COUNTY REPORTS
To The
BOARD OF AGRICULTURE

THE REVIEW AND ABSTRACT
of the
COUNTY REPORTS
to the
BOARD OF AGRICULTURE

Vol. 4. Midlands Department

by

WILLIAM MARSHALL

DAVID & CHARLES REPRINTS

7153 4368 8

This edition first
published 1815

Printed in Great Britain by
Clarke, Doble & Brendon Ltd Plymouth
Published by David & Charles (Holdings) Limited
South Devon House Railway Station Newton Abbot

THE

REVIEW AND ABSTRACT

OF THE

COUNTY REPORTS

TO THE

BOARD OF AGRICULTURE;

FROM THE SEVERAL

AGRICULTURAL DEPARTMENTS OF ENGLAND.

By Mr. MARSHALL.

IN FIVE VOLUMES.

VOLUME THE FOURTH;

(Which was first Published, in 1815, and is now combined with the other Volumes of the same Work;)

Comprizing those from the

MIDLAND DEPARTMENT.

Which includes

STAFFORDSHIRE,
DERBYSHIRE,
NOTTINGHAMSHIRE,
LEICESTERSHIRE,
RUTLANDSHIRE,
WARWICKSHIRE,
HUNTINGDONSHIRE,
NORTHAMPTONSHIRE,
OXFORDSHIRE,
BUCKINGHAMSHIRE,
BEDFORDSHIRE,
and
a principal part of
CAMBRIDGESHIRE.

York:

Printed by Thomas Wilson & Sons,

FOR LONGMAN, HURST, REES, ORME, AND BROWN, LONDON; CONSTABLE, AND CO. EDINBURGH; AND WILSON AND SONS, YORK.

1818.

THE

CONTENTS,

OF THE

MIDLAND DEPARTMENT,

SYSTEMATICALLY ARRANGED.

NATURAL ECONOMY.

* The MIDLAND DEPARTMENT, at large, might well be considered as a WIDELY EXTENDED VALE-LAND DISTRICT. On its margins, only, minor Districts are observable.

POLITICAL ECONOMY.

Huntingdon.

RURAL ECONOMY.

TENANTED ESTATES.

Oxford

WOODLANDS.

WOODLANDS.

AGRICULTURE.

Warwick,

Rye.

ADVERTISEMENT.

ADVERTISEMENT.

Mr. MARSHALL has the satisfaction of saying that in one volume, more, he shall be able, he trusts, to finish his present undertaking, and to furnish, in FIVE VOLUMES,—not only a COMPLETE ABSTRACT of what is useful, in nearly One Hundred Volumes (great and small, published and unpublished) that have been printed, by the Board of Agriculture, as 'Reports' from the COUNTIES of ENGLAND and WALES;—but to incorporate with it much practical information arising from his OWN KNOWLEDGE of the several subjects under consideration; and to CORRECT numerous ERRORS, and CLEAR UP various POINTS in dispute, among amateurs, as well as among men of more mature experience;—and moreover to appreciate, by the evidence of their own Works, the QUALIFICATIONS of MODERN WRITERS, on RURAL SUBJECTS.

DECEMBER, 1814.

THE

MIDLAND DEPARTMENT*

OF

ENGLAND.

IN an INTRODUCTION to the NORTHERN DEPARTMENT of England (recently published) I noticed, at some length, the Origin and Progress of the Board of Agriculture;—

Described the Plan and Execution of the *original* Reports; also the Plan of the *reprinted* Reports;—

Defined the requisite *qualifications* of a *Reporter*;—

Explained my Plan of Reviewing them, by DEPARTMENTS;—and sketched the Outlines and Characteristics of the six *Agricultural* Departments, into which England aptly separates.

The MIDLAND DEPARTMENT is thus described.—'This part of the kingdom, too, possesses an aptly distinguishing natural character. When compared with the great variety of soil and surface, which most of the other departments exhibits, this may be considered as one widely extended plain of fertile lands, which are almost uniformly suitable to the purposes of MIXED CULTIVATION; and without a single *eminence* within its extensive area;—excepting the Charnwood hills; which form an insulated mountain height, from whence almost every square mile of the department may be discerned, from the mountains of the northern, to the chalk hills of the southern, department; and from the rising grounds that separate it from the western, to the banks of the marshes where the eastern, department commences.

'As

* In a GEOGRAPHICAL SERIES, the MIDLAND ought to have *preceded* the EASTERN Department. In a note prefixed to the Review of the latter, I explained the necessity I had for altering the succession; namely, that of several of the Counties of the Midland Department being, at the time when they came in course to be *reviewed*, had not yet been *reported*. The deficiency, however, has since been very nearly made up; only a *fourth!* volume of DERBYSHIRE being now in arrear.

'As a wide field of Agriculture, in which every branch of the profession is highly cultivated, it has long been popularly known. Here, not only the spirit of improvement, but of *enterprize*, may well be said to inhabit. The art, science, and mystery of BREEDING has here been carried to a height which in any other country, probably, it has never attained;—the same enterprizing spirit, which led to this preeminence, still continuing, with little if any abatement.'

The REPORTS, which relate, wholely or chiefly, to this Department, are those of

	4to or "original Reports," by	*8vo or "reprinted Reports,"* by
Staffordshire	Pitt	Pitt.
Derbyshire	Brown	Farey.
Nottinghamshire	Lowe	Lowe.
Leicestershire	Monk	Pitt.
Rutlandshire	Crutchley	Parkinson.
Warwickshire	Wedge	Murray.
Northamptonshire	Donaldson	Pitt.
Huntingdonshire	Maxwell, Stone	Parkinson.
Oxfordshire	Davis	Secretary.
Buckinghamshire	James, &c.	Priest.
Bedfordshire	Stone	Batchelor.
Cambridgeshire	Vancouver	Gooch.

In all, twentyfour Volumes!

My OWN KNOWLEDGE of the MIDLAND DEPARTMENT has been accumulating during a length of years. It being situated in the Line of Road between my native County and the Metropolis, and I having, of later years, more particularly, made a point of embracing every favorable occasion to trace a fresh Line of Country; whether in travelling to the North of England, or into Scotland, or the North of Wales;—not merely with a view to curiosity or entertainment, but frequently with a tablet and pencil in hand, to acquire and retain that sort of knowledge of a Country which an experienced and attentive traveller may catch in passing over it. (see the EASTERN DEPARTMENT, p. 5.);—my GENERAL KNOWLEDGE of the MIDLAND DEPARTMENT cannot be inconsiderable.

If to those advantages be added the more fundamental acquirements obtained, in two years constant RESIDENCE and attentive PRACTICE, in one of the more central, and best cultivated Districts of the Department; and afterward, during three months, in its very Center; in order to extend, revise, and correct the mass of information that I had collected,

collected, and to digest and otherwise prepare it for the reception of the public (see my MIDLAND COUNTIES) ;—my qualification to sit in judgement on the Works above enumerated, and to abstract the useful matter they contain, will not, I trust, be deemed insufficient.

It is therefore unnecessary, I conceive, to specify the several lines which I have traced within the fortuitous boundaries of each County, in the manner I have thought it proper to do, in the preceding volumes of this Work.

STAFFORDSHIRE.

STAFFORDSHIRE forms the northwestern limb of the MIDLAND DEPARTMENT. Its northern extreme partakes of the mountain character; and has been noticed in the *Northern* or *Mountain Department*.

The southeastern quarter possesses a different character. It contains rich vale lands, which form a minor portion of what I have formerly termed, emphatically, the *Midland District*; which includes parts of Staffordshire, Derbyshire, Leicestershire and Warwickshire. See my MIDLAND COUNTIES.

The main body, the more central parts of Staffordshire, may be termed a mountain-skirt country. It is mostly broken into hill and dale, in some parts ruggedly. It comprizes no extensive range, I think, of smoothly surfaced cultivated uplands ("Needwood Forest" perhaps *now* excepted) tho many of the minor hills and the more open valleys, are of a fertile quality; giving a degree of richness, variety and of course beauty, to the surface.

It would be difficult or impossible, I conceive, to divide this County into characteristic and well defined NATURAL DISTRICTS of any considerable extent.

Staffordshire, its southeastern margin excepted, cannot be strictly termed an *agricultural* County. It is more strongly characterized by *mining* and *manufactures*.

"GENERAL

"GENERAL VIEW
OF THE
AGRICULTURE
OF THE
COUNTY OF STAFFORD;
WITH
OBSERVATIONS ON THE MEANS OF ITS IMPROVEMENT.

By WILLIAM PITT,

OF PENDEFORD, NEAR WOLVERHAMPTON.

THE SECOND EDITION.

1808."*

REGARDING the QUALIFICATIONS of this Reporter, to fill the office he undertook, much is left to conjecture. Of his previous habits and acquirements, as well as of the particulars relating to his mode of collecting his materials, the Board and himself are equally silent. And altho, as I have elsewhere intimated, a Reviewer ought to *decide* on the internal evidence of the Work before him, yet some knowledge of a Writer's *experience*, especially while writing on a *practical* and *difficult art*, may serve to lighten the labor of criticism, and tend to strengthen the mind, in deciding on matters of *doubtful authenticity*.

That Mr. Pitt, at the time he wrote, was an occupier, in agriculture, evidently appears. But to what extent, or of what description of land, or what were his objects, is not equally apparent. He sometimes writes like a *professional* man. But he certainly was not such, in estate agency; as will be seen under the ensuing head, *Estates*. With the subjects of *canals* and *manufactures* he seems to have been more particularly conversant. His favorite amusements appear to have been Rural Ornament and Botany. But in the former

* This Edition appears to have been prepared for the press, in 1804!

former of these we perceive no maturity of judgement, and, in the latter study, he was evidently, at the time of writing (as he candidly acknowledges) still in his novitiate.—Mr. Pitt, I understand is a poet. And his ideas, emanating from Congreve's Grotto, (p. 270) show that he possesses good sentiments on the art of "composing."

In regard to Mr. Pitt's MODE of SURVEY, we are, as has been intimated, much in the dark. A lengthened Tour in the Highlands of Staffordshire*, and some excursions in the Lowlands (chiefly it would seem in pursuit of plants and places) are all that we gather, ostensibly, concerning his Surveyorship. Yet from the respectable list of names that are given in his preliminary observations, as being those of CONTRIBUTORS, his visits or his correspondence would appear to have been extensive.

P. vii. "He has farther to express his acknowledgments and obligations to the following Gentlemen, Clergymen and others, for their assistance, recommendation, and the information which he has received from them, and by their means, in this business :

Mr. BRADBURNE, Pipehill, near Lichfield.
Rev. Dr. FALCONER, Lichfield.
Rev. T. GISBORNE, Yoxall-lodge, Needwood-forest.
Rev. Mr. DICKENSON, Rector of Blymhill,
Rev. Mr. WRIGHT, Bradley, near Stafford.
JOSIAH WEDGWOOD, Esq. Etruria.
JOHN SNEYD, Esq. Belmont, near Leek.
Mr. PRINCEP, Croxall.
Mr. SAMUEL WYATT, Burton on Trent.
Mr. LOCKLEY, Boscobel.
Mr. CORSER, Bushbury, near Wolverhampton.
Mr. MILLER, Dunstall, near Wolverhampton.
Mr. JOSEPH HORDERN, Saredon, near Wolverhampton.
Mr. ELLISON, Hattons, near Wolverhampton.
Mr. HIGGS, Cronkhall, near Wolverhampton.
Mr. FERRIDAY, Ettingsall-park, near Wolverhampton.
Mr. FOWLER, Erdington, near Birmingham.
Mr. CURTIS, Walsall.
Mr. HARDING, Ashley-heath, near Eccleshall.
Mr. HARVEY, Dunstall, near Abbots Bromley.
Mr. BROWMAN, at Lord DONEGALL's, Fisherwick.
Mr. JOHN SMITH, Haunton, near Tamworth.
Mr. WILLIAM WEBB, Newbould, near Burton on Trent.
Mr. JENKINSON, Stoke, near Stone.

Mr.

* For a few extracts from that Tour, see NORTHERN DEPARTMENT.

Mr. GIBBS, Leek.

Sir EDWARD LITTLETON, Bart. Teddesley-park.

GEORGE TOLLET, Esq. Swinnerton-hall, near Stone."

And, beside those, we find in going thro the Volume the following ANNOTATORS.

Mr. Sneyd, of Belmont, near Leek; under the signature S.

The Rev. S. Shaw.

R. not decyphered:—with a few others.

Touching the MATTER COLLECTED through those means, it is only requisite to say, here, that whatever I conceive to be capable of assisting in the advancement of rural knowledge, will be found in the ensuing extracts. The unimportant and irrelevant matter, with which the Volume abounds*, I leave for those who may have leisure and inclination to peruse the Work at large.

The MANNER of REPORTING, the authorship or style of the Report under notice, is superior to that of most other of the Board's publications. Repetition is its most striking blemish. But this, tho it may, by mere men of words and "letters," be deemed a high crime, is with me a venial offence.

Mr. Pitt was the original Reporter of Staffordshire, in 1794. His Report was reprinted, in octavo pages, in 1796; and, again, in 1808. The Volume before me being one of the very few Works of the Board that have reached second editions,—in the first twenty years of their labors in literature.

The number of pages three hundred and twentyseven.

The number of engravings, sixteen;—namely a Map of the County; seven of erections; eight of animals.

SUBJECT THE FIRST.

NATURAL ECONOMY.

EXTENT—P. 2. "The greatest length of Staffordshire, from the north part of Ax-Edge-common to the south part of Woods Eaves (south of the Severn), from N. N. E. to S. S. W. is 60 English miles; and the greatest breadth from

* P. vi "As an embellishment, and a relaxation of the mind from the fatigue of constant attention to one subject, the Writer has introduced a few remarks upon Natural History and Botany, and even on some other subjects not immediately or closely connected with Agriculture."

from the junction of the Trent and Dove, near Newton Solney, to the west point of Terley-heath, near Drayton, nearly from east to west, is 38 miles: the county contains in gross 1220 miles, and 780,800 statute acres."

ELEVATION.—P. 8. "The middle and south part of the county are generally level, or with only gentle eminences. To this, however, there are some exceptions; as the limestone hills of Dudley and Sedgeley, which furnish an inexhaustible supply of that material, and great part of it of excellent quality. The Quartzose, or Ragstone-hills of Rowley, furnish an excellent material for roads and pavements. The hills of Clent and Barbeacon, besides many others of less elevation, as the high grounds on Cannock-heath, the hills of Bushbury and Essington, formed chiefly of, or at least containing great quantities of gravel, Kinfare Edge, Tettenhall-wood, and some situations near Enville, also command extensive prospects. In this place it may not be improper (as it will not take up much room) to state a few particulars of a subject doubtless curious; and which, though not immediately connected, is yet not altogether foreign to the business in hand. These particulars are, the perpendicular elevation of some of the high summits, medium plains, and lowlands, of this inland county, above the level of the tide of the ocean; the Writer of this having had many opportunities of ascertaining these particulars, in many cases very accurately, and in others nearly.* The lowest points of land in the county are, probably, the Severn at Over Areley, and the Trent where it receives the Dove below Burton.

"*Elevation of sundry Points of Land in this County, perpendicularly above the Level of the Tide of the Thames at Brentford.*

Particular Spots.	Elevation. Ft.	In.
Banks of the Severn at Over Areley - - - - -	60	0
———— Tame at Tamworth - - - - -	150	0
———— Trent at its junction with the Dove	100	0
———— summit of the Staffordshire Canal -	385	0
———— summit of the Birmingham Canal -	500	0
———— summit of the Wyrley Canal, at Essington Wood New Colliery	560	0
Summit of Bushbury-hill - - - - - - - -	650	0
———— Barr-beacon - - - - - - - - -	750	0
———— the highest peak of Rowley-hills - -	900	0
———— the Grand Trunk Canal - - - - -	420 Summit	0

* A sufficient warrant, this, for inserting them, here.

Particular Spots.	Elevation. Ft.	In.
Summit of a hill called Bunster, near Ilam, in the Moorlands - - - - -	1200	0
———— Wever-hills, and some other of the highest peaks in the Moorlands	1500	0

"Many of the above are by actual observation, and others by estimate only."

CLIMATURE.—P. 7. "The air of this county I think sharp, and the cold perceptibly to the senses greater than in many other counties, particularly than in the neighbourhood of London; having often had an opportunity of making a quick comparison. The climate too may be termed inclining to wet."

P. 80. "The hay-harvest is from the middle of June to the end of July. Corn-harvest is in August and September; but in some early seasons, pease, oats, and barley, have been harvested about the end of July."

WATERS.—P. 17. "The Severn, though it passes through one of the parishes of this county, viz. Over Areley, can hardly be called a Staffordshire river; yet it receives the tribute of some considerable brooks arising in the county; the principal river, therefore of the country is the Trent, which, rising in the Moorlands near Biddulph, takes a winding course, first southerly, then easterly, and lastly north-easterly, and after washing the county for a course of upwards of fifty miles, leaves it at Burton, where it becomes navigable."—"It might be a curious, and perhaps useful subject, not unworthy the patronage of the Board, (!) to ascertain by experiment, the quantity of water falling in particular districts; and the proportion of such quantity absorbed by the earth and its products, by the atmosphere, and carried off by rivulets respectively. The quantity falling being determined by a weather-gage, the quantity running off seems not difficult to determine; for in most countries particular outlets may be fixed upon where the superfluous water of a certain district passes off. The extent of such district being ascertained, and a trusty person fixed upon near such outlet, to take, at stated times, the depth and velocity of the stream, from thence the quantity of passing water may be estimated. I think a steady excise-officer might be instructed to register such account; and that a small addition of salary might recompense him for his trouble. I know a spot in Staffordshire where the flood-water of upwards of 100 square miles passes at a particular bridge, and can go no other way; and doubtless similar situations may be found in various places."

This is another *false conception*, about the rain water which falls in a given District. See WESTERN DEPARTMENT p. p. 190, and 223.

The

The two schemes are nearly in opposition to each other; yet are equally ill grounded, and inefficacious. A part of the water which falls in a hilly, rocky country, as North Staffordshire, and which is absorbed by the earth, rises at the feet of the hills, and mixes with the flood waters; and (in the case in point) of course accompanies them to the particular bridge mentioned. In such a situation, and during a dry season, all the water which passes downward is *spring* water; the whole of which might or might not have fallen within the District of observation; while, in a chalk hill District, the whole of the rain water which falls may be said to be absorbed; and sinks to rise no more, perhaps, within the same District*.—Beside, it would require a hundred rain guagers, in one hundred square miles of surface, to ascertain, with any degree of accuracy, the quantity which falls.

Even supposing that a degree of accuracy could be obtained, over a hundred square miles, to what useful purpose could the information be applied; since no two miles of surface would absorb the like quantity. Light thin-soiled limestone heights imbibe nearly the whole of the water which falls on them; while deep clayey lands, in wet seasons, repel the principal part.

P. 18. "The county, upon the whole, is well watered, and much of its water appropriated and usefully employed; yet large quantities of it are carried of in waste by floods.

"Besides the rivers and brooks above named, this county contains one considerable lake, called Aqualate-Meer, on the borders of Shropshire near Newport, said to be 1848 yards long, and 672 broad."

P. 269. At Okeover,—"two considerable rivers, the Hamps and Manyfold, burst from under the lime-stone hills, after a subterraneous passage of several miles, in separate streams, which has been proved by throwing corks into the streams above."

SOILS.—P. 11. "The soil of this county (and probably that of every other district in the kingdom, of equal extent) is various: the arable soils may, in general, be divided into, first, the stiff and strong, clayey (argillaceous); secondly, the loose and light, sandy (arenaceous); thirdly, although the county has no chalk, yet in the limestone districts, lime earth (or calcareous); fourthly, the mixed, or compound soil or loam, composed of the above, with the addition of stones and other matter *(terræ compositio)*. Also, some uncultivated and other spots contain a thin, light

* See my Treatise on Landed Property.

light, black earth, of the nature of peat, generally lying upon gravel: this, when pulverized and dry, is very light; but when thoroughly wet, is so retentive of moisture as to resemble mud. The meadow soils are, in some places, similar to the arable, with the addition of the sediment of water when within reach of streams; in other places composed of peat earth of different thicknesses to several feet, sometimes containing trunks of trees*. This peat earth seems to consist principally of the decayed roots of aquatic vegetables, but when drained, consolidated, and meliorated, by top-dressing or irrigation, becomes valuable meadow and pasture land: the surface of this kind of land will, upon draining, sink several inches.

"The first general division of clay soils consists of two varieties: first, the strong, stubborn, harsh, tenacious clay, or clay loam; secondly, the more mild, tractable, or friable marl or loam. The *sandy* soils are more or less *light*, (!) and in some degree intermixed with loam, gravel, or other matter; the mixed soils are also various, and may be termed loam, gravelly loam, sandy loam, &c. according to circumstances."

Such is the Reporters unsatisfactory account of the soils of Staffordshire.

P. 13. "Of the 600,000 acres of cultivated land, in which class I mean to include the pasture part of parks, I estimate 100,000 acres may be meadow and pasture, and 500,000 acres arable; the arable land may be reckoned 200,000 acres of clay loam, or more friable mixed loam, 200,000 acres of gravelly or sandy loams, or other mixed, including calcareous soils; and the remainder, or 100,000 acres of light sandy, gravelly, or other soils, which though not perhaps wholly adapted to, are yet capable of producing turnip."

This statement, if it only approximate accuracy is valuable.

FOSSILS and MINERALS.—On this head, we find Mr. Pitt full of information.

P. 13. "The mines of this country are valuable and extensive, and in some articles may fairly be pronounced inexhaustible †. The *coal land* of Staffordshire, which has been proved such, and where the existence of that mineral, near enough the surface to be easily raised, has been ascertained,

"* Many curious specimens have been found of late years near Stonall, in the parish of Shenstone.—*Rev. S. Shaw.*"

"† The mines of coal, lime, and ironstone, upon the estates of Lord Dudley, are very considerable and extensive: to these mines are in a great

tained, contains a space of about 50,000 acres: of this space the quantity exhausted by consumption, from the earliest times to the present day, does not exceed a tenth of the whole; and though the scarcity and advance in price of this article, have been complained of, the scarcity of it has been owing to local causes; and the advance in price has perhaps been no more than a just proportion to the advance in the price of labour, and the machinery necessary in the trade. In the south of the county the coal country extends in length from Cannock-heath (including a part of that waste) to near Stourbridge, and in breadth from Woverhampton to Walsall. In the north of the county, the neighbourhood of Newcastle and the Potteries, Lane-end, Holly-bush, and again in the neighbourhood of Cheadle and Dilhorne. The country producing *limestone* is still more extensive; at Sedgeley and Dudley Castle Hills, Rushall and Hayhead, but above all, on the north-east Moorlands and banks of the upper parts of the Dove, where the greatest consumption or length of time could scarce apparently lessen the immense quantity. In this latter district are some veins of *alabaster*, which is also dug between Needwood Forest and Tutbury. Of *freestone* here are very good and extensive quarries. Bilstone affords a freestone of very fine grit, fit either for mouldings, building, or grindstones of the finer sort, for which last purpose it is excellently adapted. Gornal, near Sedgeley, has also plentiful

a great measure owing, the immense population of the parish of Sedgeley; such population being in a great degree supported by employment therein or thereon depending.

"These mines are from their nature almost inexhaustible; those of coal, as now worked, laying in stratums of 8, 10, and even 12 yards in thickness; and the limestone, consisting of the solid masses of extensive mountains, whose bases are upon the same materials continued to an unknown depth: this stone in some places is of a marble quality, and capable of receiving a good polish; in others composed in a great measure of helminthokthi, or petrified marine substances of the animal kind, as cardium, millepora, &c. The lime produced from either, is of a fine white, and excellent quality, the coal and ironstone, is also of a first rate quality.

"These mines could never have been worked to their present extent but by means of the artificial navigable canals, carried not only through them in various directions, but even tunnelled under the limestone mountains; which has enabled the workmen to undermine such mountains, and without removing the surface soil, to hollow out the stone in huge caverns, some of which penetrate upwards of 300 yards from the canals, under their bases, and are in height and breadth of large dimensions Large quantities of lime are carried from hence to Birmingham, and elsewhere, for building; and great quantities are used for manures; for which latter purpose, exclusive of the water carriage, it is sometimes fetched by land conveyance to the distance of 15 miles."

plentiful quarries of a coarser and cheaper freestone, used for the same purposes as that of Bilstone. Tixall produces an excellent and durable building freestone, which is easily raised in blocks of almost any dimension; and the same article is again found at Wrottesley, Breewood-park, Pendeford, and a great many other places in the county.

"*Iron.*—The strata of iron ore in the neighbourhood of Wednesbury, Tipton, Bilston, part of the parish of Sedgeley, and other parts of the coal country, are very extensive. These strata generally lay under a stratum of coal, and have occasioned some very considerable iron-works to be lately established on the banks of the Birmingham Canal, where the iron trade is very much increasing; and it is to be hoped the capital, spirit of enterprise, and exertion of our iron-masters will, in time, produce this necessary article in sufficient quantity to preclude the necessity of an importation from abroad; or at least to lessen the quantity of such importation, the balance of trade in which is very much against this country."

P. 16. "The other minerals of the county are principally those of *copper* and *lead*, of both which, considerable quantities are raised at Ecton, near Warslow, upon the estate of his Grace the Duke of Devonshire. Also a copper-mine is worked at Mixon, within a few miles of Leek, and a lead-mine near Stanton-moor."

P. 17. At Shirleywich, near Ingestree, is a considerable *salt-work*."

P. 284.—"*Rowley Regis.*—This parish exhibits a very striking singularity, being in itself distinct from any other district in the neighbourhood, or in the county. It is principally composed of an insulated mountain, ending or finishing in various peaks, pikes, or summits. The highest summit, called Turner's-hill, is the highest ground in the south of Staffordshire, but much beneath the Moorland-hills, or the Wrekin and Clay hills of Shropshire. The other highest points of Rowley-mountain are Oakham and Corney hills. This mountain has for its basis, a singular species of quartzose-stone, devoid of any grit quality, called Rowley rag-stone; large quantities of which are carried to Birmingham and elsewhere, for pavements and repairing roads. It is extremely hard, too much so to be hewn by a common tool; the colour is a rusty blue. This stone is totally void of any calcareous quality, but very probably containing a small proportion of iron. It lies in an infinite number of fragments, and some of them of immense bulk, both above, upon, and beneath the surface. The rock called Rowley hail-stone is of this quality, and of great size. Dr. Plott has most absurdly expressed a doubt,

doubt, whether this may not have been a production of art. It is evidently the work of Nature. The Rowley stone, when dug for, lies in no strata, but in rude heaps in every direction, generally beneath the surface soil, but often rising above it, with innumerable fragments both upon the lands and roads."

FALLING STONES.

ARE not those stones, and others of a similar nature, *atmospherical?* and are not the stones that have recently reached the earth, through its atmosphere, fragments thrown off from a spent, or nearly spent COMET,—at or toward its aphelion; and with a degree of velocity sufficient to overcome the attration of its remaining nucleus?

A fragment thus thrown off, whether by centrifugal force, or the force of internal gasses, would naturally travel, in space, with the given velocity, and nearly in the given direction, until its course should be disturbed by the attraction of another body, moving in the same region of space.

From the several apparently well authenticated instances of stones "falling from the atmosphere," in our own time, it is sufficiently ascertained that they enter it with a high degree of heat:—not only from their warmth when they reach the earth, but by the reports they occasion while descending;—similar to those which are caused by lightening passing through it.

In space—in vacuo—they would, it is probable retain their heat, unimpared, and would of course remain in the same ignited state in which they were sent forth, until they were plunged into the air and moisture of the atmosphere;—in passing through which they would necessarily lose some considerable portion of their heat, before they reached the surface of the earth.

The Rowley stones are certainly an object of philosophical enquiry. From the above description, they appear to resemble those stones which are known to have so descended, and which have been analyzed and described.

Since the public agitation of this interesting topic, and after the theory, here offered, occurred to me (some years ago) I have been led to conceive that many of the naked masses that are seen in grotesque shapes upon various mountains of this island, may be of cometic origin.

The rugged "Tors"—the naked rocks—of Dartmore, which are seen rising out of the summits, or sticking on the brows, of the mountain, are striking instances. And although the nature of those rocks may differ from that of the stones which have recently fallen; yet, heretofore, different species of stones, that are now seen upon, or partially

tially bedded beneath, the surface of this planet, without any connexion, and without any other probable mean of being placed in their present situation, may be of similar origin.

SUBJECT THE SECOND.

POLITICAL ECONOMY.

	Acres.
APPROPRIATION.—P 13. "The gross acres of the county, as stated before, are about	780,800
Deduct for roads, lakes, pools, ponds, rivers, canals, cities, towns, villages, buildings and yards, one acre in twenty,	39,040
Waste lands, forests, woods and impracticable land,	141,760
Deduct	180,800
Remains cultivated land	600,000
Of the waste and forest lands, it is probable that the reclaimable part amounts to	100,000"

P. 51. "The most considerable proportion of the cultivated land of this county is enclosed, very little remaining in common fields. I can only recollect the following common fields: 1. Stafford; 2. Stone; 3. Chedleton; and 4. Bloxwich; the whole amounting to, perhaps, little more than one thousand acres. I reckon in all cases, that common-field land is improved at least five shillings per acre per annum by enclosure, which will pay a good interest upon the expense of enclosing; also that its produce will be considerably greater; for common fields are generally both imperfectly cultivated, and exhausted by hard tillage. Enclosures only can effect the improvement of stock. Respecting population, I have no doubt but the means of employment are increased by enclosure, by the planting and reparation of fenses. To prove the superiority of enclosures, let us put the case of a proposal made to throw a well-fenced enclosed country into common fields, and I believe every mind would revolt at the idea."

P. 137. "The waste and unimproved lands of this county are very considerable, and certainly in the present state of population, their cultivation and improvement is very much a national object. The most extensive wastes or uncultivated spots in the county are, Needwood-forest, Cannock-heath, and Sutton Coldfield; besides a great number of commons of less extent, and some considerable

tracts

tracts in the Moorlands and elsewhere, appropriated and enclosed, but not yet fully improved."

Needwood Forest we find particularly described. It was certainly an interesting subject of description; as it was, I think, the first of English Forests:—whether viewed in the light of richness or positive beauty. It has recently been appropriated. Nevertheless, the following particulars are worth preserving. Mr. Pitt's calculations are, at least, ingenious.

P. 139. "This forest is stocked with deer, horned cattle, and horses; but no sheep are suffered to feed on it. The supposed stock may be, about 3000 deer, and 3000 of all the other kinds in summer; but much fewer in winter. The keeping of the 3000 horses and horned cattle, charged at 12*s.* per head for the summering, amounts to 1800*l.* or about 4*s.* per acre, upon the whole extent of the forest; and this sum of 4*s.* per acre is all the advantage that a neighbouring very intelligent farmer supposes the public derive from this tract; the deer not being managed in any system for the public advantage, or for the supply of subsistence and employment of the bulk of mankind. I shall add for them to the above account, 1*s.* per acre, and 5*s.* per acre as the total value of the forest to the public in its present state. I estimate the capital employed in stocking the forest at 5*l.* per head upon 3000 in number, or 15,000*l.* Although these, not being constantly kept there, cannot wholly be called forest stock, yet I will suppose that which ought to be taken off on this account, to be made good by advantages arising from the deer. The capital employed in stocking the forest will then amount to 15,000*l.* or about 1*l.* 12*s.* 6*d.* per acre, and its value to the public in its present state, as land, about 2300*l.* per annum.

"The extent of the forest, by an ancient survey alluded to by the Commissioners of Crown Lands in their last examination of it, is 9220 acres: of this, in case of enclosure, I will suppose 1000 acres ought to be reserved for woodland. This may be done about the glens and impracticable spots, and in other places where thriving oaks are the most promising: there they aught to be fenced off, and reserved in clumps and coppices, which would be both an ornament to the country, and a nursery for stout oak timber. 220 acres I will suppose occupied by the lodges, and other small enclosures. This is already in an improved state; 8000 acres will then remain for improvement. The moment that these shall have been enclosed, and buildings for occupation erected on them, they will be worth, for a term, as many guineas per annum, and

and would be improved to a higher value. The amount of capital employed in such improvement, in buildings, enclosure, crops, stock, &c. might, on this rich land be 20*l.* per acre. Deduct the present capital, 1*l.* 12*s.* 6*d.* per acre; remains increase, 18*l.* 7*s.* 6*d.* per acre: which, upon 8000 acres, adds 147,000*l.* to the national capital. By improving this tract, the increased annual product would probably be 5*l.* per acre, or 40,000*l.* per annum."

P. 146. "A general enclosure, and improvement by cultivation, of all the wastes of the kingdom, would, by greatly increasing the national capital, have a proportionable effect upon the revenue; and it is astonishing, that the colonization of distant countries should have been so much encouraged, while the cultivation of our own country remains so far from being finished or perfected."

P. 315. "In most parts of this county, there are evident marks of a cultivation far more extended than any thing known in modern times; most of our commons and waste lands have on them evident marks of the plough; marl and clay pits of great size are to be found in most parts of the county where those substances abound, and evidently made for manure. I have observed on the rubbish or spoil of these pits, timber trees of from one to two hundred years growth. No history I have read, or tradition I have heard, give any insight into the time when these exertions were made; but the traces of them are evident; and from their extent, it is equally so, that a greater strength has been employed in the cultivation of land, in some distant period, than is at present, or has been in the memory of the present generation; but from the present appearance of such common lands, and their sterile and unproductive state, it should seem that no attention was paid to drainage; and that very probably the land was cropped as long as it would bear it, and then left to Nature."

These appearances are not peculiar to Staffordshire. See my WEST OF ENGLAND.

PROVISIONS.—P. 220. "The price of provisions in this county has been in many instances very fluctuating, and their rise and fall seem owing to a combination of different causes; to the plenty or scarcity, import or export: to the plenty or scarcity also of money. Since I have been in the farming business, which is about fifteen years, I have known wheat at all prices, from 4*s.* to 10*s.* 6*d.* barley from 2*s.* to 7*s.* and oats from 1*s.* 6*d.* to 4*s.* 6*d.* and this for actual consumption; but it must be observed, that our bushel is nine gallons and a half. Butchers' meat has varied considerably in that period. Pork, or bacon hogs, sinking the offal, have sold

sold from 2¼*d.* to 4½*d.* per pound; cows, calves, and sheep, from 3*d.* to 5½*d.*"

P. 225. "Dr. Withering is of opinion, that a man, his wife, and five children, living as labouring people do, chiefly on bread, will consume a bushel of wheat per week.

"Mr. Oulton, in an ingenious pamphlet on the potteries, thinks a fair average is three stones of flour per week, of 14 lb. each, for six persons, taking in all ranks and ages, and including those who have more aid from butchers' meat; which is 156 stones per annum for six persons, or the produce of about 42 Winchester bushels. This makes the average annual allowance to each individual, seven Winchester bushels of wheat; whence the quantity raised in the county (exclusive of seed for the next year) is sufficient only for 166,000 persons, or about two-thirds of its present population, in an average season; and that this is the case at present, seems very probable, and is corroborated by every apparent circumstance. The deficiency is made out by purchase from other counties, or by oat-bread, which is eaten in considerable quantities in the north of the county, and in the potteries, though scarcely known in the south."

FUEL.—P. 226. "This is one of the most plentiful and reasonable comforts of life of which Staffordshire has to boast; the mines of coal being very extensive, tolerably near the surface, and of excellent quality: the price at the works from four to five shillings per ton; and in respect to farming labourers, the carriage of a load of near three tons weight is annually given by the farmer, for whom they work in harvest; the county is also well wooded, but little of which is burnt for domestic uses; the iron-works in the neighbourhood taking off any quantity, though ever so great, for charcoal. In the north part of the county, called Moorlands, a good deal of peat is dug for fuel; which is doubtless cheap enough, but not equally comfortable with coal. Upon the whole, fuel is a plentiful and cheap article; and the price of coal, at the works, not subject to much fluctuation: a regular and gradual advance has indeed taken place within a few years, which has been caused by an advance in the price of labour, and the materials necessary for the machinery used in the trade; and perhaps not in a higher proportion than was necessary to give a fair profit to the mine-proprietors.

"The price of coals at the Staffordshire collieries is now advanced to from 7*s.* to 8*s.* per ton, November, 1804."

EMPLOYMENTS.—P. 237. "Of the population of Staffordshire, I suppose one-third are supported by agricultural or other professions, or employments thereon depending, and two-thirds by manufactures, commerce, and mines."

MANUFACTURES.

MANUFACTURES.—As a resident in the manufacturing quarter of Staffordshire, Mr. Pitt would, in consequence, acquire a considerable share of information, respecting the nature and extent of its manufactures:—even if he had no immediate share or connexion with them. He is, at least, a manufacturer in theory, and writes intelligibly on manufactural subjects.

P. 232. "The manufactures of Staffordshire are very considerable, and comprehend a variety of articles, particularly hardware, nails, glass, toys, japanned goods, and potters' ware; also productions in cotton, silk, leather, woollen, linen, and many other articles.

"A good many of the manufacturing families at Staffordshire are resident in the country, but in no proportion of numbers to those residing in towns."

Mr. Pitt proceeds to detail the staple manufactures of the several towns of Staffordshire, and the almost numberless articles of trade (chiefly of *iron*, an indigenous and permanent material of the Island) which the County supplies; closing his Report of them with the subjoined remarks.

P. 237. "With respect to the effects of extensive manufactures on agriculture, I believe there can exist but one rational opinion, and which must be, that those effects are of the most advantageous kind, and that in every instance the value of landed property will most rapidly rise, as the demand for, and facility of disposing of its products, is increased; and with this opinion agrees every remark I have received upon the 28th query proposed by the Board, and which refers to this particular subject. The only inconveniences that can possibly be complained of are, first, an advance in the price of labour, which is always highest in manufacturing countries; and secondly, an increase in poor's-rates, which must always be highest in populous countries. These inconveniences are abundantly compensated for, by an increasing consumption of landed produce, and a brisk demand for such produce at market; and it may be farther observed, that a populous neighbourhood affords an easy means of improving the adjoining land, to almost any degree of fertility."—Yes, a *permanently* populous neighbourhood. But see the ruinous effects, even of the *woolen* manufacture (likewise a *native)* when *forced* on to excess; in the EASTERN DEPARTMENT, County of *Essex.*

"While the wind blows
O! then"—indeed.

The same page —"The woollen manufactory within this county is not very considerable, and a large proportion of the raw wool grown therein is sold into the clothing and stocking

stocking countries; yet there are wool-combers in most of the towns, and some which push a considerable business; and a good deal of woollen cloth is got up in the county by private families, though in less quantity than formerly."

Under the head "Minerals," we find the following remarks belonging to manufactures.—P. 16. "In these mines of coal, lime, and iron, and in the founderies, blast-furnaces, slitting-mills, and other branches of the iron trade, great numbers of workmen are employed, and the extension of the iron trade in particular, is of great consequence to the interests of this kingdom. The extent of the iron trade in all its varieties, wrought and unwrought, for agricultural and other internal purposes, and for home consumption and exportation, under its innumerable shapes and forms, is now so very great, as to rival even that of the great staple, wool, and to make the superiority of the latter somewhat questionable; and from the abundance of iron ore and fuel with which this country abounds, the trade, particularly so far as relates to the production of the metal, is capable of being much extended; and there can be little doubt of the possibility that this country may wholly supply itself with that article." And having noticed the copper and lead mines (see Minerals aforegoing) Mr. P. adds—P. 16. "And there are several smelting and brass works in this part of the county, particularly at Whiston, Oak-moor, and in the neighbourhood of Cheadle."

In his Tour over the Morelands, Mr. P. dropped upon the POTTERIES;—(another *native* manufacture.)—P. 277. "The Potteries are of considerable extent and population, and very much a national object. The Trent and Mersey canal, which passes through them, has been a very great convenience in the conveyance of heavy articles used in this manufacture; which circumstance, united with the genius, spirit of enterprise, and exertion of the masters and workmen, has happily succeeded in raising this manufacture in a very rapid manner, from small beginnings, to its present importance and consequence. The great improvements introduced into this manufacture by Mr. Wedgwood and others, will be for ever an honour to their memory, and rank them among the benefactors of mankind. The cream-coloured ware has all the neatness and elegance of porcelain; is in very general use, and is wrought into a vast variety of forms for purposes both useful and ornamental. The raw material used in this business being of little or no value, the amount of value of the manufactured article, which is very considerable, and a great addition to the national capital, may be considered as wholly created by the industry of those concerned and employed in this manufacture: by the success of of which, Burslem and Hanley-green, from small villages, have rapidly swelled into large market towns, and are now equal in population to Newcastle and Leek; besides which, the Pottery includes a number of populous villages scattered over this neighbourhood."

POOR RATE.—P. 239. "Respecting aids to the poor, this county is by no means backward; the property of the poor under the management of ministers and churchwardens, and left them by the charitable donations of the well-disposed, is in this county very considerable; and, as far as I know, properly and judiciously applied to the relief of those who keep themselves from being chargeable to the parish. Voluntary subscriptions have often been set on foot, and very liberally supported, in times of scarcity and inclemency of weather; and people of all ranks have come forward in proportion to their means and ability."

TITHES.—After noticing, in a general way, the evil effects of tithes, and producing, in a note, a particular instance, as follows,—N. p. 34, "I have the most satisfactory proofs, from the evidence of several respectable cultivators, that the quantity of wheat sown is affected by the tithe system; they having assured me, that they decline sowing wheat, and choose to manage their land in a grazing system, because they cannot bear the idea of paying the enormous rates that have been asked them by the titheman.—*W. P.*"—Mr. Pitt proceeds to bring forward *his Plan of Reform;* which I insert, here, with no other view than that of registering another opinion, relating to a SUBSTITUTE for TITHES. I wish to collect all the information I can respecting it: whether it may or may not accord with my own plan. See WESTERN DEPARTMENT, p. 434.

P. 35. "The following plan is proposed as the outline of an exchange of tithes for land, as land will always bear a value proportioned to that of its produce, and even the price or value of labour is measured by the same standard.

"Let an act of parliament appoint, in every diocese, an equal number of the most respectable clergy and country gentlemen, commissioners and trustees, and with a power of nominating surveyors to value all the tithes belonging either to the clergy or the laity within the diocese; and let the act give an option to the land-owners of purchasing their respective tithes at the valuation fixed on them by such surveyors: the money arising from such redemption might be invested in the funds, or other securities, until a proper opportunity should offer of laying it out in land; and where the land-owners should refuse to purchase such tithes, the commissioners might have the power of mortgaging them, or of taking up money on their security, to be invested

invested in the same way with that arising from tithes actually sold: or, after a given time, the trustees might be empowered to set apart an allotment of the land of those owners who refuse to purchase, and which, if conveniently situated for the former tithe-owner, might be so applied, otherwise sold, and the money arising from such sale invested as before, until it could be laid out in the purchase of land. The execution of some such plan would be attended with infinitely less trouble and expense than that now incurred by the annual valuation of tithes, as, should the proposed regulation be once effected, the business would be settled for ever; but under the present system, the surveyor or valuer's business is continued from year to year; and if that system should continue, will be from generation to generation. An equivalent in land must certainly be a more solid property than tithes. Land may be improved in any degree by good management and industry; tithes fluctuate or sink in value at the will of the cultivator. I think some such commutation as this may be easily effected, and that all parties would be pleased with the alteration."

PUBLIC EMBANKMENTS.—P. 253. (under the head "Means of Improvement")—"Thirdly, the embankment of rivers, to prevent the destruction of hay; with sluices constructed through such banks, to let through the water for irrigation, at pleasure. A work of this kind I had the pleasure of seeing upon the Trent below Stone; but for this business to be done in the best manner, it must be taken up in a general way: and unless the consent of all parties could be obtained, the assistance of the Legislature would be wanted. I know large tracts of meadow-land in this county, upon which I have been informed the hay is upon an average, ruined once in three years, that might be rendered perfectly secure by embanking; and at the same time watered at pleasure."

CANALS.—P. 229. "Respecting the conveniences for conveyance of heavy articles, perhaps no county in England, or even country in the universe, of equal extent, is better accommodated with artificial canals. I have marked the length upon the map of the county herewith sent, of those now in hand, as well as those which have been wholly executed nearly within the last thirty years. These canals extend about 200 miles in length, and two or three good projects of the same kind also might still be marked out within the county. They much facilitate the conveyance of bulky and weighty articles, such as coal, limestone, and lime, iron in the ore, or metal, and considerably reduce the expense of carriage. The trade in those articles has consequently been extended in a very considerable degree, and the population of the neighbourhood where those articles are produced

produced has increased. The Writer of this is of opinion, that the very rapid extension, not only of Birmingham, for the last twenty years previous to the present war, but also of the potteries, was much promoted by canal conveyance. Similar instances are to be found elsewhere: at Tipton-green, now a populous town, on the banks of the Birmingham canal; at Mr. Wilkinson's extensive works at Bradley near Bilston, as well as at the works before named in a general way, and at many others. Thus, these canals have been a means of considerably increasing population, by enabling the proprietors of mines of iron, coal, and lime, to extend their works, and by that means employ more people both in raising, manufacturing, and transporting the different articles. These canals cost in execution 500,000*l.* and upon the average pay 10 per cent. per annum to the proprietors; they consequently add half a million to the national capital, and 50,000*l.* per annum to its income; and with their consequent extension and improvement of the mines, manufactures, and commerce of the country, not less than double the sums above stated, and are certainly a great national improvement, as well as accommodation to a trading country."—And further, on the utility of Canals, see a note p. 11. aforegoing, article *Fossils.*

I here insert a paper of Mr. Jessop, canal engineer, which Mr. Pitt has placed under the head "Irrigation." It would seem to have been written, professionally, on a particular occasion. It contains little that is strikingly new, or excellent. The art of forming reservoirs, to equalize the currents of rivulets and small brooks, is as old as the making of mill pools*. It is nevertheless entitled to a place here; as the production of a professional man of much celebrity.

P. 157. "*Observations on the use of Reservoirs for Flood-waters.*—The rapid improvements which have for some years past been made in the agriculture and commerce of this country, and the happy effects derived therefrom, naturally excite a desire to investigate every means by which they may be continued and increased.

"Among the many causes which have combined to promote our prosperity, the facility of intercourse by inland navigation is a great and leading feature. All unite in admitting this as a general position; but many, from private motives, or mistaken opinions, have too often prevailed in preventing the execution of useful projects, which, if they could

* The idea of equalizing the waters of *rivers!* is truly *sublime;* as being eminently calculated to excite neverceasing *terror* throughout *inhabited valleys!*

could have been effected, would have greatly contributed to the national benefit derived from those already established.

"Among the obstacles that stand forward, none are more conspicuous, nor so generally urged, than the want of water in dry seasons. It usually happens, that where canals are most wanted, manufactures or agriculture having already taken possession of the ground, and occupied the streams of water, it is plainly to be foreseen, that, unless some means are devised to reconcile this competition, those desirable improvements must be crippled in their growth, and stop long before the age of maturity.

"It can hardly have escaped any one's observation, that streams of water used for the purpose of working mills, or the more valuable purpose of watering meadows, in the few instances where this has been practised, while they have a scanty supply in summer, they generally discharge in winter such superabundance as frequently to do material injury.

"There are in some parts of this island, exceptions to this general position. Where the soil is porous, and the substrata so open as to absorb the rains as they fall, there are no floods: the pores and fissures of the earth form reservoirs or regulators to the streams; they preserve the winter waters, and so equalize the discharge, that there is but little difference between their winter and summer state; but in clay or other similar soils, so little is absorbed, and so much suddenly glides off from the surface, that the extremes of scarcity and exuberance are the necessary consequences.

"It is now well understood, that all natural springs derive their supply from the waters of the atmosphere; and they may fairly be considered as the discharges of natural reservoirs; it is immaterial whether those reservoirs may be composed of large cavities, or minute fissures.

"Leaving expense out of the question, it is possible to conceive (however extravagant the idea may appear), that the waters of all rivers might by art be nearly equalized throughout the year; but it will be sufficient to prove, that this is practicable if applied to small rivulets or brooks, particularly where Nature holds forth a temptation, by furnishing deep ravines, or capacious hollows on the surface of the ground, capable, at a moderate expense, of being made to contain large quantities of water.

"We are taught, from the simple instinct of animals, the provident lesson of storing up the superabundant supplies of one season for the wants of another. Necessity has compelled mankind, in many countries to follow their example. In hot climates, the inhabitants could hardly exist without

without storing up the waters of winter for their use in summer*.

"There are instances in this country, where canals are in want of water in summer, while the brooks that supply them discharge floods in winter, in one day, sufficient for the supply of the whole year.

"Those who entertain doubts of the practicability of making reservoirs sufficient for the supply of canals, state their objections under three heads: the expense, the want of sufficiency of water, and the uncertainty of making such reservoirs to retain it.

"When the necessary magnitude is ascertained, the expense is a subject of plain calculation; and it is easy to determine, whether the project to which it is to be applied will bear the expense. There have been several instances, where the expenses of repelling an opposition from mill-owners to a Bill in Parliament, would have been more than enough to have made sufficient reservoirs.

"Whether they can be filled with water, may be known before they are undertaken, by an inquiry and measurement of the discharge in winter.

"The waste of water from a reservoir is in two ways; by exhalation and by leakage. The first, in a dry summer, would consume about *nine inches* (?) in depth from the surface: the making the head nine inches higher than otherwise necessary, would compensate for this. The leakage would be in few cases (where it would be prudent to attempt the scheme at all), even upon small streams, more than equal to the summer supply; and whether the water may be discharged by leakage, or by a pipe or artificial discharger, if they shall both discharge into the same channel, is not very material. In clay or other soils, where rushes grow, there will be no sensible leakage; and in soils more open, the pores of the soil would be an extension of the reservoir; and in cases where it might be necessary to discharge constantly from the reservoir, a quantity equal to the summer stream, it would, for a while, supply that discharge.

"Even in extreme cases of leaky soils, if there were any sudden floods, the reservoir would at least prevent their sudden discharge; but where the soil and strata are so close as to absorb little, and cause sudden floods (and it is to these cases that reservoirs are peculiarly applicable), there is little reason to apprehend leakage.

"The

"* At Alicant, the King of Spain has made a reservoir, the water of which, for the uses of summer agriculture, bring him in a revenue of 2000*l.* per annum. See various parts of Townsend's Travels through Spain, for the utility of such reservoirs."

" The Writer of this has lately had an opportunity of experiencing the effect of a small reservoir (not yet completed) as a regulator to a stream. It covers at present about 20 acres, and is made on a small brook, which, in dry seasons, does not furnish more water than would run through an aperture of an inch in diameter; but is subject to floods, which can hardly be discharged by a pipe of three feet in diameter.

" There is fixed under the head of it an iron pipe of six inches bore, which during the last winter has almost constantly been open; and discharged a quantity unequal no otherwise, than from the difference of pressure by the rising and falling of the water in the reservoir, at the different intervals of rainy and fair weather; and when the reservoir shall be enlarged, on the one hand, the meadows below will never be overflowed; and on the other hand, the reservoir will furnish, in the dry part of the summer, *at least twenty times* the quantity of water daily that the brook would otherwise afford.

"There is now depending in Parliament, a Bill for making a navigable canal through the vale of Belvoir to the town of Grantham, where the soil is almost wholly a firm tenacious clay, and will not require above half the water to supply it, which is necessary for canals in other instances.

" The country is subject to an extreme scarcity of water in summer, and to great superabundance in winter; and every circumstance is favourable to the intention of supplying the canal by artificial reservoirs. It is therefore earnestly hoped, that those who might be induced by their doubts to repel the intention, under the idea, that because no canal hath hitherto been *totally* supplied by reservoirs, therefore it must be impracticable, will give some credit to those who, on well-grounded information, have advised the measure; and that they will suffer it to be effected.

" It is hoped, that the execution of a canal upon this system may tend to promote the extension and continuance of those improvements in commerce and agriculture, on which so greatly depend the prosperity of this country, and which, in many instances, already have been checked, by neglecting to use the assistance of Art in remedying the defects, or rather in using or improving the bounties, of Nature.

" *Written in May*, 1792." W. JESSOP."

ROADS —P. 243. " My neighbour, Mr. Fowler, of Erdington, mentions the following obstacles, which he thinks should be removed. ' The present law, in limiting the number of horses on turnpike-roads, is not one of the least. If all carriages were limited to weight only, that must and would have the desired effect of keeping the roads in good order. Suppose six horses were allowed instead of four, two of them would

would most likely be breeding mares, or young horses likely to improve; the six would not require to be so large as if four only were kept, but of a lighter, nimbler sort, and would be kept at a less expense than four, that are required to do what the six should do. There would be more probability that the seed would be sown in due season, that he harvest would be finished quicker, and that more time would be obtained for carrying on other improvements of the farm with the horses. I also think if the tolls at turnpikes were collected by the weight drawn, it would be much fairer than the present mode of collection by the number of horses."

This appears to have been taken from BISHTON'S SHROPSHIRE. I do not find it in Mr. Pitt's original report.—For Mr. Bishton's plan at large, and my remarks upon it, see WESTERN DEPARTMENT, article Roads, Shropshire.

SOCIETIES.—P. 247. "There are no Societies in the county that I know of, for promoting agriculture. The principal iuducements are good markets, self-interest, and perhaps, in some degree, a spirit of emulation between different occupiers; from which inducements some of the farms have been brought to a pretty correct state of good cultivation, and which will be still farther improved if all the above inducements shall continue."

SUBJECT THE THIRD.

RURAL ECONOMY.

TENANTED ESTATES.

ESTATES.—P. 19. "This chapter will be short, as it is upon subjects with which the Writer is only acquainted in a general way, and upon which he made no inquiries in his excursion through the country; as not conceiving it included in the queries then proposed by the Board.

"The value of estates in this county vary greatly, from that of the great nobleman, or opulent commoner, of 10,000*l.* per annum, to the humble freeholder of forty shillings a year. I believe I could name six noblemen, and two commoners within the county, whose estates exceed 8000*l.* per annum; a good many more whose annual income is from that sum, down to 1000*l.* and other estates of every kind of value from that sum downwards."

TENURES.—P. 20. "I believe a large proportion of the county to be freehold property, but not without a considerable

siderable quantity of copyholds; considerable portions of landed property are also held on a leasehold tenure, under the bishop, colleges, deaneries, prebends, and other church dignitaries; but seldom by the occupier, being commonly farmed out again; but with the subject of tenures, I profess myself to be not accurately acquainted."

Improvements of Estates.

On this subject we find very little that is entitled to attention.

Draining Estates.—A note by Mr. Gisburne, on this operation, would have been entitled to extraction, entire, had not the subject been more amply and practically treated of, elsewhere. See my Midland Counties, and Treatise on Landed Property. The concluding paragraph, however, is interesting; as it shows the inefficacy of pipe bricks, for draining, when placed in the region of the roots of herbage; in like manner, as I have observed the inefficiency of earthen pipes for conveying water, by a subficial conduit for domestic purposes, when placed within the reach of the roots and finer fibrils of trees.

N. p. 151. "Having occasion to convey a stream (procured by boring several holes on the first ascent of a bank) about one hundred yards across a flat meadow, I laid a sough of hollow bricks surrounded with stiff water clay, some distance below the surface, for that purpose. In a few months I observed the stream, which issued at the mouth of the sough, gradually to diminish, and at length totally to fail; and a swamp began to form on the other side of the meadow, near the place where the holes whence the water issued, were bored. The sough, in which a stoppage was thus manifest, was opened; and it was found completely filled from end to end, by a cylindrical plug, composed of the roots of grass, which having entered between the joints of the bricks, were drawn out by the stream into filaments of immense length, and matted together, so as to prevent all water from passing. It was then relaid with mortar; but in the next year precisely the same circumstance recurred. It was relaid afresh with mortar, and the joints further secured by the application of broken pieces of tiles. Several years have now elapsed, and it has continued to answer perfectly. Another sough of the same kind, and for the same use, laid without mortar, has never been penetrated by roots of grass; but it lies deeper in the ground than circumstances would permit the former to be sunk.—*T. Gisborne, Yoxall-lodge, April 8th,* 1795."

Watering Grasslands.—This Reporter, it is evident, is (or was at the time of writing) not only unskilled in the practice,

practice, but unacquainted with the true theory, of Irrigation; nor does he intelligibly describe any valuable instance of practice, in Staffordshire.

For general remarks on the *qualities* of *water*, for the purpose of Irrigation, see the head, Grassland, ensuing.

EXECUTIVE MANAGEMENT.

On this general subject, too, we find Mr. Pitt deficient in practical knowledge; and the information which he has gathered is seldom of importance.

MANAGERS.—P. 19. "Respecting the management of estates; those of gentlemen of large fortunes are generally managed by stewards; and here let me introduce a remark of my neighbour, Mr. Fowler of Erdington, as it will tend somewhat to lengthen what I expected to have been a short chapter; he says 'there is another obstacle to the improvement of land, which is the employment of attorneys at law, by some gentlemen of large landed property, as their agents, who, although eminent in their professions, know little or nothing about the management of land, and consequently are unfit to give advice to tenants, unfit to be woodmen, and totally unfit to have the direction and management of landed property respecting its cultivation.'"

TENANCY.—P. 38. "Leases are often granted: those for twenty-one years are not uncommon, and some also for a shorter term exist."

COVENANTS.—P. 27. "Respecting repairs, it is very common here, upon the entry of a new tenant, for the landlord to put the farm in tenantable repair; and afterwards, the landlord finding materials in the rough, or otherwise, the tenant is at the expense of workmanship to keep it so; and in most modern contracts the tenant is bound, in case he should quit, to leave the farm and buildings in good repair."

P. 39. "The Rev. Mr. Leigh, in the letting of Russell-hall estate, has adopted a covenant which I believe quite novel: the tenant is bound to lay all the dung of the farm on the turf only; and fallows, and all loose or ploughed land, are manured with lime. It should be observed that the estate abounds with lime. The consequence has been, a very great and rapid improvement of the estate—the product of wheat, this scanty year, being uncommonly great. The soil is a cool moist loam, of tolerable depth, and has been formerly under indifferent management."

I copy the above to gain an opportunity of suggesting that, altho there may be circumstances under which a plan of that sort can be pursued with propriety, *for a while* (especially

(especially if it has been under "indifferent," or slovenly management) that is to say, until the vegetable matters with which the arable lands have been stored,—be exhausted. Yet it should be adopted with caution; and ought, I conceive, in no case, to be long persisted in.

Rents.—P. 33. "The rental of farms in this county varies from 10*s.* to 30*s.* per acre, according to its staple and condition; but as the larger half is in a backward state, the average price will fall below 20*s.*; however, I have no doubt but the average value is increasing, in consequence of progressive improvement (this in 1796). But there is great reason to believe, that from the year 1796 to 1804, the average rent of the county has advanced full 5*s.* per acre, and that the present average rental is not less than 25*s.* per acre, varying in whole farms from 15*s.* to 2*l.* and upwards, per acre."

Woodlands.

Woods.—Staffordshire is abundantly wooded. It contains within its outlines (or did contain some years ago) more *large* oak timber, I believe, than any other County in the kingdom. And Mr. Pitt has given, with satisfactory intelligence, a detail of the timber growing on the principal estates in the County. The following is his account of Lord Bagot's woods.

P. 124. "The first and best timbered estate, is that of Lord Bagot, in the neighbourhood of Abbot's-Bromley. The woods extend over many hundred acres, and almost wholly consist of oak, the ripest, finest and best that I ever saw; and I believe I run no risk of exceeding the bounds of truth, if I say the best in the kingdom. A very large quantity of oak in these woods is now quite ripe, and some even decaying. Many of the oaks carry timber to the length of sixty and seventy feet; and in Lord Bagot's park are many hundreds of very extraordinary bulk, containing from 200 to 400 feet of timber each. I could pick out many worth sixty guineas a-piece, and some even more. Some of this timber is of considerable antiquity, and mentioned by Dr. Plott, as full grown timber in 1686. I was informed upon the spot, that for these woods 100,000*l.* have been offered, and that his Lordship has half as much timber in Denbighshire. Total value of timber, 150,000*l.* which in the three per cents. at the present price, would purchase an income for ever, of more than 6000 guineas per annum. The succession woods and young plantations are very considerable, and still continuing; and as Mr. Harvey, his Lordship's steward, very judiciously observes, upon land not worth a rent of 10*s.* per acre, paying better, underwood included,

included, than in any other way; and it is upon a poor cold land of this description, that the above fine timber chiefly abounds, the soil being a moist gravelly loam, upon a clay or marl bottom." *

The other well timbered Estates mentioned by Mr. Pitt are

Chillington, the property of T. Giffard, Esq.
Beaudesert, of the Earl of Uxbridge.
Himley, Lord Dudley and Ward.
Teddesley, Sir E. Littleton.
Wrottesley, Sir J. Wrottesley.
Sandwell, the Earl of Dartmouth.
Pattershul, Sir G. Pigot; with various others.

The *prices* of timber, in 1794, were as follows.—P. 222.

			s.	*d.*		*s.*	*d.*
" Oak timber, per foot		-	1	0	to	2	6
Ash	ditto	-	0	9	to	1	6
Elm	ditto	-	0	9	to	1	6

" The other sorts, as beech, sycamore, poplar, and the different sorts of fir, according to quality and demand, plenty, scarcity, and other local circumstances of time and place, varying from 8*d.* or 9*d.* to 1*s.* 6*d.* or 2*s.* per foot."

UNDERWOOD.—In a note by Mr. Sneyd, speaking of his own estate of Belmont, we meet with a new species of the *wares* of coppice woods.—N. p. 278. " On a gently rising hill fronting the south-east, nearly surrounded by deep woods of oak, ash, elm, lime, maple, &c. with underwood of mountain ash, hazel, birch, alder, salix's of several species, &c. &c. which underwood is cut, on an average, once in six years, to make crates for the Pottery."

PLANTING.—In this art, Mr. Pitt would seem to be a keen amateur.

P. 125. (speaking of Lord Bagot's woods and plantations)—" the young plantations are made sometimes by sowing acorns with wheat, after summer-fallow; and sometimes by planting out young plants of oak, and other wood; in which case, at the end of one or two years, when such plants have taken well to the ground, they are cut off at the surface, and the second shoot trusted to for the tree; this second shoot thriving with much more luxuriance and vigour than the first, checked by transplanting. Also after cutting down a wood, the replanting is sometimes effected by striking in with the pick-axe a sufficient number of acorns

* For general remarks on the age and growth of Timber, arising from a view of Bagot Park, see my MIDLAND COUNTIES, Min. 149.

acorns and other seeds of forest trees or underwood; and all these methods have been attended with success. The young plantations are well fenced, and carefully guarded from trespass by a woodman appointed for that purpose."

P. 131. (still speaking of the Woodland Estates of Staffordshire)—" I have two more observations to make upon planting: the one relating to the proper site of ground and situation of plantations, whether intended for ornament or profit; the other on the timber best adapted to fulfil those objects, and at the same time to answer the purposes of pleasure and profit to the planter, and of utility to the public."

In these observations, however, we find nothing which has not been long before the public; one idea excepted. Their chief merit lies in urging the planting of steeps (not "precipices") of Staffordshire. And, in his tour across the Morelands, Mr. P. suggests a *rational* mode of proceeding.

P. 263. "To give any such plantations a fair chance of success, I should propose to begin, not on the summits, but on the declivity of the hills: and as such first plantations increased in growth, to proceed with fresh ones nearer the summit, till the whole should be covered: by which management the plants of strength and grown would be made to protect and shelter those of tender age."

The slow progress which this method would necessarily occasion, is its principal objection. I have recently planted the brow of a steep, in the most bleak and exposed situation, imaginable, with the view of skreening the plants to be put into the plain above; and I doubt not with success. The *top* of a mountain height is *incessantly* exposed; whereas the *face* of it has *intervals* of *shelter*; by the change of the wind. In this case, an extended breadth of the plain ground, dipping somewhat from the summit and most suitable for planting,—will in a few years receive effectual shelter from the most offensive wind, the north; whereas, by proceeding up the "precipice," a very narrow line, a few yards in breadth only, could receive benefit;—even from plants of several years growth; of course, it might be a quarter of a century, or a greater length of time according to the height and steepness of the site, before the whole of a tall steep could be completely covered with plants, in that progressive manner.

AGRICULTURE.

AGRICULTURE.

FARMS.—P. 29. "The farms of this county are of all sizes, from twenty acres to five hundred; yet it must be acknowledged that, within the last twenty or thirty years, the consolidation of small farms has been not uncommon."

Farm Fences.—P. 268. "Not far from Okeover, I observed a practice well worthy, perhaps, of imitation in other places, of washing young quickset hedges with *lime-water*, to prevent their being browsed on by cattle." Rather say with a puddle or grout of lime and water:—a good practice but not uncommon.

HOMESTEADS.—P. 24. "Respecting farm-houses and offices, little can be said in general, except that those of ancient date appear often built merely by chance, without design or contrivance, whilst those of modern construction are sometimes well contrived, comfortable, and convenient. Most of the modern ones are built with brick, and covered with tile or slate. The barns, cow-houses, stables, and offices, are laid out so as to shelter a compact-yard, and some instances occur of good convenient feeding-stalls; but most of the old ones are very defective in these particulars, and the occupier is obliged to make shift as well as he can."

Mr. Pitt offers plans for farmsteads &c. which are declared to be of his own invention, and delineation. But I perceive nothing in them of superior excellency. They are *very well*, but books of Agriculture are already *full* of such.

Building Materials.—P. 26. "The materials now very generally used in modern farm-buildings, are bricks for the walls, and the covering tile or slate."

OCCUPIERS.—P. 20. "We have in this county some gentlemen of fortune, who farm upon a considerable scale; and some others who have a turn for business; these are consequently their own stewards; but there is not perhaps a more useful or respectable set of men in the county than the proprietors of 200 or 300 acres of land, who farm it themselves; and several such I am acquainted with, who are men of business and economy, and whose farms are cultivated in a first-rate style: it is from this class, and from the first-rate farmers, that all improvements in stock, and in the introduction of new plants, and new modes of cultivation, are to be expected, and in which, when established, they will be imitated by others: this may be sufficiently

sufficiently proved by the improved general cultivation of turnips and artificial grasses, which were introduced solely by the above class of cultivators, and in which they are now very generally copied."

P. 21. "I observe in the Lancashire reprinted Survey, the yeomanry are noticed in this Chapter, as a diminishing class of men; and I have often observed, they are remarked by writers as becoming extinct. If we have lost, or are losing them in Staffordshire, I think it can be only in name. We have gentlemen of larger and smaller fortunes, occupiers of their own estates; and respectable farmers, who hire their occupations; farmers upon a smaller scale, many of them laborious and industrious; people in trade of every class, from the opulent merchant and manufacturer, to the working tradesman and day-labourer. In short, there seems no void in the body politic, but a regular gradation from the highest to the lowest class."

P. 32. "Respecting the character of the Staffordshire farmers, I do not think them at all wanting in industry, or in a readiness to adopt established improvements."

P. 79. (Article "Drill Husbandry") "The rage for farming by gentlemen of large landed property, a few years back, has pretty much subsided, in consequence of the low prices of landed produce of the last year (1803), and the high price of labour."

In a sub-article, termed "Domestic Police of Agriculture," we meet with the following enlarged and flattering view of the AGRICULTURAL PROFESSION.—P. 245. "The conducting of all business by system and regularity; both the cultivation of the land, the management of the stock, and the concerns of the family; and the dealings with others with honour and punctuality: for the situation of the practical agriculturist, affords a scope for the practice of the domestic, moral, and social virtues, and that not 'hid under a bushel, but on a candlestick,' and in a conspicuous point of view; his humanity embraces not only his friends and fellow creatures, but the brute creation; his daily employ is to raise food for the hungry, and clothing for the naked; and his industry is not only for the advantage of himself and his family, but for the benefit of his country."

PROGRESS of HUSBANDRY.—P. 72. "The most material alteration that has taken place in the cultivation of this county since 1796, has been in the pretty general introduction of the Swedish turnip."

PRESENT STATE of HUSBANDRY.—P. 313. (under the head "Recapitulation") "Upon a retrospective view of the present state of the county, it will appear that Staffordshire has

has begun to improve; and it may be added, has made some progress in improvement: that some of its intelligent and active cultivators (for such there are) have brought their farms to a pretty correct state of good cultivation, but none have by any means approached perfection; not even that perfection which they are sensible is in their power. Much remains to be done, even by those who have made the greatest efforts, and most successful exertions; and even these, are the persons who are the most sensible that we are in the infancy of agricultural improvement; who find, the more they do, the more wants doing, as one improvement paves the way to another. Much of the land of this county remains in a medium state of management much below mediocrity, and large breadths of enclosed land have never been improved at all. If to this we add our extensive wastes, unenclosed, unimproved, and uncultivated, we shall have a large set-off against our superior management, before exhibited. Upon the whole, to the eye of an intelligent agricultural stranger, familiar with a country highly cultivated, and capable of taking in at once a general view of the county, it would convey the idea of a country just emerged, or emerging, from a state of barbarism: and indeed the idea would be just, for such was very recently the state of this county; and the practice of barbarous ages may be said to be but very lately (if yet) wholly exploded. In the limits of my own observation, which can little exceed thirty years, I have known the following, a common practice on the best lands: 1. fallow; 2. wheat; 3. barley; 4. oats; and often oats repeated, and then left to Nature; the worst lands left to pasture and spontaneous rubbish: turnips and artificial grasses, scarcely at all known in farming, though now fully introduced. The person who first cultivated ray-grass in this county, and first sold the seed in Wolverhampton market, was an uncle of mine, now living; he sold the seeds of clovers and trefoils at the same time; since when, the demand for these seeds is increased, I suppose, an hundredfold. The rents of lands were then about an half of the present rents, and the population of the country not in a much higher proportion; the roads were scarcely passable, and many of the best farms were in the hands of the owners, who were unable to get tenants for them; and all this was the case within less than half a century of the present time."

For a general idea of the agricultural state of the lands of the County, at large, see the head, *Soils*, p. 11, aforegoing.

WORKPEOPLE.—P. 216. "The price of labour and the rate of wages vary in different places. They are always highest

highest in the neighbourhood of flourishing manufactures, and lowest in remote parts of the county, where no such manufactures are established. The wages of a day-labourer (in 1793) vary in this county from 1*s.* to 1*s.* 6*d.* per day, and beer. In the summer quarter, 1*s.* per day, with meat and drink; and the draught or carriage of a load of coals, is very common here. Much of the labour is lett by the great, at prices which enable a good workman to get 2*s.* or more per day, and beer."

P. 218. "The Rev. Dr. Falconer observes, that labourers' wages have lately advanced so much in his neighbourhood, that it is not easy to ascertain the average price; female servants in particular, can hardly be hired at any price; this he attributes to the numbers of women employed in the cotton mills lately erected; he says farther, 'some regulation respecting the wages of servants employed in husbandry would be of universal use.' It seems, however, reasonable, that every labouring person should be entitled to the most they can make of their labour, and that the true cause of complaint is not so much the advanced wages given, as the dilatoriness and neglect wherewith the business is done; our men-servants often fly off into large towns, where they earn higher wages, and learn to spend them all when earned; thus acquiring bad habits and a depravity of morals, without at all bettering their circumstances."

P. 219. "The following remarks on the proportion between the price of labour and provisions, are from Dr. Withering, and do great credit to his humanity: he says, 'the wages of the day-labourers are certainly very inadequate to the price of provisions, and hence arises, in a great measure, the enormous increase of the poors'-rates: I confine my observations on this subject to country parishes; a man, his wife, and five children, living chiefly upon bread, as these people do, will consume one bushel of wheat per week; the man gains from 6*s.* to 9*s.* per week, and his bread costs 8*s.* or more, when such is the price of wheat. I know the necessity, of working people whose nourishment chiefly depends upon bread, having the best kind of bread, such as affords the most nutrition. Nothing is got by the higher wages he may sometimes earn at piece-work; the man soon wears himself out by extra exertions, and his family lose his support the sooner; a day-labourer at fifty begins to be an old man: no other proof is wanting of his being over-worked. On well considering this subject, perhaps you may think with me, that a labourer should earn weekly to the amount of a bushel, and a half of wheat, and that the magistrates should at every Quarter Sessions fix the lowest price of day-labour day-labour for the three succeeding months, in the proportion I have stated, to the then price of wheat."

WORKMEN'S WAGES.

I THINK it right to observe, here, that no *one* (if *any*) price for the daysworks of laborers, could with propriety be *fixed*. Some men are worth double the wages of others:—not merely in regard to age or physical strength; but to their skill and industry. There ought, in my opinion, to be, everywhere, and on all occasions, two prices at least; namely, one for *prime*, the other for *ordinary* workmen. Nothing would tend more to stimulate the willing and the ingenious, and spur on the aukward and indolent, than such a distinction. Yet no where have I found it practised, in husbandry. But I know, from some attempts which I have made, that if the occupiers of a township, or district, would concur in such a measure, it might readily be established.

WORKING ANIMALS.—P. 208. "Horses for the purposes of agriculture, are almost universally used by the farmers in this county, and seem almost totally to have superceded the use of oxen, and are still gaining ground, and oxen at the plough are but very little used."

IMPLEMENTS.—P. 47. "Double or two-furrow ploughs are much used, and answer well on light soils, where four horses will plough two acres or more per day. These ploughs are made on a good construction, and require no holder. The single wheel plough is a very good tool, requiring no person to hold or touch it, except when it is turning at the end of the furrow: they require but one attendant, for which a boy of fourteen or fifteen years of age is sufficient. And here I cannot but remark the superiority of a plough that requires no holder but a person only to drive the horses, and turn it out and in at the end of the furrow, to one which requires to be held, and the horses of which are guided by reins. These ploughs have lately been much improved by the addition of an iron earth-board firmly screwed to the coulter, called here a flay, for ploughing turf, which takes off the turf, and turns it into the furrow, where the plough immediately covers it with earth: by this management, a turf at one ploughing has the appearance of a fallow, and harrows nearly as well. This ploughing is attended with scarcely any extraordinary trouble, but requires the strength, perhaps, of an extra horse. It is much used here for turf."

For the origin, construction, and merit of the double plow, see my MIDLAND COUNTIES. And for the architype of the flay plow, see my MINUTES OF AGRICULTURE, article Burysod Plow P. 49.

P. 49. "I cannot help thinking, I hope without partiality, that our implements in general, but ploughs in particular, are equal to any, and superior to most, which I have seen; and I have viewed those of many counties. Mr. Miller on this subject makes the following remark: 'The ploughs made in any country where the ploughmen have been most used to them, are the best; for when I came to this place, I brought with me ploughs and ploughmen out of Leicestershire, which were good ones so long as my Leicestershire-men staid: but when they left me, they might as well have taken the ploughs along with them; for Staffordshire-men could not plough with them.' This remark may serve to shew the difficulty of altering established customs, and that such alterations, even if improvements, must be gradual, and introduced by degrees; as the same workmen are not brought at once to use a new tool expertly: and unless they in some degree approve of any new practice, to make a fair experiment, the master must give his own attention, and do the business himself.

"Since drawing up the above account to the present time, 1804, Norfolk ploughs have been frequently introduced into this county; particularly by gentlemen who have made farming experiments; but though they will plough our moist soils, they are not likely to be permanently established here, and are generally laid aside, as being better adapted for lighter lands, and inferior to our own ploughs for mixed or strong soils."

The justness of the above remarks will strike every one who has had experience in these matters. Yet let them not prevent trials of improvement.

MANURES.—*Lime.*—P. 167. "This is a manure of very extensive application, and of which great quantities are annually and constantly used upon all sorts of lands."

"It is laid on at the rate of from six to ten quarters per acre: the price at the works, from 3*s.* to 4*s.* 3*d.* per quarter, according to quality of the lime, and situation of the works; and the carriage, and other expenses, nearly, and at some distances quite, as much as the prime cost. It is generally laid on tillage land, either for barley, turnips, or wheat; and is deemed best to lay it on in a quick state, soon after slacking, and to harrow it in when the land is dry: it is sometimes laid on turf land, and, it is said, with good effect. It is frequently fetched 15 miles by land carriage for manure, and is, I think, used in a more extensive way than I have observed elsewhere, and its use is still increasing."

Marl.—P. 167. "This has been much used on arable land for ages back, as is evident from the very extensive marl-pits marl-pits to be found in different parts of the county: in many places the land has been over-marled, and is rendered harsh; this, by fallowing and liming, is ameliorated, and rendered fertile. It is in general only in the loamy soils that a true marl is found; in the mixed gravelly soils is often found a clay marl, or friable brick clay, which is used on such soils with good effect."

Arable Management.

In the chapter "Arable Land, Cropping and Cultivation," are thrown together, in a somewhat chaotic manner, different items relating to this most extensive and important subject of agriculture. A very few particulars, only, I conceive, are entitled to extraction.

Species of Arable Crops.—P. 57. "The grain, pulse, roots, and other vegetables cultivated in field culture, upon the arable lands of this county, are chiefly the following:

1. Wheat.
2. Rye.
3. Barley.
4. Oats.
5. Beans.
6. Pease.
7. Vetches.
8. Buckwheat.
9. Hemp.
10. Flax.
11. Turnips.
12. Potatoes.
13. Cabbages.
14. Rape.

"To these may be added clovers, trefoils, and two or three of the real grasses. Turnip cabbage has been tried, as well as sainfoin, lucerne, burnet, and the other artificial grasses. Carrots and other garden-plants are not introduced into field cultivation, except by gardeners for the markets."

Tillage.—P. 64. "Fallowing for wheat is practised on cold, wet, or strong lands by the best farmers, and is doubtless absolutely necessary on all lands improper for turnips (which all lands are, that are not sufficiently dry to eat them on the ground by stock; for in such lands the poaching and treading, in carrying off the turnips, will do much more injury to the land than the turnips are worth); and he who shall attempt to manage such land without fallowing, will have occasion to repent his mistake. The Writer of this acknowleges himself to have been once a sufferer by too implicit a confidence in the opposite theory."

P. 85. "Summer-fallowing well managed, has a tendency to extirpate all sorts of weeds; for the pulverizing of the soil by frequent ploughings and harrowings, combined with the effects of dews, showers, and the solar warmth, disposes the seeds, roots, and prolific principles of all plants

to

to vegetation; which vegetation being effected, and the young plant in a growing state, it is completely destroyed by the next ploughing: this several times repeated, purges the land of weeds, and its whole vegetative force is in consequence directed to the support of the particular vegetable whose seed is thrown in by the cultivator; or should a few weeds remain undestroyed, they are to be drawn out, or cut up by weeding. Upon these considerations are founded two very obvious and just principles of practical agriculture, viz. 1. The necessity of summer-fallowing foul land; 2. The propriety of being very careful in the choice of seed."

SEMINATION.—P. 73. "The major part or bulk of the sowing business is done in the old *broad-cast* way, though drilling is introduced, and has made some progress. The general allowance of seed to an acre in this way, is, of wheat, two bushels, or a little more; of barley three bushels; of oats four to five bushels; of pease three bushels; and of beans, I believe, four bushels; the bushel of this county being in many places nine gallons and a half."

P. 74. "*Drill Husbandry.*—The drill husbandry, as stated before, is fairly introduced, and has made some progress. I believe I could name a dozen farmers who have drill-machines, one-half of which are within a few miles of Pendeford."

P. 77. "Respecting the advantages of drilling, and its superiority to broad-cast sowing, the following advantages are obvious: 1. The vacant spaces between the rows can be much easier cleaned by the hoe, than between the plants in broad-cast sowing; 2. The seed is laid in at a more proper and equal depth than by the harrows; and, 3. A saving of seed may be effected of, I believe, one-fourth of the whole. In some other respects, theoretically considered, the broad-cast sowing should seem to have the advantage; for, 1. The young plants promiscuously disposed will have a less distance to draw their nourishment, and will occupy the whole extent beneath the surface with less effort, and with shorter root fibres, than when crowded in rows with open spaces between; 2. The broad-cast sowing is rather more simple and easy in operation, and less liable to be obstructed by change of weather, or showers; 3. In the case of sowing grass seeds with barley, which is or should be always practised, the advantage of hoeing is lost; and in the steeping of wheat for sowing, the drying with lime is lost; in which probably a great part of the health of the operation consists; and the drying by spreading the seed on a floor, seems tedious, and a work of time. It is further to be observed, that for land to be fit for drilling, it should be be clean from root-weeds, and in a fine state of culture. I have heard a very sensible experienced broad-cast farmer remark, that when his land is in that state, he can do any thing with it, or get a good crop in any way. I have just further to remark, that I did some years back attempt the drill system, with a view of ascertaining how far foul land, or such as wanted fallowing, could be cleaned by hoeing between the rows, hoping there might be a possibility of precluding the necessity of summer-fallowing; but not succeeding to my mind in this particular, I declined the practice. I would not wish by any means to be understood to have the least wish to discountenance the attempts of others, as I consider the practice of drilling and hoing the fields in a good style as a very neat mode of culture; and he must always be esteemed an improver of the agriculture of his country, who shall obviate the difficulties attending the drill, and the objections to it, so as to render it of more general utility to the united kingdoms.

"Mr. Miller, Dunstall, is a friend to the drill husbandry, which he practises on a considerable scale. He has some barley this season which promises to be an excellent crop; it is but justice, however, to remark, that the broad-cast in the same field is equally good.

"The drill husbandry of this county remains in *statu quo*, and is nearly in the same comparative state as it was eight or nine years ago."

P. 79. "Upon the whole, there appears no probability of the drill husbandry at present becoming general."

GROWING CROPS.—P. 169. "To shew the importance of attending to this subject of weeding properly, it may be observed, that this business, if well done, will lessen every year; but if neglected, will increase beyond calculation: for—

'One year's good weeding,
Will prevent seeding;
But one year's seeding,
Makes seven years' weeding.'

"As a preventative is much better than a cure, it would certainly be an improvement in our rural polity, if it were preventable and fineable at quarter sessions, and the offender punished by fine accordingly, who should suffer weeds to run to seed on his premises, particularly those of the class *syngenesia*, which, having their seeds furnished with wings, will disperse them over a whole country."

For a striking instance of this mischief, with reflections thereon, see my MIDLAND COUNTIES, Minute 76. See also the head, Tillage, p. 39, aforegoing, relative to the prevention of weeds.

PRODUCE

PRODUCE of ARABLE CROPS.—P. 73. "The returns or products vary; but to be deemed a good crop, should be, of wheat, twenty-five bushels per acre; of barley thirty; of oats thirty to forty; of pease and beans various. Much greater quantities than the above have been obtained in particular cases, and a bad crop full as often gives less."

BARLEY.—P. 59. "I have been informed that the following tillage for barley in these soils (strong loams) has been attended with success, though not practised to any great extent. After summer fallowing for wheat, and harvesting the wheat crop, those who practise it plough up in the November following the wheat-stubbles in a proper form for sowing, lay them dry by proper furrows or gutters, and sow barley the April following, without farther ploughing, as the amelioration of winter frosts disposes the land to work kindly under the harrows without more tillage."

CULTIVATED HERBAGE.—In a list of Pasture and Meadow Herbage, we find remarks on the two following plants.—P. 96. "The *Crowfoots (ranunculus's)*, so very abundant in our meadows and pastures, and which, though in themselves so acrid and pungent, are notwithstanding most certainly a grateful and desirable admixture. They seem intended as seasoners and correctors, and to be adapted to uses in the animal economy similar to that of salt, mustard, pepper, and vinegar, at our tables; to correct the flatulent or putrid qualities of the more palatable and luxuriant dishes on the great table of Nature. It is said in Withering's Botany, of the *ranunculus acris*, that 'cows and horses leave this plant untouched, though their pasture be ever so bare.' I believe this to be only true of the flower stem, or when there is not a sufficient admixture of other more palatable herbage."

Neither the Reporter, nor his friend Dr. Withering, appears to have been sufficiently acquainted with the *agricultural* qualities of the ranunculus tribe; they being equally strangers, it would seem, to the valuable nature of the RANUNCULUS *repens;* which, is peculiarly affected by cattle; being free from acridity; having neither mustard nor pepper! in its composition. It might, I doubt not, be cultivated with greater propriety than many of the plants that have lately been recommended.—The Glocestershire cow farmers appear to have been the first to make the discovery. See my GLOCESTERSHIRE. Also MIDLAND COUNTIES.

P. 100. "*Hogweed**, or *cow parsnip (heracleum)*. This plant

"* A good plant for neat beasts, which they are very fond of when cut young. If this plant had the advantage of tillage it would answer well to the farmer, and would bear cutting two or three times in the season.—*S.*"

plant (Variety 2. the *angustifolium)* is very abundant in an upland mowing meadow near Dudley-castle; and though I believe cattle will eat it without injury, yet it is certainly too coarse and weed-like to be suffered to abound in well managed land."

This, under proper management, is a nutritious valuable plant. In mowing grounds if suffered to run up, without a check, it becomes a dry kex, and an encumbrance to the hay crop; but if cut out while the crop is growing (and collected as green food) the aftergrowth will afford hay of the first quality.

For its high estimation among farm workpeople, as *hog food*, see my SOUTHERN COUNTIES, District of Petworth.

I have lately raised it in rows, and have cut it repeatedly in the course of the summer. Not only hogs, but cattle, and horses are partial to it; when it is cut before it run up, or while it is running up to seed. Where hogs are confined to a yard, or where their outlet is narrowly circumscribed, it will be found a valuable species of herbage, in a farm yard garden.

In the Reporter's Catalogue raisonné of "Artificial Grasses," some remarks on the two following species are noticeable.

P. 102. "Burnet *(poterium sanguisorba)* has been sown by many persons of late years, and by some on a broad scale. I know it from experience to be a valuable addition to cow pastures, hardy, and strictly perennial. Cows prefer it to clover, and it is doubtless wholesome for them; sheep and horses prefer clover; and it is by no means so productive as the broad-leafed red clover. A very attentive friend and neighbour of mine, who keeps a very large dairy, and has for some years back sown large quantities of this plant, is so very partial to it, that he would this year have sown ten hundred weight of the seed, could he have procured it."

This is an application of Burnet which I have not before met with. For other purposes, it certainly ranks among the meanest of cultivated herbs.

P. 103. "Rib-grass *(plantago lanceolata)* is also sown in considerable quantities, and by many approved as a good mixture with clover and ray grass. There is good authority for asserting that cattle will not eat its leaves alone; but it is believed to be a grateful mixture with other herbage*."

As

"* Rib-grass: I am lately informed by a very considerable and attentive grazing farmer, that the greater value of this plant is in its seeds, which when formed, are eagerly sought for and greedily devoured by cattle and sheep, and that they are very nutritive."

As a pasture plant for cattle and sheep, it has its merit. But in a mowing ground, it may be considered as a troublesome weed. It is among the last of meadow herbs to lose its sap; and when it has entirely lost it, moulders to dust.

Grass Lands.

P. 88. "The low lands adjoining all our rivers and brooks, come naturally under this head of meadows and pastures, as well as considerable tracts of flat land, which, by the backing on of water in former times, have acquired a stratum of peat on their surface.

"Considerable tracts of meadow land, lying near the larger brooks and rivers, are improved, and kept in sufficient heart by the natural overflow of the streams; but this advantage is enjoyed at the risk of having the whole crop occasionally swept away by untimely floods, a misfortune too, which occurs pretty frequently.

"The fertile meadows on the banks of the Dove, are an object considerably interesting. This river, which separates for many miles the counties of Stafford and Derby, rises from springs under the limestone hills of the Moorlands and the Peak; and at times receives an amazing addition, from torrents rushing down those hills after heavy rains or the melting of snow. Its channel has a great declivity, and in many places this river comes tumbling over the rocks in cascades; and in its greatest swell pushes on with astonishing rapidity, which continues to below Rocester, where the water has a greyish cast, apparent to the eye, from its being impregnated with calcareous earth, to which undoubtedly may be attributed the extraordinary fertility of its banks: for after receiving the Churnet, a considerable stream from a part of the Moorlands, not abounding with limestone, its water becomes diluted; and although its banks still continue excellent, yet they visibly decline in richness, and the extraordinary fertility ceases. Immense quantities of limestone are found both on the banks and in the channel of the Dove, in the first part of its course: this limestone has fallen in length of time from precipices, which overhang the river. The fertility of land on the upper parts of this river, about and above Rocester, is, and always has been proverbial; 'as rich as Dove,' being an epithet applied to any spot highly forced *. This land has a perpetual verdure, and the spring-floods of the river are very gratifying to the land-occupiers, who have this proverb, 'in April, Dove's

"* The farmers are accustomed to say, that it is scarcely possible to overstock a few acres of Dove land.—*Rev. Stebbing Shaw.*"

Dove's flood is worth a king's good.' It is also said of Dove banks in spring, that a stick laid down there over-night shall not be found next morning for grass. It is very certain this river fertilizes its banks like another Nile; but sometimes rises so high in twelve hours as to carry off sheep and cattle to the great alarm of the inhabitants; and in as few hours abates, and returns again within its own channel. Below Rocester, where this river receives the Churnet, the plain spreads very wide, and continues so with variations to below Uttoxeter. The plain here, on either side the river, is composed of deep rich mellow loam, impregnated with, if not wholly formed of, a rich sediment of mud and calcareous earth. The herbage is very fine, without any mixture of rushes or aquatic plants. The grasses are of the common sorts; but the foxtail, the vernal grass, the *poa's*, the dog's-tail, and the meadow *bromus's* predominate. It contains also rib-grass, meadow and white clover, upright crowfoot, and the common herbage of other meadows: not without a mixture of the cursed or common thistle, or saw-wort, (*serratula arvensis*), so common in every soil and country. The plain within the reach of the floods of the Dove, extend, in some places to near a mile in breadth, particularly opposite Uttoxeter, and amounts to several thousand acres, almost entirely pastured with cows, sheep, and some horses; very little of it being mown for hay. The uncertainty and suddenness of the floods make the risk of hay too great. The rent of the Dove land generally rises to near forty shillings per acre; and I was informed by an eminent grazier on the spot, that were it not for the inconvenience of floods, the land, equally rich as at present, would be worth ten shillings per acre more, even for grazing: as it sometimes requires a sharp look-out to preserve the stock from drowning, even where there has been little or no rain on the spot. A sudden rain or melting of the snow on the Moorland or Peak hills, is sufficient to inundate large breadths of land near this river: as the declivity or fall is great, the swell of water is sudden, but soon over, and the largest floods continue but a few hours. It is to be remembered, however, that the extraordinary fertility of these lands is owing to this circumstance, however complained of as an inconvenience."

General Remarks on Calcareous Waters.

I insert the above extract with greater satisfaction, as it serves to strengthen the theory which I have long entertained; namely, that calcareous waters fertilize, and that astringent waters (collected from heathy mountains) tend to sterilize the grass lands over which they are spread*.

The unadulterated waters of the Dove enrich to the highest degree. But after they mix with those of the Churnet, they lose a part of their fertilizing quality.

Subsequent observations in the district of the western chalk hills of the southern counties (in Wiltshire and its environs) proved the theory, and raised it to scientific certainty.

It is not the river tumbling over the rocks, or falling from precipices, that causes the fertilizing quality of the Dove, but the rain waters that have filtered through the pores and fissures of the calcareous strata of which the hills are formed and that rise at their feet, loaded with limey particles,—taken up, chemically, in their passage downward;—principally, it may be conceived, from the loose eflorescent matter, with which limestone hills abound.

The pulverized limestone which is of course washed off the roads across the hills during heavy rains, together with the dung of sheep, which is generally scattered plentifully in such roads,—may give the "greyish cast" mentioned, and *add* to the general fertility.

GRAZING.—P. 106. "Staffordshire is not considerably a feeding" (fatting) "county, at least not in any degree comparable with the adjoining one of Leicester; yet there are some gentlemen who farm, and considerable farmers, who think much of the trouble of a dairy; who fatten a good many cattle and sheep; calves and hogs are fattened upon most farms; the horned cattle fattened here are principally heifers and cows, with no considerable proportion of bullocks; these are mostly bred in the county, which I suppose breeds more cattle than it consumes, as a considerable number of in part fed cattle are sold to dealers, who drive them towards the metropolis."

ORCHARDS.—P. 119. "The orchards of Staffordshire are inconsiderable; little or no cyder or perry is made, and upon the whole, I believe the produce of the county is insufficient for its own consumption even at table; this ought doubtless to be censured as a neglect; as many soils and situations are unquestionably well adapted for fruit of any kind: the farms and other country houses have generally fruit trees for their own consumption; but not sufficient to supply the markets, which are principally furnished from Worcestershire

* See my MIDLAND COUNTIES, Minute 42; which was written when that theory was in its infancy; and on the very lands that are now under notice.

shire. An extraordinary circumstance I have been told from good authority, which is, that upon a hit of fruit in Worcestershire, two thousand pounds have been paid in one season for tonnage of apples upon the Staffordshire canal, in their way to Lancashire : the tonnage demanded is about *5s 6d.* per ton ; whence the quantity conveyed must have been near 8000 tons. The parish of Over Areley, in this county, which adjoins Worcestershire, has formerly been famous for fruit, especially apples ; but the orchards have been suffered to decline, though some recent attempts have been making towards reinstating them, and the soil and aspect are doubtless well adapted for the purpose."

P. 122. "Large tracts of this county are well adapted for the growth of fruit ; deep rich friable loams are the natural soils for the best cyder apples and pears, for the production of perry ; and on lighter soils they will well succeed, especially if a good cart-load of marl be dug into the earth, and incorporated with the soil previous to the planting of each tree : in the hedge-rows of pasture land they would, I think, do no kind of injury ; and even planted at proper distances in grazing fields, they would little interfere either with the production or consumption of the pasture herbage ; and even in arable lands, a fruit tree I conceive to be less injurious than any of the kinds of timber trees."

Growing barley in hedges, and wheat where barley is now grown (the favourite idea of the Reporter) may seem to be a self evident improvement. But experience, in the cider counties, have not found it such. Somersetshire is now the only County, I believe, in which apple trees are raised in hedgerows ; and, there, they are mostly planted *by the side* of, not *in* the hedges. There are two evils of fruit trees in hedges. They are certain destruction to the fences (unless very tall stemmed and the hedge kept down to fence height) ; and the fruit grown in such situations are troublesome to be gathered.

LIVESTOCK.

HORSES.—P. 208. "The draught breed of horses being those only whose use is applicable to agriculture, of the others I shall say nothing, and of these bnt little, as conceiving there is nothing very remarkable in our breed ; though we have a sufficiency of good stout horses, for the use both of the carrier and the farmer. The colour is most generally black or brown, each being equally esteemed and equally useful ; and, indeed, as the old proverb says, 'a good horse is never of a bad colour,' some valuable stallions are kept of each colour. But in respect to the breed

breed of horses, I think this county must yield the palm to the neighbouring ones of Leicester and Derby; and indeed, breeding horses is by no means a main object here, and carried little farther than to supply the county, and also the neighbouring fairs with a few. There are some considerable shows or fairs, where a great number of excellent colts and horses are offered to sale, particularly at Stafford*, Burton, and Rudgely."

For the general economy of the disposal of young horses, in Staffordshire, &c. see my MIDLAND COUNTIES.

CATTLE.—On this fashionable topic, in the Midland Department, we find nothing to instruct, and little to interest, in the Report under consideration. The extractable matter is too inconsiderable to undergo the processes of analysis and digestion. I therefore insert the passages which I have selected, progressively, as they stand in the Report.

P. 173. "The *horned* cattle of this county, are very generally of the long-horned breed, varying in value and quality in proportion to the attention of the breeder and his resources for keeping."

P. 174. "The cattle stock of this county hath for years back been (and is at present) in some degree improving; but all general improvements must be gradual, and a work of time. It is not in the power of every farmer, or even of the generality of them, to pay the prices for prime stock; and if they could, the improvement of their meadows and pastures should go hand in hand with that of their stock. Mr. Miller's idea, which I cannot but approve, and wish to see in practice, is, that gentlemen of fortune should procure, for the use of their tenants, the best bulls, rams, stallions, &c. This, if they did not choose to do *gratis*, might easily be thrown upon a plan to indemnify expenses, and would tend very much to facilitate the improvement of the stock of the smaller farmers."

This plan of improving the livestock of an estate, has, in various instances, I believe, been practised. But certainly not in the general and liberal manner, in which it might be adopted with great profit; not merely to an estate, but to the district in which it is situated.

P. 175.

"* Two year old colts are sold at Stafford fair in great numbers, and with good profit to the farmer who breeds them; the poorer sort of lands in the Moorlands answer well for breeding; and a few acres of rich feeding land on the banks of the Dove, pushes up the young stock surprizingly; they generally produce thirty pounds a pair or more at the fairs, at two years old; a very fair profit, and inducement to the farmer to attend to this discrimination of poor and rich land for the breed and improvement of his live stock.—*Rev. S. Shaw.*"

P. 175. "The cows of this county will generally give from eight to twelve quarts of milk at a meal (and in some instances more), and two meals per day; but this only in the prime season of grass, May and June; they decline afterwards to three-fourths, one-half, and one-fourth of that quantity, and for two or three months are quite dry."

P. 176. "It is said that five hundred weight of cheese per season, will be sometimes made from a cow; but I believe in general the produce will be nearer half that quantity. Dairies extend from ten, fifteen, and twenty cows to forty, and in a few instances to more, even to seventy cows.

"No great number of oxen are fatted in this county; the few bred therein are generally sold at the neighbouring fairs, and driven to fat nearer the metropolis.

"The above account is meant to apply to the general cow-stock of the farmers of this county; some few instances are to be found, where the breed has been carried to a much greater perfection, especially in carcass. The following instances of capital or superior stock came under my observation."

The "cow-stock" of Mr. Princep of Croxall, of Lord Donegall, of Lord Bagot, of Sir E. Littleton, and of Messrs. Huskinson, Miller, and Dyot,—are mentioned by Mr. Pitt; but I perceive nothing in his detail, nor in the remarks that follow it, which requires to be noticed, here; excepting what relates to Mr. Miller's hornless variety.

P. 178. "My neighbour, Mr. Miller of Dunstall, has the largest and best dairy that I know in the county. The number of his milkers are upwards of seventy, mostly of the long-horned breed; with six or eight cows without horns*."

Several portraits of highbred longhorns of the Leicestershire breed, are given. But we meet with no account of the "Staffordshire heifers," by the means of which the suckling farmers of the southern Counties have long been supplied with cows.

SHEEP.—On this head, we find Mr. Pitt an intelligent Reporter of the County of Stafford; and conveying to his readers a satisfactory account of the distinct *native breeds* of the County. P. 182.

"* Mr. Miller has since entirely adopted the polled breed, and given up the long horns, having now upwards of fifty dairy cows of this breed; they are large heavy cattle, and good milkers, and will fat to twelve and fourteen score the quarter; and he believes with as little keep as the long horns. He does not know of their being of any particular country, breed, or descent, having selected the originals at fairs and markets where he could, and bred the rest himself; he has now a succession stock of from twelve to fifteen young cattle of each different age of this breed, having reared so many every year. He thinks they milk equally well with the long horns, and fat generally to a greater weight."

P. 182. "First, the grey-faced without horns, with fine or clothing wool. Secondly, the black-faced horned, with fine wool. Thirdly, the white-faced without horns, with long or combing wool. Fourthly, the mixed, common, or waste land breeds. Fifthly, the pasture sheep, of different breeds and crosses.

"First, the *grey-faced without horns*, are the native breed of *Cannock-heath*, Sutton Coldfield, and the neighbouring commons. The distinguishing characteristics of this breed are in general, grey faces, lighter or darker, varying from white to black, with all the shades of colour between. The legs of the same colour with the face. The wool fine, closely and compactly covering the carcass, without horns, and of a moderate size. Those from a sound part of the walk, and from a managing master, have a good disposition to fatten, and produce mutton at the table equal to that of any breed in the kingdom. The better breed of these sheep very much resembles the breed of the South Down, and are, doubtless, originally from the same common stock; and perhaps the superiority of the South Down to some of the best Cannock-heath and Sutton Coldfield flocks is very questionable, and cannot readily be admitted. The general fault of this breed has been the want of thickness in proportion to their length. Sir Edward Littleton, with a patriotism and public spirit highly commendable, has for several years back been setting the example of improving this breed, by crossing with Ross rams; by which the carcass has not only been thickened, improved in form, and increased in weight, but the wool improved in a very high degree."

P. 185. "The *Sutton Coldfield* sheep are doubtless from the same original common stock with those of Cannock-heath, but have been pushed to a larger size and weight. Mr. Fowler of Erdington, who, though in Warwickshire, is very near the borders of this county, and summers several hundreds on the Coldfield in either county promiscuously, was so kind as to shew me his own and his neighbours' flocks. His rams are stout, broad-backed, wide on the rump, and well made, with fine wool to the very breech: the largest of them would, I believe, fatten to more than thirty pounds the quarter; and the smallest would be considerably more than twenty. Great attention has been paid for several years past to improving this breed both in wool and carcass, and the principal farmers have endeavoured to excel each other in these particulars.

"Mr. Fowler thinks the breed is now pushed rather too far in bulk and weight, for the pasturage of the common, or even of the neighbourhood, unless they are driven into better land for fatting."

P. 187

P. 187. "I have farther to observe, that Sutton Coldfield is but a barren sheep-walk; containing in some large tracts scarcely any other plant than heath; in other places, fern, gorse, whortleberries, and rushes, with grasses in small proportion.

"Secondly, the *black-faced horned sheep*, with *fine wool*, are peculiar to the commons on the west of the county, towards Drayton, in Shropshire, particularly Maer-heath, Ashley-common, and the other wastes in that neigbourhood. They have black and rather long legs; are light in the carcass: the rams are horned, and have been bred, I apprehend, with little attention, and are certainly capable of great improvement, especially in the thickness and form of the carcass. I think them, in their present state, much inferior to the grey-faced polled last described; their walk, with the herbage thereon, is, however, poor, and ranks with the worst parts of the commons before-mentioned.

"Thirdly, *the white-faced polled*, with *longer combing wool*, considered as occupying waste or unimproved land, are peculiar to the east parts of the Moorlands. Upon the calcareous or limstone bottom, they are strong heavy sheep, and, I think, the most valuable and best sheep on waste land in the county: inferior to the New Leicester, as being much heavier in the bone, and coarser in make; but, by proper crossing with well-made rams, may be improved into an excellent breed of sheep.

"Fourthly, the *mixed common* or *waste-land breed*, consists of the sheep upon the wastes, or upon the uncultivated enclosures in the west part of the Moorlands, and on the grit or gravel bottom. These are much inferior to those on the limestone or calcareous ground, and are, indeed, of a very different breed. These appear to have originated from the ancient breed of the Moorlands, continued without attention, and have some white, and some grey or dark faces, with legs generally of the same colour: some with, and some without, horns: the wool too coarse to be called clothing, and too short for combing wool. The walk on this west part is inferior to the other, as being in part composed of peat moors, on which sheep are, doubtless, subject to rot. The breed is, nevertheless, capable of being much improved by attention in selecting rams, which appears to have been, in a great measure, neglected.

"In the mixed breed, too, may be included the sheep upon the walks and commons in the south of the county, as on Clent-hills, the commons near Stourton, Swindon, and Wombourn, Kinver Edge, &c. the sheep on which are a mixed breed, not deserving commendation; apparently bred with little attention, with faces of all colours, white, grey,

grey, and black; some with, and some without, horns: the wool is tolerably fine, and of the clothing sort. Some of the rams have large horns, as heavy as their heads; and even the young lambs often have a strong horn growing with great luxuriance."

P. 189. "Fifthly, amongst the pasture flocks of different breeds and crosses, in regular flocks, or as stock yearly changed, I first name the *Leicestershire-breed*, of which there are many regular flocks in different parts of the county."

P. 194. "In this populous manufacturing country, the considerable demand for lamb, as well as mutton, has induced a great proportion of farmers to keep none other than an annual stock of sheep, consisting of ewes bought in at Michaelmas, from Cannock-heath, Sutton Coldfield, the commons of Shropshire, and sometimes even from Gloucestershire, Wiltshire, and Dorsetshire. These ewes are immediately put to a ram, and the lambs in spring suckled till they are fit for the butcher; they are then sold, and the ewes kept in good pasture, fatted, and sold after them, and the whole flock generally cleared off within the year."

This is a valuable practice; where a good market for fat lamb is at hand. It may, indeed, be said to be the general practice of the kingdom, under such circumstances. It therefore requires no comment, here. But the note appending to the above passage is entitled to especial attention.

How inconsiderate, and unpardonable, in a public Reporter of *country* concerns, to give circulation to such *mere town talk*, as that which is therein contained. I do not accuse the Reporter of Staffordshire as the *inventor*; for the silly idea has frequently been thrown out, by ignorant town writers on rural subjects.

The proposal for a restrictive law! arises most inappropriately out of the practice here reported; as the lambs, in this case, would not exist under such a law. The aged ewes, that are usually employed in such a practice, would alone be sent to the butcher. Farmers who follow it, have seldom any rearing ground; and it is principally followed on lands that are too cold and moist,—are unsafe—to rear sheep upon. Of course, under such a law, neither mutton nor lamb would go to market from lands of that description. And, on sheep land, on which a breeding flock is kept, such a law would not be the means of increasing the quantity of mutton at market. For if the occupier was obliged to rear all the female lambs which he should happen to have dropped, no matter whether one two or three by each ewe, he would of course keep fewer breeding ewes. His sheep lands being of a given extent, it is of course unable to support more than a limited number or weight of sheep.

The same or a similar train of reasoning would produce the same conviction, in regard to calves.

How painful and difficult it is to prove self-evident positions; and to *sap* those that have *no foundation.*

The Reporter speaks, in detail, of Mr. Tollet's flock of Spanish sheep.—P. 194. "In addition to the account of sheep, I have now to add the particulars of Mr. Tollet's flock, of Swinnerton-hall, Staffordshire, who has, with great industry and perseverance, raised from a small number of the true Merino breed, a large flock of fine-woolled sheep. He has procured Spanish sheep from His Majesty's flock, from Lord Somerville, and from other quarters, the breed of which he has kept distinct, as far as it goes; but to increase his flock, he has put Spanish rams to South Down and Ryeland ewes, the latter originally from the Ross (Hereford) breed, so well known for its fine staple of wool. The last season (autumn, 1804), Mr. Tollet had 414 fine-woolled ewes put to real Spanish rams, and his shearing the present season (June, 1805) included 730 fine-woolled sheep.

"At shearing, June 6, 1803, Mr. Tollet, then resident in Gloucestershire, had a Merino flock, consisting of 24 ewes and 2 rams of the full blood; 19 shearlings and 2 rams, half Spanish and half Ryeland; 7 shearlings and 2 rams, half Spanish and half South Down."

Mr. Tollet has great merit in his strenuous endeavors toward growing Spanish wool in England; and thereby not only avoiding the extravagance and disgrace of paying away immense sums, in the purchase of it; but rendering it an indigenous or native produce of the island; and of course enabling this country to command a supply of it, IN TIMES TO COME, without being liable to the ill blood, caprice, or interest, of any other; and tenfold merit will Mr. Tollet have, if *his discovery (?)* of growing long wool on fine wooled sheep can be profitably practised, on a large scale; so as to give a high degree of excellence to the WORSTED MANUFACTURE. See the EASTERN DEPARTMENT, p. 195, on that subject.

P. 200. "Mr. Tollet has made a few experiments of this superfine wool acquiring length, by growing on the sheep's back more years than one, which may be done without endangering the animal; and he has this season left a few fleeces unshorn, to continue the experiment.

"A ewe fleece, pure Merino, two years' growth, average length of the staple, 10 inches; shorn 1804:—manufacturer's turer's opinion, that it was the finest long wool ever seen; has been manufactured into a shawl (which is now at Swinnerton), of extreme fineness and delicacy of texture.

"A wether fleece, half Spanish, half South Down, three years' growth, was exhibited by Mr. Tollet this season at Holkham, on the sheep's back, and there shorn; weight 13¼ lb.; besides which, 1¾ lb. at least, was supposed to have been lost in specimens, making 15 lb.; pronounced by the manufacturers worth any thing, if it succeeds in their hands as may be expected. *7s. 6d.* per pound was named; and it was observed, that the price of the raw material was scarcely an object where extraordinary products might arise. This fleece is now in the hands of a manufacturer for experiment."

I recollect to have seen a specimen of Mr. Tollet's fine long wool (I think at Woburn) and it bore every appearance of being capable of becoming a valuable material of the manufactures of England.

Diseases of Sheep.—P. 205. "The disorders to which sheep are most subject in this county are, the rot, the scab, the foot-rot, and striking or dying in the blood."

P. 206. "Mr. Bradburne has been successful upon lands subject to *rot* sheep, by a plentiful use of lime, and in laying the land in a form for the rain water to pass off quick."

P. 207. "The striking*, or dying in the *blood*, is a very serious complaint, and generally happens to sheep in a growing and fatting state, often in turnips in winter, or in clover in the spring season, and is, I suppose, of the apoplexy kind."

This malady of sheep has ever appeared to me to be occasioned by a plethora, or over fulness of blood. Bleeding, exercising (see my WEST of ENGLAND) or lowering their pasture, would therefore seem to be the most likely preventative.

P. 322. (in a paper of "Mr. Town, a gentleman of the medical profession," inserted in the Appendix) "I have known oil of turpentine prove successful in the prevention and cure of the *rot* and dropsy; half a meat spoonful given for

"* To prevent this complaint, bleed the sheep in the nostril, about three times, each spring, and give each three spoonfulls of salt and water, made rather strong. To young lambs, give one spoonfull to each. The above remedy to be applied at other seasons of the year, if necessary.—*T. Webb*

"N. B. The first bleeding, &c. should be in about a week after the sheep are put to good keep. The second about a fortnight, or three weeks after, &c. Ewe and lambs to be omitted, till the lambs are full three weeks old, but should not be kept too well, during that time."

for a dose now and then, has cured some, and prolonged the lives of others; a dose to every sheep in the beginning of winter is said to be a preventative. Tapping might be of service."

RABBITS.—After having said to his readers, p. 212 "on the management or profit of rabbits, I know but little,"—the Reporter ventures to tell them, p. 213. "Rabbits are certainly a species of stock unworthy of being cultivated, or bred in any considerable numbers, on enclosed and cultivated land; yet doubtless deserving considerable attention on impracticable sandy or rocky precipices, which may at the same time be *planted*;* and when properly fenced in, and *thus stocked*, (!) such land seems in a system of the highest improvement of which it is capable."!!—See my MIDLAND COUNTIES, Minute 124; where it will be found that hares and rabbits are the well known and most mischievous enemies of young plantations.

POULTRY.—P. 213. "The profits of poultry are a matter of but little consideration, in or any where near the populous parts of Staffordshire; for though a sufficient quantity, both of poultry, ducks and geese are kept as breeding stock, yet the risk of having their progeny carried off by thieves is so great, and is so often actually the case, that little attention is paid to them as an article of profit. I have known some considerable farmers, who have had their stock of this kind pretty completely cleared off in this way, two or three times a year, and few escape an annual visit or two: so that it is often difficult to reserve a reasonable supply for the table; this business being always done in the night, the parties are seldom detected, and when they are, have been generally discharged with a whipping, and so enabled to proceed again in the same way. I have sometimes thought the value of farms in this country are lowered five per cent. by this circumstance, as all kinds of poultry are dear in the markets. The remedy, in my opinion, would be to have the poultry-house under the command of a lodging-room window, where fire-arms were kept in readiness, and a dog chained near."

PROFITS of FARMING.—P. 40. "Respecting the expenses and profits of farming, it can hardly be expected that actual accounts should be produced; the divulging of the domestic concerns of persons in any business, seems a matter of considerable delicacy; and whether that business be farming, manufacture, or trade, will seldom be consented to,

* A favorite improvement of Mr. Pitt. See *Woodlands* aforegoing.

to, or admitted as proper, by those who are interested therein. It is, however, not difficult to form ideal estimates of expenses and returns; and if such estimates are founded on experience, and a judicious application of such experience to average disbursements and receipts, such estimates may be equally useful with actual accounts.

"Previous to making such estimates I have to observe, that in this country, few fortunes are making merely by farming, and perhaps none at present upon modern rents, unless the farmer is connected with some other employments, in which, by enterprise, judgment, diligence, and industry, large sums of money may be annually turned, and a good profit often obtained: this is frequently done by engaging in the miller's and malster's business, by dealing in the various kinds of live stock, fat and lean, or grass seeds, particularly clovers, in which very large sums are turned annually; by dealing in cheese, butter, bacon, and other necessaries of life, for which there is a great demand in populous countries. The dealers in all the above articles are certainly very useful to society, as without them it would be impossible to obtain a regular supply, at least in the present system of things; and lastly, I shall add, the surveyor's business, in which, connected with farming, money has sometimes been made. Some instances I have also known of people of property hiring a good farm, with an income sufficient to pay the rent; in such case it is no wonder if systematic management and economy should save money. The case of a person occupying his own estate has not always succeeded; in such case, turning gentleman, and neglecting the regular system of business, has soon been followed by involved circumstances; and I have known an instance of a person occupying a pretty good and clear estate of his own, till he has been obliged to sell it; and have heard of other instances, where such seller has hired it again to farm, at a fair rent, and done pretty well. If a person even occupies a farm of his own, and means to thrive, he must remember that he is a man of business, and must act as such: how much more, then, the person who hires a farm at rack-rent.

"That some pretty good properties have been raised simply by farming, must certainly be admitted; several such instances having come under the Writer's observation, and similar instances must be in the recollection of every attentive person. In such cases, I believe there has always been a combination of all, or most of the following circumstances: 1st, An easy rent; 2d, A pretty good or extensive farm; 3d, Economy and industry; and 4th, Length of time. An

An easy rent affording the first profits, these would be increased by the after circumstances; and every calculator is acquainted with the astonishing accumulation of small sums in length of time at compound interest.

"In the present system of farming, at a modern rent, with the additional accumulated expenses of high taxes, partilarly poor's and malt tax, house and window tax, additional price of labourers' and servants' wages, high amount of tradesmen's bills necessary to agriculture (such as the wheelwright, blacksmith, collar-maker, and all others); and even the luxury of the times, by which not only the food and clothing of the family, but even the boarding of servants, and workmen occasionally, is at increased expenses; under all these circumstances, *the writer of this knows from experience*, that it requires not only the most diligent industry, but also the most prudential economy, to keep the balance on the right side.

"It is an idea often expressed, and I believe a good deal credited, that the profits of farming are enhanced and rendered enormous by the high price of provisions, both at present, and in all similar cases. This, I believe, will not be generally found a fact: high prices are, doubtless, the result of unproductive seasons; and a scanty produce, at a high price, may make less money than a plentiful one at a moderate price. It may certainly occur, that a lucky hit of a great crop, in an unproductive season, may be advantageous to the grower: from whence appears the superior advantage of keeping land always in good heart, as in such circumstances, the growing crop is much less liable to be affected by unkindly seasons."

After those exordial remarks, of which every man of experience or extensive observation, in the country, must see the justness, the Reporter proceeds to *calculate*. But, on calculation of that sort, I have repeatedly spoken my sentiments, in the former volumes of this work. I therefore pass over Mr. Pitt's, and merely copy the conclusion which he has drawn from them.

P. 45. "From the above estimates, which are founded on experience and attention, it may be inferred, that whoever hires a farm under an idea of suddenly acquiring a fortune, will probably find himself disappointed; and that it is only by industry and regular management, that a result equally favourable to that of the above calculations can be expected."

The only remark that I have to make, further, on this subject, is that I have rarely found a farmer making a fortune, by his profession, alone; unless on FRESH LAND; —on virgin marsh,—old grazing ground,—ancient sheep walk,—

walk,—or well soiled common; on land that has never been "plundered" (to use the strong expression of the knowing ones in the art)—of its native, or long horded treasures:—a fortune, I mean, any way resembling that which, with the same ability and industry, and with a small share of the outset capital, he would have been making by trade, manufacture, or commerce.

DERBYSHIRE.

DERBYSHIRE.

THIS strongly featured County naturally separates into MOUNTAINS, UPLANDS, and VALELANDS; the last being principally confined to its southern extreme; and forming a part of the Midland District, mentioned aforegoing.

The mountains of Derbyshire form the southernmost extremity of the northern mountains of England; and have been spoken of as such in the NORTHERN DEPARTMENT.

In general appearance they resemble the limestone mountains of North Wales; but are inferior in elevation and grandeur.

Its uplands, whether on the east or the west side of the County, bear a strong resemblance to the rotund, flat-topt swells of the South Hams and other parts of Devonshire. In the Ashbourn quarter, round Ballidon, lie a range of calcareous heights of that description; and, in the Chesterfield quarter a charming plot of country, in a similar style, is observable. The more central parts of the County, round Matlock, the surface is more abruptly broken into hill and dale.

"GENERAL VIEW

OF THE

AGRICULTURE

OF THE

COUNTY OF DERBY;

WITH

OBSERVATIONS ON THE MEANS OF ITS IMPROVEMENT,

BY THOMAS BROWN,

OF LUTON, IN BEDFORDSHIRE.

DRAW UP FOR THE CONSIDERATION OF THE BOARD OF AGRICULTURE AND INTERNAL IMPROVEMENT.

1794."

THIS is the original Report that was sent in concerning Derbyshire; and which I have, before, had occasion to notice. See NORTHERN DEPARTMENT, District *Southern Mountains*.

To

To the QUALIFICATIONS of this Writer no guide is given. An entire stranger in a County, as Mr. Brown would seem to have been in Derbyshire, at the time he made his transient tour of enquiry (as Mr. B's evidently appears to have been) might, without severity, be said to disqualify him for the office of drawing up a report of its "agriculture and internal improvement." The blame, however, must not lie wholely on Mr. Brown, who makes an apology for the deficiences in his performance.

In a letter to the President of the Board, Mr. B. says, p. 7. "I flattered myself, from what you informed me, that I should receive much assistance from the well known abilities of a Gentleman, whose local knowledge of the district would have rendered the task much less arduous. This Gentleman being very much engaged during the time I spent in Derbyshire, I could not obtain more than an hour's conversation with him; yet, in justice to his politeness, I have to acknowledge, that he rendered me every service and recommendation, which the short time he had to spare could possibly lead me to hope for.—Under this disappointment, I look to the indulgence and candour of the Board of Agriculture, as well as to that of the gentlemen and yeomanry of Derbyshire, to forgive every inaccuracy, misinformation, or omission, that a stranger must be liable to in executing the agricultural survey of a county."

It is but justice to Mr. Brown to observe that his Report contains evidence of his being acquainted with rural subjects. And he speaks of his "experience in other Counties" (p. 18.) This, and the *brilliancy* of style which he occasionally employs, point out, pretty evidently, his profession.

The number of pages seventytwo.

A map of soils and another of rivers and canals; and

One plate of a farm-yard, implements, &c.

NATURAL ECONOMY.

DISTRICT, SOILS and EXTENT.—P. 9. "The soil of the County of Derby is various, as nature in her most capricious mood could form:—to trace these variations in agricultural language, or to attempt to mark them accurately on a plan of about six miles and an half to an inch, are difficulties of which every one must be sensible. These difficulties, though great, ought not however to damp all attempts to investigation. Nature in her most capricious mood observes something like universal laws; and we find this

this county *demarked* by what she has thought fit to elevate and depress—high and low—hill and vale. These the natives of Derbyshire have (taking a general view of the county) long ago denominated High Peak and Low Peak, leaving the more fertile parts of the county undistinguished by either: so that, generally speaking, to make a distinction of soil, the county admits of three parts, which I shall (as an introduction to observation and improvement) call—the Fertile,—the Low Peak,—and the High Peak. It is however remarkable, that in all of these, nature has made some marked varieties in the nature of the rock with which this county abounds: the agriculturist distinguishes them by lime-stone and grit."

The first division (the High Peak) naturally belongs (as has been said) to the southern mountains of the NORTHERN DEPARTMENT. The other two divisions of Derbyshire are natural portions of the MIDLAND DEPARTMENT.

P. 9. "*Fertile Soil*—is not inaccessible to the plough; it consists principally of a red loam on various *sub-soils*, approaching (in patches) nearer to marle, to clay, to black loam, to sand or grit, or to gravel, as may happen from the sub-stratum, or the atmospherical exposure; and these soils admit of other variations, from their proximity to springs, to rivers, or to stagnant water.

"*Low Peak*—is more difficult of access, but in no instance inaccessible to the plough; it is however more strongly tinctured with quick transitions, but chiefly consists of drier sands or grits. The clays and loams here are in general more valuable (perhaps from being more scarce); and where they are not too much elevated, are certainly inviting for the husbandman to pulverize and subdue."

P. 36. "Following the three grand divisions of the soil, I find that what I have called the Fertile part of the county, contains about - - Acres 213,120

What I call the Low Peak land, contains about - - - - - - 231,680

And what I call the High Peak land, contains about - - - - - - 275,840

Making the whole county about - - 720,640"

CLIMATURE.—P. 11. "From the description that has been given of the soil and situation, a faint idea of the climate may be inferred—in general it is wet and cold. The degrees of cold vary more than are easily conceived; and although I am sensible that our feelings are not the proper scale by which we are to form our judgment of the different degrees of heat and cold, yet finding mine so sensibly affected, I could not help remarking that in travelling from

from Sudbury to Ashborn I found a pleasing temperature: passing through Ashborn, in my way to Buxton (without any apparent change in the atmosphere), before I had left Ashborn three miles, I found an additional coat absolutely necessary; and this sudden transition is every where felt, on ascending into atmospherical elevation. The fertile part of the county is salubrious and temperate, though inclining to wet. The mountainous part is cold, enveloped in clouds, and during the winter months much incumbered with snow; but during my tour I was not fortunate enough to meet with any regular account kept of the quantity of rain or snow; nor did I hear of any meteorological journals being kept in any part of the county. I have long been of opinion, that to ascertain the quantity of moisture that falls, and above all the proportion of time that the surface of any country is wet and dry, the hours of sunshine, and the hours of clouds, would in a great measure ascertain what the natural productions of the climate are, and fix some data for improvements in all situations." These are ingenious, and, what is more, sensible remarks.

FOSSILS.—See the first extract, above.

MINERALS.—Mr. B. has wisely confined his observations to the surface; notwithstanding the temptation, in Derbyshire, to dip beneath it. He, however, very properly notices the ancient, but now absurd and mischievous LAW of MINING:—an unwarrantable immunity of miners, which is not confined to Derbyshire; but is still more diffusively spread over the western peninsula of the island.

P. 53. "In a large part of the county, denominated the King's-field, every miner has a power of entering at all times upon the lands, and searching for ores, and this even when the corn is growing."

POLITICAL ECONOMY.

APPROPRIATION.—P. 33. "Within the last 15 years, I believe that above one-fourth part of the whole county of Derby has been inclosed—the two districts which I have denominated Fertile and Low Peak, are almost entirely inclosed. The High Peak remains a field, in many places, for that improvement."

P. 38. "If we deduct one-eighth part for roads, rivers, wastes, woods, and hedges, in the Fertile and Low Peak districts, and two-third parts of the High Peak, for wastes and unprofitable lands, which it is believed is about the fair proportion, it makes the heaths, wastes, moors, woods, roads,

roads, rivers, and lands, not employed in husbandry, to consist of about 239,492 acres (nearly one-third of the whole), leaving 481,148 acres for arable and pasture; of which not more than one-fifth part is annually cropped with corn, the four-fifths being either old sward, or artificial grasses."

PROVISIONS.—P. 42. "From the number of inhabitants, the quantity of unprofitable soil, and the numerous manufactures carried on in this midland part of the kingdom, provision in general is full as dear, and in the article of corn, dearer than in the metropolis:—without some means be discovered to keep up the increase of food with the increase of its consumption, in consequence of additional population, I think we may reasonably expect that the price of provision is more likely to rise than to fall. The new breed of cattle, which certainly requires less time, and consequently less food to fat them, is no doubt the only rational mode by which we are enabled to account for butcher's meat not being, with regard to price, in the same predicament with corn.—To enumerate the prices would be to give a return of the different markets in the year, and which will, in all probability, vary every succeeding market."

RURAL ECONOMY.

TENANTED ESTATES.

ESTATES.—The subjoined brief, and well written history of landed property, in Derbyshire, I insert, here, on Mr. B's authority.

P. 12. "This county originally was in the possession of perhaps as few individuals as any part of the kingdom of an equal extent: we are told that at the time of the Norman survey, it belonged wholly to seventeen individuals; and some of the present possessions have lineally descended from those individuals down to their posterity, the present proprietors, but with considerable diminution in point of territorial extent. The acquisitions of the church, under the Roman superstition, took considerable root in this soil; but the distribution of her property, after the suppression of religious houses, seems to have fallen into many hands. The enterprising spirit of trade, cherished by a wise and excellent constitution, established at the glorious revolution, has diffused those immense possessions, dividing the territory, and hiding what used to be the ancient gentleman in obscurity. But by well-concerted marriages, hereditary possessions are in many instances wisely preserved; and in the

the county of Derby we find some rent-rolls upwards of 20,000*l.*; several upwards of 10,000*l.*; many of more than 3,000*l.*—Those families possessing a rental of 1000*l.* or under that sum (where there are not other resources), risking their estates in trade, and bringing up their children to manufactures and commerce; and (what is too often the case) wherever agriculture is clogged with difficulties which require property and talents, they carry that property and those talents of which they are possessed into trade; leaving the improvement of the soil to men of less property, and consequently of less power.—Fatigued with trade, the mutability of the human mind, previous to the approach of old age, frequently drives men of this description to gratify a second change of sentiment, and search for something new in the sequestered vale; and every where we find small habitations decorated with plantations, on a confined scale."

TENANCY.—P. 45. "The largest estates in this county are without leases; and in general leases are wearing out of use. On some estates of considerable extent in the High Peak, I found a printed lease, where nothing remains but for the steward to fill up quantities and names.—By these leases, the tenant enters upon all the arable and meadow grounds from the 13th of February, and upon all the pastures from 5th of April, except a specified close, which the *way-going tenant* has for foddering his cattle in, under the name of a boosey pasture; and this *boosey* pasture, with the house, buildings, yards, orchards, and every other part of the premises, the way-going tenant surrenders to his successor on the 12th of May."

WOODLANDS.—P. 41. "A great part of those districts which I have denominated Fertile and Low Peak, are wooded, and well calculated for the production of timber.—Kedleston park stands unrivalled in the county for timber and plantations; and is a striking instance that even the best pasture land may be planted without diminution of the rental of a family estate. (?) In general through the county, timber though small, is valuable; but from the plenty of coal and wood for fuel, will not answer for cultivation. However, the ingenuity of the natives renders the stub of the ash, the hazle, the sallow, and other shrubs, of more value here than in the southern counties where they are cultivated for fuel; and many parts of this county send tools made from these shrubs into counties where they are more plentiful.—The mines render every piece of timber, though ever so insignificant in itself, truly valuable; and those who do not sacrifice every thing to immediate convenience, very laudably attend the increase and improvement

ment of their woods, by regular falls, and keeping up a succession.—But generally speaking, the quantity of timber and woods are upon the decrease: land becoming more valuable than formerly for corn or pasture, every one is engaged in rooting up all those brambles, thorns, and bushes, which are the natural guardians of the oak, the ash, and the elm in their infant state."

AGRICULTURE.

FARMS.—*Sizes.*—P. 14. "Generally speaking, there are in Derbyshire farms of a sufficient size to occupy that capital which forms full employment for a farmer; much of the county, however, is occupied in rather small farms (under 100*l.* a year)."

HOMESTEADS.—*Rural Architecture.*—P. 52. "In laying plank floors in barns, a practice has been followed and communicated to me by a very intelligent gentleman, who has the management of large estates in the county of Derby, which I think preferable to our common method of laying them hollow, or bedded on chalk. He causes the earth to be taken out and replaced with stone or brick, laid in mortar, and grouted; in this foundation he rests the sleepers, and builds them firmly into it, perfectly level with the surface of the stone, the whole is again grouted, and the plank pinned down to the sleepers in the grout; he assures me, that plank floors laid in this way, will last more than double the time we usually reckon them to do when laid in the common way."

For what would seem to be the origin of this new and excellent practice, see LOWE'S NOTTINGHAMSHIRE, ensuing.

OBJECTS of HUSBANDRY.—See *Appropriation*, p. 63, aforegoing.

P. 15. "In the fertile part of the county, about one-third is in tillage, the remainder being old sward, or resting under artificial grasses.

"In the Low Peak, a greater part of the land is in tillage, the pastures being poor, they usually have two-thirds in tillage, the other third being employed as pasturage for the dairy or breeding of stock."

OCCUPIERS.—The smaller farms Mr. B. observes, p. 14, are occupied "by men engaged in pursuits distinct from improvements in agriculture:—men either pursuing the riches of mines; men employed in the mechanical operations of manufactures; or men labouring for the tradesman, and whose attention is more immediately engaged in the operative

operative part of manufactures than in the improvement of the soil they occupy. There are, however, in this County occupiers of another description, very properly styled yeomen; men cultivating their own estates with a sufficient capital, or employing a considerable capital in the occupation of the ancient hereditary estates of the gentry."

PLAN of MANAGEMENT.—P. 15. "This varies according to the nature of the soil; the circumstances of the occupier, and the nature of his tenure." (Tenancy.)

On the "rotation of crops," we find a few pages. By the subjoined passage, it appears that the practice of the central district of the Midland Counties extends into Derbyshire; namely, that of employing the land in producing arable crops and temporary herbage, alternately.

P. 17. "In some parts of the Fertile Soil, we find the following rotation of crops, on breaking up the land after the natural grasses are exhausted, or become unprofitable, and as preparatory to its being relaid; 1. oats, 2. fallow, 3. wheat, 4. turnips, 5. barley; and again rested under artificial grasses."

Mr. Brown is an orthodox Fallowist.

WORKPEOPLE.—P. 38. "Derbyshire abounding with mines and manufactures, the labouring hands find no other employment beside agriculture; consequently the price of labour to the farmer fluctuates according to the briskness or stagnation of trade, and the different demands for the produce of the mines.—The most general prices seem,

"*Labourers* from Candlemas to Martinmas—1*s.* 4*d.* to 1*s.* 6*d.* per day: hours of work from six to six. From Martinmas to Candlemas, 1*s.* 2*d.* per day, working from daylight till dark."

P. 39. "*Hired Servants.*—The best man-servant from ten to twelve guineas a year; a woman from four to five guineas."

ARABLE CROPS.—Scarcely a word is said on this principal branch of agriculture; excepting on what relates to one crop; and this crop I have not before known to be an object of husbandry; as it appears to be in Derbyshire. I therefore thank Mr. B. for the opportunity he has given me of registering its cultivation, here.

CHAMOMILE.—P. 28. "Finding in Chesterfield, and some of the adjoining parishes, particularly in that of North Wingfield, in that district which I denominate the Low Peak, many acres planted with

"Chamomile,—and conceiving it not usually cultivated as a field crop, I shall begin with observing, that a loamy soil is chosen for this purpose; that after the ground is well prepared by thorough cleanings (which however is not

always

always practised), about the end of March, the roots of an old plantation are taken up, and divided into small slips, which are planted in rows about eighteen inches asunder, and about the same distance in the rows. The plants are kept clean by frequent hoeing and weeding with the hand. In September, the flowers are fit to gather; their perfection depends upon their being fully blown, without having stood so long as to lose their whiteness; the flowering continues till stopped by the frosts. The gatherings are repeated as often as a succession of flowers appears; this depends very much upon the season, dry years furnishing more, and wet or dull weather fewer successions of flowers. When gathered, they are carefully dried, either in kilns very moderately heated, or on the floors of boarded rooms, heated by slow fires; the object is to keep the flowers white and whole; and this is done only by drying them as slowly as possible. The produce varies from two hundred weight, or even less, to four, five, and in some (though as I have learned but in few instances) to six hundred weight per acre: the price has also varied from 40*s.* to 7*l.* per cwt. From the best accounts I have been able to obtain, four cwt. at 4*l.* per cwt. may be considered as the average produce and price. The plants usually stand three years, of which the first affords the smallest, and the second the best and greatest produce. Sometimes the same plants are continued beyond three years, but the ground gets foul, and the flowers are weak and bad. The flowers when dried are packed in bags, and bought up by persons in the neighbourhood; by whom they are sold principally to the druggists in London. Some persons have used them in brewing, as a succedaneum for hops; and others contrive to mix them with hops. I am informed they will not answer the end, and that few people approve the taste, even when mixed. From the information given me, I apprehend that about two hundred acres of land here are employed in the cultivation of this plant."

LIVESTOCK.—Several pages are appropriated to this subject. But the different species are spoken of too *pleasantly*, to afford even a passage that would well assimilate with the more thoughtful and instructive materials of this register. Fortunately, however, the livestock of the lowlands of Derbyshire are so similar to those of Leicestershire, that a studied description of them is the less required.

THE DAIRY.—*Cheese.*—On this species of the produce of livestock, Mr. Brown has gathered some practical information. He has briefly minuted the practices of three dairy women:—not, however, in such a way as to enable a stranger to the art, to manufacture good cheeses from the sketches given. Nor do I perceive any particular of the processes reported,

reported, that could profitably add to the ample and methodized accounts, concerning the art of cheesemaking, that are already before the public.

Whey Butter.—On this profitable branch of the cheese dairy, Mr. B. has reported the practices of four dairies. I transcribe his notes, as they comprize a few particulars of practice which differ somewhat from both the GLOCESTERSHIRE and the CHESHIRE practices.

P. 50. (Head "Miscellaneous Remarks,") "*The first* gathers no butter from the green whey, but from the *crushings* which she sets up in pans for twenty-four hours, then skims off the cream or thick part, and immediately *boils it*; then before it is cold, she puts it into an earthen pan, in which she collects a week's cream for churning; she likes her cream to be sour, and for that purpose saves a little of the last week, which she puts in the bottom of the pot, and adds the next week's cream to it; she also puts her cream into the pot before it is cold, and in winter sets it near the fire; in summer she churns her milk and whey butter together; she also makes her milk cream as sour as possible. It has been recommended to her by an experienced mistress, to put a small quantity of saltpetre dissolved in water into her milk which she sets up for cream, as a good thing for making the milk throw up a greater quantity of cream, making it churn easier, and giving the butter a better colour; it was also told her it was a good thing for preventing the butter from having any disagreeable taste, such as arise from the cow eating turnips, cabbage, &c. She has tried the experiment, by putting about the size of a hazle nut of saltpetre into as much cream as made six pounds of butter, and approves of it very much; but did not put it into the milk as advised, thinking it would spoil it for family uses.

"*The second* sets up all her whey, as well green as white, for cream, which she gathers every twenty-four hours, into large earthen cream pots; she boils hers only twice a week, and differs from the first by wishing to keep it as sweet as possible, and for that purpose changes it into sweet pots twice a week; she gathers a small quantity of milk cream, which she churns together with the whey cream; her butter is very good and very little inferior to real milk butter.

"*The third* gathers all her whey, as well green as white, into a large brass kettle, over a fire, and as the top or thick part begins to rise, she takes it off with a brass skimmer full of holes; when her whey is near boiling, she puts into it about a quart of cold spring water, and as much cold sour butter milk, which makes it throw up more top or thick curdy cream; she sets it by till cold, then puts it into her cream pots for churning; her cream pots have all tap-holes at at the bottom, by which she twice a day draws off the thin whey that has settled there. She likes to keep her cream sweet, and for that purpose sets it in a cold place, and changes it into clean sweet cream pots every two days. In summer she churns her milk cream and whey cream together once a week; her butter is very good, and from her cheese being coloured, it always looks well, and she sells it for the best price in the market, and mostly to the same persons who have bought it before.

"Another mistress of a dairy, equal for her good management and civility, informs me that she sets both her green and white whey by, for skimming, twenty-four hours; when skimmed, she puts about a gallon or six quarts of boiling clean water to a *panchion* (an earthen vessel that holds about six quarts) of cream, and stirs them together well; the water will settle to the bottom, and when cold she takes the cream from it, and puts it into cream pots for churning; she stirs it well in the cream pots once or twice a day, and changes it into clean ones twice a week, to keep the cream as sweet as possible. This is a very much approved mode of making whey butter."

"GENERAL

"GENERAL VIEW
OF THE
AGRICULTURE
AND
MINERALS
OF
DERBYSHIRE:

WITH

OBSERVATIONS ON THE MEANS OF THEIR IMPROVEMENT.

DRAWN UP FOR THE CONSIDERATION OF

THE BOARD OF AGRICULTURE

AND INTERNAL IMPROVEMENT.

BY JOHN FAREY, SEN.

MINERAL SURVEYOR,

OF UPPER CROWN STREET, WESTMINSTER.

VOL. I. AND II.*

1811."

TO speak of Mr. FAREY'S QUALIFICATIONS to undertake the Survey of a County, with regard to GEOLOGY and MINERALOGY, might be considered as superfluous, if not officious; they being, already, pretty generally known to the public. Mr. Farey it appears, in the Work before me, has written, more or less, on those subjects, in most of the superior public Journals, and other widely circulated Works, of the present day. He mentions the Philosophical Transactions, Doctor Rees's Cyclopedia, the Edinburgh Cyclopedia, the Philosophical Magazine, the Transaction of the Geological Society, the Monthly Magazine, &c.

As

* JANUARY, 1814. The examination and abstraction of the first volume were done in June and July, 1812.—After waiting nearly twelve months for the second volume (which had been promised) I learnt that a third was still to be *expected!*—Judging, however, from what I found in the second, the disappointment at not being able to treasure up, here, the good things of the third, has been the less felt. *Livestock* is the principal agricultural topic left untouched; and Derbyshire having *now* no breeds that it can call its own, the loss, I conceive, will be light; and my readers, I trust, after having been truly informed of the contents of the second volume, will not lament it.

As a Surveyor of the AGRICULTURE of a County, however, I may I trust be allowed, after having examined, with attention, the two first volumes of his General View of Derbyshire, to offer my opinion on his abilities to fill that office.

Were it strictly just, it would be unmannerly, bluntly to assert, that he was, at the time of his Survey, altogether unfit for such an undertaking. But I think it may be fairly said, that he was, at that time, wanting in four essentials of an agricultural Surveyor. We find neither proof, nor substantial evidence, of his, then, possessing *matured experience, widely extended observation, competent reading* on the subject itself, nor a sufficient acquaintance with its *relative sciences.* Of chymestry, a near relation of Mineralogy, and a cousin German, at least, of agriculture, we perceive nothing in the volumes under view, to convince us that the Surveyor possessed, even the slightest knowledge. And in botany, likewise allied to agriculture, and which, occupies some sheets of the work, palpable errors meet the eye.

Derbyshire, however, as Staffordshire, is not, emphatically speaking, an *agricultural* County. *Mining* and *manufactures* being its characteristic distinctions;—unless in its southern extremity; and this, as has been said aforegoing, forms one quarter only of an extensive and well defined natural district. The *public*, therefore, have to regret that Mr. Farey's valuable time, when rightly applied, should have been unprofitably employed.

Mr. F's means of COLLECTING INFORMATION, concerning the various objects he had in view, appear to have been chiefly two; namely that of surveying the County and its environs, as a GEOLOGICAL MAPIST; and that of examining the estate of Ashover, the property of Sir Joseph Banks,—as a MINERALOGICAL SURVEYOR.

His notices in AGRICULTURE would seem to have been taken, incidentally; every thing which happened to be seen or heard, concerning it, while pursuing his vocations, appearing to have been indefatigably put down. It is, therefore, the less to be wondered at, that his Report should be swelled out to three volumes; for his communications, with the resident inhabitants, of every class, may be said to be universal. He has furnished lists, amounting to seven or eight hundred! CONTRIBUTORS;—principally, it is true, to the subjects of mining and mineralogy; but not less than two or three hundred, to that of agriculture, alone.

The *marginal notes* of the original Report are lost to the public; Mr. Brown having, we are told, refused to give them up!—Vol. II. p. vi. "It becomes necessary for me to to state in this place, as mine and the Board's apology, to those Gentlemen who took the trouble to return the copies of the Original Report, either to the Board or to Mr. Brown, containing their several marginal corrections and additions, that none of such are acknowledged or inserted in the pages of this Report: that the same is owing to the whole of such corrected copies having gone into Mr. Brown's hands soon after their transmission, and my repeated applications thro' all the proper channels, having failed, in procuring the return of them; and I would add, that I have copied or taken nothing from such Original Report, without expressly quoting it."

On the QUALITY of the MATTER COLLECTED, I have little to remark. That which relates to MINERALOGY appears to be, principally, a collection of materials for a "larger work"—a "mineral history." My estimation of what regards AGRICULTURE, will sufficiently appear in the smallness of extractable matter, comparatively with the bulk of the materials collected.

Regarding the AUTHORSHIP employed on these volumes,—the way in which the multifarious mass of matter they contain, has been prepared to meet the eye and understanding of the public,—a few remarks (conformably with the established rule of this Work) will be required. The arrangement of the chapters may nearly accord with the ill judged "plan of the Board." But the never ceasing references, from chapter to chapter, are intolerably teazing*. The language of the first volume,—the mineralogical phraseology—there made use of,—is such as a *miner* may, it is possible, readily comprehend. But it will often pause an ordinary reader. Indeed, the present nomenclature of mineralists is, at best, an uncouth kind of babylonish jargon.

On agriculture, the author being possessed of more words than correct ideas, his language is frequently diffuse and talkative. Yet there is, almost throughout that part of his work

* REFERENCES.—The above remark may bring to the mind of the reader, as it does to mine, the numerous references that appear in my present work; and I may not find a more favorable opportunity, than this, of explaining the sort of necessity which gives rise to them.—In the ill digested state in which many or most of the Reports have been sent to the press,—subjects, that have no scientific connexion, are inseparably placed in the same paragraph; and, of course, without REFERENCES (made, let me say, at the expence of much care and solicitude) one or more of its members would be lost to the subject to which it immediately belongs.

In a well digested *original work,* references of that sort can seldom be required.

work, much want of required detail, and circumstantial description; and, in every part, a deficiency in *analytical* information.

The EDITORSHIP (*or* the authorship*) of the first volume must have been censurably negligent; as appears by a list of acknowledged *errata*, prefixed to it, of nearly three pages in length; and, in the second, is found a further list, filling two closely printed pages, of "errata in the former list of villages, &c."

I have only further to say that, in making the few extracts, relating to *rural* concerns, I have used the same consideration and caution, that I have invariably exercised on all similar occasions.

The subjoined is the opening and most essential part of the author's own account of his undertaking.—Vol. I. p. v. "The present Volume, is mostly the result of a Survey of the County of Derby and its environs, which was undertaken in the summer of 1807, at the instance of the worthy President of the Royal Society, in order to examine minutely its Stratification and Mineral Treasures; and appears, in consequence of the President of the Board of Agriculture having, previous to my setting out on that Survey, engaged me to collect at the same time, the necessary facts and particulars for a Report to the Board, on the Agriculture and Rural Concerns of the County."

The number of pages of the first volume, five hundred and seven; of the second, four hundred and ninetyfive.

In the first, there are two geological maps: one of superficial appearances, and the other of substructures; and three of stratifications. In the second, one of building, one of implements, and one of utensils.

VOLUME THE FIRST.

SUBJECT THE FIRST.

NATURAL ECONOMY.

EXTENT.—P. 76. "Derbyshire contains about 972 square English miles, or 622,080 statute acres, which is the result of a careful scaleing of my large map." This map would seem to be intended for Mr. F's "larger work."

SURFACE.

* There is a peculiarity in the *orthography* of these volumes, which frequently arrests the attention of the reader:—I mean the obsolete abbreviations—won't, don't, can't, &c. which cannot now be "errors of the press." They doubtlessly serve to convey an idea that the writer is a *plain man*.

SURFACE.—On the striking features of the face of Derbyshire, Mr. Farey has bestowed nearly five sheets of paper and a map; describing the principal *ridges*, and its several *hills*; and noticing the *valleys* and other appearances of its surface; the two first being marked on the map, and the whole listed in the letterpress! a laborious undertaking.

P. 4. "*The Surface* of Derbyshire is much diversified, yet far less *enormously* * so, than many writers have represented it: full one half of the County, taken at its southern end and nearly along its eastern side, might rather be represented as a flat country than otherwise, yet having on the whole an easy ascent towards the north-west end of the County, whose elevation is certainly considerable, the surface advancing gradually in height, to the *Grand Ridge* or waterheads of our Island, which enter the County from Staffordshire on the middle Axe-edge Hill, about a quarter of a mile north-west of Dove-head on the Leek and Buxton Road, and pursues a N N E and serpentine course across the County (as shewn in the Map of Ridges facing page 1) to 'the Trough,' at the head of the main or east branch of the Derwent River, and the head of Littleclough water (before mentioned, p. 2), where the Grand Ridge enters Yorkshire, after having separated or cut off the very large parish of Glossop, Chapel-en-le-Frith, and parts of Hartington and Hope parishes, as belonging to the western drainage of the Island."

P. 5. "On the *Grand Ridge* (coloured Vermillion) the three principal eminences of the County, Axe-edge, Kinder-scout, and Blakelow-stones are situated, the latter *appearing to me* †, to be considerably the highest of the three, and Axe-edge the lowest, which seems equalled in height, if not exceeded, by Goyteshead Tor, on the N of Stoney-lane Toll Bar on the Macclesfield and Buxton Road, which hill is situated on a branch from the Grand Ridge near Axe-edge into Cheshire, which will be mentioned hereafter. From the western side of the Grand Ridge in Glossop and Chapel-en-le-Frith, there spring four or five ridges

* Mr. Farey, it would seem, entered Derbyshire under the delusive expectation of finding in it the semblance of the Alps of the old, or the Andes of the new world. It appears not to have been enough, in the eye of the Surveyor, that the "grand ridge" which "enters Yorkshire in its majestic progress towards Scotland" (p. 8.) occupies some considerable share of its surface.

† We find no estimate of the ELEVATION of any of the "Derbyshire mountains."

ridges of considerable height; but they are too short to require further notice for the present."

Having given in the devious manner, which may be caught in the above extracts, a general description of the more prominent ranges of hills, Mr F. inserts (p. 11.) a list of the "Names, situations and lengths of the several principal RIDGES or Waterheads, in and near Derbyshire, in alphabetical order." The numbers inserted in this list are fortyone.

Next succeeds (p. 16.) "an Alphabetical List of the Names of the several Mountains, HILLS and Eminences throughout Derbyshire, or in the borders of the adjoining Counties, describing their situations, the STRATA on the top of each, and referring by numbers to the RIDGES to which they severally belong."—This list fills nearly fifty pages; the number inserted being upward of seven hundred!

That long list of hills is followed (p. 64.) by "an Alphabetical List of the Names of the principal narrow and Rocky VALLEYS, or Defiles, with precipitous Cliffs, in and near to Derbyshire, describing their Situations, the STRATA exhibited in their Sides and Bottoms, and the Names of the most noted ROCKS, CAVERNS, &c. in each." The number fiftysix.

The above list is accompanied with the following sensible observations.—P. 72. "I have selected the above, as specimens of the narrow and precipitous Valleys of Derbyshire and its environs: the neighbourhoods of Ballidon, Brassington-pastures, Brushfield, Dowall, Flagg, Hartington, Pike-Hall and others, present similar Dales, some of considerable length, and not less striking than many of the above, and which I have visited, but don't happen to have learnt their particular Names; otherwise they would have been included, on account of the facility which such Lists give, of recording a number of highly curious and interesting phenomena, of which Travellers may in future avail themselves: it is to such Valleys also, that Mineralogists and Geologists must principally resort, to become acquainted with the different Calcareous and Basaltic Rocks of this County, to draw materials for the Natural History of each, and for settling the important and contested questions respecting the origin, and mode in which Valleys were excavated and formed.

"It must not be inferred, that high and precipitous Rocks and Cliffs are peculiar to or confined to the class of Valleys of which I have been speaking, since the sides of the wide Valleys, also, abound with Rocks and Cliffs, some of them highly picturesque and beautiful, but such Rocks seldom

seldom continue far, without the intervention of grassy or cultivated slopes, such as the sides of Valleys usually present, in districts where no durable or permanent Rocks exist in their strata: whereas, in the narrow Valleys above, such slopes, or interruptions to the continuity of the Cliffs on each of their sides, are rare, and in some instances do not occur at all, within the distances which I have named. The Grit-stone Rocks of this district, seem particularly disposed to appear and disappear repeatedly on the surface at their edges, or in tracing their Bassets through the country; and except of the 1st or lowest Grit Rock, it is a rare thing to find a continued Grit-stone Cliff of any length: some of them, indeed, are so disposed to moulder and fall, on exposure to the air, rain, frost, &c. that Cliffs of such Rocks are never seen; but where *Slips* or slidings have happened, in comparatively modern times, of which there are numerous and striking examples in Derbyshire, particularly in the Shale and shale Grit districts; and as it seems of the utmost importance in Geological researches, to distinguish between Cliffs or Facades of equal antiquity with the valleys themselves, probably, or such as have originated with, or been increased by, subsequent and sudden Slips, or by the gradual and recent undermining of currents of the Brooks and Rivers, I shall here give a List of such SLIPS, or modern sliding and sinking of tracts of ground on the sides of Hills, as I have noted in the course of my Survey."—This list of Slips (a natural and good term) closes the section " Surface."

CLIMATURE.—P. 95. " A disposition to the marvellous, seems to me to have pervaded all the accounts of the Climate and Surface of Derbyshire which I have read; there is certainly a sensible difference between the Climate of some of the middle and north-westerly parts of the County and the remainder of it, owing to their difference of elevation; but this is far from being so great or striking, that cultivation in most instances, and successful improvements in every instance, cannot be practised, as I shall take occasion further to explain in the Twelfth Chapter.

" The name *High Peak*, seems almost generally misunderstood by strangers to Derbyshire, and even by a large portion of the Inhabitants of the Southern part of the County itself; the greater number understanding thereby, a certain alpine and inhospitable region; while others have imagined *the High Peak*, to refer to some frightful Mountain or Precipice, which, like that of Tenerif, lorded it over all the surrounding Country, instead of its being the Name of one of the Hundreds of the County."

Indeed!

Indeed! This is a discovery. But what has agriculture, or mineralogy to do with the Hundreds of a County? It is well for magistrates and chief constables, who act within them, to be able to trace their fortuitous boundaries: no matter how unnatural, inconvenient and irrational they may *now* be. But what ordinary person who hears of the "High Peak of Derbyshire," is not, and ought not to be, impressed with the idea of an *English mountain*;—especially one who has been in the habit of seeing its "grand ridges" from the low vale lands of the Midland Counties. If, instead of criticising former Writers, Mr. F. had given us (as doubtless he could) a sufficiently accurate division of the County into MOUNTAIN, UPLAND, and VALE, and noticed the climature of each, he might have done English agriculture some service.

P. 96. "At New Haven in Hartingdon, I was informed by Mr. T. Greenwood, that the Harvest with them, both for Hay and Corn, is a fortnight later on the average, than it is about Derby."

Unfortunately, however, we have no intimation, as to what time harvest usually commences about Derby.

The subjoined is the Surveyor's account of the Climature of the "High Peak;"—by which no doubt is meant the HIGHLANDS of DERBYSHIRE;—and not a political division of the County.

P. 96. "Frequent mention has been made, of Corn remaining out in the Fields of the High Peak at Christmas, indeed I saw myself, Oats standing in the Shock, and covered by Snow, on the 25th of November, 1808, between Buxton and Hartingdon."

P. 98. "*Thunder* or *Lightning* does not seem to be very prevalent in Derbyshire; I heard or saw but little, while I was in the County."

Rain.—P. 99. "By the kindness of his Grace of Devonshire, and of his Agent, Mr. Knowlton, of Edensor, I am enabled to present a very satisfactory abstract of the Rain which fell at Chatsworth during 50 years past, ascertained by an excellent and well-attended Rain-Guage in the Gardens at that place, the funnel of which seems to be about 18 feet above the Ground, and about 60 feet above the Derwent River at Chatsworth: the depth of Rain is registered by the Gardener every morning at nine o'clock, which has fallen the preceding Day and Night. The following are the yearly totals, viz. in 1761, 26.525 inches; in 1762, 23 399 inches; and in

"1763

Years.	Inches.	Years.	Inches.	Years.	Inches.
"1763 ...	36.399	1779 ...	24.582	1795 ...	23.531
1764 ...	34.262	1780 ...	19.443	1796 ...	24.280
1765 ...	27.536	1781 ...	23.065	1797 ...	30.129
1766 ...	25.235	1782 ...	39.115	1798 ...	27 562
1767 ...	30.723	1783 ...	29.526	1799 ...	30.995
1768 ...	39.919	1784 ...	22.976	1800 ...	27.732
1769 ...	27.255	1785 ...	23 162	1801 ...	28.345
1770 ...	29.446	1786 ...	30 676	1802 ...	23.340
1771 ...	22.433	1787 ...	32.068	1803 ...	24.270
1772 ...	30.842	1788 ...	19.856	1804 ...	47.904
1773 ...	31.281	1789 ...	36.309	1805 ...	22.232
1774 ...	31.522	1790 ...	26.892	1806 ...	30.182
1775 ...	33.749	1791 ...	34 698	1807 ...	26.365
1776 ...	29.892	1792 ...	34.740	1808 ...	28.509
1777 ...	24.794	1793 ...	24.316	1809 ...	29.911
1778 ...	29.895	1794 ...	30.769	1810 ...	27.984

"The total depth of Water fallen in this period, including melted Snow, being more than 119 feet, and giving a yearly average of 28.411 inches; the greatest yearly depths being 39 919 inches (in 1768), 39.115 inches (in 1782), 36.399 inches (in 1763), 36.309 inches (in 1789), &c.; and the least, 19.443 inches (in 1780), 19.856 inches (in 1788), 22.232 inches (in 1805), 22.433 inches (in 1771), &c.

"The monthly average depths during these 50 years appear to be, January, 2.23 inches; February, 2.15 inches; March, 1.62 inches; April, 2.00 inches; May, 1.98 inches; June, 2.09 inches; July, 2.70 inches; August, 2.64 inches; September, 2.77 inches; October, 2 95 inches; November, 2.74 inches; and December, 2.54 inches."

Chatsworth is one of the few *show* places of the kingdom which I have not seen. It is situated somewhat considerably to the northward of the center of the County. But at what elevation above the tide, or its relative situation, with respect to neighbouring hills, does not appear, in the Report.

WATERS.—*Running Waters.*—Mr. Farey bestows eighteen or twenty pages on descriptions of the rivers, brooks, and brooklets of Derbyshire; or rather of their beds, or the bottoms of the valleys, through which they run; noticing the different strata which appear or may be found, in each: thus furnishing, in addition to the geological facts contained in the List of Valleys, abovementioned, a valuable collection of data which cannot fail of being greatly useful to *practical miners;* but which, in a Work on *Agriculture*, is a heavy encumbrance. If the almost infinite items of information are faithfully given (and they *read* as if they were) they are creditable

creditable, in the highest degree, to Mr. Farey, as a *mineral Surveyor.*

P. 489. "I shall close this account of the *Rivers* in Derbyshire, by an alphabetical List, of those above enumerated, with the portion of Derbyshire, nearly, which each drains, viz.

	Acres.
" Amber (except a part in Notts.)	31,000
Ashop	13,000
Bootle	8,000
Bradford and Lathkil	20,000
Dane (upper part)	580
Derwent (except a part in Yorkshire)	111,500
Dolee (except a part in Notts.)	15,000
Dove (only the E side)	81,000
Ecclesburn	15,000
Erewash (only the W side)	17,000
Ethrow (only the S side)	10,000
Goyte (only the E side)	31,000
Hipper	7,000
Idle (upper parts)	21,000
Mease (intermixed with Leicestershire)	16,000
Morledge	13,000
Noe	15,000
Nutbrook	10,000
Rother (upper parts)	45,000
Schoo	10,000
Sence (in Ravenstone)	2,000
Sheaf (upper part)	5,000
Shelf	10,000
Trent (middle parts)	70,000
Wye	45,000
Total of Derbyshire	622,080"

The following apt and sensible remarks, on the rivers of Derbyshire, are entitled to a place, here.

Temperature.—P. 487. " It has been often remarked, that some of the Rivers of this District are *warmer* than usual, and rarely freeze, the Derwent in particular, owing as it is said, to the many warm Springs which vent into them: when, however, the very inconsiderable quantity of such warm Spring Water and its small elevation of temperature is considered, as also, that there is nothing like a general warmth perceivable in the Strata any where, as those fond of deriving Toadstone and every thing else from subterranean Fire have pretended, it seems more natural to refer the circumstance, as far as it is true, to the great depth and narrowness

narrowness of the Valleys, preserving the temperature longer than in more open situations."

Or may not this circumstance, "as far as it is true," be owing, in part at least, to the numerous springs which rise in the river beds, or immediately on their banks; issuing from the bases of tall and steep masses, on which the outward air can have no influence, and with temperatures of course much above the freezing point.

Drought.—P. 487. "After long dry weather the Rivers and Brooks here, as might be expected with such rapid falls, suffer considerable *Droughts*, and are quite dried up often, in places where at other times the torrents are tremendous: a remarkable drought is recorded in the year 1661, in which it was said, but not truly I think, that the Derwent was dried up at Derby."

Floods.—"It has been remarked, that considerable *Floods* usually follow Rain with the wind blowing down the course of the Rivers.* The Dove seems particularly subject to sudden Floods, which inundate its fine expanse of Meadows. Under this head it may be proper to mention, that in 1587 the Derwent was greatly swelled by a Flood, which carried away St. Mary's Bridge: in 1610, and again in 1673, the Morledge was so swelled by sudden Rains, as to do much damage in Derby: Nov. 5, 1698, the Derwent was greatly flooded: also on the 21st of November, 1791 †, when it carried away Toad-moor Bridge above Belper."

Standing

* Land Floods.—The above remark is not singular. The effect, I apprehend, is principally to be accounted for, not by the wind *hastening* the flood waters (the idea in *this* district) but by the direction in which the rain approaches the high grounds that feed the river. If it come over the collecting surface, to the place of observation, not only the quantity, in ordinary cases, will be greater, there, than at the feet of the hills, (where perhaps little rain may descend) but its fall will be *earlier*, according to the strength of the wind which conveys it. If this be moderate, or nearly stationary, the flood will be said to be SUDDEN, as being unexpected, and may thereby become injurious, on the flat river banks of the country below. Whereas, with the wind and rain coming in the opposite direction, the reverse of those circumstances will naturally take place.

In a case like that now under notice, (and cases of a like nature are common) it would be no more than ordinary precaution to employ a person or persons who reside among the hills which send down the flood waters, to give notice, to the occupiers of the lower grounds that are liable to be flooded, of heavy falls of rain; and thus warn them of approaching floods. For the serious mischiefs to which the banks of the Dove are liable, see p. 45, aforegoing.

"† The Register kept of the Rain at Chatsworth, on this River, of which I have given an account at page 99, in the Week preceding this Flood, was as follows, viz. on the 14th = .173 inches, 15th = .141, 16th = 494, 17th = .058, 18th = .378, 19th = .612, 20th = 2.062, and 21st = .074, total of the week 3.992 inches."

Standing Waters.—Lakes.—P. 490. " Neither Derbyshire or its environs furnish any natural Pools of Water deserving of the name of Lakes, nor is there the least appearance of deep Lakes which have been filled up, either by *native* Gravel (see p. 132) and earthy deposits, or by the growth of Peat."

Pools.—P. 491. " In the Rocky Limestone Districts of Derbyshire, which are coloured Vermillion Red and Orange in the Map of Soils and Strata, facing page 97, the Farmers and Inhabitants set great store by certain ancient Ponds or Meers of Water, which rarely if ever fail, and yet few of them have any perceptible Stream running from them: few of these Meers exceed an Acre, and many of them are less than a Rood in extent, and generally are but a few feet deep in the middle or deepest part. It seems to me, that most or all of these are the work of art, in part at least, in deepening the bottom and raising a head, where a slight Spring and natural wet flat place appeared, either on the basset of one of the Toad-stone Strata, or on alluvial patches of sufficient extent and tenacity to catch and hold up the Rain-waters. The period when these Meers were made is probably very distant, the tradition even of which is lost, and they are generally considered as natural Meers or Pools of Water."—Mr. F. gives a List of twentyfive places, where he says " I observed these *ancient Meres* of Water." He gives a List of fifteen or twenty of such pools.

The following information is very interesting; and may serve, perhaps, to account for all, or many, of the " ancient Meres," abovementioned.—P. 495. " Upon the high East Moor, on the south side of the very ancient Grindstone Quarry in Ashover, which is noticed as such in the Doomsday Survey of William the First, a very entire artificial Pond was discovered in 1808, almost concealed under Peat, in making a Drain in Sir Joseph Banks's new Plantations; the head or artificial Bank of which was *puddled* in the centre, in a very complete manner, no ways differing, apparently, from what has been erroneously said to be a modern art, introduced on our Canals by Mr. Brindley. The situation of this Pond, close to the ancient Road which led to this Grindstone Quarry, leaves no room to doubt, but it was constructed for the use of the Cattle, employed to carry Grindstones from this inhospitable Moor into the South Country."

Mr. BRINDLEY may, nevertheless, be entitled to all the praise he has received, and to all the gratitude due to him, for the quantity of good which he has occasioned in his country, from the time he established the practice, to the present day. If it could be *proved* that Mr. B. did *not discover*

cover the art of puddling, but *copied* after the *ancients*, his merit, as an *inventor* would certainly be less. But, otherwise, the honors he has acquired are as much his own, as if the art had not before existed.

P. 496. " Mr. George Toplis, in draining his allotment on the Green in Brassington, on Shale, has made some very complete Watering-places, by fixing long Stone Cisterns, 18 inches wide and 9 inches deep, in the line of his Underdrains, and sloping away the ground and paving the easy descents to them each way, by which means the Cattle can approach the water from either side, and are not liable to be injured by a master Beast, attacking them while drinking, but can readily escape across the Cistern. Mr. John Blackwall, of Blackwall, in draining his Farm, on Shale, has conducted the Drains to proper places for Cisterns by the Fences, causing the water to enter at one end just level with the surface, and pass off at the other; and finds, that the constant change and agitation of the surface of the water by this stream across it, prevents freezing in the severest weather, a thing of much importance to the health of Cattle."

This beneficial effect would seem to arise from the water issuing from a depth beneath the influence of the frost, as well as from its motion in the trough.

Springs.—P. 500. " Few subjects are of more practical importance, than the Theory and Knowledge of *Springs*, to the Miner and the Agriculturist, who want to discharge them from the interior or the surface of the Ground, to the Civil Engineer, the Miller, or the Inhabitants, who want to discover and collect them for the supply of Canals or Mills, and for domestic and rural purposes; and yet few subjects have been incumbered with more wild and fanciful Theories, or been more superficially treated by Authors. That filtration of the Rain Waters through porous Strata, till interrupted and thrown out by other water-tight Strata or Faults, is the original cause of all Springs of Water, is doubted or questioned by no practical Miner, Well-sinker, or intelligent Drainer; and of which, no subject that I am acquainted with in Nature, admits of stronger or more conclusive evidence."

Having presented us with " an alphabetical List of the noticeable Springs of Water, in or near to Derbyshire," Mr. F. favours us with a *glimpse* of what appears to me an important fact in Geology.

P. 506. " The particular nature or proportions of the mineral impregnations, in the Springs mentioned in the above List, I have not had the opportunity of enquiring into, but have set them down according to obvious appearances, or as they are reputed to be: much less shall I say

any

any thing here on their Medicinal qualities: those who visit Buxton, Matlock Bath, or Keddleston-Inn, will be at no loss for publications setting forth their respective virtues, or for the advice of Professional Men who have especially turned their attention to these subjects; and to the proper regimen and treatment of invalids, to whom these Waters are likely to prove serviceable. I ought here, however, to acknowledge the kindness of Dr. Buxton, of Buxton, in communicating to me his observations on the great Fault which ranges through the Baths there, and the state of the Hot Springs, at the time that the foundations were digging for the Crescent, and other Buildings adjoining it, in the year 1781." *

Might not a sedulous investigation of this striking fact, lead toward a rational theory of the nature of hot springs?

A List of *Cascades*, and a "List of *Water-swallows*," or "Holes in the Rocks into which Streams of Water fall and disappear in and near Derbyshire," are found in the First Volume of this indefatigable Writer.

GEOLOGY.

This has ever been with me a favourite subject, since I read, at an early age, "BURNET'S THEORY." I have, since that time, incidentally dipped into other Works on the subject; and have not failed to contemplate what has been termed the face of Nature, in traversing the surface of this island, and viewing, I may say, with little latitude, its every feature.

The *formation* of its fractured shell, however, has been with me a secondary study; and my remarks upon it have rarely (excepting in a comparatively few instances) been admitted into my registers;—any farther than as they appeared to be useful to AGRICULTURE, and the other branches of RURAL ECONOMY; with which GEOLOGY, as an abstract science, has (in one instance only which will be noticed) but a slender connexion; and still more irrelevant to those subjects are FOSSILOGY and MINERALOGY; unless so far as they are capable of assisting to furnish *implements, manure* and *fuel.*

The arts and mysteries of MINING, which has not inaptly been termed the "curse of agriculture," can have no pretension to be incorporated with it. Oil and water are scarcely more repugnant to each other. Yet no inconsiderable portion

* P. 503. "Buxton Town, hot, 82°, and Baths; Chalybeate, 52°, to 55°, in Shale, these on opposite sides of the great Limestone Fault: W of Buxton, Cold, and a Bath."

tion of the Work under review, is occupied by the *Practice* of *Mining*;—an odious interruption, in a Work on Agriculture.

The art of DISCOVERING valuable fossils and minerals may, however (or may not) be useful to land proprietors. I shall not, therefore, entirely overlook Mr. Farey's Strictures on Stratification.

The subjoined is Mr. F.'s definition of "stratified masses." I insert it without any other *comment*, than that of confessing I do not clearly comprehend the justness of it.

P. 106. "A number of extended and continuous masses applied upon each other in contact, constitute a stratified mass, whether the strata composing it are plane and of equal thickness throughout, as the leaves of a book, or are of irregular shape and thickness, as the annual layers of wood round a tree, and its several knots or the insertions of its arms or principal branches; or the several concentric coats round an onion. In the two latter cases, the strata or lamina composing the tree and the onion, return into themselves or form rings, in one of their dimensions, while in the opposite one, they spread into roots and branches, at their different ends."

This definition is succeeded by introductory remarks "on the Sections of stratified Masses;" in which the same analogical manner of explanation is used.

The Author next enters, "in a general way," on "the stratifications of England," as explained by Mr. SMITH,—whom Mr. Farey styles his "master and instructor in mineral surveying."

P. 108. "It is now about 19 Years since, that Mr. *William Smith*, of Mitford, near Bath, contemplating the great regularity of the numerous strata in the Coal-works, in the superintendance of which he was then employed, in the neighbourhood of High-Littleton, in Somersetshire, and the generally prevailing *dip*, or descending of strata toward the east-ward, and consequent rise and crop or basset of them towards the opposite point; happily conceived the idea, and shortly after began putting it in practice of actually tracing the edges of a certain number of the most conspicuous strata, from the place of their entry on our Island on the south Coast, to their exit again therefrom in the German Ocean. In a few years he had so far succeeded in this attempt, as to have traced, several strata, and delineated their entire British course on his Map, from one Sea to the other, as he expected."

In a note, p. 109, we are informed that "the Rev. John Mitchell made a list of 11 principal strata in their order, before Mr Smith took up the subject, but carried it to no useful conclusions, that I can learn." Mr.

Mr. Farey "attempts a concise account of the upper part of the British series of strata, as they have been ascertained and taught by Mr. Smith."

The first stratum, mentioned in his account, is *Gravel*; which we had previously been told (p. 109) is "composed of the ruins of strata, which he found so plentifully distributed over the surface of England, but forming quite a distinct class from the regular Strata, *among or under which it never is found.*"

Thus far I can go with this account; but cannot proceed farther in it, with the like satisfaction. I have, as many others doubtlessly have, been long waiting for Mr. Smith's *own* account of these matters; of which *Mr. Farey* thus speaks, at the close of *his* account of them. P. 116. "And here close my account of *Mr. Smith's* meritorious labours and discoveries, lamenting my inability to do any justice to them, in the imperfect sketch which I have presented, which I cannot however do, without sincerely hoping, that such a desire may speedily be excited, for the publication of that Gentleman's valuable Maps and Papers, and descriptions of his Fossils, illustrative of the British Strata, as would induce him to lay by his professional engagements, in order to publish them, or which should dispose him to give them up, to such persons as would speedily bring them before the public."

The regular strata of Mr. Smith, the names of which appear in succession, in Mr. F's account (accompanied by a few remarks) p. 111, are these.

1. Sand of Bogshot Heath, &c.
2. London Clay.
3. Blackheath Sand.
4. Flinty Chalk.
5. Hard Chalk.
6. Chalk Marl.
7. Aylesbury Limestone.
8. Sand, and several Clays and Sussex Marble.
9. Woburn Sand.
10. Clunch Clay.
11. Bedford Limestone.
12. Clay and Ragstone.
13. Limestone and Grey Slate.
14. A Sand Stratum.
15. Bath Freestone.
16. Sand and Clays.
17. Maidwell Limestone.
18. Lyas Clay, containing blue Lyas Stone and white Lyas Limestone.
19. Sand.

20. Red

20. Red Marl:—a bad name, this, for the red substrata of England, which are in a manner destitute of calcariosity; as appears by analyses, in different departments of the kingdom. See my Registers of their Rural Economy.

This "Red Marl," from the account here given, would seem to be the lowest of Mr. Smith's strata, and the highest of Mr. Farey's.—P. 116. "A natural division of the British strata being thus as it were marked out, by the basset or first appearance of the Red Marl on the Surface, from under the edge of the Lias Clay, I shall reserve what I have further to say upon this stratum, until I come to speak of my own observations on the Derbyshire strata, of which this Red Marl is the highest stratum."—But not strictly so, as will be seen.

Here, as in various other parts of this Report, we are *at fault,* as a huntsman would say; and as a miner says (as if it were after him) when he comes to a BREAK, in a seam or stratum. Mr. Farey, however offers, in the present instance, a reason for this "dislocation:"—another term of Mineralogists, for FRACTURE, and a want of continuity of parts.

P. 116. "I shall be unable to proceed, in detailing the series of strata which appear from below these, in Derbyshire and its environs, without first resuming the subject of *Stratified Masses,* in order to point out the effects of *breaking and dislocating* such masses, and afterwards of cutting and *denudating* them in various directions; a subject which I have never seen touched upon in any Author, and must therefore claim the indulgence of my Readers, in order to go somewhat particularly into it, as the Theory or foundation of Mineral Surveying, by the application of which, I propose, to explain the number and position of the principal strata in Derbyshire and its Environs, from the examination which I have made of their surface."

This bold and arduous undertaking does Mr. Farey great credit, as a Mineralogical Surveyor. A large plate (in effect, but divided into two parts for the conveniency of folding into the Report) on which is engraved fiftysix figures of stratified masses; each part being entitled "A Sheet of Figures for explaining the nature of FAULTS, or DISLOCATIONS and TILTS of STRATA, and of the subsequent denudating and excavating of the terrestrial Surface, to its present shape."—"By John Farey, Senior, Mineralogical Surveyor."

These figures represent double piles of strata, of a somewhat cubical form; each pile or mass being formed of twelve distinct strata; their edges being aptly distinguished, to the eye, by different colors.

One mass or pile of each figure is intended to represent the

the strata in their "fixed," or "unmoved" state,—shall we say their *natural state.*—These are mostly drawn, horizontally, or nearly so; while the other, composed of the same number of laminæ, bearing the same colors, is intended to exhibit the same strata, in a *broken* and *dislodged* state; by being sunk somewhat below, or raised somewhat above, the fixed strata; without altering, perhaps, the general line of inclination, or horizontality.—Or the fragments broken off are "tilted," so as to form an inclined plain, dipping toward, or from, the general line of surface, &c. &c.—No two of the fiftysix figures show exactly the same form and articulation of strata. Indeed, the variety of fractures, positions, and articulations of strata, found in sinking shafts, and working mines, must, I conceive be infinite *. Those which Mr. Farey has delineated and described (not very *intelligently)* will doubtlessly tend to convey a more precise idea of them, than the mere imagination of one who is unpractised in the work of mining, could form. But, without intending to lessen Mr. Farey's merit, as a mineralogical surveyor, I cannot refrain from saying, in language which at this moment is familiar to me,—that, in a work on AGRICULTURE, they are an obtrusive mass of fault stuff.

We now come to Mr. Farey's *own* "description of the principal strata, in *Derbyshire* and its environs,"—P. 131.

These strata, or masses of strata, are nine in number; namely,

1. Gravel or other alluvia.
2. Lyas clay and limestone strata,

3. Red

* A specimen of GEOLOGICAL ANOMALY, or in words more appropriate, geological confusion, is seen in the subjoined passages.—P. 174. "The Coal-Field round Ashby-de-la-Zouch in Leicestershire, is one of the highly curious, but perhaps not uncommon occurrences in the Red Marl districts, a tract entirely surrounded by a Fault or Series of Faults which unite, seems lifted up through the Red Marl strata, and denudated, the Coal strata having *rapid dips* in various directions, while the surrounding strata of Marl are *horizontal,* or as nearly so as may be. On the north-eastern and northern border of this Coal-Field, the yellow Lime, its upper strata, are seen lifted up with it, from Grace Dieu to Ticknall, and perhaps also to Decoy Wood in Bretby." Other specimens might be pointed out. Some will appear in the ensuing extracts.

In every extensive district of the island anomalies might be detected, to show how difficult it would be to make out "a british series of regular strata,"—even were the fault stuff, and the several strata *transparent;* so as to show distinctly every part; and still more difficult must be the task, under the existing circumstance of *opacity.*

I am not saying this to discorage Mr. Smith, or his pupil Mr. Farey, or any one else, in proceeding in the meritorious attempt; but rather to stimulate their diligence in the undertaking.

3. Red marl strata.
4. Yellow limestone strata.
5. and 6. Coal measures, or strata.
7. Gritstone and shale strata.
8. Mineral limestone and toadstone.
9. Fourth limestone.

We find no *general section* of those strata, to show their several thicknesses, and the manner in which they bear upon each other; and thereby to give the reader a clear idea of the justness of the above arrangement.

A *section* of the *three lowest masses*, however, is given, on a small plate,—entitled " a Section of the three lowest assemblages of Strata known in Derbyshire;—showing the thickness and position of these several Strata, as they appear across Matlock Bath Dale."

This sketch is highly satisfactory. In it we see the NATURAL ARRANGEMENT of the strata, and the proportionate depths that they bear to each other; scales of lengths and thicknesses being added*.

Nor do we find any *sections* of *shafts*, or of *slips*, or of *precipices*,—such as might reasonably be looked for, in a work of this nature.

What, however, is much more interesting to AGRICULTURE, Mr. Farey has furnished his work with a map of the County and its environs, showing by outlines, numbers and coloring, where the several strata APPROACH the SURFACE.

This map is entitled " a map of Derbyshire, and parts of the seven adjacent counties; showing the principal STRATA and SOILS."—The last word, however, is ill placed; but perhaps it was inserted (by whom I cannot say) to give the map a more *agricultural* appearance. In some places, the word SUBSOILS might have been accurately put. But, more generally, the BASES or the SUBSTRUCTURES of the SOILS would have been more appropriate.

Nevertheless, for this map many thanks are due to Mr. Farey,

* SECTION of STRATA.—The *thicknesses* of the several strata, comprised in that sketch, as measured by the scale at the foot of the section, are these

No. 7. First grit rock 120 yards.
Limestone shale 140.
No. 8. First limestone rock 50.
First toadstone 20.
Second lime rock 50.
Second Toadstone 30.
Third lime rock 60.
Third toadstone 30.
No. 9. Fourth limestone rock 120 yards.

The greatest *length*, shown in the sketch, is more than one mile and a half.

Farey. It is chiefly in supplying the cultivators of the surface with plans of this nature, that GEOLOGY can be materially serviceable to AGRICULTURE. It is well known, by men of experience, that, in the productiveness of LAND, more depends on the *subsoil* and *base*, than on the *surface mold.*—Thus far, as to GEOLOGY, abstractedly considered.

FORMATION of SOILS.

It may be said to be natural, and is not uncommon, for a man who has two subjects before him, one of which is familiar to him, the other not, yet inseparably connected, —to ascribe too much to that which has long occupied his mind, and to which his habits are enured,—and too little to the other.—Thus, Mr. Farey, in speaking of the "origin" or formation of soils, seems to consider them as the mere decomposition of "perishable strata."—He says, speaking of clayey soils, p. 303, "the clayey Soils of Derbyshire owe their origin, 1st, to Clayey Gravel, which is indiscriminately strewed over the County, but most extensively in the local patches of the tracts coloured brown, in the Map facing page 97, to the S and SW of Derby; the others are mentioned in the List, page 134: these are generally found difficult soils, either to drain or improve. 2nd, to Red Marl Strata, in the southern district, coloured Lake Red (page 148), frequently on Lands too much marled at a former period; these are capable of a high degree of improvement, by draining and liming. 3rd, to Coal Shales, and the other argillaceous and perishable Strata, which accompany Coal (see page 161 and 181). 4th, to the great Limestone Shale, in the districts coloured Purple, page 227); which, when it has a proper degree of tenacity, makes excellent Land, as about Hassop, Ashford, Bakewell, Ashburne N, Newton-grange, &c. &c. and very poor Land in others, as observed above. And 5th, to the decomposition of Toadstone on the surface, see page 278, as on the E of Fairfield, and other places: this Clay is said to be very unfavourable to the growth of Oaks. Cold clayey soils in this County, have numerous Pewets or Lapwings, flying and screaming over them, whence such are often called pewety soils."

Now, it has long appeared to me that the surface soils, the cultivated molds, in this and every other cultivated country, are of *vegetable* rather that of *mineral* origin; but partake of both.

By aquatic plants, a soil, altogether vegetable, may be created in a few years. And, seeing the length of time, the millenia of years, which the surface of the principal part of this kingdom, while in a state of nature, or when thinly inabited,—

inhabited,—was covered with wood (and coarse deep-rooting herbage) whose leaves annually fell to the ground, and whose dead branches, stems and roots were, in the ordinary course of nature, converted to vegetable mold,—the origin and existing depths of soils, might, by a mere vegetist, seem to be well accounted for, without calling in the aid of mineral substances. For, supposing the leaves, decayed branches, and the roots of annual and of aged plants, to increase the depth of soil, only one hundredth of an inch, annually,—the increase, in one thousand years, would be ten inches: a depth which the majority of soils do not reach.

Let us, now, endeavour to explain how far mineral and fossil substances have been instrumental, in the formation of soils. The first plants which took root, after the present figuration of the surface of the earth was cast, were of course nurtured by the substances that were exposed upon it; and it would be a length of time, in most situations, before vegetable productions arrived at the state of luxuriance, in which we now view them; and this may serve to account for the thinness of soils, at the present day, in various situations, and for the great variation in their depths, in a general view.

Where natural clays, or other loose earthy strata, of a fertile quality, were exposed on the surface, there, vegetation would soon gain strength. On the contrary, where indurated strata, or those of a nature unfriendly to vegetation, though of a plastic or loose texture, occupied it, there, it would long remain destitute of covering. Again, where water lodged in the substratum, so as to give an ungenial coldness to the surface, or where the surface was a blowing sand, or where the elevation was so great as to check vegetation, though the exposed surface were of a fertile quality,—in such situations the growth of plants, and the accumulation of vegetable mold, would be slow; while on sounder and better textured grounds, more genially situated, the *growth* of *soil* would be rapid; and its depth would of course become comparatively great.

But although the more fertile parts of the generality of soils, must necessarily, I conceive, have been produced in the manner above suggested. Yet there can be few instances in which their entire bulk can be of vegetable origin. For, even in the state of nature, the substratum on which the vegetable mold was produced, would be raised and mixed with it, by moles, worms, and other inhabitants of soils; and, in the state of cultivation, the subsoil or base is still more liable to be turned up, and intimately blended with the vegetable matter, by the operations of the plow, and other implements.

Hence there can be no risk in concluding that (unless where the accumulation of vegetable mold has been of extraordinary depth) cultivated soils partake more or less of the mineral strata on which they rest; and this might not inaptly serve to raise in the minds of mere mineralogists the idea that the entire matter of soils may have been produced by the perishing and decomposition of those strata.

The *animal* matter which has been accumulating on the surface, from the time of its being inhabited, I have refrained from mentioning; as it is of *vegetable origin;*—vegetable mold highly elaborated and rendered capable of giving a superior degree of fertilization to soils.

I have embraced the present as a favorable opportunity of explaining my ideas respecting the origin, increase, and component parts of cultivated soils. I have, for some length of time, been in possession of them; as may be seen in my SOUTHERN COUNTIES, district *Weald* of *Sussex*, article Soil; but have not until now, deliberatively discussed and digested them.

FOSSILS and MINERALS.

FINDING nothing, in Mr. Farey's remarks on *Soils*, that could add to the value of this register,—they being directed to the "improvement" of them, rather than to their *specific qualities*, or to an accurate *mineralogical description* of them,—such as might have been expected from a mineralogical surveyor,—I pass on to matters with which he is evidently better acquainted.

In this instance, I unite fossils and minerals under one head; Mr. Farey having made no distinction between them. My motive for having usually separated them has been that *fossils* are many of them valuable in *agriculture;* whereas minerals on the contrary, are its bane (as will presently be seen)—coals always excepted. The distinction I make between them is, that *fossils* are *dug out of pits* and *quarries,—minerals* extracted from what is figuratively, but not analogically, termed the "bowels of the earth,"—by the means of *shafts* and *drifts*.

In the two lists, subjoined, we see the numerous kinds of *subterranean*, or, in better geological, because more scientific, language, *subficial* matters, (if the phrase will be allowed) which one of the smaller Counties of this kingdom and its immediate environs afford.

P. 219. "The following is a general List of the Minerals, and articles produced by the valuable *Coal-districts*.

"Argillaceous Sand-stone.	Bind, of several kinds.
Bakestones (of Shale).	Black Chalk (Bind or Shale).
	Brasses

Brasses (Pyrites).
Brick Clay.
Cant-stone.
Canney-Coal (Sparkle, Branch, Splint).
Chalybeate Springs.
Clay.
Clunch.
Coals.
Crowstone (Ganister).
Crozling Coals (Smithy).
Fire Clay.
Fire Stone (Pot-stones).
Freestone.
Grind-stones.
Gritstone.
Hard Coal (Stone Coal).
Hones (Ironstone).
Ironstone.
Marble (Muscle Ironstone).
Marl (Bind).
Micaceous Gritstone.
Ochrey Springs.
Paving-stone (flags).
Peacock Coal.
Pipe Clay (White Potters').
Potters' Clay (white, yellow, Red).
Pyrites (Brasses).
Sandstone.
Shale.
Slate grey (micaceous grit).
Soft Coals (Sleck).
Sulphureous Springs.
Tile Clay.
Whetstones."

P. 299. "I shall close this account of the *Lime and Toadstone Districts*, as I did that of the Coal-measures, by a general List of the Minerals, and Articles produced in the Mineral or Mountain Limestone Districts,

"Antimony?
Arsenic?
Asphaltum.
Barytes (sulphate).
Bastard Limestone (Dun-stone).
Bird's-eye Marble (Entrochian).
Bitumen (hard, soft, and elastic).
Black Jack (Zink Ore).
Black Limestone (stinking).
Black Marble.
Black Wad (Manganese Ore).
Blend (Zink Ore).
Bloodstones (alluvial).
Blue Limestone.
Blue John (coloured Fluor).
Brazil (Pyrites).
Brick Clay (decomposed Toadstones).
Bur-stones (chert Screw-stones).
Calamine (rusty Zink Ore).
Calcareous Sand (crystallized).
Calcedony.
Carbonate of Lead (white Ore).
Cawk (Sulphate of Barytes).
Chert (black nodules, and white blocks).
China-Clay.
China-Stone (white Chert).
Clay (Brick, China, Fire, Tile).
Copper Ore.
Crystallized Limestone.
Diamonds, Derbyshire (Quartz Cry).
Dod-tooth Spar.
Dunstone (bastard Lime and Toadstone).
Figured Marbles (shelly).
Fluor Spar.
Freestone (Hopton-wood, &c. Harboro).
Galena (blue Lead Ore).
Geodes.
Gravel (on Surface).
Green Lead Ore.
Grey Limestone.
Grit-stone (Harboro Rocks).
Gypsum, plumose, &c.?
Hot Springs.
Jasper.
Iron Ore.
Lapis Calaminaris (rusty Zink Ore).
Lead Ore (blue, green, white, yellow).
Limestone (black, blue, grey, white, yellow).
Magnesian Limestone (2nd Rock).
Manganese Ore (black, and rusty).
Marble (bird's-eye, Black, Blue, Dove-coloured, Figured, Grey, Purple-veined, White).
Marl (soft Tufa).
Mock Ore (Zink Ore).
Molybda?
Ochre (red, yellow).
Onyx?
Petrified Wood.
Petrifying Springs.
Petroleum.

Phosphate

Phosphate of Lead (green Ore).
Pyrites (Brazil).
Quartz crystals.
Raddle (Ochre).
Rottenstone (on black Limestone surface).
Scowering Sand
Silver (formerly, separated from Lead Ore).
Slickensides (on Lead-Ore, Lime, and all other substances).
Stalactites.
Stalagmites.
Steatite.
Stink-stone (black Limestone).
Sulphur.
Sulphureous Springs (corrosive, near Shale).
Swine-stone (black, stinking).
Talk ?
Tallow Mineral ?
Tigre-stone Fluor.
Toadstone.
Tufa.
Warm Springs.
White Limestone.
White Marble.
White Lead-Ore (wheat-stone).
Yellowish Limestone.
Yellow Lead-Ore.
Zeolite.
Zink Ore (Black Jack and Calamine).

" Some articles in the above List, either rarely found, in combination with other substances, or doubtful, are marked (?)"

Most of the articles, inserted in the above lists, are noticed directly, or indirectly, and some of them repeatedly, in the course of the volume; but not with any thing resembling systematical arrangement. I will therefore examine its pages, and make my remarks (where I think remarks are required) miscellaneously, as they appear.

GRAVEL.—P. 131. " The first substances which claim our attention in describing the strata, are the *Gravels* and other *Alluvial Matters*, as being the uppermost, and occupying indiscriminately the surface of nearly every stratum in the County, in different patches. The principal mass of Gravel within the limits of my Map, is situate in Nottinghamshire, the higher and more barren parts of which are known by the name of Sherwood Forest "

P. 132. " In all my examination of this immense Mass of Gravel, except on the very surface, I did not perceive a single Pebble which belonged to the neighbouring strata, or to any strata which I have seen in England !"*

P. 134. " The surface in Derbyshire which is covered by Gravel, I find, by a careful scaling of my large Mineral Map, to amount (including the alluvial or river Flats, within the same) to 77,000 acres very nearly, being the 4th Soil in point of extent, in the County.

" Besides

* P. 307. " No Strata of CHALK exist in Derbyshire, or nearer to it than the neighbourhoods of Market-Raising and Caistor, in Lincolnshire, W N W, or of Baldock, Hitchin, Donstable, Tring, &c. S S E, in Hertfordshire and Bedfordshire; while towards the S E, these Strata retire still further from the district comprised in my Map; and yet, such has been the astonishing distribution of Alluvial Matters, that bolders of hard Chalk are sometimes met with, and Flints very commonly, with numerous Organic Remains peculiar to the Chalk Hills, in many of the gravelly tracts."

"Besides the above connected tract of Gravel towards the southern parts of the County, there are many small detached hummocks or patches of Gravel, of various kinds, in the other parts of the County and in those which adjoin, which are curious in many respects, but particularly, as proving the important Geological Truth, that Gravel and alluvial matters, are peculiar to no particular sub-stratum, but *are deposited alike on all strata**, and in almost all situations; on which account, I beg to present a list of all such issolated patches of Gravel, as I have noted in my survey of the district contained in the annexed Map.

"An Alphabetical List of detached Patches or Hummocks of GRAVEL not shewn in the Map of Soils, with their Situation, their Nature, and that of the Strata which they cover."—The number inserted is more than one hundred.

LYAS CLAY. P. 114. "The *Lyas Clay*: this stratum is of considerable thickness, forming generally a light yellow tenacious surface, cold, and much disposed to Ant-hills, when laid down in pasture: a part of this stratum approaches within 3 or 4*m.* of Derbyshire, which has enabled me to introduce it in the Map of Strata and Soils facing page 97. It is there distinguished by a blue colour, through a part of Leicestershire and Nottinghamshire, from Wigstead to Cotgrave. This clay is rendered remarkable, by a *Limestone* in thin blue beds, called *blue Lias*, which it contains; two or three of which beds make a Lime, which is superior to any other that is known, for Sluices, Locks, Piers, and other waterworks, on account of its property of setting almost immediately even under sea-water, and continuing to harden." See my GLOCESTERSHIRE, MIDLAND COUNTIES, and WEST of ENGLAND.

RED MARL STRATUM.—Mr. Farey notices an interesting circumstance belonging to this valuable base and substructure of English soils; it being common to many parts of the kingdom; namely, p. 147, "that it is in almost all parts very nearly horizontal. In all my numerous observations upon it, I found but two places within the limits of my great Map, where it had a considerable dip, and this only in small patches."

P. 156. "In Derbyshire, the Red Marl occupies about 81,000 acres of the surface."

GYPSUM.—

"* A late writer on the Wernerian Geognosy, in the article *Fletz*, in Dr. Rees' new Cyclopædia, classes *Gravel and Sand* in Werner's *Fletz Trap Formation*: and this writer asserts, the dogmas of his School, to be as superior, in truth and excellence, to all which others have written on Geology, as the Astronomy of the moderns is to the Astrology of the Ancient! See *Geology* in the work above quoted."

GYPSUM.—P. 149. ("Red marl strata")—GYPSUM, or Alabaster, is a *produce* of this Red Marl, in which it forms thin beds or strata in particular spots, sometimes finely striated transversely to the strata, in other parts the Gypsum is accumulated in vast nodules, or irregular and confused crystals forming hills, where the covering of Marl has been stript off."—Different places are mentioned in which it is found, in Derbyshire and its environs.

SIENITE.—P. 151. "*Sienite*, or the Granite of Mr. Playfair and some other Authors, next claims our notice as a *produce* of the Red Marl strata."

SLATE (Shistus) P. 152. "*Slate*, of a very dark blue and of various grey and greenish tints, is also a *production* of the Red Marl stratum, which I am describing: it appears in small low peaks, piercing through the Marl, as has been described respecting Sienite, over the whole of Charnwood Forest, except at its southern end, where there are large sienitic masses intermixed with it, as above mentioned: like the Sienite, these Schistous Masses, appear as nodules, or huge rude crystals in the Red Marl, and often adjoin close to the Sienite, without any order of super-position, but they seem placed side by side."

It is not probable, I think, that Mr. Farey should really believe that the three fossils, above named, are all of them actually *produced* by the earthy stratum in which they are found, in Derbyshire, or its environs. I have faithfully transcribed his *words;* about which, by the way, he is too frequently negligent.

YELLOW OR MAGNESIAN LIMESTONE.—To this stratum, it would seem, belongs the limestone of Breedon Hill, in Leicestershire; about the agricultural properties of which different opinions prevail. See my MIDLAND COUNTIES.

This peculiar and interesting stratum appears, on Mr. Farey's Map, to form the substructure of an extended range of Country, in Nottinghamshire, Derbyshire, and Yorkshire; the Breedon and Cloud Hills of Leicestershire being, doubtlessly, fragments or nodules that have been, in some convulsion of the earth, detached from that "yellow stratum."

P. 157. "Towards the bottom of this series several beds of compact *blue Limestone*, imbedded in blue Clay, and abounding with Anomia and other shells, some of them, have been discovered to differ entirely in their properties from the yellow or red beds, and to be much more proper for agricultural purposes, particularly on the yellow Limestone Lands."

P. 158. "The knowledge of these blue beds of Stone, and that Coals can in every instance be procured from beneath

neath them, to burn them into valuable Lime, along the whole line of Country from Strelly to Wetherby, which I have mentioned, cannot fail ere long, I hope, of proving a source of great benefit to the owners of the Quarries, and to the agriculture of a wide district on each side of them."

The hillocks of Ticknall (see as above) and Caulk are, with equal probability, fragments of this "blue stratum." Thanks to Mr. Farey for this information.

COALS.—Concerning this first of minerals (ironstone I consider as a fossil)—Mr. Farey has entered into a minute detail, which, had not his labors been interrupted by the "impatience of the Board," * could not, if completed, have failed of being most instructive to the *coal miners* of *Derbyshire*, at present, and in times to come †.

The *qualities* of Derbyshire Coals are described. But not with sufficient intelligence.—P. 177. "The quality of the Coal-seams, in many instances, change, from *hard* to *soft* or *crozling* Coals, and *vice versa*, similar to what Mr. Richard Martin has observed in the South Wales Coal-Field, Basin, or Swilly (see Philosophical Transactions, 1806): thus, on the banks of the Erewash, at the southern end of the great Derbyshire and Yorkshire Coal-Field, hard Coals abound, and crozling or melting Coals are very rare; but as we proceed northward to Staveley, the crozling Coals become plentiful, and Hard or stone Coals rather scarce, and still more so as we proceed further North into Yorkshire."

Mr. Farey would seem, by the above remarks, to be unacquainted with the nature or specific quality of the stone coals of Wales, which are as different from what he denominates "stone coals" of Derbyshire and Yorkshire, as *unburnt*

* P. 162. "These difficulties," (some points that remained to be cleared up,) "and the impatience of the Board for the completion of the Rural Observations throughout the County, which are the more immediate subjects of their Reports, necessitated me to leave several parts of this and other Coal-districts, where the colour is dark Green, in an unfinished state, with respect to the colouring of the numerous *Grit-stone Rocks* which traverse them, and divide the country into intervening strips of argillaceous strata, which I call *Coal Shales*, for the sake of distinction; and which is the reason, that in the parts coloured dark Green, several Hills in Sect. 1. (p. 16), of this Chapter, and several Collieries in the List of them which follow, are without the usual denominations of their strata, or are marked, some of them, with a ? as being somewhat doubtful."

† How could the veteran in useful science, whom Mr. Farey proudly styles his patron, commit him to the guidance of one whom he must well know to be a mere pretender in science:—a species of literary *at-all*, who, in the multitudinosity of his attainments, and their consequent superficiality, necessarily taints every thing he touches,—mars every thing he meddles with.

burnt wood is from *charcoal;* which the Welch stone coals resemble; both in the manner of burning, and in the deadly gass which they emit. They do not flame or blaze, nor send up smoke;—they require no other chimney, than a small wooden trunk, six or eight inches square, that is usually seen rising through the thatch of cottages, in any part of the roof most convenient to carry off the gas; which, otherwise, would suffocate the inmates; as charcoal, burning in a close room ever does—Numberless instances are mentioned of its deleterious effect.

The fracture, too, of the Welch stone coals differs much from that of the large *block* coals of Derbyshire, &c.; the former resembling that of hard close-grained stones; the latter that of tainted wood.

Mr. Farey has given (p. 188) an alphabetical "List of Collieries which are or have been in work in Derbyshire, and in such parts of its seven adjacent Counties, as fall within the square of the Map of Strata and Soils;"—"which List (p. 215) contains the Names and Situations of five hundred Collieries."

The superficial *Extent* of the Derbyshire "Coal Fields."—P. 219. "A careful scaleing of my large Map, shews, that the three lowest Coal Shales and their covering Grit Rocks, which are coloured light Green in the Map, extend in Derbyshire over 60,000 acres of its surface, and the remainder of its Coal-fields coloured dark Green, over 130,000 acres, making in the whole 190,000 acres of Coal-measures in Derbyshire."

Are we to conclude from this statement, that there has once been an extent of one hundred and thirty thousand acres of workable coal seam (or seams) or *that* extent of the sorts of strata among which coals are usually found?—Some estimate of the original quantity of workable coals, deposited, and one of the quantity already raised, though such estimates might have been, in some considerable part, conjectural would have been acceptable; and might not, unreasonably, have been expected, from Mr. Farey.—See Mr. BAILEY'S Estimates, in *Northumberland*, in the NORTHERN DEPARTMENT.

Some idea may be formed of the present *exhaustion* from the subjoined partial account.—P. 185. "One of the Coal-masters, shewed me the general account rendered to him from the weighing Office, for 12 months to the end of June 1808, from which I extracted the following particulars, viz. That in that space of time, 8286 boat-loads of Coals passed on the above three Canals," (Cromford, Erewash, and Notts) "in their way towards the places of consumption, which contained

"Hard

" Hard Coals - - - - - - - -		205,006	Tons.
Soft Coals - - - - - -		37,289	——
Cobbles - - - - - - - - -		27,161	——
Cokes - - - - - -	24,384	——	Quarters.

The value of which amounted together, to 122,838*l.*"

IRON STONE.—P. 218. " The Ironstone above, is principally in flat balls, laying often, like paved floors in the Bind or Shale, in which it is found; but there are a few thin beds or strata of it. Several of the Coal Shales produce Iron-stone Beds, which at their basset or out-crop are called Rakes, the workings of which, can often be traced through the fields for many miles together."

Mr. F. having previously given (p. 217) a List of places (seventyfive in number) " where I have observed *Ironstone Rakes,* either now or formerly worked."

GRIT ROCK.—P. 220. " *Millstone Grit* Rock, which by its thickness and its hardness, and truly indestructible properties, gives rise to the greater part of the Silicious Rock Scenery in Derbyshire, and the adjacent parts of Staffordshire, Cheshire and Yorkshire. In several places this Rock has been proved to be 120 yards thick, composed for the greater part, of a very coarse-grained white, yellowish or reddish Free-stone, which is easily worked, considering the extreme hardness of its particles, and its great durability, which appears to me superior to that of any Free-stone which I have seen used in England. What are known all over England by the name of *Peak Mill-stones,* are from this stratum, and though formerly these were dug and prepared from various parts of the stratum, from Belper northwards, yet now, few if any Millstones are made, but at Old-Booth Edge, and other places near Nether Padley in Hathersage, in a very inaccessible part of the County; principally, as it seems to me, because here, by long working, a superior part of the stratum has been reached, to what is generally met with on the surface: for the fact is, that fine blocks of this Rock, of every size that can be wanted, are so plentifully met with, loose and above ground, that any thing like a Quarry in it is almost unknown, except in Hathersage."

FREESTONES.—P. 221. " Some of the beds of this 1st Grit Rock, which have usually spherical stains in them of a light Red colour, are perfectly infusible, and form the best *Fire Stone* which is known, for lining the Hearths of Iron-Furnaces and others, where an intense heat is kept up. Roches Quarry, near Upper Town in Ashover, is particularly famous for these Fire Stones."

" GREAT OR LIMESTONE SHALE."—P. 229. " But the most extraordinary anomaly attending this great Shale is, the great masses

masses and accidental beds of dark blue or black Limestone which it *produces*, and which therefore I call the *Shale-Limestone*."

P. 232. "Some of the beds of this blue Shale Limestone, make a Lime which sets in Water, and is little inferior for water-works to the famous Barrow Lime."

ROTTEN STONE.—P. 231. "*Rottenstone*, which is used in polishing different substances, is a produce of this stratum, and seems owing to a decomposition or change which the Shale Limestone undergoes in some places, on or near to the surface."

The following suggestion is highly creditable to Mr. Farey, and entitles him to the best thanks of the landed proprietors of Derbyshire.

LIMESTONE.—P. 235. "Before quitting this great Shale, which covers so large a portion of the district under consideration, and to which *Lime*, as an ameliator of its Soil, seems quite essential, I beg to mention, what occurred to me, on seeing such great and meritorious exertions making by the Farmers in carrying Lime over this very uneven Country, viz. that the great depth of the excavated Valleys in several places, and the rising of the Strata into some of the adjoining Hills, seem to render it more than probable, that Tunnels for Tram-waggons might be driven into the hills, in some instances, and reach the excellent Limestone Rock, which every where underlays this Shale, and that thus Limestone might, in some places, be procured in the vicinity of Coals, to the incalculable benefit of the Agriculture of the districts so circumstanced."

MINERAL LIMESTONE and TOADSTONE STRATA.—(see p. 88, aforegoing.) It would seem to be in this mass of alternate strata, that the *metals* and *semimetals* are chiefly found.

P. 243. "*Veins of Lead, Zink, Manganese, Copper, Iron, Fluor, Barytes, &c.*—The Strata which I am now describing, and sometimes those immediately above and below them (viz. Shale and 4th Lime), contain great numbers of Mineral Veins, which are of three distinct kinds; the most common, is called a *Rake Vein*, which is in fact, a straight and vertical crack or fissure in the Limestone strata, filled with Spar and Ore, &c.; a *Pipe Vein*, which is a cavity, often horizontal nearly, between the beds of Limestone, filled in like manner, having a narrow rake vein, or rake-leading from it, to the surface of the stratum, and a *Flat-work*, which is a horizontal cavity in the strata, filled with Spar and Ore, without the rake-leading peculiar to Pipe Veins. This last kind of veins are rare in Derbyshire, wherein I heard only of three, viz. Cross Flat, Maury, and Robinstye Mines.

The

The late Mr. John Williams could therefore have been little acquainted with the Mines of this County, when he mentions much of the Ore here, being found in Streek or *Flat* veins. See Min. Kingd. 2d edit. I. 345, 282.

"The *Rake Veins*, which are far the most numerous, generally preserve a pretty straight course on the surface, and they often run parallel with each other, having others crossing them almost at right angles. It is now supposed, by many practical Miners, and so they construe their Titles to the Veins, that every principal vein extends through the whole series of Limestone Rocks, as from the top of the 1st to the bottom of the 4th Rock, but not without interruption, since the three Toadstone Rocks are very rarely broken through, I believe, so as to connect the veins above and below them, except where *Faults**, have since happened to follow the ranges of the veins."

LEAD ORE.—P. 252. "A List of Lead Mines † which are or have been in work in Derbyshire, and in such Parts of its adjoining Counties, as fall within the Map of Strata and Soils."

In this List, the names and situations of about three hundred Mines are inserted; noticeing the stratum, in which the lead is found; and the other mineral substances raised; in each.

The subjoined considerate and well intentioned remarks follow the List.—P. 270. "What I have said in the pages preceding this List, and what is to follow in this and the next Section, respecting Minerals, makes it necessary here only to observe, that the Strata or Measures which I have mentioned above, have not all Ore, or even the Vein found in them, in every case, but occur only in the sinkings of the Shafts, in many instances, being here enumerated, for pointing out so many opportunities of examining or enquiring into the thickness and nature of the Strata mentioned by those who may wish to examine the truth of my general description of these important Strata, or by those who

"* I am more surprised every day, at the little notice which writers on Mines, seem to take of *Faults*; it cannot be said that M. Werner's "New Theory" of Veins, notices these grand Geological Phenomena, except it be, to confound their appearances and effects, with Mineral Veins."

This is not the only place where Mr. Farey speaks with warmth, or a degree of ire, on the "New Theory" of the "WERNERIANS."—Several occasions, too, are found to correct Mr. WHITEHURST, Mr. WILLIAMS, and others. Religion would scarcely seem to be more productive of *opinions* and *sects*, than is Geology.

† In the head line it stands, "Lead, Zink, &c."

who may laudably concur with me, in the great labour, of collecting materials for a complete *natural history of each Stratum*, a task which can only be fully effected, by the united labours of many resident and critical observers of the Strata, as they happen from time to time to be penetrated by Shafts, Wells, Mines, Quarries, &c.: and which probably will remain long unattained, without the establishment of local Geological and Mineralogical Societies, as recommended page 217;"—where Mr. F says "the establishment of a *Geological and Mineralogical Society* in the district, for collecting and methodizing such accounts, and arranging and preserving Specimens of the several Measures proved in sinking Shafts, Quarries, Wells, &c. and of the Organic Remains which they contain, could not fail of proving highly beneficial to Science, and to the interest of Mining, at the same time that it furnished a most rational and delightful amusement to the Members."

First Limestone Rock.—P. 271. "The upper *beds* of this Rock, are often dark coloured or black, and stink much when struck with a hammer, the Swine-stone of some Mineralogists."

Second Limestone Rock.—P. 273. "In this Rock, several of the beds contain Magnesia; a specimen taken from some of the upper beds, on the W side of Matlock-Bath Dale, by Mr. Tennant, yielded on analysis, 22 per cent. of Magnesia (see Philosophical Transactions, 1799, p. 308)."

Third Limestone Rock.—P. 274. "The most extraordinary circumstances attending this 3d Lime Rock, are the beds of *chance Toadstone* which it contains, similar to what I have shewn with respect to the anomalous Masses of the Red Marl."

To me, there is nothing extraordinary in that circumstance; which appears to be one of the ordinary anomalies in Geology. In the instance above noticed, the Toadstone became embedded in the calcareous matter (doubtlessly, I conceive, formed at the bottom of deep water) while yet in a plastic or pappy state; even as the various substances, before mentioned (p. 95,) became bedded in the "Red Marl," and as fragments of chalk are found, in other earthy strata.—See my West of England, &c. &c.

The following observations show that Mr. Farey's mind is well matured in mineralogical knowledge.

Toadstone.—P. 277. "The *Toadstones* of Derbyshire shew strongly, the labour and difficulty which will attend the assigning of Mineralogical characters to *Strata*, however easy it may be to apply such to *hand Specimens* in a Cabinet, since a large Cabinet might be filled with Specimens, whose external

external characters differ materially, and a volume almost might be filled, with minutely describing the various substances and appearances which these curious strata present. Their most general appearance is that of a compact, hard, and ferruginous Stone, somewhat of the colour of the back of a Toad, whence the provincial Name most in use, and which I have used herein, as preferable, as a general Name for these Strata, to any of those which different Mineralogical Writers have assigned to particular substances, nearly if not exactly resembling some Parts of these Derbyshire Toadstone Strata."

To the above, the subjoined is attached, as a Note. "The Mineralogical and Provincial Names alluded to are, Amygdaloid, Black-Clay, Black-Stone, Basaltes, Bolder-stones, Brown-Stone, Cat-dirt, Channel, Chert, Clay, Dun-stone, Ferrilite, Fiery-dragon, Freestone, Jew-stone, Lava, Rag stone, Toadstone, Trap, Tuft-stone, Whin-stone, &c. &c. Dr. Millar denominates them *Secondary Traps.*"

Those things, let it be said, tend to show in what an unscientific state, Mineralogy at present remains.

P. 279. "Though in the general, the strata of Toadstone are as true and regular, as Mr. Whitehurst's several Sections, and mine in *Plate* V. facing p. 129, represent them, and are so calculated upon by intelligent Miners in their operations, yet in several instances, they have proved of very great thickness, and in others, as much thinner than usual; but in no place could I find, that the three Toadstones were wanting entirely, in their proper places; while the anomalous or chance beds of Toadstone, to which these Limestone Rocks all seem liable, may perhaps explain most of the wonderful stories which have been related, as to its irregular and uncertain thickness."—Remarks like those are worth laying up.

Mr. Farey estimates the superficial extents of the three upper Limestones, and the three Toadstones, at 51,500 acres.

The FOURTH LIMESTONE ROCK.—P. 280. "The fourth Limestone strata" (stratum) "is the lowest, and by far the thickest, without beds of a strikingly different character, of any which occurs above it in the British Series; I have myself seen no lower Strata, and from all which I remember to have read or heard, am *inclined to think*, that this thick 4th Lime Rock, is the lowest which is any where seen in England."

P. 297. "The 4th Limestone Rock has very different characters, from either of the three Lime Rocks which are above it; though regularly stratified, the beds are generally of considerable thickness (except a few beds which make flag paving on Brassington Common, and at Wetton, in Staffordshire), and form in general a *Freestone*, or one which cuts or breaks with equal ease in any direction, a property which is very rare in the other three Rocks."

P. 299. "The ease with which the excellent free Limestone of this Rock can be quarried, and broken small enough for the Lime-Kiln, compared with the grey, hard, and bedded stone of the other Rocks, is one reason why it is preferred by the Lime-burner; and has occasioned the Peak-Forest Rail-way to be cut for ¾ *m.* through the 1st and 3d Rock, until it has quite passed the Grand Ridge, in order to reach this Rock at Dove-Hole, on the edge of Peak Forest."

P. 292. "The great degree of *shrinking* which this 4th Lime-stone seems to have undergone, has opened in it vast Shake-holes and Caverns in different places, as may be gathered from what has been said above; the other Lime Rocks have also their Opens and Caverns, though in a less degree: it may amuse some, and be useful to others, to present the following, viz. A List of remarkable Natural Caverns and Holes in the Rocks, in and near to Derbyshire."—These Caverns are twentyeight in number.

Can Mr. Farey believe that Castleton Cave, and other caverns that are mentioned in his List, have been formed by the mere "shrinking" of the Limestone?

P. 299. "From the scaleing of my large Map it appears, that the 4th Lime Rock, coloured Orange, makes a surface in Derbyshire of 40,500 Acres."

In the subsection, fourth Limestone strata, the GREAT LIMESTONE FAULT of DERBYSHIRE is described,—in a manner, and with minute tracings, which cannot fail (admitting them to be accurate) of being greatly valuable to practical Miners*.

IN a distant part of the volume, Mr. F. speaks of "VARIOUS MINERALS." I will look over his pages and endeavor to extract what may be valuable to this concentration of things

* Not only the above remark but the entire article of review of the First Volume of Mr FAREY'S DERBYSHIRE, was written before Mr. BAKEWELL'S INTRODUCTION to GEOLOGY,—an elementary work of considerable merit,—was published. My surprize was of course great, when I read the following passage in Mr. Bakewell's book.

P. 212. 'Mr. Farey, in his Survey of Derbyshire, has described a great Fault commencing near Nottingham, and extending in a westerly direction, by Ashbourn, and from thence into Cheshire, where it turns northward,

things useful in Rural Economy. They are separated into "Metals, Stones, and Earths." Among the former are mentioned Zinc, Manganese, Silver, Arsenic, Antimony, Molybda.

Stones.

Limestones.—P. 408. "In this class of Minerals, the *Limestones* claim our first notice, as well on account of their vast quantities and varieties, as their important usefulness. They occur of various colours, as white, grey, yellow, red, blue, and black, of different hues, and are of different qualities, as Compact, Porcellanic, Granular, Crystalline, Shelly, Magnesian, Pozolanic or Water, Stinking or Swine, &c. The following is a List of the principal Limestone Quarries in or near to Derbyshire."—Nearly one hundred are mentioned.

Marble.—P. 413. "Several varieties of the Limestones of this district, are in repute as Marble for chimney-pieces, slabs, &c."—A List of Marble Quarries are given. About twenty in number.

Freestones.—P. 415. "The *Freestones*, or those capable of being broken or hewn with equal ease, or nearly, in any direction, for use, and thence often called Building-stone, or Ashler (in distinction from Beddy-stone, Flags or Paviers, and Slate or Tile-stones, which will split only in one direction, or Canks, which are too hard and brittle to be cut), are in this district all silicious or sand-stones, except occasional beds in some Quarries of the Limestone Strata, and the Tufa of Matlock Bath, &c. used in Buildings there and at

northward, and extends to Lancashire or Yorkshire. This he has called the great Derbyshire Fault, and has traced its course on a Map of that part of England.

'I confess I could discover no indications of the existence of this Fault, having attentively examined part of the Country through which it is said to range; nor has Mr. Farey stated any particulars respecting its thickness, or the mineral substances with which it is filled. So far from any dislocation of the strata being perceptible, the beds of the Sand Rock at Nottingham are nearly horizontally divided, by seams that contain rounded pebbles; the strata at Ruddington Hills, on the opposite side of the Vale, are but little inclined; the strata in the Vale are nearly horizontal, wherever wells or excavations have been made. No disturbing force appears to have changed their position since their formation. Had a Fault existed which rent the Island, from Nottingham to Macclesfield in Cheshire, it would have left no dubious marks of its existence in every part of its course.'

It concerns one to find two men, who appear to possess superior natural abilities, and much acquired knowledge of the same science,—differing, irreconcilably, concerning a natural fact belonging to it, which requires only leisure and assiduity to be fully ascertained.

at Alport, &c. The following is a List of Free or Building-ing-stone Quarries, or Delphs."

In this list, comprising from one hundred and fifty to two hundred quarries, are alphabetically inserted, agreeably to the names of the places where found, whether the specific nature of the stone is shistous, siliceous, or calcareous.

P. 423. "Respecting the Freestones of this district, it may be proper to remark, that the several Grit-stone or Sand-stone Rocks in the Coal-Measures have Argillaceous Cements (except the 1st, and the 3rd in a slight degree), and often won't stand the weather; the 4th Rock, however, generally produces a good Building-stone, when pursued to a proper depth below the surface. The stone from the yellow Limestone strata, is generally very durable, and so is that from the 4th Lime. The Shale-freestone is generally pretty durable, and in some Quarries is variegated with concentric streaks of yellow red, so as to have a pleasant effect: Chimney-pieces are sometimes worked of this stone from Callow (Hascar-side) Quarry, for the Inhabitants, who improperly call them Marble: in Sheffield I also saw some new Houses faced with it, at Portobello, from Stannington (Lydyate), there called Marble, from this variegated appearance."

FLAGSTONES.—P. 424. "PAVIERS, Flags, or Layers;—these are flat beds of stone which naturally split up or rise in the Quarry, so plane and flat, as to serve for paving Foot-paths, Yards, Out-houses and even Dwelling-houses, with little labour, and often without any, applied to the faceing of them. The following are the places where I noticed these kinds of Quarries or Delphs." Upwards of fifty.

ROOFSTONES.—P. 428. "SLATES—or Tile-stones: these, in the district where the lamellar stones abound, are mostly used instead of Tiles, or blue Slates for the Houses and Buildings. At Sheffield these white and grey Slates are exclusively used, and give the Town a novel" (heavy) "appearance to a stranger approaching it by the Mansfield Road."

A list of slate quarries is inserted, in which the Swithland blue slate (shistus) is intermixed with the stone slates of Derbyshire and West Yorkshire, which have no mineralogical connexion; the former being the very best, the latter among the very worst of coverings; as requiring a serious waste of timber to sustain them; and as giving a town the appearance of an extensive stone quarry.

FREESTONES (again). P. 432. "The more perfect Freestones of this District, are applied, in many Quarries, to the making of *Cisterns* or Troughs, hewn out of the solid stone,

stone, the larger and deeper of which are used for holding Water for domestic purposes; others, of a medium size, for supplying Cattle with Water; and the smaller and shallower ones, for Pig-Troughs, &c."

P. 433. "At Ellaston, Mansfield and others of the Quarries above, shallow circular *Pig-troughs* are made, having a round smooth lump of stone left in the centre, which throws the Wash or Milk to the outer edge all round, and enables a number of Pigs better to obtain their share from the same trough, without fighting:"—not peculiar to Derbyshire; but eligible.

SHALE FREESTONE.—P. 228. "This Stratum" (great or limestone shale) "is subject to great and curious *anomalies*; the first and most general of which are, accidental beds of fine-grained Silicious Freestone, very full of Mica in minute plates, and stained with various concentric rings of different shapes and shades of yellow and red. This stone, which I call the *Shale-Freestone*, or Shale-Grit, from the circumstance of its always alternating with Shale, forms the most beautiful and perfect Freestone which is known in this district, as Chatsworth-House, Buxton-Crescent, Wirksworth Low-Peak Hall, and numerous other Buildings in the County will shew."

FILTERING STONES, edge stones (rolling mill stones) grinding stones (which form a considerable export by the canals of Derbyshire) sithestones, with many others, are among the useful fossil productions of this part of England.

The last having now become a sort of necessary, in English husbandry,—having at length reached this northern quarter of the kingdom,—and Mr. F. having described the manufacture of them, with unusual diligence and success,—I will here insert his description.—

SITHESTONES.—P. 438. "The dexterity displayed, in cleaving out and forming the Scythe-stones, the process of which I examined in Morley-Moor Quarries, is rather surprising. The workmen use very sharp-pointed Picks, which require sharpening every quarter of an hour, and a number of very small Wedges and a Hammer. A proper block of stone being selected, two or three of these small Wedges are set in a row, by gentle blows of the Hammer, which are successively repeated, until the stone splits in two, by a straight and plane joint; the Wedges are then set into this new face in a straight line, and the stone cleaved again; a race or nick being first scratched with the point of the Pick, where the Wedges are to enter, when the pieces grow slender, and in this way the subdivisions are continued, until a piece remains, large enough to make two Scythe-stones, each 1½ inch square, and 11 or 12 inches long;

long; this stone the workman holds nearly upright in his left hand, and with the point of his Pick, races a deep nick down the middle of first one side and then the other, and then by a slight blow with the point of his Pick in the nick, it is separated into two rough Scythe-stones, which is so dexterously performed, that seldom more than three or four are broken in the 120, in cleaving. Those intended for round Rubbers are then reduced to an octagon nearly, by the point of the Pick, and are then handed over to women and boys, who grind or rub them with water in a notch in a hard stone, until quite round: the square ones are ground in like manner on a flat stone, and have their arriss taken off, and the ends ground flat and to the proper length; when they are sold at 10*s.* per long hundred (120)."

WHETSTONES of grit, and finer ones of ironstone, and

BAKESTONES of shale,—are enumerated among the other productions of the Derbyshire hills.

CLAYS of different qualities and uses are noticed; as china clay, pipe clay, potter's clay, fine clay, tile and brick clay.

BLUE TILES.—P. 453. "In the Pottery District of Staffordshire, a kind of plane *Tiles* for Buildings are manufactured, which have a very dark dull purple colour, very like new Cast Iron; they are made with two projecting nobs at the upper end to catch on the laths, instead of holes and wooden Pins, as is usual in other Districts; these Tiles, from their neatness, somewhat resembling Slate, and being very sound and durable, are in great repute in the southern parts of Derbyshire;"—and in the Midland District. They form a light durable, and not unsightly covering.

MARL.—A short list of places, in the southern parts of Derbyshire, where Mr. F. observed red marl pits, "used by the farmers of the present or former generations," is inserted.

Calcareous-Spring Marl.—Extraordinary mounds of this fossil-like production of the present arrangement of the earth's surface, are found in Derbyshire.—P. 457. "TUPA, Tophus, Puff-stone or Marl-stone, is a porous soft stone of modern formation, which the Springs of Water issuing from the calcareous Rocks have deposited, in some of the Valleys, enveloping the Horns, Bones, Teeth, and other parts of Animals, and Leaves and Stems of Plants, &c. The largest accumulation of this kind is at Alport, near Yolgrave, occasioned as I think, by a Spring which issued from the Rock, extending towards Haddon Field, but which, probably owing to the works of the earlier Miners, is now diverted into other channels; this Spring seems to have deposited

deposited a large Hill of Tufa, and to have spread the same quite across the channel of the Lathkil River, just at the junction of the Bradford River with it, and has dammed up the Lathkil, so that it falls suddenly 15 or 20 feet into the Bradford, though a much smaller River: at Matlock-Bath the mass of Tufa is very considerable, and is yet accumulating, by the Derwent side. The following are the places where I observed large masses of *Tufa*."—Twelve places are noticed.

For a description of the manner in which this production is formed, and of its virtues as a manure, see my YORKSHIRE; article *Newtondale Well*.

The Derbyshire *water stone* has already been mentioned, among freestones, as a building material. In one part of the County, it is applied to a peculiar purpose.—P. 458. "A kind which is found in the bottom of Tideswell Dale, is applied to the making of Chimney-tops; a hole being drilled through a block, and a narrow turning saw used, to saw out the inside in a cylindrical form; the outside is then sawn to shape, either round, square or octagonal, and these make very durable and handsome substitutes for Chimney-Pots."

Mr. F. says, p. 457, the softer parts of it, according to tradition, were formerly used as marl; "but the practice is quite laid aside, I believe." Limestone, probably, prevails in the neighbourhood*.

SAND.—P. 462. "There is not, I believe, in the whole Series of Strata within the limits of my Survey, any regular stratum of Sand, except that below the Lias Clay, mentioned page 115, notwithstanding the numerous Sand or Grit Stone Strata, which consist of grains of Quartz, slightly cemented together."

MINERAL TALLOW.—P. 466. "Is said to be found at Brown Hill in Warslow, Staffordshire, in the Limestone Shale, of a brown colour. In a fissure or sort of small Rake Vein in the 3rd Toadstone, N E of Hopton Hall, a light yellow flexible substance is found, almost like white Leather, in appearance."

BITUMEN. P. 467. "This singular inflammable substance is found in various degrees of induration, sometimes elastic, and in others resembling Jet almost: see Mawe's "Mineralogy of Derbyshire," p. 91. It frequently occupies the centre of hollow nodules of Limestone, in the lower part of the great or Limestone Shale and sometimes druses

* How could Mr. Farey register these facts, without perceiving in *calcareous waters* a valuable species of *manure*.—See the head, *Irrigation*, ensuing.

druses or cavities in the 1st Limestone Rock, as in the Limestone Quarry, $\frac{1}{4}$ *m.* S of Ashover Town, and in Gregory Mine at Overton, and Odin at Castleton: it is frequently as liquid as Tar, or more so, and is called Rock-Oil in such cases: the quantity of this inflammable liquid was so great, in the driving of Stoke Sough, near Stoney Middleton that it swam on the surface of the water, and would take fire from a Candle, and burn for a time, hence called a Burning Spring by Mr. Bray, in his Tour, p. 176. The following are the places where *Bitumen*, Rock-Oil, &c. has been observed."—Ten in number.—P. 468. "The Miners of Derbyshire applied liquid Bitumen or Rock Oil to fresh wounds, with great success, towards their cure, as is said." See WESTERN DEPARTMENT, p. 194.

SULPHUR.—P. 468. "Considerable quantities of this Mineral are combined with the Lead and other Metals, and the Shales, of this District, and some specimens of native Sulphur have also been found in Virgin Mine in Bradwell, and in Odin Mine in Castleton."

MINING.

ALREADY have I thought it right to censure the plan of the Work before me, in uniting, in the same volume, Agriculture and Mining. I will here draw together such evidence as the Work itself affords, to show the unnatural connexion.

MINING LAWS and CUSTOMS.—P. 356. "These Laws or Customs, which are very ancient, seem originally to have authorised any Man, or set of Men, to enter at any time on any part of this King's Field, comprising the greater part of the Mountain Limestone district of Derbyshire, to dig and search for Veins of Ore, without being liable or accountable to the Owners or Occupiers of the Soil, for any damage which they did to the surface, or even to growing Crops. At present, however, it is held, that unless a Miner procures Ore enough, from any search he may make after a Vein, to *free* the same, that is, to pay to the King, or his Farmer or Leasee, a dish of Ore, he is liable to the Occupier for all damage he may have done him: and fortunately for the Farmers of the present day, the searches were so repeated and universal in former times, under the sanction of these Laws, as observed page 314, that no one now thinks of digging or delving on the Limestone surface as formerly, in search of new Veins of Ore, although the Agriculturalist is most materially annoyed by their operation in another way, which I shall mention further on.

"In the King's Field, there are several Officers appointed, called

called *Bar-Masters*, and Mineral Courts held, at which a Jury of 24 Miners, decide all questions respecting the duties or Cope payable to the King or his Farmer, and to the working of the Mines, by those to whom the Bar-Masters has given Possession, and even decide on, and enforce the payment of, Debts incurred in the working of the Mines, in certain cases. These Laws or Customs were printed at London in 16mo., in 1688, under the title of the "Complete Miner;" in 1734 they were reprinted in 8vo., with additions by George Steer; and again, in 1772, by William Hardy, &c. These Laws bear evident marks of having originated in the very infancy of Mining, and were adapted to the working of the Mines entirely by manual Labour.

"A person having found a Vein of Ore, made certain crosses on the Ground, as a mark of temporary possession, and then went and informed the Bar-Master, who attended and received a measure or dish of Ore, the first produce of the Mine, as the condition of permitting him to proceed in working his *Meer*, or measure of 29 yards in length of the Vein; the Bar-Master, at the same time, taking possession of the next adjoining 14½ yards, or half Meer of the Vein, for the King. And if the Vein seemed promising, it often happened, that at the same time, or soon after, there were various applicants to be admitted each to free his Meer, or 29 yards in length of the Rake Vein in succession. It was a condition, that each person or company possessing their Meer or Meers in partnership, called Groove-fellows, should immediately begin and continue to work at their Mine, as in case of intermission for three successive Weeks, the Bar-Master was authorised to dispossess them, and give the Mine to another.

"As these first Mines, were all in the districts where the Limestone has no other cover but the Corn-soil, each Miner went to work, and with Mattocks or Picks, and with Hammers and Iron Wedges in the harder Veins, loosened the Ore and Spar, and threw out the latter into a bank or ridge of their Vestry or Bowse, on each side of the Vein: proceeding thus to sink and throw out the Vein-stuff, as deep as was practicable; when a square frame, composed of four narrow planks of Wood, laid across, and pinned together at the corners, on which two others were erected, with holes or notches to receive the spindles of a turn-tree, or rope-barrel, for winding up the Ore in small tubs; this apparatus, called a *Stowse*, being erected on each Meer or Mine, the sinking was further continued, and the heaps on the sides of these *open works*, or open-casts, increased, until in numerous instances a perpendicular ditch of the width of the Vein, and

and many yards deep, was opened, with proportionally large heaps of rubbish on each side, for many hundred yards in length, with other similar Veins and heaps parallel to, and crossing them at certain angles. Great numbers of the Mines thus opened, proved too poor in their produce of Ore, to be sunk lower than Men could throw out the stuff, before the Miners abandoned them, and others, after some progress had been made in deepening them by means of Stowses. But as in after times, other adventurers might appear, who would resume the work, the strictest Laws were made and enforced by the Mineral Courts, for preventing the Occupiers of the Soil, or any other persons, from meddling with the dangerous ditches, or throwing in the unsightly heaps of barren white Spar and rubbish, which the Miners had left on the land. Some of which shallow Mines, opened apparently in the very earliest periods of Mining in Derbyshire, still remain, and until within a few years past, most, if not all, of the Veins which had been tried to a few yards depth and abandoned, remained in this state, or altered only by the treading of Cattle, and natural mouldering of the sides, except where Roads, and the Fence-wall dividing properties, crossed them."

P. 360. "The Mining Laws, which, previous to this time, had required a working *Stowse*, and its actual use, at least once in three weeks, in drawing Ore on each Meer of ground, became now relaxed, so far as to allow models of Stowses, or small *sham* drawing apparatus, made of thin laths of wood, which the Bar-master provided, to be used as the means of keeping possession of all the Meers but one, on a consolidated Mine: a custom which prevails to the present day, and is so rigidly enforced, that a Mine on which large Steam-Engines and powerful Horse-Gins, and other expensive apparatus, may have long been used, is not held to be legally occupied, unless one of these pigmy memorials of the primitive mode of drawing Ore, is constantly kept 'in sight of all Men,' as the Laws express it, on or within a certain distance of the Drawing-shaft (where a Stowse worked by Men is not used), and others on each of the Meers of ground, or lengths of 29 yards, of which the Mine consists.

"The Laws of the King's Field punish by Fines, all such Persons as are detected in removing or destroying the Bar-Master's Stowses, though placed across the middle of a cultivated Field, a Common, or on the Fence-wall next a public Road, as is very commonly the case: but the noble Horse and the sturdy Ox, disregarding such puny representatives of property and authority, continually tread them to pieces, while Travellers and Strangers, the Servants of

of Gentlemen who are travelling, in particular, as commonly bear them off from the Roads, as curious memorials of the folly or superstition of the Inhabitants. The Bar-Master furnishes such Models, which to be effective must have no nails used in their structure, but be pinned together with wood, according to the state of actual Stowses, when these were first introduced as their representatives, for each of which he charges a small sum, and the Miners are obliged to be very particular, at short intervals to replace all such of their possession Stowses as are broken or gone.

"If a known unoccupied Vein crosses the choicest Paddock which a Farmer has, or even his Garden, or the Park of a Gentleman within the King's Field, he must take it of the Bar-Master, by the payment of a Dish of Ore, and erect these sham Stowses, and even a real one, and make periodical attempts, however slight or colourable they may be, to work the Vein; or any other person, by application to the Bar-Master, may dispossess him of such Vein, and enter on his Lands, and without mercy dig, delve, and make poisonous Buddle-Ponds, Ways, and Roads therein."

P. 363. "Another misapplication of these Mining Laws, is I think to be seen, in suffering Miners of the lowest class, without the requisite property, or any intentions of opening and further exploring ancient and disused Mines, to take possession of such from the Bar-Master, only for the purpose of delving in, and *Buddling* the old Hillocks on the surface, in search of small particles and quantities of Ore which had been thrown away by the first Miner, and perhaps by one or two previous sets of Cavers like themselves, who had in modern times, to the great damage and vexation of the Farmer, turned over and spread these barren Mine-Hillocks without remorse, *over the surface of the cultivated Lands;* on the W side of Wensley I saw some shocking doings of this kind, as well as in other places."

P. 364. "The King, or his Farmer of the Mineral duties, now seldom works his half Meer of ground on the new freeing of a Mine, but usually the same is valued by two or three experienced Miners, named by the Bar-Master, and the same is offered to the finder or owner of the Founders-meer, at from 1*l.* to 100*l.* according to circumstances, and generally is purchased by him and worked with his other Meer or Meers. The Duke of Devonshire is the present Leasee of the High-Peak Mineral Duties; those of the Low-Peak, or Wappentake, have *very lately been sold under a Decree of the Court of Chancery*, during the currency of the present Lease, and are supposed to have been purchased by Richard Arkwright, Esq." So

So still, it seems, this mischievous mummery is carried on;—and sanctioned by a decree of the Court of Chancery;—in this "augustan age" of England.

P. 376. "*Buddling.*—The process of separating the very smallest particles of Lead Ore from the dirt and Spar with which they are mixed, by means of a small stream of water, is called Buddling, and the best of the Ore so obtained is called Hillock Ore, or Pippin, a bad sort of Smitham, and the dust Ore so separated is called Belland: a very inferior species of Ore, little if at all adapted, to the Hearths, or Furnaces, which were used for smelting Ore in Derbyshire prior to the year 1747, whence it seems, probable, that Buddling was little or scarcely at all practised till within the last 50 years, much as it has since prevailed, to the vexation and annoyance of the Farmers in numerous instances," (as mentioned p. 112,) "and indeed to every class of the Inhabitants, to a degree, by thickening and bellanding or poisoning the Brooks, and even the large River Derwent, at the times when the Buddlers let off their thick water and buddle sludge. I have myself seen every part of the Derwent River at Matlock Bath, which was before beautifully clear, and limpid, suddenly made as thick and yellow as a strong solution of Gumbouge, and so continue for hours, from the Buddling operations of the Miners about Wensley, 4 *m.* higher up the River; by which, as I was told, the Fish are entirely poisoned, or driven away in dry seasons. I heard also of such losses by Farmers, from the Bellanding or poisoning of their Cattle, which drink at Brooks and Streams polluted by the Buddlers of old Hillocks and Wastes, that it is suprising nothing has yet been done to put a stop to the practice; except, perhaps, where performed on a small scale on regular Mine-hillocks, for obtaining the last portions of Ore from their Buddle-holes, Buddling ought no longer to be suffered. There were periods, when the Limestone District of Derbyshire was a vast *Mining Waste*; but now that the same equals, perhaps, the average of all England in Agricultural Improvement and produce, surely the antiquated and inapplicable Customs, or Laws as they are called, which permit such doings, ought to be revised and amended."

P. 187. "The Coals in old inclosed parishes, in some instances belong to one person, and the land to another, and even the Iron-stone is again separated by Leases as in Somercotes and some other places: in such cases, the cultivation suffers severely, from the want of any common interest between the Farmer and the Miner."

See also *Lead Mines*, ensuing. May not mining, under existing law, be rightly termed the "Bane of Agriculture?" See p. 83.

DISCOVERING

DISCOVERING MINES.—This, as has been said aforegoing, may (or may not) be beneficial to land proprietors.—I will here insert Mr. Farey's directions for that purpose.

P. 313. "The admirable provision of Nature, in the basseting or out-burst of Strata, for exposing to the knowledge and use of Man, the Mineral treasures which the Earth contains, has evidently first led to the discovery of Mines, in almost all situations where they are known, arising however from two very distinct causes: in the case of stratified or Stratigenous Minerals, or those which compose seams, beds, layers, measures or strata, as Coal, Iron-stone, Limestone, &c. the edge or basset of the Mineral appeared, in or under the vegetable soil, or thin alluvial covering, and from thence has been traced, or followed by its dip or inclination compared with the surface, until it has, as the Colliers express it, taken or got cover (of upper strata), and under which, generally speaking, Mineral Seams are more perfect and valuable than near their bassets, in the open-works or shallow Pits whence in the first instances, such Minerals were procured: the others are, the Venigenous Minerals, which instead of forming Strata, approaching to the horizontal, are applied as coats or linings to fissures and cracks or cavities, often nearly vertical, in certain rocky strata, the latter class only are denominated *Mines* in Derbyshire; the other class, when deep and worked under-ground, being denominated *Pits*, as Coal-Pits, Ironstone-Pits, &c., and where shallow, are called Open works, Quarries or Delphs, and Pits also in some cases, as Clay-Pits, Marl-Pits, &c. It rarely if ever happens, that a Mineral Fissure or Vein, does not extend from the top to the bottom of the stratum in which it occurs, completely dividing it, for considerable distances, in most instances; hence it happens, that Mineral Veins all appear on the surface, where the planes or tops of the strata peculiar to them, are exposed, or form the surface of the Earth; and such was the avidity, with which the early Inhabitants of this County, explored the surface of its Mineral Limestone Strata, under the sanction of ancient Laws or customs, which authorised any one to remove the Soil and dig in these districts, as will be mentioned further on, that I believe it may be truly said, that no Mineral Vein in the County is of modern discovery, all of them having a communication with the surface in some part of their course, and where they were anciently known and tried by the old Men, as the Miners term it. In early times, the Veins in the 1st or upper Limestone Rock, were traced or followed from the Limestone surface, under a cover of Shale, in some instances, increasing in width and richness

richness of Ore, as the Mine got deeper under Shale; and in more modern times, the Veins of the 2nd, 3rd, and 4th Lime Rocks, have been traced from the naked surfaces of Limestone, under the Toadstone stratum, which covers each of these respectively.

"It is maintained by many of the best informed Miners, that in all the great space which has been explored under Shale and Toadstone, in the different Limestone Rocks, by the working of Veins which emerge from under the Shale or Toadstones, or by the driving of Soughs or Water-levels to Mines, or by Drifts, Headings, or Tunnels of considerable length made on purpose to search for Mines in different situations, that numerous as the cross-veins are which are found, all such if pursued, owing to their obliquity to the edge of the Shale or Toadstone Stratum above them, or to the indentations in the edges of such strata, are found to appear somewhere, above ground: and this circumstance has given rise to an opinion, that such appearance to day, or at the grass, as Miners often express it, is essential to the filling or richness of Mineral Veins, at the least, if not to their formation, or the rending of the Rock also, in which they are found: after comparing however the phenomena presented by the Denudations, Faults, Slickensides, Riders, Hades, Squints, &c. in these Mineral tracts, I cannot subscribe to this opinion, but think that the Veins of Derbyshire were formed and filled in most or every instance, as they appear at present, prior to the removal of the vast load of different Strata, which once covered this Mining District, at a period when no parts of these Veins had access, even to the waters of the universal Ocean, much less to the atmosphere, as at present. This question is however worthy of the most rigid and extended investigation, on account of its importance to the subject in hand, viz. the discovery of Mines, since, if the Miner's opinion above quoted be well founded, we have little but disappointment to expect, from further searches after Mines, except on the surface of the naked Limestone Strata (already and thoroughly explored), or near to their bassets from under the Shale and Toadstones: while, if the contrary opinion be true, we have much to hope, from the driving of Soughs or Tunnels in or upon the 1st Limestone Rock, in search of new and profitable Lead Mines, even at considerable distances from the districts to which they have been considered as peculiar; at the same time that Lime, an article still more important to the Country, as a stimulant of Vegetation, would thereby be discovered and obtained, as explained page 235.

"At an early period, divining Rods and other superstitious

stitious means were resorted to by the Miners, when searching for Mines, and even in later periods, certain atmospheric phenomena, have been denominated Burning-drakes by the vulgar, and their apparent fall to the Earth, was thought to point out the situation of rich and undiscovered Veins of Ore: by which class of persons, whistling in a Mine, was supposed to frighten away the Ore, or lessen its chance of continuance: and hence they say arose the custom, that however Miners may sing or halloo when at their work, no Boy or Man is to whistle, under pain of severe chastisement from his fellow Miners.

"Some valuable Mines of Lead and other Ores may yet, it is plain, lye concealed under Gravel and other alluvial coverings, and so of some Coal-seams, as hinted page 159; but a more common cause of the concealment of Coals and other stratified Minerals, is the Faults, or vertical derangement of the piles of Strata, as will be fully comprehended by such of my Readers, as have the patience to study the various Formæ in *Plates* III. and IV. facing page 113, to whom it must appear plain, that the learning of the character of each individual Stratum, the permanent Grit Rocks in particular, and their relations to the known Coal-seams, is the best, if not the only true method of discovering Coal-seams, and of successfully opening and conducting Collieries or Coal-pits."

To those liberal strictures*, on the discovery of Mines, succeed more practical directions, for

Boring	Air Shafts and Gaits
Sinking	Damps, or foul air
Ginging and	Steam Engines—Wimseys
Timbering Shafts	Gins, &c.
Driving Soughs or Levels	

General Remarks.—But as well might practical directions for making and working spinning mills, and conducting the business of those pestiferous "institutions," cotton manufactories, have been thrust into a Report to the Board of Agriculture.

This is not said in contempt of mining and manufactures, generally considered. Particular branches of each are, in the present state of society, essential to the health and comforts of mankind. Nor are they intended to lessen the value of Mr. Farey's labors. But surely the result of them ought to have been sent into the world, in a detached state; for the use of those whom they solely concern. It is unreasonable to expect that a miner or practical mineralogist should

* See Western Department, p. 202; where less liberal sentiments are noticed.

should be obliged to purchase three expensive volumes, professedly on Agriculture, about which he cares not, to be able to get at half a volume of instructions how to improve his own practice.

Mr. Farey, it is true, speaks of his "large Map" and his "larger Work." But seeing what a length of years it requires to compleat a large work, and the time which his friend Mr. Smith has already expended on his, added to the uncertainty of a man's *capability*, who designates himself *senior*,—he surely ought to have adopted some method of making his endeavors more immediately useful, to that class of the existing generation, who alone can profit by them, in their present state;—rather than to suffer them to lie a *dead letter* (to *miners* at least) in the warehouses of the Board.

WORKING MINES.—This subject, having stolen in upon me, and being willing to concentrate, here, whatever may be advantageous to the "landed interest" (a term, in political economy which is now nearly obsolete) I have thought it right to abstract from the mass of information that is drawn together, in the Volume under view, a few particulars which may serve as hints to large proprietors, in different parts of the island.

Coal Mines.—By whom worked.—P. 182. "The Coals in Derbyshire and Nottinghamshire are, for the most part worked by Leasees: the Duke of Devonshire, Lord Middleton, Earl Manvers, Edward Miller Mundy, Esq. William Drury Lowe, Esq. Rev. Henry Case Moorwood, and Rev. Dews Coke, are the only considerable Land-owners who work Coals on their own account, except it be in a small way, for their own and neighbours' consumption.

"The mode of letting Collieries in Derbyshire generally is, by the Acre of Coals that are worked, ascertained annually, by a survey and measurement of the subterranean works: the prices which I heard mentioned, were from 50*l.* to 180*l.* per acre, according to the number and thickness of the seams, their quality, depth, quantity of Water, distance from a Market, &c. &c. Other Coal-owners let their Coals, reserving a fixed rent per Ton for all which are sold: the prices in these cases vary, as I was informed, from 4*d.* to 16*d.* per Ton."

Method of working.—P. 188. "The greater part of the Coals in Derbyshire are worked, in what is called the *long way*, or by banks of several yards in length, in which method, under favourable circumstances, but a small part of the seam is left in the ground: but in some places, particularly where the roofs are bad, or the strata which immediately cover the Coal are tender and soft, the method of *posts and stalls*,

stalls, or leaving large pillars and excavating chambers between them, is resorted to; and even in some extreme cases of bad roofs, mere Galleries are driven in the Coal, and only a small part of it obtained, as at Borelane, &c."

In page 341, after having given practical directions, mentioned above, concerning preliminary operations; as boring, sinking shafts, &c. &c.;—operations belonging to mining in general; Mr. F. enters minutely into the

Methods of working *Coals*.—Here, we find Mr. Farey writing as a man who is perfectly acquainted with his subject. His descriptions are clear, and his directions circumstantial; yet not prolix. They are such as may be understood by the amateur, the student, and the working miner. How absurd to suffer them to lie buried among the Board's Reports.

Markets for Coals.—P. 340. "Here it may be proper to remark, that Coals are often sold at the Pits, to the Inhabitants who send their Teams, called the Land-Sale, by so much per Corfe, or box in which they are drawn, instead of being weighed: but more commonly, a certain number of Corves are supposed to make a Ton, and by that denomination they are sold: in many instances the Coals are laid in separate heaps, on the Pit-Hill, of a Ton or Ton and half, &c. according to the usual loads of their customers. In most large works they have Weighing-Engines erected to weigh the Tram-Corves as they are drawn, or to weigh loaded Carts or Waggons; and where such are not provided, it is not unusual to determine the weight, by the Toll-man's account at the nearest Turnpike Weighing-Engine."

P. 185. "The *Hard Coals* are almost the only Coals which the buyers for the Midland Counties south and east of Derbyshire will purchase, and only such are deemed hard Coals, as can be loaded into the boats in pieces from near the size of a man's head, at the smallest, to the largest pieces which can be lifted by two or three men. The soft Coals of these districts do not crozle or melt together in burning, except in some few instances (when they are called *Smithy Coals*, as at Benty-field, Dunston, Hollingwood-common, Swadlincote, Treway, and other places), and are tender, and liable to break small by keeping, or unless moved with the utmost caution; yet I see no reason to doubt, that by some of the care that we in London are obliged to use, in moving Coals and in mixing the large Coals of one sort with the small of another, owing to the high Duty we pay on the article (from which the districts alluded to are wholly exempt), that a large portion of the soft Coals, now nearly, if not entirely wasted, in the working of the hard Coals here and about Wednesbury in Stafford-

shire

shire, and numerous other places, might be sold and used, and this invaluable article be by that means husbanded, for the use of future generations, as well as rendered cheaper to the present. The waste of soft Coals to which I allude, in hurrying after the hard seams because more saleable, exceeds all belief, and is a subject to which the owners of the soil ought more to attend than they do, and perhaps the Legislature ought to take up the subject; allowing soft Coals which do not crozle, to be brought to London by Canals, or carried generally by sea coast-ways, at considerably lower duties than hard or crozling Coals, would perhaps go far towards remedying this crying evil, which cannot be fully seen or understood, without entering into the under-ground operations of the Collier, although enough of it may be seen on the wharfs and rail-way branches, of the Nutbrook Canal in particular, to satisfy any one that a change is wanting."

P. 182. "Vast quantities of Coals are annually sent out of the Counties of Derby and Nottingham southward, by means of the Cromford, Derby, Erewash, Grantham, Leicester, Melton-Mowbray, Nottingham, Nutbrook, and Trent Canals or Navigations."

For a partial account of this export, see p. 97, aforegoing.

Copper Mines.—These, it appears, do not properly belong to Derbyshire. "The quantity of Copper Ore which Derbyshire produces, is very small," p. 352.—"The famous Ecton Mine" is in Staffordshire.

This long celebrated mine is now nearly worked out.—P. 353. "The body of Copper Ore seems now nearly or quite exhausted in Ecton Mine, but the thick skirts to the Vein, and numerous scrins and small Veins, or strings, branching therefrom, which the Miners neglected to follow when the Copper Ore was in such plenty, still produce considerable quantities of Lead Ore, which is smelted at Ecton, and about Ore enough to produce a Ton of Copper weekly at Whiston; where, about 1781, 12 Tons of refined Copper were produced weekly from this Mine."

Lead Mines.—A List of three hundred Mines of this metal in Derbyshire and its environs, have been noticed, aforegoing.—P. 355. "Within a few years past, the Miners of Derbyshire have discovered a White Lead Ore, which was previously taken for a useless Spar, and was either left in the Mines, or buried in the old Hillocks, from which very considerable quantities of White Ore have since been extracted."

Methods of working Lead Mines.—On this *adventurous* employment, as on coal mining, Mr. F. has given practical directions,

directions, and in the like technical manner,—adapted to to the understanding of working miners.

Manorial rights respecting Lead Ore.—P. 370. "The Owners of Manours and Estates within the King's Field, who are possessed of Mineral Rights, none of them commute with the Miners for fixed Rents, but all take their Cope, or share of Ore in kind, at each Ore-weighing, as the King, the Sougher, and the Tithe-owner do."

Tithe of Lead Ore.—P. 370. This "impost is paid only in Eyam parish, and in Wirksworth, including Cromford and Middleton. The pretence of claiming *Tithe of Lead Ore*, is said to have been, that the Ore *grew and renewed* in the Vein! About the year 1780, the Gentlemen Miners, or Maintainers, as they are called, in Wirksworth, met the Clergyman, and agreed on $\frac{1}{20}$ as the Tithe-owner's share of saleable Ore from the Mines, but the working Miners, when they came to hear of it, all met, and unanimously resolved to pay no more than $\frac{1}{40}$ of their Ore as Tithe, which the Clergyman, the Rev. Mr. Tillard, much to his credit, accepted without further dispute, and the same has continued ever since to be the proportion paid in that parish. In Ashover, Matlock, Darley, and other parishes, expensive litigations were carried on by the Clergy previous to this time, for enforcing the Tithe of Lead Ore, but without success."

The ore having been raised to the surface, and the dues to the King, the Lord of the Manor, and the Tithe-owner, having been discharged, the Engineer proceeds to describe, and give directions concerning the

Dressing of Lead Ore, p. 372.

Buddling, p. 376.

Mode of Selling, p. 378.

Smelting, p. 380.—Here a history of the ancient boles or hearths (together with a list of them): also a description and list of modern Cupolas, in and near Derbyshire,—are furnished.—The Section closes with the following information.

P. 392. "The great draught of air which the High Chimneys of the Cupolas occasion, seems to render the operation inoffensive, to the Smelters employed *in* the Cupola Buildings, as their appearance, and the length of time which they continue to work at them, sufficiently prove, where they live at a distance from their work, as usually is the case; but the noxious fumes of the Cupola and Slag-Mill Chimnies, descending by their weight on the ground, for a quarter of a mile or more round them, poison the herbage, so that Cattle are affected, and if continued there, soon die, of a disorder called the *Belland*, which will be noticed in Sect. 2, of Chap. XVI., as affecting also the health

health of the inhabitants, in some cases. As the Cupola Owners are obliged to pay a rent to the adjoining Farmers for the damage their Smoak does to the Lands, the most barren and rugged spots are of course chosen for the erection of Lead Smelting-works, and they ought also to be in more sequestered and unfrequented places, than many of them are found in. After a Lead-work has existed for a long time, it so affects certain spots where the fumes alight, that neither wood or any other vegetable produce, can exist in such spots."

Mr. F. I think, has not attempted any estimate of the produce of the Derbyshire Lead Mines.

Iron Works.—Under this head, also, some account of the ancient and modern practices of Derbyshire, is found.—P. 393. "In very early periods, the Ironstone of Derbyshire seems to have been known, and *Charcoal Furnaces* and *Bloomaries* to have been erected for the smelting of it, and making wrought Iron in various places. The first mode of working or getting Ironstone, seems to have been, by removing the soil, clay, &c. and laying the Ironstone Beds bare, called Open-works, or Open-casts; in the conducting of which, little or no regard was paid to the subsequent levelling of the ground, from which circumstance, and the great length of the basset which was thus run over, without obtaining much Ore, especially in rising grounds, or where the Measures dip fast with regard to the surface, it becomes easy now to trace most of the rich Ironstone Beds, by the marks of these primitive Open-works, or Rakes as they are called. After the bassets had thus been all worked, a method of working was adopted, called *Bell-work,* in which a round Pit, of the usual size of a Shaft, is sunk, until the Ironstone is reached, from 3 to 10 yards deep, the first two or three yards being made cylindrical, and the part below it conical, in order to reach a larger surface of the stone, which being got below the shaft, and a drain laid across it for connecting with the next Pit, the Workmen, or Ironstone-men, begin to hollow out the Measures all round the Shaft into the form of a Bell (whence the name), throwing the refuse into the centre, and getting the Ironstone as far under as possible on all sides."

P. 395. "Until about 40 years ago, small Furnaces and Bloomaries, heated by Charcoal of Wood, were alone used, for the making of either Cast or Bar Iron in these districts. At Wingerworth, one of these Charcoal Furnaces continued in some use, blown by means of a Water-wheel, until the year 1784, this work, or others in the site of it, having been used more than 180 years; and at Walley in Bolsover, another was used, until about the year 1770. The following

ing is a List of 23 Places where I have observed the Slag and remains of *old Bloomaries and Charcoal Furnaces*."—The number twentythree.

P. 396. "Numerous as these Charcoal Iron-Furnaces were at one period, before they had well nigh exterminated the Wood of the Country, in 1806 their number was so far decreased, that from the returns made to the Deputies for opposing the Excise Duty, then proposed to be laid on the manufacture of Pig Iron, there were but 11 such remaining in all England, at which Iron was then made.

"Iron is now made in and near to Derbyshire, only in tall Furnaces, heated with Coke of Pit Coal, and blown by Cylinder Bellows worked by Steam-engines."

Produce of Iron.—Mr. Farey has inserted a list of Iron Furnaces, in Derbyshire, in 1806 (twelve in number) with the tons of Pig Iron made, annually, in each. The aggregate quantity being 10,329 tons; which, Mr. F. says, p. 397, "is just a 25th part of the Iron which was at that period made annually, by 221 Coke and 11 Charcoal Furnaces then standing in Great Britain."

A General Remark on Mr. Farey's Report of the Natural Economy of Derbyshire.

What appears to me as a principal defect in Mr. Farey's First Volume, is the silence which prevails in it, regarding the component parts,—the varying natures and specific qualities of what he has termed (not improperly) Fault Stuff,—of "the extraneous matter filling faults."

It strikes me, forcibly, that many data, and corroborative evidences, might, by assiduous examinations, be detected by Geologists, in those fortuitous, and of course more or less heterogeneous, masses. The Hot Well at Buxton, and other incidental mentions, are sufficient to excite this idea, if common sense did not suggest it. That the clefts which have been formed, by the breaking and separation of strata, are the conductors of subficial heat, rising from internal fires,—not only to hot springs but in a more general and less perceptible manner, to the atmosphere,—is in my apprehension, highly probable.—See my Minutes of Agriculture, &c. Art. *Weather*, first published in 1779. 2d Edit. Note, p. 259 *.

VOLUME

* March, 1814. I think it right to mention, here, that the above remark was written some months before I saw Mr. Bakewell's Introduction, or Sir H. Davy's Elements.

VOLUME THE SECOND.

SUBJECT THE SECOND.

POLITICAL ECONOMY.

APPROPRIATION.—Mr. Farey inserts, in p. 71, a LIST of INCLOSURES that have been made in Derbyshire, amounting to about one hundred and thirty.

And, in p. 77, a LIST of the open *Arable Fields* now remaining, in the County.—" Bredsall, the southern part on Red Marl, the remainder on Coal-measures.

" Dalbury Lees in Dalbury, on Red Marl.
Hollington, in Longford, on Red Marl.
Langley (Kirk), on Red Marl.
Little Chester, in St. Alkmund, on Red Marl.
Little Eaton, in ditto, on Coal-measures.
Roston in Norbury (and Common Meadows by the Dove), on Red Marl.
Shirley, on Red Marl.
Smithsby, on Red Clay, in the Coal-measures.
Snelston, in Norbury, on Red Marl.
Stenston in Barrow, on Red Marl.
Whittington, on Coal-measures.
Whitwell, on Yellow Lime.

" None of these are of considerable extent, and many of them must remain in their present open, unproductive, and disgraceful state, (though principally on the best stratum in the County,) until less expensive means can be resorted to, than at present, for effecting their division and allotment. In Hollington it was pointed out to me, that repeated attempts had been made there towards an Inclosure, and Ten Pounds an Acre was offered to be advanced by the Proprietors for the general Expences, but, on calculation, it was found quite insufficient!"

In the chapter " Wastes," we find the following remarks on their present state.—P. 341. " The quantity of Moors, or waste and barren unfenced Lands, remaining in the County, is now far less than has been supposed, and perhaps one-half of these are not Common, but Private Property, belonging exclusively to the Duke of Devonshire, in the Woodlands of Hope, and to the Hon. Bernard Edward Howard, in Glossop Lordship, adjoining.

" The

"The principal tract of Common Moors, is called the East-Moor or the High Moors, and extends northward from Ashover and Darley Parishes, almost to the bounds of the County, within the Manors or Liberties of Great-Rowsley, Brampton, Barlow, Holmsfield, Totley, Baslow and Curbar: the extensive Moor in Hathersage, north of them, being now under Inclosure, and I believe by this time allotted; and so is Beeley Moor. The following is, I believe, a pretty accurate List of the Places now having *Open Commons*, or Moors, with the principal Soil of each Common."

This List comprizes thirtysix open *Commons;* some or most of which, it would seem, are of small extent.—The subjoined observations follow the List, and show the want of a more facile mode of removing the disgrace, which these nuisances incur, than is at present known to the laws of the Country.—P. 343. "Elmton Common exhibits one of the most lamentable instances of deep Cart-ruts, and every other species of injury and neglect, that can, perhaps, be shown, on useful Land: part of it has been ploughed at no distant period, as completely exhausted as could be, and then resigned to Weeds and Paltry.

"Hollington Common, of 20 or 30 acres, though overgrown with Rushes through neglect, is on a rich Red Marl soil. Some of the Farmers having common right here, let to Cottagers the run of a Cow on this Common, from May-day till Harvest is ended, at 30*s.* to 42*s.* The truly impolitic and unnecessary *fees* and expenses on Inclosure Bills, doom this Common to its present state of neglect.

"Langley (two) Commons, on similar soil to the last-mentioned, have the obstinacy of an Individual, opposed to their improvement, as I was told, as well as Parliamentary and Lawyers' *fees.*

"Roston Common, near to Birchwood-moor, is miserably carted on, cut up, and in want of Draining: in wet seasons it generally *rots the Sheep* depastured on it; few can stand it two or three years; and on this account it is probably injurious, rather than beneficial, in its present state, both to the Parishioners and the Public."

On the *principles* and *business* of Inclosure, we find the following scattered notices.—P. 3. "In the Act for Inclosing Matlock in 1780, it seemed to me rather a singular provision, that all encroachments from the Commons, of twenty years standing or upwards, were to become Copyhold, and their fixed Rents to be ascertained by the Commissioners: this I afterwards learnt, was principally intended, for securing the extensive Premises which had been erected on on the waste, at Matlock Bath, to the Persons who erected them."

P. 78. "In the Act for the Inclosure of Ashover (1779), the Commissioners were directed, to mark out and describe in their Award, 600 Acres of the best of the Commons, to be subject to immediate Tithes, and the Allotments on all the remainder of the Commons were declared exempt from Tithes, for the ensuing Seven Years. The Act for Matlock, in the year following, directed, that 350 Acres of the worst of the new Allotments should be exempt from Tithes for Eight Years, and the remainder pay Tithes immediately."

P. 81. "Before I close this Section, it may be right, to state a few particulars, respecting the reservation and adjustment of *Mineral Rights* on Inclosures, in addition to what is mentioned respecting Brassington, vol. I., p. 406.*

"In Hartington Act, the Coal, Ironstone, and all other Minerals, except Lead Ore (which belongs to the Crown), in the new Allotments, is reserved to the Lord of the Manor, who is to pay the damage occasioned to the Occupiers by his Mines, assessed by arbitration; which is not an unusual provision.

"In Ilkeston Act (1794), the Coal, Ironstone, and other Minerals under the new Allotments, and the right of sinking Pits and Shafts, making Soughs and Drains, Stacking, Coaking, taking and carrying away all such Coals and other Minerals, and all necessary Roads and Ways for such purposes, are reserved to the Lord of the Manor, without any compensation whatever (because he was subject to none such on the Common). And it is provided, that when damage is done to any Allotment by the Lord's Mining, on notice given in the Church, all the other Proprietors of Allotments are to appoint one Arbitrator, and the injured Person another, who are to ascertain the damage, and assess a rate on all the Proprietors of Allotments, according to a Schedule to be set forth in the Award, by the Commissioners, of the value of each and every Allotment, for raising such compensation. On the contrary, in Heanor Inclosure, the Commissioners made a specific Allotment to the Lord of the Manor, for the estimated damage to be done, by the getting of his Coals and other Minerals, and he is made liable to compensate the owners or occupiers of Allotments, for all the damage his Mining may occasion.

"In

* Which stands thus: "In Brassington Enclosure, in consequence of 1-18th of the Common being allotted to the Lord of the Manor, the future rights to the Calamine, China-Clay, &c. was assigned to the Owners of the New Allotments."

"In Stretton Act (1777), the Mines of Coals and other Minerals in the Allotments, are reserved to the Lord of the Manor, on paying for all damage done by the getting of them, by Arbitration: and it is provided, that Pits, Shafts, Holes, or Hills of Rubbish, or Roads disused for Twelve Months, on the Allotments, may be levelled by the owners of them, and the expences are to be repaid by the Lord of the Manor: and it is enacted, that no Land shall be again 'entered and broke up, under pretence of getting Coal, after the same shall have been once worked, cleaned, and levelled, as aforesaid.' It is easy to see, that under the last provision, the Lord may be deprived of deep Seams of Coal, that may hereafter become very valuable, and without their becoming the property of any one else. In Barlborough, previous to the Inclosure, the Coals, &c in the old Inclosures, and in the Common Arable Fields, belonged to the owners of the individual lands: and the Act made no provision for valuing and transferring the Minerals along with the Allotments, but simply reserved every Person's Minerals, by which, besides the Owner of a Field, there is now as many Coal Owners in it, as formerly it had single Lands, almost, in the common Fields! and scarcely any persons are able to get or avail themselves of their Coals, in these Allotments, owing to these intermixtures."

TITHES.—P. 30. "About Matlock, Darley, &c. it is usual, for the Clergy to have a Survey made annually previous to Harvest, by a Surveyor, who charges certain rates per acre on the different kinds of Crops of each occupier: these have been, Hay from 2*s*. 6*d*. to 4*s*. 6*d*., Wheat 12*s*. to 14*s*., Oats 7*s*. to 10*s*. 6*d*., Barley 10*s*., &c. Sometimes the Surveyor fixes a gross sum on the Tithes of a place, and agrees with the principal Occupier for the same, leaving the adjustment of the sum to be paid by each Farmer, to be settled among themselves, at a meeting: and it argues I think no small degree of liberality and knowledge, among them, that this is generally done with readiness, and with great fairness,"

INLAND NAVIGATION. Vol. I. p. 470. "The lowest five miles of the Trent, where it bounds upon Derbyshire, from the mouth of the Erewash River to the entrance of the Trent and Mersey Canal, at Wilden-Ferry in Shardlow, is now the only *Navigable River* remaining in or near to Derbyshire, the Navigation from Wilden-Ferry up to Burton Bridge, which was made by the Earl of Uxbridge, in pursuance of the Acts of the 10th and 11th of William III., having been discontinued in the year 1805, in consequence of an agreement with Hugh Henshall and Co.

the

the Proprietors of the Trent and Mersey Canal, which runs by its side; and the Navigation on the Derwent River, from Wilden-Ferry up to Derby, having been discontinued since 1794, when the Derby Canals were finished. From this five miles of Navigation on the Trent River, the Loughborough Navigation, by the side of the Soar, branches to the south, and the Erewash Canal on the north, nearly opposite to each other."

EMBANKMENT.—A proof of the *want* of embankment is seen in the subjoined extract.—Speaking of the water formed lands of the Dove, &c. Mr. F. says, p. 176. "About Hoon Hay and other places near Tutbury, it is not uncommon to form mounds of earth in each Meadow, two or three yards high, for the Cattle to retire to, in case of a sudden Flood, which frequently happens in the course of a night, and sometimes when little or no rain has fallen thereabouts. Mr. Thomas Harvey, instead of these safety mounds in the low Meadows, prefers having each field so set out, that a part of it extends on to the gravelly flat that edges these Meadows, somewhat above the height of the floods, on account of the difficulty of removing the Cattle from these mounds, or of supplying them there with food, should the flood continue several days, as sometimes happens." See Note page 80, aforegoing.

SUBJECT THE THIRD.

RURAL ECONOMY.

TENANTED ESTATES.

ESTATES.—*Purchase.*—P. 1. "The *prices* at which Estates appear to have sold of late, is thirty years purchase on the Rentals, where of considerable magnitude."

TENURES —P. 3. "*Freeholds* almost generally prevail thro' Derbyshire, and the quantity of *Copyholds*, or of Lands held under *Church Leases*, is very inconsiderable, I believe."

P. 35. "The granting of Leases for three Lives, probably had some prevalence formerly in Derbyshire; at present three Farms in Parwich, and one at Mackley in Sudbury, are the only remaining instances that I heard of: though several such had not long been extinct in Brailsford."

IMPROVEMENT of ESTATES.

MEANS of IMPROVEMENT.—The following suggestions,—which are not always so proper to be pursued, as the writer of

of them would seem to have conceived,—are entitled to a place, here.—P. 360. "On the general subject of this Chapter: I wish to impress on the minds of Land-owners, the propriety, whether we consider their own interests, that of their families, or their country, of setting apart a sum of money to be expended annually, in effecting permanent agricultural improvements on their Estates; selecting either the Farms of the poorest and most deserving of their Tenants, or those where the greatest expenditure seems wanting, to be first began upon, and to charge an interest on the sums thus expended, in addition to the Rents, as a practice, much to be preferred (as long as any such improvements remain wanting on their Estates) to the expending of every few hundred pounds that they can spare, or even by mortgaging, as many do, to buy up adjoining Estates, and add to the number of acres on their Rent Roll, rather than to the productiveness of what they already possess: since, how much better would it be, to double the productiveness and income from what they already possess, than by doubling the quantity of land, to delay, for perhaps all the remainder of their time, the improvement of any part of it, when they might have fully improved their own, and have had the satisfaction, perhaps of seeing some other purchaser do the same, by the adjoining Estate that he purchased."

P. 361. "Mr. William Cox of Culland, who occupies a large and highly improved Farm, and acts besides as Land Steward to different Gentlemen, expressed to me his opinion, that in most instances, Tenants had better pay six per cent. additional Rent for the Landlord's Money expended in draining, irrigating, liming, or other expensive and permanent improvements on their Farms, than sink their own money, though it were on a 40 years lease, that might so much better be employed in plenty of good Stock, superior Cultivation, artificial Manures, and other improvements, of quicker return to them: and this Gentleman is, of course, a strenuous advocate for this mode of improving Estates, wherever he is consulted."

This principle I have been acting upon, and recommending, for some length of time.—See my TREATISE of LANDED PROPERTY, &c. &c. &c.

DRAINING Estates.—On this subject, it would not be unreasonable to expect that a *Geologist* should throw out new ideas, and point out superior principles of practice. After examining, however, near forty pages,—the extent of Mr. F's section, "Draining,"—I have not found any thing of excellence, which has not been, for many years, before the public. The main part of those pages tends to underrate

rate Mr. ELKINGTON'S practice! but as well might Mr. Elkington's have written as many pages, to underrate Mr. Farey's knowledge of mineral surveying.

IRRIGATING Estates.—On this subject, as on draining, the Reporter has presented his readers with a full-bodied section; and this without convincing them that he possessed, at the time of writing *one practical idea* upon it. From a *Geologist*, and particularly from a *Mineralogist*, it was impossible not to expect some *new lights*, respecting the QUALITIES of WATERS for IRRIGATION; and some information respecting the strata out of which waters of value are wont to issue; with suitable tests for trying them. These expectations, however, must necessarily render greater the disappointment, at finding a man, doubtlessly possessing much subterranean science, wholely unacquainted with the specific qualities of waters for that purpose —Nay, a very infidel, in regard to there being any specific difference belonging to them!—*Quantity* "plenty of water" is all he asks. P. 462.

P. 463. "Calcareous, Chalybeate, Ferruginous or Ochry, Sulphureous, Peaty or Bituminous, Saline, &c. which have been so much insisted on, to the *impediment* of this Art, exist only in such comparatively small quantities, and are visible only in such small and very *slow running springs*, that the using of such alone, is out of the question."

Here we see *calcareous* waters classed with those that are, or have been supposed to be, *noxious!*—Some of *these*, it is true, rise above ground, in such "comparatively small quantities," that, though noxious in themselves, they become, when mixed in a large stream of purer water, in a degree inoffensive.

But do calcareous waters usually rise in "small quantities?" The Reporter must, in his time, have seen oceans of water (if collected) which was abundantly charged with the calcareous principle; and, of course, superiorly adapted to the purpose of fertilizing grass lands, wherever suitable soils and substrata could be found to receive them. Almost every chalkhill district has its brooks, if not rivers, of such water. And where ranges of limestone heights are seen, there brooklets and smaller streams, of the same, are generally observable; conveying sufficient quantities without admixture) to produce, if rightly applied, valuable advantages to lands that lie beneath the levels of their sources.—It is not QUANTITY or QUALITY, alone, but the two combined, by which superiorly profitable irrigation may be, with certainty, expected.

I cannot refrain from intimating, in this place,—that had the Mineralogist of Derbyshire met with a man who had hardihood enough, to hold out, that all mineral substances, are

are equally proper for the melioration of arable land, as the purest marl, or lime itself,—what heavy censure would not have befallen him.—Yet, in my mind, equally censurable is he who, in effect, holds out, that all waters are as fit for the irrigation of grass lands, as those in which lime is chemically suspended.—Whatever beneficial effect calcareous earth *in substance*, has on ARABLE LAND, the same or a similar effect has lime, *suspended in water*, on GRASS LANDS.—In either case, much depends on the nature of the land to be ameliorated, and on the method of *applying* the *manure*.

MANAGEMENT of ESTATES.—*Managers*.—P. 2. "The *management* of Estates were principally entrusted, until of late years, either to Persons expressly employed as Agents, or to Land Surveyors, or others who had different rural concerns of their own and others to manage: but here, as is I fear too commonly the case in other Counties, the Salaries and Allowances made to Land-Stewards, were so small, that many of the Persons best qualified for such trusts, are reported to me, as having given them up; others were on the point of doing so; and that the management of the Land was rapidly falling into the hands of the Attornies of the District, who cannot in general be considered as properly qualified, for many of the essential duties of this important Office: to me it seems surprising, that any Gentleman of Landed Property should fail to discover, that where, for the sake of securing his own Law business, and that which can be made among his Tenants, a Gentleman of that Profession, is willing to undertake the care of his Estates, at a Salary greatly below what any Man of humbler, tho' not less important and useful pursuits, is disposed to accept, that the best Interests of himself and the Community are likely to suffer, in a much higher degree than his apparent savings amount tō."

TENANCY.—P. 35. "The number or those Land Owners who see the propriety of granting Leases, for their own and tenant's benefits, are comparatively very small, and unfortunately, their number seem rapidly decreasing, in Derbyshire, as well as elsewhere; the example of the Duke of Devonshire, who grants no Leases, and yet is considered one of the best, as well as the largest Landlord in the district, having probably contributed a good deal, to bring them into disuse. That those steady principles of honour towards his Tenants, and vigilance to check any occasional deviations therefrom in his numerous Agents, which happily seem to have grown hereditary in the Family, should have left his Grace little to wish, or to expect, of the benefits which usually result from Leases, I can readily conceive,

conceive, from having witnessed upon various parts of his Estate, such expensive improvements making by *his* Tenants at Will, as I should scarcely have believed from any one who mentioned them: Houses and Premises Built, or completely Repaired, Fencing, Draining, Liming, Planting, &c., to the amount of some Thousands of Pounds on single Farms, and even Collieries effectually opened, on a good scale, by Tenants at Will!"

Covenants.—P. 174. "The prevalence of Grass Land in Derbyshire, seems little if at all enforced by the Covenants in the few Leases that subsist, or in the positive or implied terms of letting Farms, as is the case in most of the more Southern Counties, where custom seems to authorise the Landlord, to consider the breaking up of an old Pasture, or even any Pasture that *was such* at the time of entry, however unproductive, without his special consent, as one of the most heinous offences his Tenants could commit: whereas in Derbyshire, the Tenants seem almost universally at liberty, and in the practice of ploughing any and every piece of Pasture on their Farms, in rotation, which they think will be more profitable in that state: the only rule or customary restriction that I heard on the subject was, that one-third of a Farm ought to be left at quitting, in grass, either old or laid down in proper rotation in an husbandlike manner."

Time of Entry.—P. 27. "The Farms in Derbyshire, appear to be pretty generally held from Lady-day to Lady-day."

WOODLANDS AND PLANTATIONS.

TO this minor department of Rural Economy, the Reporter has appropriated nearly one fourth of his second volume. Yet, on these subjects, as on that of irrigation he appears to be little more than an amateur. It must be observed, however, that his deficiences are not quite so palpable on this, as on the former topic.

Whatever I may find of judicious *report*, concerning the present state and practice of *Derbyshire*, I will extract;—and leave the *general matter*,—what might be termed the fillings; as well as the puffings of Mr. Pontey, on "Forest Pruning"—(as if it were of *his* invention)—undisturbed.

WOODS.—P. 219. "Spring Woods, as those are here called which bear Underwood as well as Timber, and are cut at stated periods, are well distributed throughout this County, except on the Mineral or Peak Limestone District, and

and the Shale and Coal-measure District to the North of it, as will appear by the following List of Places, where I noted ancient Woods, principally of Oak, but often with a mixture, of Ash, Sycamore, Elm, Beech, Poplar, Alder, Spanish Chesnuts, and a few other Trees; and Underwood, consisting for the most part of stems of Oak, Ash, Nut-hazel, Birch, Sallow, &c."

This list contains nearly a hundred woods; but their *extent*, either severally or aggregately does not appear.

P. 222. "Almost throughout Derbyshire, the principal appropriation of the Underwood is to *Puncheons*, or Supports for the Coal-Pits, and for which purpose the Underwood requires to stand from 21 to 28 Years old, or about 25 Years on the average; the *Stemples* and Fails used in Lead-Mines, and the Ladder-shafts, Soughs, Gates, &c., leading thereto, occasioned also a very considerable demand for stout Underwood Poles, until within a few years past, when the Mines have so much declined: the smaller *Poles* find a vend for making *Fleaks*, or Hurdles, for *Broom-sticks* and *Hedge-stakes*, and other similar uses, and nearly all the remaining Underwood and Lop of the Wood Trees, are cut into Cord-wood, and converted to Charcoal near the spot.

"The Woods in this Country are principally, if not entirely, in the hands of the Owners, managed by their Agents or Bailiffs, tho' often the Wood is valued previous to sale, by professional Wood-valuers; of course *Rents* for Wood Lands are here little known.

"The Duke of Devonshire, the Duke of Portland, Sir Thomas Windsor Hunloke, Bart., the late Sir Sitwell Sitwell, Bart., Francis Hurt, Esq., and others of the principal Proprietors of the Woods above mentioned, divide their Wood Lands into 24 or 25 nearly equal parts, or falls, one of which is cut every Year, so that by the time the last Fall is cut, the first will be ready to cut again, and so on in succession, by which means the Colliers and other consumers, are supplied with nearly equal quantities annually, and the Owners can also reckon upon nearly as regular an annual income from their Spring Woods, as from any other equal extent of their Estates that are let in Farms:* great fluctuations in the prices of Puncheons and other articles, and of Oak Timber in a degree, are also thereby prevented."

The following mode of sale is new to me.—P. 229. "In Glossop, the Timber and Wood is sold standing, as by that means

* While the mines remain productive.

means the Auction Duty is avoided: but more commonly the sale is by *Ticket*, the process of which was described to me by Mr. Matthew Ellison, Agent to the Hon. Barnard Edward Howard: the buyers and the vendor being assembled at a public-house, the vendor puts a folded Ticket, containing his price of the Lot about to be sold, into a Glass on the Table; each of the buyers do the same, and then the vendor opens all the Tickets but his own, and declares the name of the highest bidder, but not the amount of his offer: a second delivery of Tickets by the buyers then takes place, and the name of the highest bidder among them is again declared; and then a third delivery, which, according to the practice about Glossop, decides the Sale; unless on opening the vendor's Tickets, none of the biddings come up to it, when the Sale is void, unless the highest bidder, or the next or following in succession, should agree to come up to the vendor's price in the Ticket, the amount of which is not however declared, unless a disposition manifests itself among the buyers, to further advances: it has rarely happened of late, that the biddings in this district have not exceeded the valuation and the seller's Ticket price, or that he is necessitated to accede to that of the highest bidder, who is considered as bound to take the lot in such case."

At the close of the section, "Copse Woods," Mr. F. has, —perhaps sarcastically—inserted the subjoined passage.

P. 236. "I heard of no instances of the *Grubbing* up or Stubbing of ancient Woods, to cultivate their sites, tho' from what I have said in page 225, such a measure seems advisable on some of the best soils now occupied by Spring Woods; and the same arguments would apply, with greater force, to many Plantations made within the last half century."—And for which Mr. F. might have added—splendid premiums have been given.

Planting.—P. 237. "A very laudable spirit has pervaded the Land-owners in this County, for improving and ornamenting their Estates by Plantations, made within the last 50 or 60 years, but principally so in the latter half of that period; and in general, steep, rocky, and barren Lands, have been selected for this purpose, which could scarcely be otherwise improved: but instances are not wanting here, as in most other Counties, of too great a breadth of even and useful soils for Husbandry, having been appropriated to the growth of Wood, and most of which, the rapidly increasing Population of the Country calls alike loudly with the private interests of their owners, for their being cleared again, as soon as circumstances will admit."

These

These are judicious remarks; no matter whether they are original or copied. So far as the PLOW, the SICKLE, and the SITHE can go, there let planting be prohibited. Those who deal out premiums for planting "ARABLE MEADOW and PASTURE LANDS" ought to be made liable to penalties, *or* a certain mode of *imprisonment*.

The following account of an extraordinary property of "cedar wood," is entitled to a place in this register. The story is not, however, intelligently told.

P. 247. "Cedar *(pinus cedrus)*, seems to be scarce in the County; near the east front of Bradby Hall, there is a large and remarkable one, supposed to have been planted about the year 1682, its trunk for 17 feet high measures 13 feet 2 inches circumference, on which rises three prodigious upright branches, nearly of equal sizes.

"The well known property of this Wood, to drive away or destroy insects, probably arises from its Resin or Turpentine being slowly volatile, at the ordinary temperatures, as William Strutt, Esq. of Derby, rather disagreeably experienced a few years ago, on having new Cases and Drawers of this wood made for his Mineral Collection, and on examining of which, after an absence of some months, particular Fossils in the Drawers were found so completely coated with soft and sticky Resin, that it had run off them and in part filled the small paper trays, in which such Fossils lay, and what seems extraordinary, other Fossils appeared to have attracted none of this volatile Resin, nor was the Papers or the surface of the Wood of which the Drawers were made, sensibly soiled by it.

"This property of Cedar Wood, is noticed in the Philosophical Transactions, No. 110, an exactly similar thing having happened to Dr. Lister in 1674; and I have lately experienced the same disagreeable effect, tho' in a smaller degree, from a number of new blacklead pencils that were kept together in a tin case, which they lined with their sticky Resin."

Now *pinus cedrus* is the Linnean name of the cedar of Lebanon, whose propensity to *spreading* is proverbial; and the wood of blacklead pencils is usually that of the Bermudian cedar *(Juniperus Bermudiana)*—a tree that will not thrive in the open air of this climate. Is the wood which produces this extraordinary effect that of a Pinus or of a Juniperus? or is it common to the cedar of Lebanon and the Bermudian cedar?

AGRICULTURE.

AGRICULTURE.

FARMS.—Sizes.—P. 25. "The number of Farms in Derbyshire of considerable size, is small, and there are none that can with propriety be called *large* Farms."

P. 26. "In Ashover it is computed, that the Farms average under 50 acres: Sir Joseph Banks has, for a Rental of 1613*l.*, no less than 97 Tenants in that Parish: and such small occupancies are by no means uncommon, in other places."

Farm Fences.—The subjoined notice is entitled to attention.—P. 86. "Mr. James Dowland, of Cuckney, Notts, mentioned to me, from observing that bank-set Quicks, with a northern aspect, succeeded much better than those with a southern aspect, he had ascertained, that the Winter and early Spring Sun was very prejudicial to young White-thorn Sets, in prematurely exciting them to vegetate, from which those with a northern aspect were free."

Gates.—The following is something new.—This might be *literally* termed the *iron* age.—P. 235. At Mr. Samuel Tudor's at Coxbench, and Mr. Richard Harrison's at Ash, I saw a new sort of *Fleak Hurdles, made of Cast Iron*, four feet high, with five light yet strong ribbed bars, two yards long, with dove-tails at top and bottom of the heads, by which these Fleaks are effectually locked together, as they are set, and to iron Stancheons pointed for driving into the ground: these Fleaks were cast at Bridgenorth in Shropshire, by Messrs. Hezledine and Rastrict, and cost 9*s.* each delivered at Stourport (whence they came by the Canals); Fleaks of similar form but of less dimensions, for Sheep, 7*s.* each."

HOMESTALLS.—Roofing Material.—P. 14. "I saw but one remaining instance, of the *Shingles* of cleaved Oak, or wooden Tiles, which probably was once much more common, and that was on the Church at Walton on Trent."

Rural Architecture.—Vol. I. p. 423. "At the following places there are *Saw-Mills*, worked either by Water or Steam, for sawing Stone for the various purposes of Building, Paving, &c." Seven in number.

Vol. I. p. 427. "At most of the Saw Mills mentioned above, considerable quantities of Paving-stone are sawn from blocks of Freestone; and at the following places they have also apparatus, worked by their Mills, for scowering or smoothening, and at some for *polishing* the better kinds of Paving and Marble Slabs." Six in number.

Vol.

Vol. I. p. 463. "At Buxton, large edge or rolling Stones are used for crushing Grit-stone, to make Sand for Mortar, and other purposes."

STATE of HUSBANDRY.—P. 94. "It has been estimated, that so large a portion as four-fifths of the surface, in Derbyshire, is in grass, and one-fifth of it only in aration; but I think it probable, that the proportion of ploughed Lands is greater than this." See *Covenants*, p. 131.

P. 174. "The proportion of Grass Land to that under tillage, is considerable in this County, owing to the high lands in the northern part of it being better adapted to pasture than to the cultivation of Corn, and to the great prevalence of Cheese-making, or Dairying as it is called, in the southern part of the County, and in a degree throughout the whole of it."

TILLAGE.—P. 102. "The system of periodically fallowing Land, which many have been disposed to decry, is still much adhered to in Derbyshire, tho' the number of naked fallows are now comparatively few, Turnips, Cabbages, and other green crops, having become pretty universal on the fallows. Mr. John Webb of Barton-Blount Lodge, considers fallowing superior to any other system of management on the Red Marl, even if clean. Mr. William Smith of Foremarke-Park, is also a steady advocate for this process. On the Coal-measures about Alfreton, Mr. W. Jessop, jun. estimates, that every fifth field of Arable Land is fallowed each year."

MANURE.—*Lime.* This is a point in the wide field of Agriculture, on which the Reporter of Derbyshire is prepared to speak with intelligence, and useful effect. He appears to be fully aware of the nature and value of Lime, in *a palpable state*, as an amelioration of soils, unacquainted as he may be with its properties, in a *state* of *solution.* See *Irrigation*, aforegoing.

Magnesian Lime.—P. 185. "In Plesley, I noticed the thick water from the Roads mended with Magnesian Lime, to be carefully collected into Pits by the Road sides in wet weather, to drop its sediment*, and which, when the Water was dried away from it, was mixed with Dung, as a Compost. by the Farmers."

Derbyshire abounding, in an extraordinary degree, with limestones and coals, and with water carriage, to convey the lime prepared from them, to a distance, we are the less surprised to read of the extensive *lime works* that are observable

"* Which probably contained a large portion of *Magnesian Earth*, and which renders the alleged noxious quality of this Earth to vegetative life still more doubtful, than it is said by others to be."

observable in the County. And, in the subjoined description, we see the great advantage of *canals* to agriculture.

P. 426. "Samuel Oldknow, Esq. has very extensive Lime Kilns for burning Stone of the 3d and 4th Rocks, brought from *Bar-moor* and *Dove-hole* Quarries, in Peak Forest, above-mentioned: the structure and arrangements of these Lime-works are the most complete that I have seen. Where four Locks occur near together on the Canal, a branch has been taken out of the upper pound to a Dock, where the Stone and Coal Boats lie to unload, level with the tops of the Kilns, which are 12 in number, and can burn 2500 bushels of Lime daily! From the bottoms of the Kilns, Rail-ways are laid, and conducted, some into a Boat-house, over two Boats that can lay in a Dock connecting with the lower pound of the Canal, and have their lading of Lime tippled or turned over into them from the Trams on the Rail-way, under cover from rain; others of the Rail-ways are conducted into a Lime-house over four or five Carts or Waggons that can stand at the same time, and have the Lime tippled into them, secure from the weather: and others to Tipples without covers. The Kilns are rather egg-shaped, 36 feet deep, 13½ feet diameter at top, and 14½ feet in the belly or widest place at nine feet down; diminishing thence, to 3½ feet diameter at bottom. Iron shovels are used to draw the Lime at 20 inches above the floors on which the Rail-ways are laid. Between the bottoms of the Kilns, roomy arched Stables are constructed, in some of which the Farmers feed and rest their Horses, while their Carts and Waggons are loading, and others are let to the Boat-men for their towing Horses."

The *boat-shaped kiln*, which is described below, appears to be an improvement of the Brotherton kiln (see my YORKSHIRE); as the greater the body of fire collected together, the less proportion of fuel is of course required.

P. 440. "Mr. Timothy Greenwood uses a great deal of Lime, and burns it in Pye-kilns, or Pudding-pyes, as some call them. His process is as follows:

"In a Stone Pit, if on an eminence rather, and open to the West the better, for saving carriage of the Lime, and procuring more draught of air, and if Carts can come into the West side of the Pit, still better, as then the Pye is to be constructed along the Eastern side of the Pit: those I saw were thus situated, and sixteen yards long, six yards wide at top, three quarters of a yard wide at bottom, and three yards deep, shaped much like a Boat, with swelling ribs; the sides of the Pit having been roughly cut or quarried, to form the East side and the ends, and the West side

side formed with a rough wall of Limestones: three openings or door-ways being left in the length, in building this Side-wall, which openings are built up with Stones, previous to charging the Pye. Along the bottom of the Pye, a Channel is formed about half a yard wide, and as much deeper than it, like the keel of a Boat almost, and from this, three similar channels branch, to pass under the three openings or door-ways; these are for admitting air, and lighting the Pye: whose previous preparation for charging as above, has cost Mr. G. from 60*s.* to 70*s.*

" Preparatory to charging the Pye, the Trenches above mentioned are covered over by dry branches of Wood, and Heath or Straw spread upon these, to receive a floor or layer of Coals three inches thick, all over the bottom of the Pye: then six inches thick of Stone, broken rather small, is spread on this; than another three inches of Coals, succeeded by a seven or eight inch layer of Stone, which may increase in size of pieces to the middle, where they may be pretty large, if set up edge-ways. In the above manner the alternate layers of Coals and of Stone are continued, the latter increasing in thickness to 14 feet above the bottom, along the middle of the Kiln, and the last layer of Stone may be 14 inches thick, and should be pretty well broken, and the top layers should diminish above the walls, so as to form a regular surface, almost like a Boat five feet deep, turned bottom upwards. This surface is then to be covered with Sods, laid with the Grass inwards, and lapping close over each other, except along the ridge at top, to about six inches thick.

" Lighted Straw or dry Heath is then introduced to the middle of the Pye bottom, by means of the three side channels, and the Pye is left to burn for five days, if good Coals from the Wharf at Cromford are used, or ten days if the Thatch-marsh Coals are used: one or two days more are generally enough to cool the Lime, sufficiently to begin drawing; which commences, by backing the Carts against the side wall, and the men with Shovels throw the Lime into the Carts, until got some distance below the side Walls; the temporary Walls in the three openings or Doorways, are then removed, and a Cart backed to each, enables the remainder to be readily drawn and loaded."

On the *application* of lime, in Derbyshire, there is nothing in the work before me, that requires to be noticed, here.

Yard Dung.—P. 456. " *Long Dung*, and fresh or rotten? The late Mr. Joseph Wilkes of Measham, used the Dung of his Horses, long and unfermented, as is stated by Mr. W. Pitt in the Leicestershire Report, p. 191 and 192.

Mr.

Mr. Thomas Logan, late of Buxton, used to boast of his success with long and unfermented Dung, on Grass Lands: but from the very exhausted and foul state of his Lands when I saw them, then recently in the occupation of Mr. William Wood, and the many *hoaxes* which he is known to have passed on Agricultural inquiries," (!!) "I dare not adopt his statements."

Query, have not many of the silly tales that have been told, about the *charms* of "long dung," arisen from the same *prolific source* of *errors* in *Agriculture?*

WHEAT.—I feel myself more and more gratified, as I procced in my REVIEW of WRITTEN AGRICULTURE, to meet with a useful idea that is new to me; the number of course decreasing, as I advance. The practice of the North Derbyshire farmers, as noticed in the subjoined extract, is probably well founded.—Vegetables as animals have, in many instances, a natural tendency to transmit their acquired habits, in a greater or less degree, to their offspring; and the seeds of corn that has ripened early, in a forward climature, may possibly have acquired a natural proneness to early ripening; even in a more backward situation. If its produce ripen only a few days earlier than the corn raised from seeds which matured in the same climature, it may, in some seasons, repay well the labor of going to a distance to fetch it. The proof lies open to any man who farms in a backward climature.

P. 114. "The advantage of having Seed from early Districts, is understood by many Farmers in the Northern part of Derbyshire, and who annually procure their Seed Wheat from Dunstable in Bedfordshire, and from other Southern Districts."

I insert the following instance of practice; not so much with a view of recommending it, though it may not, in some cases, be improper; as to caution those who may be willing to adopt it, against following it implicitly.

Stubbles of Wheat.—P. 124. "Mr. John Blackwall of Blackwall, uses a Paring Plough on his Wheat and other stubbles, immediately after Harvest, and then harrows and rakes out all the straw, roots, and weeds, carts them home. and spreads them in the bottom of his fold-yard, to be trodden into muck: by which harrowing and raking, the shed Corn and seeds of Weeds, immediately vegetate, and prove of some use to the Sheep late in the Autumn; which, and the severity of the following Winter, effects the destruction of *most* of what might otherwise prove detrimental, by vegetating next Spring."

To cart off the seeds, and creeping roots, of weeds, and deposit them, in the bottom of a dung yard,—to be there covered

covered up, and in that way deprived of the power of vegetating,—is unpardonably imprudent. Laying them in heaps to decay, and afterward mixing lime with them, to form a compost for grass lands, would render the practice under notice, especially on light free working lands, unexceptionable.

GRASS LANDS.—For an evidence of the value of old grass lands, in the estimation of the occupiers of Derbyshire, see the head *Covenants*, p. 131, aforegoing. Also p. 135.

Destroying Rushes.— P. 195. " Mr. Francis Blaikie of Bradby Park, breast-ploughs rushy patches very thin, when the surface is slightly frozen in the Autumn, and strews hot Lime for more effectually and quickly destroying the Roots of the Rushes."

PROFIT of FARMING.—There is not a passage, in the two volumes which I have now, I trust, rightfully appreciated, that impresses me with a firmer idea of Mr. Farey's good sense and judgement, in matters concerning *Agriculture*, than his decided opinion regarding its profits.

P. 40. " The propriety never appeared to me, of asking particular questions, whose answers were to be stated under this head, nor do I see the necessity now, of adding anything to the many general or hypothetical Calculations on this subject, which my Colleagues in the Reports on some of the adjoining and many other Counties, have furnished. I may remark, however, that Farming seems to have been a far less profitable pursuit, than the many species of Manufactures carried on in the district; and that where great numbers of the latter class have risen into considerable opulence: an instance of a Farmer (Mr. George Allen, of Stubbingedge in Ashover) who had acquired a large Sum of Money, was pointed out to me, as a very rare occurrence: and here even I suspect, that the successful cultivation of Chamomile-Flowers, and other things that can hardly be called Farming, and perhaps the fortunate investure of his property since it began to accumulate, has done more towards it, than Farming has ever done."

FINAL REMARK.

SHOULD the Author of the Work, which I am now finally closing, think it too severely dealt with, in regard to some particular points of Rural Economy, he ought, perhaps, to take the blame (if any) upon himself; as the spirit of harsh criticism (if detectable) may have been imperceptibly inhaled, from the rough stream of censure which runs through his volumes.

I have only to add, that, in reviewing the Report of Derbyshire, I have observed the same rules of estimation, as as I have kept in view, on all similar occasions; and, further, that in revising, for the press, the remarks and observations that were, in consequence, made upon it,—I have rubbed off such prominent points of censure, as I conceived might *reasonably* be the cause of offence to the Writer or his friends.

NOTTINGHAMSHIRE

NOTTINGHAMSHIRE.

THERE are three well defined NATURAL DISTRICTS, in NOTTINGHAMSHIRE :—

The Red Hills, or "Clays;"
The Forest; and
The Vale of Trent, Nottingham, or Newark.

The remainder of the County may be considered as the outskirts, or margins, of other natural Districts.

"GENERAL VIEW

OF THE

AGRICULTURE

OF THE COUNTY OF

NOTTINGHAM,

WITH

OBSERVATIONS ON THE MEANS OF ITS IMPROVEMENT.

DRAWN UP FOR THE CONSIDERATION OF

THE BOARD OF AGRICULTURE

AND INTERNAL IMPROVEMENT.

BY ROBERT LOWE, Esq.

OF OXTON.

1798." *

HERE again (as in Staffordshire) we are almost totally in the dark, respecting the ACQUIREMENTS and HABITS, as well as of the MODE of SURVEY, of the Author of the Work under view; saving what the Work itself affords.

The CORRESPONDENCE, which constitutes no inconsiderable part of the Volume, is almost wholely addressed to "Sir RICHARD

* Mr Lowe was the *original* Reporter of Nottinghamshire, in 1794.

RICHARD SUTTON, Bart.;" not to Mr. LOWE*. There are few ANNOTATORS, on this Report, though a "reprinted" one. The names of some of the CORRESPONDENTS will appear in the following abstract.

The number of pages—one hundred and ninetytwo; fortyeight of them being comprised in an Appendix.

A Map of the County, divided into Districts; see the head Soil and Surface ensuing.

No other *engraving*: two *cuts* of implements.

SUBJECT THE FIRST.

NATURAL ECONOMY.

CLIMATURE.—The passage of the Report that first strikes me as being entitled to extraction, is creditable to Mr. Lowe, as a Reporter.

P 2. "Being situated between fifty-two deg. fifty min. and fifty-three deg thirty-four min. north latitude, it may be supposed to be later in its harvests than the more southern counties. There is however an exception to this with regard to oats and rye, which, in the warm gravels about Newark, are as early as in most counties, being often brought to Newark market before the first of August. The seed time and harvest may in general be stated as follows: Wheat seed time, from the latter end of September to the beginning of November, and often later; spring seed time, from the beginning of March to the beginning of May; turnips from the middle of June to the latter end of July; hay harvest, from the middle of July to the middle of August; corn harvest, from the beginning of August to the latter end of September. The only particular circumstance that seems to deserve notice in the climate, is its dryness. From my own observation, and that of many experienced persons I have consulted, I have reason to conclude, that much less rain falls in this county, than in the neighbouring ones to the west and north, which may perhaps be naturally accounted for by the clouds from the western ocean breaking upon the hills of Derbyshire and Yorkshire, and exhausting themselves before they reach Nottinghamshire; and even those from the German ocean may be supposed not unfrequently

* Oxton is in the neighbourhood of Norwood Park, the residence of Sir Richard Sutton.

quently to skim over this more level country, and break first on the hills before mentioned: the greatest rains are observed to come with easterly winds. The drought of the summer 1793 was particularly experienced in this county."

In Tables, transmitted by Mr. THOMPSON, of West Bridgeford, the following striking results appear.

P. 146. "*Quantity of RAIN which fell in the following places in the year* 1794.

	London.	West Bridgford *.	Lancaster.	Kendal.
"January	1,64	0,58	3,00	7,29
February	0,94	1,68	6,16	13,47
March	1,26	1,33	3,37	4.53
April	1,52	2.80	3,66	4,18
May	2,54	1 15	2,08	1,99
June	0,50	0.10	2.16	1,45
July	0,62	3.10	2 66	4 16
August	2,42	2,66	3,75	5,34
September	3.71	3,00	6,83	7,67
October	3.36	3,65	7 94	7.32
November	4,44	4,02	3.83	6,01
December	0.37	2,20	5,33	6,20
Total inch.	23,32	26,27	50,81	69,65

"*Quantity of RAIN which fell at the following places in the year* 1795.

	London.	West Bridgford.	Lancaster.	Kendal.
"January	0,47	1,60	4,00	0,98
February	2,55	1,80	2,21	5,41
March	1,74	1,60	3,02	4,30
April	0,49	2,10	3,33	3,75
May	0,27	0,90	1,50	1,51
June	3,33	3,07	3,75	4,73
July	1,40	1,75	2,47	2,69
August	1,85	1,92	4,58	6,10
September	0,08	0,54	1,06	1,05
October	2,53	4,95	7,08	7,14
November	2,42	3,02	8,50	10,27
December	0,97	1,39	7,48	10,00
Total inch.	18,15	24,64	48,98	57,98"

A REMARK on CLIMATURE.—If these statements are nearly correct, and they correspond well, with others which I inserted,

" * In Nottinghamshire.—At Langar, in the same county, the FALL was 29,62."

serted, in the NORTHERN DEPARTMENT, p. 251, they seem to prove, substantially, that soil, or the vegetable economy (or the two combined), is capable of accommodating itself to the climature to which it is habituated. In the Vale of London, arable crops, in ordinary seasons, experience no general inconveniency, from want of moisture. And, in the vale lands, between Lancaster and Kendal, where, according to those Tables, *three times the quantity of rain falls*, crops of equal or greater luxuriance are seen. And, in the year 1798, they were nearly as forward as those in Middlesex, though situated almost three degrees of latitude, farther north. See NORTHERN DEPARTMENT, p. 243. The lands there, it is true, are mostly of an absorbent nature. And so are many of the lands, in the neighbourhood of the metropolis. Should three times the usual quantity of rain fall in the Vale of London, what would be its effect on the crops?

WATERS.—P. 6. "This county may be said to be well watered for different purposes. The navigable river Trent enters the county near Thrumpton and runs through Nottinghamshire on both sides, till a little below N. Clifton, from whence to the northern point of the county it forms the boundary between it and Lincolnshire.

"The Erewash forms the boundary between this county and Derbyshire for ten or twelve miles down to its junction with the Trent, a little below Thrumpton.

"The Soar forms the boundary between Nottinghamshire and Leicestershire, for seven or eight miles above its junction with the Trent, a little above Thrumpton."—Mr. L. enumerates several minor brooks and rivulates.

SOILS and SURFACE.—Under this head, Mr. Lowe has undertaken to divide the County into DISTRICTS; and his endeavors, in this respect, have proved more availing than those of most others of the Board's Reporters, who have aimed at the same difficult point. He separates it into seven distinct Districts.

It has, however, been said, aforegoing, that Nottinghamshire comprizes only three *natural* and *entire* Districts; namely, the *Forest*, the *Red Clays*, and the *Vale of Trent*. The other parts of the County are merely outskirts that are cut off, by *fortuitous* lines, from the *natural* Districts which happen to enter partially within those lines. This impropriety, however, originates, not with Mr. Lowe; but with the plan of *reporting by Counties*.—I insert the Reporters ideas in succession, as I find them. They are not very methodically arranged.

P. 2. "The surface of this county, except the level through which the Trent runs, is uneven, and may perhaps be said

to

to be hilly, though none of the hills rise to any considerable degree of elevation.

"In point of soil this county may be divided into the three districts of 1. Sand or gravel. 2. Clay. 3. Limestone and coal land.

"The sand or gravel may again be conveniently divided into, 1. The Forest country, or the borders of it. 2. The Trent Bank country. 3. The tongue of land east of Trent, running into Lincolnshire.

"*The forest district*—consisting of the ancient forest, and the borders of it, of the same kind of soil, is in length about thirty miles, and in breadth from seven to ten, more or less in different places.

"*Trent Bank land.*—I consider as Trent bank land, the level ground accompanying the Trent, from its entrance into the county, down to, or a little below Sutton upon Trent, where the clay soil comes down to the river on the west side; and on the east, a poorer sand runs in a tongue-shape into Lincolnshire. I include in it, likewise, the level grounds running up the river Soar, from its junction with the Trent, up to Rempston,—as the townships of Ratcliff upon Soar, Kingston, Sutton Bonington, Normanton, and Stanford; and those lying on the back of them,—as East and West Leak, Cortlingstock, and Rempston, which though on higher ground, are much lower than the Woulds, and of a good mixed loam, convertible, and equally fit for tillage or pasture; not let at less than twenty shillings an acre throughout, taking upland and meadow together; as well as the strip of higher land, on which are the townships of East Bridgeford, Kneeton, Flintham, and Stoke, which, though above the level of the rest, are of a mellow mixed soil, different from the clay of the vale of Belvoir, adjoining. This level is, in general, of a mellow soil or vegetable mould, on sand or gravel, though in some places these rise to the surface. It is of different breadths; in some places, not above a mile and a half; in others, three, four, and five miles wide; and is mostly inclosed.

"*The tongue of land east of* Trent, is of a sandy soil, in some parts rather better than others, but in general very poor. A great part of it is taken up by low moors, much flooded by rains.

"*The clay country* of Nottinghamshire may properly enough be divided into

"I. *The clay north of Trent*, consisting of the north and south clay divisions, and the hundred of Thurgarton.

"II. South of Trent, comprehending 1. The Vale of Belvoir. 2. The Nottinghamshire Woulds.

"I must observe that the *clays north of Trent*, are in general

general not of so tenacious a nature, as in many counties, being more friable, from containing a portion of sand and falling more readily by the weather; particularly the red clay, of which there is a great deal in the country round Tuxford, and in the hundred of Thurgarton, which might perhaps be more properly called a clayey loam, and a blackish clay soil, commonly called a woodland soil, in which there is plainly a mixture of sand.

"*The Vale of Belvoir* having no precise known boundaries, as soil with me is the chief distinction, I shall call by that name the country lying between the hills called the Nottinghamshire Woulds, and the strip of land running along the Trent on which stand the towns of East-Bridgeford, Kneeton, Flintham, and Stoke; which, though not on the same level with the rest of the Trent bank land, is of a mellow mixed soil which will bear the same cultivation, quite different from what I term the Vale. The soil of this latter is generally a clay or loam.

"*The Nottinghamshire Woulds.*—Are a range of high bleak country; the townships are some open, some inclosed. The soil is generally a cold clay.

"*Lime and Coal Districts.*—The lime-stone and coal district may be defined to lie to the west of a line drawn from the river, at Shire-Oaks, pretty nearly south by west to the river Lene near Woolaton and Radford, no lime being found east of the Lene. The lime-stone, which may be called a hungry lime-stone, rising up to the vegetable mould, commencing at Shire-Oaks, and beginning to abutt on the coal near Teversall runs afterwards between it and the sand. The line of coal begins a little north of Teversall, runs about south and by west, to Brookhill; then south to Eastwood; afterwards about south east, or a little more easterly to Bilborough, Woolaton, and the Lene. This line is scarce above a mile broad in this county, and above the coal is a cold blue or yellow clay. Between this and the sand of the forest, is the strip before-mentioned of lime-stone."

FOSSILS.—P. 5. "*Stone.*—At Mansfield is got a very good yellowish free-stone, for the purposes of building and paving, staddles, &c. and for cisterns and troughs, a coarser red kind. At Maple-beck, is a blueish stone for building, of which Newark bridge is built, which bleaches with the air to a tolerable white. At Beacon Hill, near Newark, is a blue stone for hearths, approaching to marble, which also burns to lime. At Linby is a coarse paving stone, much used at Nottingham.

"*Coals*—are got in the line described in the Coal and Limestone district, and conveyed by the Erewash and Nottingham canals, as well as by land carriage. The price of them is of late

late greatly raised at the pits, owing probably, in great measure, to the enlarged demand occasioned by the extension of the navigation into Leicestershire, and the supply by the opening of new pits, not yet corresponding with it, but that evil is beginning to remedy itself, as many are now going to be worked, and the price is already considerably fallen at Nottingham.

" *Lime*—is made of a weak *kind, for land* at Kirkby, Skegby, Mansfield Wood-House, and Warsop, of a better more soapy kind at Hucknall. On Beacon Hill near Newark, of a good kind, from a blue stone.

" At Linby is exceeding good *lime for building*.

" *Gypsum or Plaster*—is got of an excellent kind, on Beacon Hill near Newark, and much used for plaster floors.—A good deal of it is sent to London in lumps for the colourmen, and of the white, ground, in hogsheads for other uses. At Red Hill, at the junction of Trent and Soar, is a fine plaster quarry, from which Mr. Pelham, of Brocklesby in Lincolnshire, now Lord Yarborough, had columns of twenty feet high, in three pieces, used in his mausoleum. Lord Scarsdale also used the same in his house at Keddleston.

" Plaster is found also at G. Markham, and the Wheatleys, and in many other places, amongst the red loam; but I do not know of its being got for sale any where else than near Newark and at Red Hill.

" *Marl*—Marling land is not used in this county, nor do I know of any marl pit opened; though there is reason to believe that there is much of it in the clay soil, as a red crumbling stone, and a blueish, are both found at Halam, Kirklington, Oxton, Gedling, and in many other places; effervesce strongly with the vitriolic acid, and if found in sufficient mass, there can be no doubt of the improvement of land from the use of it. The blue is in narrower veins than the red, and has a smell of sulphur when the acid makes it work.

" N. B. I am since informed that Mr. Green of Bankwood, has lately found good marl on his farm at Saxendale in the Trent bank district, and is now beginning to lay it on his grass lands."

SUBJECT THE SECOND.

POLITICAL ECONOMY.

APPROPRIATION.—On this subject, a variety of remarks are found scattered throughout the Volume. Those which relate to the FOREST of SHERWOOD, are the most *interesting*;

teresting; and may serve as items of history concerning forests in general; which, whether or not they were founded in reason and right, are, under the present circumstances of the country, shamefully wrong.

The notices respecting *the Forest* appear in four different and distant parts of the book. I will here insert them miscellaneously as they are found, in passing through the Volume.

P. 21. "There was always about each forest village a small quantity of inclosed land in tillage or pasture, the rest lay open, common to the sheep and cattle of the inhabitants, and the king's deer.

"*Forest Breaks.*—It has been, besides, an immemorial custom for the inhabitants of townships to take up breaks, or temporary inclosures, of more or less extent, perhaps from forty to two hundred and fifty acres, and keep them in tillage for five or six years. For this, the permission of the lord of the manor is necessary, and two verdurers must inspect, who report to the Lord Chief Justice in Eyre, that it is not to the prejudice of the King or subject. They are to see that the fences are not such as to exclude the deer."!

P. 51. "The principal remains of the ancient forest woods are, the Hays of Birkland and Bilhagh, being an open wood of large old oaks, most of them decaying, or stag headed, and without underwood, except some birch in one part; it extends about three miles in length, and one mile and a half in breadth. By a survey taken for the crown, in 1790, there were found in both together, ten thousand one hundred and seventeen trees, valued at 17,142*l.* The land on which they grow is one thousand four hundred and eighty-seven acres, and is supposed would be worth, when cleared of wood, and inclosed—Birkland, eight shillings, and Bilhagh, twelve shillings an acre.

"In a survey of 1609, were found 21,009 trees in Birkland, and 28,900 in Bilhagh; the trees in general were then past maturity. By a survey in 1686, there were 12,516 trees in Birkland, and 923 hollow and decayed ones. In Bilhagh 21,080, and 2797 hollow trees.

"By a survey in 1790, there were in Birkland and Bilhagh together, 10,117 trees, at that time estimated at 17,147*l.* 15*s.* 4*d.* In the year 1609, there were in Birkland and Bilhagh, 49,909 trees; so that in seventy-seven years, to 1686, had been cut down 12,593 trees.

"There are now and then opportunities of knowing the ages of oaks almost to a certainty. In cutting down some trees in Birkland, letters have been found cut or stamped in the body of the tree, marking the king's reign, several of of which I have in my possession. One piece of wood marked J. R. (James Rex) was given me by the woodman who cut the tree down in the year 1786. He said that the letters appeared to be a little above a foot within the tree, and about one foot from the centre; so that this oak must have been near six feet in circumference when the letters were cut. A tree of that size is judged to be about one hundred and twenty years growth. If we suppose the letters to be cut about the middle of the reign of James the First, it is 172 years to the year 1786, which added to 120, makes the tree 292 years old when it was cut down. The woodman likewise says, that the tree was perfectly sound, and had not arrived to its highest perfection. It was about twelve feet in circumference. I have been told that J^{n}. R. (John Rex) have been found cut in some of the oaks. One piece said to be marked with John Rex, and a crown, I have in my possession; but it is not sufficiently made out to be inserted here as a fact, though the person from whom I had it assures me, from his having seen others more perfect, that it is marked with Jo^{n} Rex. Others have had C. R. and several have been marked with W. M. (William and Mary) with a crown."

P 96. "The ancient royal forest of Sherwood is in extent, from Nottingham to near Worksop, about twenty-five miles; and in breadth, seven, eight, or nine miles, more or less in different places. Several tracts of land, particularly in the north part as far as Rossington bridge, lying in the same waste state, have been usually called forest; but from the survey of 1609, appear not to have belonged to the forest, or to have been disafforested before that time. In it are comprehended several parks taken in at different times, as Welbeck, Clumber, Thoresby, Beskwood, Newsted, Clipston, and several villages or lands belonging to them. The whole soil of the forest is understood to have been granted off from the Crown to different lords of manors, reserving only, in forest language, the vert and venison, or trees and deer.

"The latter were formerly very numerous, all of the red kind. Within the memory of persons living, herds of one hundred or more might be seen together; but as cultivation increased, they diminished gradually, and are now entirely extirpated. The vert and venison are under the care of four verdurers, chosen by the freeholders of the county."

P. 156. "The following account of the extent, jurisdiction, and officers of the Forest were communicated to me by Hayman Rooke, Esq. well known to the literary world.

"The

"The Forest of Sherwood is the only one that remains under the superintendance of the Chief Justice in Eyre North of Trent, or which now belongs to the Crown in that part of England.

"In a survey of 1609, it is described as divided into three walks, called North Part, South and Middle Part.

"North Part contains the towns of Carberton, Gleadthorpe, Warsop, with Nettleworth, Mansfield, Woodhouse, Clipstone, Rufford, and Edwinstow; the Hays of Birkland and Bilhagh, towns of Budby, Thoresby, Peverelthorp or Palethorp, and Ollerton.

"Middle Part, town of Mansfield, Plesly Hill, Skegby, Sutton, Hucknall, Fulwood, part of Kirkby, Blidworth, Papplewick, Newsted, part of Linby and part of Annesley."

"South Part, town of Nottingham, part of Wilford, with Radford, Sneinton, Colwick, Gedling, Stoke, Carleton, Burton, and Bulcote; Gunthorp, Caythorp, and Lowdham; Lambley, Arnold, Basford, Bulwell, Beskwood Park, Woodborough, Calverton, and Sauntesford Manor.

"FOREST OFFICERS.—*Lord Warden*, Duke of Newcastle, by letters patent from the Crown during pleasure.

"*Bowbearer and Ranger*, Lord Byron, by the Lord Warden during pleasure.

"*Four Verdurers* elected by the Freeholders for life.—Sir Francis Molyneux, Bart.; J. Litchfield, Esq.; Edward Thoroton Gould, Esq.; William Sherbrooke, Esq.

"The verdurers have each a tree out of the King's Hays of Birkland and Bilhagh, and two guineas to each verdurer attending the inclosure of a break.

"*Steward*, J. Gladwin, Esq.

"Nine keepers, appointed by the verdurers during pleasures, having so many different walks.

"The keepers have a salary of twenty shillings, paid by the Duke of Newcastle, out of a fee farm rent from Nottingham Castle.

"Two sworn woodwards for Sutton and Carlton. Thorney-Wood Chace is a branch of the forest. The Earl of Chesterfield is hereditary keeper by grant to J. Stanhope, Esq. 42 Eliz. The wood and timber of the Crown are under the care of the surveyor-general of the woods. His deputy in the forest is Geo. Clarke, who has a fee tree yearly, and a salary of twenty pounds per annum out of wood sales.

"Forest towns, villages, hamlets, or lands belonging to them included in the Sand and Gravel District.

"Carberton, Gleadthorpe, Warsop, with Nettleworth, Mansfield, and Woodhouse; Clipston, Rufford, and Edminstow;

stow; Budby, Thoresby, Peverelthorp, or Palethorp, Ollerton, part of Kirkby, part of Papplewick, Newsted, part of Nottingham, part of Radford, part of Basford, part of Bulwell, part of Arnold, and part of Calverton."

Thorney Wood Chace.—P. 85. "A branch of the forest of Sherwood, of which the Earl of Chesterfield is hereditary keeper, by grant of 42 Eliz. comprehends most of the towns mentioned in the southern part in the survey of 1609. It is well stocked with fallow deer, as the rest of the forest was formerly with red deer, which appear not to have intermixed. It has been hitherto well wooded; but the recent inclosures of Lambley and Gedling, when completed, will reduce it to very little. *In point of soil,* only the towns of Carlton, Gedling, Burton, and Bulcote, Lowdham, Lambley, Woodborough, and part of Arnold and Calverton, fall within this district. The deer since the late inclosures are all destroyed."

The scattered notices, relating to the appropriation of *parochial commons* and *common fields*, in Nottinghamshire, I likewise insert miscellaneously; without attempting to digest them.

P. 19. "Inclosure is going on rapidly in this county. There is seldom a session of parliament in which three or four bills are not passed for inclosing common fields."

P. 96. "Little waste land is now left in this county, much the greater part of the forest being inclosed. What remains is chiefly in the line between Rufford and Mansfield, and between Blidworth and Newsted, and is mostly poor barren land.—A good deal of it is in rabbit warren; and it is to be doubted whether it would answer so well in any other shape. Some part has formerly been taken into cultivation, and thrown up again. Planting might perhaps be found to answer.

"In the tongue of land east of Trent are some low flat commons, very much drowned in winter, and not easily improvable without good drainage, and whether the outfall is sufficient seems questionable."

The following sensible remarks are extracted from a letter, addressed to Sir R. Sutton, by W. Calvert, and dated Darlton, Feb. 5, 1794.—P. 165. "Having been much employed as surveyor and commissioner for inclosures, you may expect much information on that subject. The improvements are as various as the circumstances under which we find the lordships to be inclosed; the difference proceeds from the disproportion of their soil, quantity of commons, goodness of, or impracticability of making good roads without an enormous expence, contiguity to markets, &c.

"A lordship chiefly consisting of good land, with extensive commons belonging thereto, may be said to be the most capable of improvement; a clay one, with a great quantity of common, the next; and a clay one, with scarcely any open common, the least of all; though even the worst, upon an average, will increase about one-fourth in value, after deduction of all expences attending the inclosure, whilst some lordships, under the first description, in a few years have more than doubled their value before inclosure."

PROVISIONS.—P. 133. "Provisions are here much on a level with the neighbouring counties. They have been for a year or two past enormously high; beef and mutton sixpence, and even sixpence halfpenny per pound: but are now (in the latter end of 1797, and beginning of 1798) got down to fourpence, and fourpence halfpenny; and pork in the same proportion."

FUEL.—P. 134. "The fuel used in this county is, almost universally coal. A good deal is produced in the Lime and Coal District; and a good deal brought out of Derbyshire, by the Erwash, Cromford, and Chesterfield canals. Some is brought by water from Yorkshire, from the river Air; and some is distributed, by land carriage, from the pits. It is observable that since the canals have been opened, coal is become much dearer to all places, within a certain distance of the pits, the price having been greatly raised at the pits themselves. At Southwell, those that used to be laid down at ten shillings, and ten shillings and sixpence a ton, are now at fourteen shillings, and fifteen shillings.

"At Mansfield and Worksop, coals are also risen. On the other hand, at Newark and Retford, and other places at a good distance from them, they are fallen.

"In general, this county may be said to be supplied with fuel at a reasonable rate."

MANUFACTURES.—P. 138. "The malting business is carried on to a great extent in this county, particularly at Nottingham, Newark, and Mansfield, and in many other places. A great deal of malt is sent up by the Trent and the canals, into Derbyshire, Cheshire, and Lancashire. At Newark are great breweries, which vie with Burton upon Trent, in the trade to the Baltick and other parts. At Nottingham is a brewery, and another going to be established on an extensive plan.

"*The Stocking Trade*—is the most anciently established manufacture in this county; the frame for knitting stockings having, it is said, been invented by one Lee, of Calverton. It occupies a great many hands at Nottingham, and the villages for some miles round; as also at Mansfield, Southwell,

Southwell, and other places in its neighbourhood. Many new works of different kinds have been lately erected, as follows: many cotton mills worked by water, to prepare the thread for the Manchester manufacture, and for stockings, and other purposes, as at Gamston, Lowdham, Papplewick, Southwell, Newark, Fiskerton, Mansfield, and Basford.

"At Cuckney is a mill for combing wool, and another for spinning worsted, and one for polishing marble. At Arnold is a large woollen mill for both the former purposes: at Retford is a mill for combing woollen. These two are worked by steam. At Nottingham silk mills worked by horses. At Mansfield is a great trade in stone. Artificial marble is likewise made, and a considerable thread manufacture carried on, as also of British lace. At Nottingham is a white lead work, a foundery for making cast iron ware out of the pigs brought from Colebrook Dale, a dying and bleaching trade, and a manufacture of British lace by frame work. At Sutton, in Ashfield, a considerable pottery of coarse red ware, for garden pots, &c. At Upton, near Southwell, is a starch manufactory. At Retford, a sail-cloth manufactory."

For an observation on the *Stocking Manufacture*, as it effects AGRICULTURE, see the next Head.

I insert the following frightful List of Seminaries, that are most *ingeniously* calculated, not only to propagate diseases of the body and mind, and to sap the morals and health of the rising generation, who are unfortunately drawn within their walls; but to bring on, prematurely the decline and fall of a prosperous nation.

P. 170. "COTTON MILLS IN NOTTINGHAM.

"Dennison and Co.
Green and Co.
J. James
Cox and Co. stands still
Hippinstall
Pearson and Co. stands still
Morley
Harris.

"NOTTINGHAMSHIRE.

"Stanford and Burnside. Mansfield
Ditto Ditto
Stanton's
Robinson's upper mill
Old mill
New ditto
Middle ditto
Forge ditto
Nither ditto
} Papplewick and Linby

"Unwin's,

"Unwin's, Sutton in Ashfield
Also a mule factory at Sutton
Co. of hosiers, Radford
Thomas Caunt and Co. Southwell
Mr. Chambers, Fiskerton
Handley, Sketchley, and Co. Newark
Late Hardcastle and Co. mule factory, Newark, stands still
Burdin's, Langworth
Hall's and White, Basford
Salmon, Chlevell (nearly finished)
Walsh, Bulwell, part built, but remains unfinished
Rod and Co. Worksop
At Gamston, near Retford, a mill which occasionally spins worsted, cotton, and bump
Lambert's, Loudham, and Gonalston
Worsted mills
Bagshaw, Mansfield
Toplis, Cuckney
Davison and Co. Arnold
Retford mills."

POOR RATES.—P. 15. "Poor's rates vary extremely in different parishes. It is impossible, as well as useless, in a work of this kind, to enter into the detail of them: I can only observe in general, that they do not run so high as in many counties, where manufactures have formerly flourished, which are now come to decay: but at the same time, it is a matter of concern to observe, that the manufactures, particularly that of stockings, whilst they increase the population, increase at the same time the burthen of the poor's rate on the occupiers of land; which may be ascribed to the lower manufacturers too frequently spending all their earnings, without looking forward to a time of old age and infirmity. The most obvious remedy for this evil, appears to be the extension of the Friendly Societies, which have already met with the encouragement of parliament; or the making of some more comprehensive provision by the legislature, on the same principle."

TITHES.—P. 15. "Tithes are in many places taken in kind, but are more frequently compounded for, at a much lower rate than they could be valued at by any surveyor. In the new inclosures, land has universally been given in lieu of tithes. As in other counties, there are modusses for different kinds of products, and some lands, which were anciently in the occupation of religious houses, are tithe free."

P. 141. "Some persons have considered tithes as a great obstacle to improvement; and a law to compel a general compensation

compensation for them, as a money, or corn rent, as a remedy.

"I must, however, beg to offer my doubts, as to the propriety or efficacy of it.

"The right of tithes to the clergy, or lay impropriators, is as much fixed, and guarded by law, as any other property; and, consequently, no alteration should be attempted against their inclination, but for very cogent reasons indeed. It must be allowed, that the taking tithe in kind tends to impoverish the lands of those that pay it, by depriving them of so much straw for manure, whilst it enriches those of the rector, or impropriator, or their lessee. It may likewise sometimes discourage the growing of some particular valuable crops; though, in that case, the rector will generally find it in his interest to come to a composition. The legislature has, indeed, interfered; and, for the encouragement of valuable crops, fixed a certain sum, in lieu of tithes, as in the case of madder.

"But what weighs most with me is, that in this, and, I believe, most other counties, more tithes are paid by composition, than in kind. These compositions, from the desire of Clergymen to live well with their parishioners,* and partly perhaps from habit, are much lower than the real value of the tithe. If, therefore, a general compensation is to be fixed by law, which must necessarily be by understanding persons upon oath, I apprehend much the greater part of the occupiers would, instead of being relieved, find themselves charged with a much heavier expence than before; and, consequently, instead of a general satisfaction, a general complaint would ensue."

I have inserted those remarks, faint and futile as they are. I am desirous to furnish my readers with every particular which the Board's Reports afford, whether for or against a SUBSTITUTE for TITHES.

PUBLIC DRAINAGE.—P. 98. "In the new inclosure bills, drains are ordered by the commissioners, and provision made for their being properly kept up, which is more effectual than the old laws of sewers, of the neglect in the execution of which there is great complaint here, as well as in other counties."

The subjoined extract of a letter, by RICHARD DIXON, addressed to John Holmes, Esq. Retford, shows, in a more explicit manner, the want of new regulations, and a GENERAL LAW of PUBLIC DRAINAGE.—See my Treatise on LANDED PROPERTY, &c. &c. &c.

P. 98.

* Yes, perhaps, of those who *do* live with their parishioners. But the nonresidents and the lay tithers feel little of that desire.

P. 98. "The following remarks respecting the general drainage of this county, I leave you to dispose of in such manner as you think most proper. The drainage of every country greatly depends upon the state of the streams and rivers flowing through the same. There are many rivers flowing through this county, from west to east. Their average fall is from twenty inches to a foot in a mile, from their source to the tide's way. The rivers and main drains in the north part of the county are inspected by a jury, called a water jury, twenty-four in number, being freeholders of the county, possessing ten pounds per year of landed property, who make a survey of the rivers, &c. four times in a year. They make their report to a court called a court of sewers, which is holden at certain times of the year. I have frequently conversed with several of these jurymen respecting the business of their surveys; who say, they go upon that business because they are obliged so to do; that they do not understand the nature of rivers, and the best method of improving them—that they seldom see the rivers a mile together; they order a few sand-beds to be removed, especially at the tails of mills; and as they are appointed only for one year, they slip over it as easy as they can. The effect produced in the last twenty years makes good this assertion.

"In other parts of the county the rivers are committed to the inspection of one person, which I have known some years ago to have been very little attended to, being persons not conversant in that business. Was the improvement of the rivers of this county to be committed to the direction of professional men, there might be more improvement made in a very few years to drainage of lands, and facilitating the discharge of the flood-waters, than will be effected by the water-juries and inspectors, as before-mentioned, in a century. Men of experience might be employed in improving and repairing rivers and drains in a country, as advantageously as surveyors of high-roads."

Inland Navigation.—P. 136. "There is a great trade carried on in this county by water, by means of the river Trent, and the different canals.

"*By the Trent* are carried—*downwards*, lead, copper, coals, salt, from Cheshire, cheese, Staffordshire ware, corn, &c.—*Upwards*, raff, or Norway timber, hemp, flax, iron, groceries, malt, corn, flints from Northfleet, near Gravesend, for the Staffordshire potteries.

"*By the Canal from Chesterfield*, to Worksop and Retford, and to the Trent at Stockwith—*Downwards*, coal, lead, Steetley stone, lime, and lime stone, chirt-stone, for the glass manufactories, coarse earthen ware, cast metal goods, and

and pig metal, oak timber and bark, and sail cloth.—*Upwards*, fir timber and deals, grain, malt, and flour, groceries, bar iron, and Cumberland ore, wines, spirits, and porter, hemp and flax, cotton-wool and yarn, Westmoreland slate, and various sorts of small package.—*Upwards and Downwards*, bricks, tiles, hops, and candle-wicks ; other articles, however, bear but a small proportion to the coal downwards; and the corn, groceries, foreign timber, and iron, upwards.

" *By the Erwash and Nottingham Canals—Downwards*, coals from the Nottinghamshire and Derbyshire pits.—*Upwards*, corn and malt, for the consumption of the country at the head of these navigations, which is very populous, are carried up by the Erwash canal, and are likely to be so by the Nottinghham, when completed.

" Great advantage is expected from their junction with the Cromford canal, in bringing lime from Crich, and other places in Derbyshire.

" N. B. This is now completed, and found to answer, particularly with regard to lime."

SUBJECT THE THIRD.

RURAL ECONOMY.

TENANTED ESTATES.

ESTATES and their MANAGEMENT.—P. 8. " Estates in this county are from about 12,000*l.* downwards to the smallest amount.

" Nothing particular occurs in the management of them.* Gentlemens' estates are, as in most other counties, under the care of stewards. Some considerable, as well inferior yeomen, occupy their own lands."

TENURES.—P. 8. " Lands are holden as in most other counties, under a variety of tenures—freehold, copyhold, and leasehold.

" A

* In a note p. 160, however, we are informed of their *mismanagement*, " I am sorry to say, some land-owners are so jealous of any profit accruing to the tenant, that they are constantly enquiring into his profit : and without considering his losses, expences, &c. &c. by advancing his rent on the least suspicions of advantage, he is driven to the waste and destruction of his farm for his own present support."

"A good part of the small copyholds are borough English, *i.e.* descend to the younger son.

"There are many leaseholds for three lives absolute (or freehold leases) holden under the archbishop of York, or the church of Southwell. Some pretty considerable estates formerly belonging to the priory of Thurgarton are holden by lease for years under Trinity College, Cambridge."

SODBURNING.—From a number of notices brought forward, on this subject, it would seem to be the prevailing idea of the County, that, in breaking up rough sward, this operation is useful, or in a degree necessary; but that, afterward, it is injurious.

IRRIGATION.—On this subject, too, some notices are brought together; but, on neither of them, do I find any thing extractable,—after the ample details (especially respecting the former) that have already entered into the preceding volumes of this Work.

TENANCY.—P. 16. "The greater part of the lands in this county are, I believe, let to tenants at will, who in general do not feel themselves uneasy under their tenure, and frequently succeed to their farms from father to son for generations. Where there are leases, the covenants are the usual ones, as to repairs, not cross-cropping, &c. without any special provision that I am acquainted with.

WOODLANDS AND PLANTING.

NEARLY one fourth of the Volume is occupied by papers, and incidental remarks, on the woods and plantations of Nottinghamshire.

Some of those papers relate to the methods of planting pursued on the larger estates: among them Mr. SPEECHLEY's valuable paper, descriptive of the practice followed on the *Welbeck* estate, is inserted (see my Treatise on PLANTING). But the greater part of them are minute details of the woods and plantations of minor estates; as well as those found in different Districts of the County. Plots of a few acres, down to two or three, are enumerated in these lists; which, as facts in the topography of the County, may, hereafter be interesting. But, in a concentration of useful ideas, in the rural knowledge of the Midland Department of England, they are inadmissible.

WOODS.—The remnant of woodlands of *Sherwood Forest* are mentioned aforegoing, p 149.

The *aggregate extent* of NATURAL WOODS in Nottinghamshire,

hamshire, is not expressed by Mr. Lowe. It is not great, I conceive.

On the *management* of those woods, little is said. The subjoined extracts contain what I think requires to be transcribed into this Register.

P. 84: " *In the Clay District, north of Trent*, there are considerable tracts of woods, which are chiefly sprung. Of these I have inserted in the following pages a general and particular account, with the management of them as far as I have yet been able to learn. I may observe in general, that the principal value of spring woods in this country, arises from the ash for hop-poles; and the stakes and bindings, flakes, &c. for farmer's use. From the universal use of coal for fuel, brush and cord wood are of less value than in many other counties; the bakers even having learnt to heat their ovens with coal. The timber in most of the woods in this district having been cut within these twenty years, and the underwood hurt by the growth of the timber, they have been reduced in value; but are now, in general, improving by new planting and taking care of the underwood, and young oaks are getting up for timber being left for standards. Vacancies are generally filled up with ash. Some charcoal is made."

The following is taken from a letter addressed to Sir R. Sutton, by Mr. DENNISON, dated Ossington, Jan. 26, 1794; giving " an account of the extent and manner of occupation of his woods, to assist Mr. Lowe in his survey."

P. 89. " They are nearly four hundred acres ash and oak; about twenty acres are annually cut down for hop-poles, round poles, and country uses. Such oaks as are stag-headed, and not likely to improve against another fall, are felled at the same time. The hazels and thorns are afterwards mostly stubbed up, and young ashes planted in their stead; by which mode, with the addition of draining the wet parts, these woods have been very considerably improved. I last year completed the whole round on this plan, which has taken an immense number of plants. I have some years planted from eighty to one hundred thousand, and mean still to pursue the same plan, though in a diminished proportion. Some of the young plants make poles the first fall; but in general, they are not supposed to be productive till the second, and many die. Oaks in this soil do not grow to any girth, but are mostly straight, solid, good hearted timber."

PLANTATIONS.—These might be termed the pride of Nottinghamshire; which exhibits a greater extent of tall-grown PLANTED WOODS, I believe, than any other county in the kingdom; mostly in a flourishing state, and many of them fast

fast approaching to the state of timber. They are principally found on lands that are properly adapted to planting; namely, those whose surface soils are of inferior value, for the purposes of agriculture; yet on which, or rather in whose substrata, trees find ample store of pasturage.

P. 53. "The spirit of planting has prevailed much in this district since about forty years. Unfortunately, the first plantations were chiefly of firs, whether from the desire of making an early appearance, or from the notion that forest trees were not easy to rear in this soil. It has, however, been found since, that trees of all kinds, well planted and properly sheltered, succeed very well.

"His Grace the Duke of Newcastle's plantations within Clumber Park, amount to one thousand eight hundred and forty-eight acres."

P. 69. "The uncultivated lands which have been improved by agriculture and planting, by the Duke of Portland, within the last twenty-five years, amount to between two thousand and two thousand five hundred acres; of which number about one fourth consists in plantations."

The subjoined account of propagating the *Birch* may be useful in bleak and barren situations. It is conveyed in a letter from George Neville, Esq. addressed to Sir R. Sutton, dated Feb. 1, 1794.

P. 34. "My birch is felling from November to the beginning of March, though the sooner the better, as it is very early in its sap in the spring, bleeding exceedingly if not cut before March. I first let the twigging to the besom makers at so much per bottle (or bundle), measuring four feet in the girth. The twigger lets the bottles lie till March, then takes them away, and stacks them like corn, and thatches them. They must, however, be tolerably dry before stacking, as otherwise they would be apt to heat and mould in the stack. The besom makers suit their own convenience as to the time of working up the twigs, generally beginning the latter end of the year, as soon as they become properly dry and seasoned for use. The making up is winter employment generally. I then cut out the shafts or staves, which I sell by the thousand or hundred. The tree thus dismembered I sell to the brush-makers, which is converted into brush heads, painters' brush handles, bannisters, spindles, distaffs, &c. and short pieces are worked up by clog makers and shoe heel cutters, &c. I sell these poles by the score, or by the groce of the articles they are converted to. In the last case they are cut up in the rough before they are carried from the woods. The refuse is kidded up for the bakers and family use; the nogging ends unconverted, are brought into my own yard and burnt as coal,

coal, making the quickest and best burning fire possible, and the pleasantest, never sparkling or flying in the least. I used to raise a great quantity from seed. In this case I used to pare and burn a piece of my worst land, on which I sowed turnips, eat them off early, and ploughed the ground immediately, and harrowed it well. By this means the land was immediately in order for the seed, which I harrowed well in any time before the winter, which I prefer, as the plants will grow the sooner and make greater progress by coming out of the ground earlier than if this business was delayed till the spring. They will grow in great abundance sown broad-cast like corn, and be a nursery for years, leaving a sufficient quantity for a plantation at last. The seed may be easily taken from bearing trees, by cutting the branches before it is quite ripe in August, and may be threshed out with a flail as corn, as soon as the branches dry a little. By this means I can, in the course of a few hours, get as much seed as would sow an acre or two of land, at the rate of two strikes or bushels to the acre. I raise few in this way now, as I can furnish myself with seedling plants at one shilling per 1000 for taking up and planting the same at three shillings per ditto. These are taken up with small balls of earth."

P. 35. "I make rails of my *birch*, tray," (?) "and gate bars, first shaving off the bark. The rails frequently are used to get up a second quick hedge on my bad land, so well do they wear; and I prefer them, for this purpose, to any oak or ash sapling rails whatever. They make very light and useful bars for inward gates for farmers, and with oak heads will last many years. I have corded a great deal of this wood, where it is not kind enough for riving for farming purposes, and it charrs very well."

For the uses to which the *birch* and the *willow* are applicable,—see *Gates* and *Fences*, ensuing. The latter is strongly, and properly recommended by Mr. Lowe.

P. 118. "The willow I recommend as most advantageous on every account—is the *broad leaved, red hearted, Huntingdonshire willow;* every other species I have tried, and find reason to give a decided preference to this."

P. 120. "The times of planting must be from January to the end of March; but the sets for that purpose should be cut from December to the end of February; when the sap is down*. If however there are people so injudicious as

"* And the reason is, that if poles are cut in the spring (the sap being up) the stool will at last be weakened by bleeding, if not killed; and of course prevented from shooting so vigorously as if cut at the preceding time."

as to sell sets in spring, it will be to the advantage of the purchaser to plant them, as the sap is then in the poles. The reason why many are induced to cut at that time, is on the supposed account of their pealing better; but I can affirm from experience, that poles cut in December, January, or February, and laid in rows upon the ground, or the ends put in water, will peal as well in the spring as at the usual time."

The neglect of land proprietors, in not raising *timber trees* in *hedgerows*, is certainly to be lamented.—P. 19. "It is to be lamented, that in the new inclosures very little attention should have been paid to raising hedge-row timber, which is done at first with no more expence of fencing than the raising of the quick.

"Whole tracts of country may be seen without a single tree growing up for farming use."

AGRICULTURE.

FARMS.—*Sizes*.—P. 14. "The farms may, in general, be said to be small, few exceeding 300*l*. per annum, and more being under 100*l*. a year than above that sum; many (especially in the Clays) as low as twenty pounds, or under.

"The largest farms, as might be expected, are on the forest in the poorest lands, and which have been lately brought into cultivation."

Plans of Farms.—P. 9. "Farm houses and offices are in general not very spacious, and in most parts of the country, *except in new inclosures*, situate chiefly in the villages, and not contiguous to the land."

Homesteads.—P. 9. "Houses and barns generally, (except in the strip of country adjoining to Derbyshire, where there is plenty of stone, which is applied to that purpose) are of brick, and tiled, sometimes thatched. Poor cottages and barns, in the clay country, now and then of stud and mud; but new buildings of all sorts are universally of brick and tile. Ground floors are generally laid with stone or brick: chamber floors almost always with plaster, which is a great preventive against fire. Excellent plaster is got at Beacon Hill near Newark, and is run at nine-pence per square yard, or six pence a strike."

Barn Floors.—The following circumstantial account of a new method of laying barn floors is entitled to a place, here.

A

A theoretical objection to it is that of *fresh* mortar "eating away the wood," as workmen term it. But this, perhaps, may happen only when *hot* lime is applied to *unseasoned* timber; and where a free communication of air assists in the decomposition. Moist, *stale* cement, however, may, by completely sheathing the wood, entirely exclude the air; and thus prevent the evil. The method recommended, I conceive, must necessarily be a preventive of what has been thoughtlessly termed the "dry rot;" but which, in the account under notice, is more properly named the *damp rot;* as its effect is evidently occasioned by a *vegetable* which cannot grow without air, and moisture; nor, of course, without sufficient space in which to extend itself.

P. 10. "Mr. Chambers of Tibshelf, in a letter to Sir Richard Sutton, describes a particular method of laying barn floors, as under:

"'Sir,—About twenty years ago I laid a barn floor with oak beams, fourteen inches square, and three inch oak plank, the plank was fourteen inches hollow from the ground, and the beams about two feet asunder; in two years after, some part of the plank broke down, without any other use than common thrashing upon; I examined the reason, and found the under side of the plank decayed by the *damp root*, nearly through; upon which I had the floor taken up, and found all the planks in the same situation, and the beams almost totally perished; upon which I consulted a very experienced architect, who advised me to lay the next floor still higher than the former, and if possible to admit a circulation of air under the same, as the situation of the barn must be very subject to the damp rot. I relaid the floor with new beams and plank of the same thickness as the former; the beams were fixed upon brick pillars, fourteen inches high, so that the floor lay twenty-eight inches hollow; and under each door-sill was two grates, about one foot square each, that gave a current of air under the floor through the barn, and by the beams being laid upon supporters of brick, the whole floor was hollow except the nine inch pillars.

"'The current of air was not through the middle of the floor, as the doors were more to one side than the other. In about two years the planks that were farthest from the passage of air fell down, all reduced to rotten wood, but about $\frac{3}{8}$ of an inch at the upperside; upon taking up the floor, I found the beams nearly reduced to rotten wood, except those that lay near the current of air, which were very sound, as was also the plank that lay over them in that situation.

"'After

"'After these trials in the usual way of laying barn floors, I determined upon the following experiment:—to lay the next floor solid, in lime and sand mortar; upon which I removed every part of the former materials, and fixed fresh beams upon a spreading of mortar, at about six feet asunder, so as to suit the piecing of the planks to pin to; between each beam I filled the space with stones and thin mortar, that the whole was made solid with the upper sides of the beams; when this preparation was sufficiently dry, I culled the best of the remaining planks from each of the former floors, and before the workman laid down each plank, the space that I covered was spread with fine mortar, even upon the beams; then the plank was laid down and pinned; so that every hollow part, either in the beams, or decayed parts in the planks, was filled solid with the mortar. The floor has now laid about sixteen years without any amendment, except one of the planks being so weak in sound wood, that it started from the pins a year ago; after taking the same up and examining the underside, I found such of the plank that was sound when last laid down, was still perfectly so, and the rotten part was firmer and stronger than when laid down.

"'I have mentioned the above circumstance to several workmen, &c. but few will follow the practice without peremptory orders, which I have followed up, with twenty different floors in sixteen years; some of oak, and some of deal planks, in different situations, and all appear as if they would stand for ages, unless they wear through from the upper side.

"'About ten years ago I ordered a floor to be laid, with ash plank (in the method above) as oak could not be got without cutting down oak trees to considerable loss; the Ash was fallen, sawed up, and laid down in the floor immediately, as the saw had left it; the joints did not open much before the last summer, upon which I had the floor taken up and relaid, as the plank must be well seasoned in nine years use; the under side of which was as sound as when first put down.

"'There are other advantages by laying barn floors solid with lime mortar, as a barrier against rats and mice, worms, &c. Prevents the joints from wear, by quivering, &c. and also prevents any loss in the corn through the joints.

"'I am pretty confident that the same method will hold good in laying ground floors with boards, in gentlemen's houses, that I have frequently seen them rot and eat through with worms in a few years. Both of these maladies the lime mortar will prevent, and will make the floor warmer also.

"'It

"'It will hold good to cover the lath and pin, or nail, in the under side of slate and tiled roofs, by starting or rough drawing the same, so as to cover the lath, &c. close My first observation of this simple method was about twenty years ago, being witness to the pulling down of an old timbered house, dated 1564; between each beam was pieces of ash wood, with split ash and hazel laths, and plastered on each side with lime or plaster mortar; where the plaster was free from cracks, the laths and the bark of them, was as sound and fresh as if they had not been cut down three months, but where the cracks had admitted the air, every part of the lath, &c. was reduced to nothing. I have lost no opportunity since my first observation, to examine the old ruins, and where I have found any old timber within those walls that had been run with thin mortar, the same has been sound and fresh, though the building has been in ruins for two centuries.'"

Having bestowed considerable attention, on the nature and operation of the FUNGUS ROT*, I was so fully convinced of the probable efficacy of Mr. CHAMBERS' DISCOVERY (as it here appears to be) from the first reading, that I have, since, not only laid a *room floor*, in his manner; but have fixed up a *dwarf wainscot*, on the same principle (in refitting up a room)—thus:

The back of the wainscot having been previously studded with small rose-headed nails, coats of lime-and-hair mortar were firmly spread over it with a trowel; so as to fill every vacuity, and render the surface perfectly plane, and smooth; and the wall having been in like manner prepared, the two plane surfaces, while the last coat was plastic, were pressed close, and skrewed together; by the means of wood bricks, laid into the wall, in the usual manner;—the lime and sand having been made up several weeks previously to the operation.

GATES and FENCES.—P. 19. "*Gates* are generally of oak, but willow with oak posts is found to make very durable gates, which have the advantage of lightness, and not damaging themselves by falling to."

Fences.—P. 19. "In poor soils, which are particularly favourable to the growth of birch, birch has been found to answer very well for hedges, which may be pleached, and resist light stock, and also serves for light gates and rails."

The willow and the birch,—the former in genial and moist, the latter in alpine, situations, rank among the first of

* FUNGUS ROT.—This term may not be strictly botanical. But no matter, if it will serve to convey a striking idea of the nature and operation of the most mischievous destroyer of timber.

of woods for the farmer's use:—not for gates and rails only; but for tools and light implements of various kinds. —See *Planting*, p. 161, aforegoing.

OCCUPIERS.—P. 14. "Many of the principal farmers carry on agriculture with great spirit, adopting the best practices of other countries; nor can it be said that the lesser farmers are backward in following good examples, of which they have seen the success. A very great difference may be seen from the face of husbandry twenty years ago."—See the following article.

STATE of HUSBANDRY and general PLAN of MANAGEMENT. —Mr. Lowe has been very attentive, and is commendably intelligent, concerning the progress and existing state, of the Nottinghamshire Husbandry. I will select what appears to be of general interest.

P. 21. "*In the Forest District*, the land being of a convertible nature, very little remains permanently in grass, except in the bottoms near rivers or brooks for meadow, and homesteds about farm houses for convenience."

Forest Breaks.—P. 21. "Before the introduction of turnips and artificial grasses, (generally called here, simply, seeds) which is scarce so old in the kingdom as the beginning of this century, and much later in this county, it was usual to get five crops running; oats or peas, barley, rye, oats, and lastly skegs, then leave the land to recover itself as it could by rest. The introduction of turnips was of great improvement in insuring a good crop of barley after being fed off with sheep; but still, till within these few years, it was not usual to lay down with seeds. At present, the culture of a break, well managed, may be stated to be —Break up for, 1. turnips, laying ten quarters of lime an acre; 2. barley; 3. rye, sometimes wheat; 4. oats, with seed, *i. e.* white clover, and rye grass, which are mown for hay, and then thrown open. But the greatest improvement has been made in the forest lands permanently inclosed.

"Amongst these deserves to be named, in the first place, Clumber Park, belonging to his Grace the Duke of Newcastle, between ten and eleven miles round, and containing in the whole about 4000 acres, which may be said to be a new creation within these thirty years; at which time it was a black heath full of rabbits, having a narrow river running through it, with a small boggy close or two. But now, besides a magnificent mansion, and noble lake and river, with extensive plantations, which will be particularly noticed hereafter, above 2000 acres are brought into a regular and excellent course of tillage: maintaining at the same time between three and four thousand sheep, and are all in his Grace's own occupation."

P. 23.

P. 23. "Beskwood Park, containing 3700 acres, which before that time was little cultivated, except in breaks, was about nineteen years since taken on lease by a Mr. Barton, of Norfolk, who brought a colony of Norfolk labourers; but on some differences between them, they left him in a year or two. Mr. Barton is since dead, but the lease continues in his family; the land is now divided into eight farms. Many other tracts of ground have, in the course of twenty-five years, been inclosed from the forest and borders of it; some under acts of parliament, some by private proprietors without act, and some are now in agitation."

P. 28. "*In the Trent Bank District.*—The occupation is mixed of arable and grass, though more of the latter, especially contiguous to the river.

"*The Arable* is generally calculated for the turnip husbandry, and kept in those courses, producing good crops of barley, and remarkable fine ones of oats, eight, and sometimes ten quarters an acre, particularly about Muskham and Balderton. They are so remarkably good, as to be distinguished by persons of knowledge from any other. Weight of the best, fourteen stone of fourteen pounds the sack; wheat is but eighteen. Oats are picked by hand by curious persons for seed. If the top one is a single oat, the rest on that stem will be so; the double ones are rejected. It is a strong instance of the improvement of husbandry, that about thirty years ago, the sand lands in Gressthorp Cromwell and Muskham fields, were not worth more than two shillings and six-pence an acre, covered with wild sorrel, and lea lay for six or seven years. The alteration is to be ascribed to turnips and clover."

P. 37. "*In the Clay District, North of Trent,*—there is a great intermixture of open field and inclosed townships; but more of the former.

"In the open field, the common course of husbandry is pursued as 1. fallow; 2. wheat or barley; 3. beans, pease, or both mixed. The latter crop is very common in this country. The reason given for it is its smothering the weeds; but I have always observed the crops to be very foul.

"Folding is little used. Few farmers, indeed, have stock enough of sheep to do it with any effect."

Same Page. "In some places, of late years, clover has been sown with the barley, and mown the third year, instead of the bean crop, which, in lands that have been long in tillage, is often very poor. The old way, in Oxton fields, was the usual one of two crops and a fallow, there being only three fields. In consequence of the act for cultivation of common fields, of 1773, they have now sown broad or red clover with their wheat or barley, (except a few who chuse

chuse to have their old crop of pease and beans the next year) they mow the clover the second year, and then stock it with three horses to two acres; or else two cows, or six calves, or three sturks to an acre, and then fallow, except a few persons who let the clover lie another year, and then sow it with wheat."

P. 38. "The following course has also been tried with success: 1. fallow; 2. barley or wheat; 3. beans; 4. red clover; 5. wheat. The clover crop sown with the beans, and the wheat crop, have both been remarkably good—at Norwood Park, by Sir Richard Sutton; by Mr. Musgrave at Halam; and at Red Hill, by Mr. Cook."

Same Page. "Mr. Turnell, of Stokeham, in inclosed lands, tried crop and fallow alternately, for twelve years; but did not find it answer."

P. 44. "*In the Vale of Belvoir district*—The country is part open, and part inclosed. In the open fields, the course of husbandry is generally, 1. wheat or barley; 2. beans; 3. fallow. In Elston are four fields, as 1. wheat; 1. barley; 1. bean; 1. fallow. In the inclosures there is almost universally a mixture of arable and pasture, and a little dairying.

"Clean fallows are generally made in rotation, as in the open fields. Sometimes red clover is sown with barley, and broken up instead of a fallow. Sometimes white clover, rye-grass, and rib-grass, or narrow leaved plantain, is sowed with the barley, and let lie three years."

P. 144. ("Conclusion"). "I have now only to add, that I am happy in being able to say, that of late years a great spirit of improvement has arisen in this county, not only amongst gentlemen and considerable farmers, but also amongst the inferior ranks, who begin to have their eyes opened by example, and in many instances have been ready to leave the old beaten track, and adopt better practices in agriculture." See also the preceding article.

P. 158. (In a letter from Mr. Calvert, inserted in the Appendix) "Lands under tillage in this county, whatever may be their rotation of crops, are generally fallowed the third or fourth year from the preceding fallow; and it is, and has been the custom, to lay upon such fallows the manure arising from the lands in tillage upon the same farm, and to plough in the same. This practice has been exploded by many, yet discontinued by few."

WORKPEOPLE.—P. 133. "The prices of labour are so various in different parts of the county, that nothing satisfactory is to be said on the subject. Within these few years, day labour is raised from one shilling to sixteen and eighteen pence a day; and, for the three harvest months,

to

to two shillings. In harvest they expect likewise some beer. Task work is raised in proportion. Threshing is now for wheat, four shillings per quarter; barley, two shillings and sixpence; oats, one shilling and sixpence; which were, a year ago, three shillings, two shillings, and one shilling. The hours of labour are the common ones. The ploughing is generally done at one stretch. Boarding labourers in harvest, as is done in some counties, is not usual here."

P. 140. "There are few counties in England where they will be found better lodged, clothed or fed, or better provided with fuel. Most cottages have a garden, and potatoe garth, and few of them are without a web of cloth of their own spinning: many of them, particularly in the Clay District, have a few acres of land annexed to their cottage, which enables the cottager to keep a cow or two, and pigs. The poor here may be said to be industrious: they may be often seen themselves, or their children, collecting the horse dung, casually dropped on the roads, for their gardens, or to sell."

WORKING ANIMALS.—P. 130. "*In the Trent Bank District*—Some horses are bred, chiefly a middling kind of black cart horse, though the breed begins to be improved by Leicestershire stallions.

"*In the Clay District*—Most farmers raise a foal or two every year, but of a middling kind of black cart horse, which calls for improvement.

"Dr. Coke, of Brookhill, in the Lime and *Coal District*, says, 'The breed of black horses is much attended to, and a great number of them are sold to the southern dealers, who come down to buy them.'

"*Horses*—The business of agriculture in this county is almost universally done by horses: those generally made use of, are a middling sort of black cart horses. Such fine teams are not seen here as in many of the southern counties. Mr. Jones, who rents the great tythe farm at Arnold, about 800 acres, performs all his work with nag horses, which he finds to work with more expedition on light land. It is become, within these few years, the general custom in the sand land, and begins to be so in the clays, to do all the latter orders with two horses a-breast, without a driver.

"*Oxen*—are so little used, as scarce to make an exception. Mr. Bower, of West Drayton, however cultivates a forest farm of 100 acres entirely with four oxen, and is very well satisfied with them; they work wholly on straw and grass, and do an acre a day in winter, and five roods in the spring. They are used two in the morning, and two in the afternoon. The Duke of Newcastle employs some

some beasts in Clumber Park, particularly in getting out his wood. Sir Gervase Clifton has a team of Devonshire oxen. Sir Richard Sutton, Mr. Stubbings, of Holme Pierrepont, and Mr. Wilson, of Shelford Manor, employ some, and perhaps some few other persons who have not come to my knowledge."—For *Working Hours*, see the last article.

IMPLEMENTS.—P. 17. "The plough generally used in this county, is the Dutch swing plough, which is found to answer very well, their gate or bottom being from two to two and a half feet, with a pair of hales or handles, at a proper height to hold.

"In the Vale of Belvoir the two-wheeled plough is used, which is made at Moor Green, near Nottingham. A one-wheeled plough is used near Nottingham, south of Trent, with two horses. A one-wheeled drill plough for turnips, is likewise made at Moor Green, which is much approved. The one-horse plough (on the recommendation of the late Charles Chaplin, Esq. of Tathwell in Lincolnshire) has been tried with success at Averham, Farnsfield, and Norwood Park."

MANURE.—*Lime.*—P. 105. "As to the effects of Lime on the Clay Soil, I have received the following imformation:

"Mr. Calvert, of Darlton, on a cold clay soil, has laid from one to as far as twenty chaldrons of lime an acre, and found no benefit whatsoever." (!) "He used the Knottingly soapy lime from Yorkshire, which is much esteemed. He tried it for several years, having had two or three sloop loads. As he informed me, Mr. Cartwright of Marnham, by persisting in it, spoiled a close entirely.

"Mr. Musgrave, of Kirklington, one year, on purpose for a trial, limed in Kirklington for his mistress, and in Halam for himself, two chaldrons, or sixty-four strikes* an acre, some of Newark and some of forest lime; and in another part no lime, on a summer fallow red clayey loam. He dressed all with dung at the same time. He saw no difference in the crop: but where he laid the heaps of lime, nothing has grown since.† His own land has never come about since that time. He apprehends many are drawn into lime by example only. If of any service, it is to lighten; but good fresh soil laid on is much better."

This is certainly *strange* report. It may nevertheless, be *true;* and I have thought it right to give it a place, here.

"*Gypsum,*

* Too small a quantity, for strong land.

† Probably *magnesian*

"*Gypsum*, or *Plaster*."—P. 110. "*In the Trent Bank District*—Gypsum or plaister, the best of which is produced at Beacon-Hill, near Newark, has been tried by Mr. Sikes three years together, in the same manner and with the same bad success, as Sir Richard Sutton and Mr. Calvert had, as mentioned hereafter.

"*In the Clay District*—it was tried by Sir Richard Sutton for three years running, without success."

P. 163. (Mr. Calvert's account) "*Gypsum or white plaster* threshed in an unburnt state, I have tried as a manure upon grass land, about three years ago, according to the rules prescribed by a pamphlet published concerning the use and good effects of that mineral in America; and am convinced, whatever virtues it may possess in America, it has none here; at least the native plaster which I made trial of had not. I began by laying on six pecks to the acre, and increased the quantity till I expended six bushels per acre, yet no visible alteration of the herbage could be discovered even to this day."

Burnt Bones and "*Dove Manure*," are enumerated, as being in use, in Nottinghamshire.

For a proof of the INVOLATILITY of vegetable manure, or *dung*,—see *Turneps* ensuing.

TILLAGE.—For the hours of team labor, in plowing, see Workpeople, aforegoing.

WEEDS.—For a method of killing *fern—brakes—breckans*—(PTERIS *aquilina*)—see *Grass Lands*, ensuing.

ARABLE CROPS.

P. 45. "The crops usually cultivated in this county are the common ones, of wheat, rye, barley, oats, beans and pease."

WHEAT.—P. 45. "The kinds of *wheat* commonly sown are, the red lammas, and white chaffed, or Kentish; two strikes, or Winchester bushels, sown to the acre. It is very difficult to form an average of the product of this, as well as other grain, from the great difference of soil and management.

"The crops in common fields, may be said to be from two to three quarters, or more. In inclosures from two and a half to four.

"A good deal of bearded wheat, here called Yeograve wheat, used to be sown particularly in the clay open fields, but is now much left off. It is a stronger stemmed hardier wheat, but coarser grained."

RYE.—P. 46. "*Rye* is but little sown, being scarce at all used for bread. Chiefly in the Trent bank land, about Markham, &c. and on the forest. There are two kinds; a black,

black, and a white or silvery sort. The latter has been sown in the spring with success.—Two strikes sown, crop from three quarters to four."

BARLEY.—P. 46. "*Barley* is much sown—No particular kind is distinguished. The Fulham rathripe, or early barley, has been tried in a few places; but though ten days or a fortnight earlier, has not answered in point of quantity of produce, or boldness of grain, so as to recommend the practice.

"Four strikes are sown, produce per acre, from three to six and seven quarters."

OATS.—P. 46. "*Oats* of various kinds are sown.—In the Trent bank chiefly the Poland; in other parts the Friesland Holland oats, brown oats, black oats in cold lands, and a few Tartarian, which will grow on worse lands than others, but are later in ripening, and coarser grained.

"Four strikes are sown; crop from four to seven; sometimes as high as ten quarters.

"*Skegs*, a species of oats, are I believe confined to this country. Eight strikes are sown; and yield a crop double that of other oats, in quantity; but not more than equal in weight.—They will grow in the poorest land, and are reckoned very sweet food. They are seldom brought to market; but esteemed by farmers for their own use, and are often given in the straw."

P. 148. (In the Appendix II. Mr. Lowe's account?) "Skegs appear to be the *avena stipiformis* of Linnæus, described by the Botanical Society at Litchfield, in their translation of the System of Vegetables.

"Pannicled, calyxes two flowered, awns twice as long as the seed, culm branchy, stipe form.

"They are sown on the worst land; sometimes on a lea, sometimes after turnips, often taken as a last crop. On bad land they may produce about four quarters per acre, which are generally about two thirds of the price of oats. They answer to sow on good land, producing fourteen and fifteen quarters per acre. The kernel is reckoned remarkable sweet good food for horses. They are sometimes threshed, sometimes cut in the straw. They are chiefly grown about Carberton, and will grow where nothing else will."—— Query, is Skegs a provincial name of the Tartarian, or Reed Oat?

P. 38. In the clay district, "scarce any oats are grown."!

TURNEPS.—P. 103. "Robert Ramsden, Esq. of Carlton, observes that it has been long a practice with strong soils, to plough in manure in the winter; but very few people have followed that method upon hot sandy soils: it however answers

answers very well even upon such lands after a wheat crop, which is intended for a summer fallow with turnips, and which land is afterwards worked very much in the hottest weather to get out the twitch grass. This has been fully proved in a farm near Carlton, for several years past and particularly the last year, by part of a field which was so managed, upon which there was a much finer crop of turnips than upon the other part, which was managed in the general way, viz. by ploughing it in winter, without any manure, making a clean fallow in the hot weather in summer, and ploughing in the manner immediately before sowing, the turnips."—Does not this show, in a convincing manner, the futility of the chemical notion, about 'long dung, and carbonic acid gas'?

RAPE.—P. 38. "Rape is sometimes sown instead of them," (turneps) "for sheep feed; sometimes for a crop, yielding half a last, or five quarters, often four; medium price, twenty-five pounds a last; sometimes thirty-three pounds, sometimes fifteen pounds only. Rape has lately been employed with success to feed beasts, giving it to them mowed under sheds in the winter, and leaving the stalks to afford sprouts for sheep feed in the spring.—Query, if borecole might not afford a greater produce?"

HOPS.—P. 38. "*Hops.*—Are a considerable article of produce in this district, principally in the part about Retford, and some about Southwell and its neighbourhood. They are generally known among traders, by the name of North Clay hops; they are much stronger than the Kentish, going almost as far again in use; but those who are accustomed to the latter, object to their flavour as rank. The quantity grown is fluctuating, some yards being laid down every year, and others taken up. It is supposed there are not so many now grown as thirty years ago, but that the culture has increased within the last ten years. Mr. Bower, to whom I am indebted for the accurate account of the management of them in the following letter, supposes the number of acres now so employed in the whole county 1100: others carry them as high as 1400."

I here insert, with readiness, Mr. Bower's letter.—The culture of the "North-clay Hops," as I have elsewhere said (see WESTERN DEPARTMENT, *Worcestershire*, art. Hops, note p. 377.) is the only remaining practice, of the HOP CULTURE of ENGLAND, which has not fallen under my inspection; and this letter, I fear, will be all the information I shall be able to collect, concerning it,—in going through the Boards Reports. It will at least tend to convey some general ideas of the practice. And an additional letter, from the same to the same, will furnish full and

and satisfactory detail of the *extent* of the culture, in Nottinghamshire.

P. 39. " *West Drayton, January*, 7, 1794.—SIR,—When I had the pleasure of spending a few hours with you at Clumber, you desired me to procure you an account of the number of acres planted with hops in this county, and likewise the expence of their cultivation. According to the best information I can get, there is about 1100 acres of hop ground. It consists of different kinds of soils, but chiefly strong clay, and bog or black earth. This, (the Eastern) part of the county is strong clay: The plantations here lie in vallies and wet lands for the most part, not very valuable for other purposes. The common price of first taking up, or converting grass land into hop ground, is fifty-shillings per acre; exclusive of sets, planting, and draining, which cost about as much more. Poling new ground is the heaviest expence; it will (if new poles are used) cost at least twenty-five pounds per acre. The best managers here set but two poles at each hill, (and where the bind is strong) but two binds upon each pole.

" The common price of what is provisionally called, 'looking after an acre of hop ground,' is from forty to forty-five shillings: this work only consists of digging, picking, cutting, poling, twigging, once hilling and hoeing, and poles stacking. Good managers add at least two hoeings more, which cost half a crown an acre each. Then there is the draining every other, or every third year, with fresh earth getting, catch poles sharping, carrying in, and setting, with many other little works, which are for the most part here done by the day. The men's wages are fourteen pence from Michaelmas to May-day, and eighteen pence from thence to Michaelmas again. It is to be observed, that the shopman has the grass that grows on the drains, with the broken pole ends, and often the binds. Upon taking an average of the expence of labourage of my hop grounds for four years, I find it cost me four pounds per acre; for the working part only. The poles, manure, rent, and tithe, about nine pounds ten ten shillings per acre; which brings a certain expence of thirteen pounds ten shillings per acre; if there is not a hop grown.

" The crops in this country, in the best years, are very small, compared with the Kentish plantations, and do not in the very best of years average eight hundred weight per acre; owing I apprehend more to the number of small planters, who have neither knowledge or purse necessary to this intricate and expensive culture, than the badness of the land. With respect to manures, the greater difficulty in the

the management of this plant, is to procure hops of a large size. The bind is easily forced by the use of rags, but they, if not properly used, will make the hops small. I apprehend the best way of using them, to prevent that evil, is not to lay more than eight hundred weight per acre, mixed with three or four cart loads of good virgin earth, of a light black soil, or strong land. This composition to be made at least six months before laying on, and turned two or three times, then laid upon the hills after the tying before Midsummer.

"I have used the scrapings and parings of oil leather, instead of rags mixed as above, and have found them excellent manure.

"Malt culm I have likewise used, and think it a good manure, and particularly so, where land is subject to the small snail or slug, which eat the young bind on its first appearance; for it sticks so fast to their slimy bodies, that they cannot creep over it to the bind. Where land is subject to grow small hops, I am well satisfied the best method, (where it can be got even at a very high rate) is to dig in, in winter, from twenty-five to thirty cart loads of good dung, and if it is not quite so rotten as to cut with a spade, I thing it is the better for strong land. If this method, with good drainage, and keeping the land clean from all kinds of weeds, has not the effect of making the hops a good size; I should apprehend the land is either not congenial to the growth of this plant, or otherwise has been planted too long, and wants laying down to rest.

"The worst evil that attends the culture of hops, is the smitt, which nobody seems properly to understand, and for which no effectual remedy has ever yet been found out; neither do I think it would tend to the profit of the planters, whatever it might do to the public at large, to have such a remedy, as either more than half the land must be laid down, or hops would want a market.

"I am afraid these few observations, from their being well known to every observant and practical hop-planter, will not be worth your acceptance; but if I can be of service to you in any future inquiries upon this, or any other business, I shall always be happen to give such assistance as my small experience and abilities enable me to give, and am with the greatest respect,

"SIR, Your most obedient humble Servant,

"MARTIN BOWER,

"*To Sir Richard Sutton, Bart.*"

P. 42. "*West Drayton, Feb.* 1, 1794. SIR,—I am favoured with yours, and in answer inform you, that the hop

hop plantations beginning at the north end of the county are chiefly situated in the following parishes:

Barnby-Moor,	East Drayton,	Bothamsell,
Tiln,	East Markham,	Walesby,
Lound,	West Markham,	Willoughby,
Welham,	Milnton,	Kirton,
Ordsall,	Tuxford,	Boughton,
Eaton,	Egmanton,	Ollerton,
Gamston,	Bevercoats,	Edwinstow,
Headon cum Upton,	Haughton,	Wellow,
Askham,	Elksley,	Eakring,
Woodcoats,	Southwell,	South Markham,
Rufford,	Halam,	Laxton.

"'There may be some single plantations in some other townships; but these are the principal.'"

LIQUORICE.—P. 28. *Liquorice*—was formerly much grown about Worksop, but is now entirely left off."

CULTIVATED HERBAGE.—P. 49. "The method I pursued last year in laying my land down with grass seeds was attended with great success. Instead of sowing my land with barley and seeds after turnips, as usual, after one ploughing, which was about the last week in April, I sowed half a peck of rape seed, mixed with it one stone of Dutch clover, and one of trefoil; the rape got sufficiently high to shade the young plants from the sun. About the second week in July were turned upon ten acres, one hundred and thirty wethers and ewes, part of which went fat to Rotherham market, about the 11th of September, and the remainder I should have sent the latter end of the month, had not mutton fallen in price."

This instance of practice is not noticed in the original Report, in 1794. It therefore probably took place, between that time and 1798.—See my WEST of ENGLAND; Ed. 1796.

GRASS LAND.—P. 29. "*Grass Lands* are employed more for feeding" (fatting) "than the dairy, except along the Soar, where, and in the towns on the south bank of the Trent, as far as Nottingham, viz. Thrumpton, Barton, Clifton, and Wilford, as well as at Attenborough, and Chilwell, on the opposite side of the river, are large dairies, milking from twenty to twenty-five cows, chiefly employed in making of cheese. The island between the towns of Averham, Kelham, Muskham, and Newark, is remarkably fine feeding land."

Grazing Grounds.—P. 43. "Mr. Turnell, of Stokeham, has a particular method of feeding which deserves to be mentioned. He feeds" (fats) "about eighty head of beasts a year, from twelve to twenty of his own breed. He always buys

buys in at spring, takes care to have twenty to thirty fresh beasts, or incalved heifers, mostly of both sorts, that are sure to go off before the middle of July; when he lays in, *i. e.* shuts up about forty acres, to finish or make fat all his beasts that went lean at Spring*. These go off in succession till Christmas. The land laid in (where good) will be very often ready to pasture again in six weeks."

Hay Grounds.—P. 42. "The grass grounds along the Trent, in the open townships, are generally shut up at Lady-day, some part opened for stinted pastures at old May-day, some kept for hay, and all commoned from old Lammas."

On *salting hay*, for sheep, see the head *Sheep*, ensuing.

Pasture Grounds.—P. 117. "Mr. Wright, of Ranby, in the Forest District, to destroy bracken or fern, a very troublesome weed there, uses the following method: He has at the end of a stick, a blade with dull edges; a woman uses this to strike the stems and bruise them, and will do several acres in a day: this is repeated two or three times in a summer; the next morning a gummy consistence is found to exsude, and the bracken gradually disappears."

CATTLE.—Nottinghamshire cannot be emphatically termed a cattle County. And it would seem, from Mr. L's account, to have no particular breed that it can call its own;—nor any prominent practice which requires to be detailed. We are therefore the less disappointed at finding a paucity of information, on this topic.

The notices adduced, being of too miscellaneous a texture to admit readily of analysis, I will here insert them as they occur in the volume.

P. 42. "Most farmers have some dairying keeping, from five or six to ten or twelve cows, in general perhaps eight cows to 200 acres, chiefly a woodland breed; but it is not their principal object, except about Fledborough, and from thence close along the Trent, down to Gainsborough, where

"* This practice agrees with that of fogging, mentioned in the Cardiganshire Report. Sir R. Sutton has tried it with success for keeping his stock in winter. Many years ago being in the practice of buying in Highland Scotch bullocks about October, which he began to kill for his family about that time twelvemonth, he used to give them the first winter straw and sometimes a little hay, and did not find them go on to his mind. It seemed indeed to be the opinion of the neighbourhood that they would not feed kindly. His bailiff falling into conversation with a Scotch drover, and telling him how he managed them, the drover told him he would spoil them if he gave them any dry meat at all. It would (as he expressed himself) dry them up. Since that they have never had any thing the first year but such fog as they could pick up, and have had a little hay to finish them, only when the weather has been very hard frost or snow."

where the numbers kept (especially at Fledborough) may run as high as thirty."——

"A good many young cattle are reared. In some places, particularly in the north clay, there is more feeding." (fatting.)

P. 123. "Few are reared in the Forest District. For feeding, after trying various sorts, Mr. Wright prefers the good sort of Irish cattle. He would not buy any that would not feed to fifty or sixty stone, of fourteen pounds.

"Not many black cattle are bred in *the Trent Bank District*. On the Soar bank the breed of cows used to be indifferent. Of late they are got into a pretty good long-horned breed. They rear almost all their female calves; which, when young, are pastured amongst the sheep, and at three years old are taken into the dairy, and the old ones fed off.

"Some persons have improved their stock by the Dishley breed. Mr. Breedon, of Ruddington; Mr. Bettison, of Holme Pierrepont; with three others, bought the Garrick bull, at Mr. Fowler of Rollwright's sale, for two hundred and five guineas. The bull called Young Garrick was bought by Mr. Rowland, of Stamford, in September last, for one hundred and fifty guineas. A bull was bought at the sale of Mr. Paget, of Ibstock, in Leicestershire, for four hundred guineas; of which Mr. Sandy, of Holme Pierrepont, had a sixth part.

"Mr. Bettison, of Holme Pierrepont, observes that much improvement may be made in the breed of beasts and black horses in this part of the county. For such as are the occupiers of small farms, and desirous to improve their stock, and not able, the most obvious mode presents itself for the landlord to form a committee out of the most intelligible class of tenants, who shall procure either by *hire* or *purchase*, such and so many male stock, of different sorts, as shall in their judgment be most proper for the improvement of different breeds. The landlord to be answerable in the first instance, for such *hiring* or purchase, and the tenant in proportion to the quantities of their respective stocks, contribute so much in return annually to the landlord, and according to chances in general to reimburse him with interest.

"The beasts reared in *the Clay District* are generally of a poor coarse kind, commonly called wood land beasts. Some gentlemen and principal farmers are endeavouring to introduce a better sort.

"Peter Pegge Burnel, Esq. of Winkborn, a gentleman very understanding in husbandry, keeps the Yorkshire short horned breed, and computes that they are worth at least,

as

as much at three years old, as the old breed at four. Mr. Turnell of Stokeham rears the same.

"*In the Vale of Belvoir*—A good many beasts are still reared, though that business is on the decline; a mixture of the long and short horned breed which generally wants improvement.

"*In the Lime and Coal District*—The black cattle are very indifferent; a mixture of long and short horned woodland beasts."

P. 165. (Extract from Mr. Calvert's letter)—"I am sorry I cannot give you so much intelligence upon the dairy as I wish to have done, not having had sufficient early notice of the enquiry, as it would require a due observation for some years, to come at the production of a dairy farm, people not being in the habit of either keeping clear accounts or burthening their memories with the profits or losses incident thereto. At Fledbro the farms are not very large, perhaps from eighty to one hundred and fifty acres in a farm; the principal occupation is confined to the dairy, though some of them feed very good bullocks thereon. The most correct account I can make out, respecting the production of cheese is, that one cow will produce about three hundred pounds weight of cheese, upon an average, during the summer season.

"Calves are much better fed" (fatted) "upon linseed pottage mixed with new milk, in the proportion of one third of good mucilage to two-thirds milk; they thrive much better, rest a great deal, and the veal is generally finer; at least the butchers who purchase mine thus fed, tell me so. I have also bred" (reared) "calves in the same manner, only with this difference, when three weeks old, we give them old milk instead of new, and the same quantity of the linseed, viz. one-third. The linseed is put into cold water, and heated over a slow fire (one pint to two gallons) for two or three hours, scarcely suffered to boil, then passed through a hair sieve. Warming the linseed saves the trouble of warming the milk."

SHEEP.—*Breeds.*—On this subject Mr. Lowe is commendably explicit.—P. 124. *Sherwood Forest.* "The old Forest breed are a small polled breed (though some are horned) with grey faces and legs; the fleeces of which may run from thirteen to eighteen to the tod of twenty-eight pounds; the wool fine, the price of 1792 being from thirty-four to thirty-six shillings; that of 1793, from twenty-nine to thirty-one shillings. The carcases fat, from seven to nine pounds a quarter. In the inclosed farms, the breed has been much improved of late years, by various crosses; sometimes the Lincolnshire pasture sort, but of late more the new Leicestershire, or Dishley."

Vale

Vale of Trent.—P. 126. "The sheep have been much improved for many years past, by tups of the Lincolnshire and new Leicestershire sort; but of late many more of the latter. It is become of late a principal object of attention, and many breeders are spreading the improvement, by letting out their tups, some at as high a price as one hundred guineas. Amongst other, Mr. Breedon of Ruddington; Messrs. Stubbings and Bettison, of Holme Pierrepont; Mr. Deverell, of Clifton; Mr. Buckley, of Normanton Hill; and Mr. Maltby, of Hoveringham, are noted."

North Clays.—P. 129. "The fallow sheep are a poor breed; a mixture generally between the forest and Lincolnshire pasture sheep. In the inclosures many farmers have raised their breed, by getting more into the Lincolnshire, and of late into the new Leicestershire sort; particularly in Thurgarton Hundred, adjoining to the Trent Bank country. Mr. Turnell, of Stokebam, breeds in the same manner as Mr. Wright in the forest, viz. large Northumberland ewes with Dishley tups.

"*In the Vale of Belvoir*—the sheep are much improved of late by the Leicestershire cross."——

"*In the Lime and Coal District*—As to sheep, an improved breed has not been much attended to.

"On the Limestone, pretty good ewes, fat, weigh from fifteen to sixteen pounds a quarter; wethers, (if not mixed with the forest breed) up to twenty pounds; fleeces, about seven to the tod; wool inferior to the forest; last year about twenty-four shillings. The sheep formerly consisted of the small forest, and the large Gritstone breed, which is now giving way to that of the Leicestershire. The coal land is much subject to rot sheep; lime stone much sounder.

"Mr. Chambers has known hundreds cured of themselves on limestone land not eaten too bare; their livers healed again*."—This is highly interesting information.

Further on the *Rot.*—P. 127. "Mr. Sikes always keeps *salted hay*; has standing racks for his sheep, which he fills the beginning of September, and keeps on till Christmas: two pecks of salt are used to a load. He once led his clover, supposed to be quite spoiled with wet, and salted it. He put one hundred and twenty hogs (*i. e.* lambs after five or six months) to turnips, with his hay in racks, in a very wet season. He did not lose one by the water. They eat every morsel of it." This

"* This information is very valuable, as it leads to a discovery of what may possibly prove the cure of this disease in other counties. Water impregnated with the fixed acid of lime in proper quantities, with change of pasture as soon as the disease appeared, might remove it.—Mr. *W. Fox.*"

This strikes forcibly as a probably valuable practice.

RABBITS.—P. 131. "There were formerly many rabbet warrens in the Forest District. Those at Farnsfield, Clumber Park, Beskwood Park, Sanson Wood, and Haywood Oaks, have been destroyed. The following remain: Clipston, Peasefield, Inkersall, Oxton, Blidworth, Calverton, and Newsted. The land of some parts is so bad, that it is not likely to answer if taken up for husbandry. Some of it indeed has been tried and thrown up again."

SWINE.—P. 131. "Hogs are no great object in this county except for home use; no hams, bacon, or pork being sent out of it to my knowledge. The breed for bacon is the old lopped-eared sort. For pork, the Chinese dunky, or swing tailed sort. A mixture with the old sort has been much introduced."

POULTRY.—P. 131. "Poultry has never been made an object of particular attention. Few turkies are bred. Fowls are commonly of a bad breed, generally the game sort; which are raised as much for the diversion of cock-fighting as the table. Geese are reared for home use only, or the neighbouring markets, not to be sent away in droves, as from many northern counties."

PIGEONS —P. 132. "*In the Clay District*—more pigeons are kept than are probably in any part of England. It is a well attested fact, that some years since, seven hundred dozen were sold on one market day at Tuxford, to a higler from Huntingdonshire, at the price of sixty-three pounds, or guineas."

BEES.—P. 132. "Bees are very little attended to in this county. Indeed the climate of England seems very ill adapted to them, from its variableness. The bees are tempted out to their destruction by the fine warm days, which we often have in winter. Of particular persons who have applied themselves to the keeping of bees, I have observed the stocks, of late years, to have been much diminished, perhaps from above twenty to under ten."

PROFITS of FARMING.—P. 16. "The expence and profit depend so much on the particular management of individuals, that I cannot pretend to enter into the subject."

This brief reply, to an ill judged head of enquiry, shows, among many other instances, as my readers must now be well aware, the good sense of the Reporter.

LEICESTERSHIRE.

LEICESTERSHIRE.

THE County of Leicester occupies the center of the MIDLAND DEPARTMENT, of which it forms a *fair* specimen. Its outlines are almost uniformly filled with what I term VALE LANDS; and those, mostly, of a superior quality; saving the extraordinary pile of *mountain materials*,—the CHARNWOOD HILLS,—which are situated in its northwestern quarter. Its most western margin forms a part of the *Midland District*, which has been repeatedly mentioned, aforegoing.

"GENERAL VIEW

OF THE

AGRICULTURE

OF THE COUNTY OF

LEICESTER.

WITH

OBSERVATIONS ON THE MEANS OF THEIR IMPROVEMENT.

BY JOHN MONK,

(Late 19th Light Dragoons)

OF BEARS-COMBE, NEAR KNIGHTSBRIDGE, DEVON.

1794."

THIS is one of the original Reports which have not been reprinted; and it might, without intending to give offence to its Author, be deemed one of the least interesting of those sketches. Why a gentleman, from the western confine of Devonshire should have been appointed to explain to the Board of Agriculture, and the public, the rural affairs of a Midland County, in which it would seem, from the internal evidence of the Report, he was a stranger, and who, judging on the same evidence, possessed no one superior qualification

tion that is requisite to the task,—is to be looked for among the numberless acts of folly which have been heaped up, by the conductor, or conductors, of the literary labors of the Board.

Seeing the inconsiderable quantity of matter which can claim admission into this Register, it may appear to be unnecessary to reduce it to analytical arrangement. But, without this, it would not assimilate with the other materials of the volume, in the general Table of Contents.

Number of pages seventyfive.

NATURAL ECONOMY.

I FIND nothing of sufficient intelligence, on this division of my general subject, to require a place, here.

POLITICAL ECONOMY.

APPROPRIATION.—Mr. Monk speaks, at some length, and with much propriety, on the inclosure of Charnwood Forest, and Ashby Wolds. But they are, now, no longer a disgrace, to the country.

P. 46. "Waste lands amount nearly to 20,000 acres, and the whole capable of considerable improvement; which, in their present state, are of very little value, being depastured with a bad sort of sheep and some young cattle, unrestrained as to quantity."

In the Appendix, the Reporter has inserted "Particulars of the Lordships;" being an alphabetical List of the several (query, the whole?) of the Lordships of the County; showing, in columns, their names, the number of acres, whether inclosed or not, (the dates of inclosure being added to many of them) and the names of their several proprietors, or principal proprietors; but without drawing from them any general information.

By whom this table was formed (it could scarcely be done by a stranger) does not appear. If nearly accurate, it might form a valuable article in a topographical history of the County;—as a similar statement of the appropriation of the several Counties of the kingdom, or the island, would be to political economy.

P. 45. "Tenants are partial to inclosures, because they are tithe-free (in all the new inclosures they throw a certain quantity of land in lieu of tithes), and they can cultivate their

their estates without fear of a drawback on that head; and another advantage is their lying so very compact."

POOR RATES.—For the effect of the *stocking manufacture* on the poor rates, see the head *Manufactures*, ensuing.

TITHES.—In Bills of Appropriation, the tithes have generally been *substituted* by *land*. See *Appropriation*, aforegoing.

MANUFACTURES.—P. 56. "Manufactures of woollen yarn and stockings are lately much increased, and the landed interest much benefited thereby. Within these few years cotton mills also have been erected by Mr. Wilkes, which employ a great number of the industrious poor of all ages.

"A gentleman informed me, in some few parishes the poor-rates were considerably increased of late years, and, from a pretty attentive observation he had made of the habits and manners of the poorer classes, that a very small proportion indeed of expence was to be attributed to the sober industrious poor, whether labourers or manufacturers. The immoral were generally idle and profligate, and there were now few villages where their bad habits were not kept in play by the facility with which they could spend their earnings in those public nuisances to every manufacturing village (in particular), the alehouses; and those were the persons who upon every little occasion fell upon the parish."

Thus, even while manufactures florish, they are sapping the foundation of the "landed interest."

PROVISIONS.—P. 49. "The price of provisions is regulated a good deal by distant markets, Smithfield, Birmingham, &c. The average price of beef (prime) for some years about 3¾*d.* mutton 4¼*d.* veal 4*d.* lamb 4½*d.* pork 4½*d.* bacon 8*d.* poultry of all sorts dear; fish very scarce, very indifferent, and very dear; cheese 5*d.* *per* pound; butter according to the seasons; wheat flour (the general bread flour) best at this time, 2*s.* 6*d.* *per* stone (about two years ago it was 1*s.* 9*d.*); fourths now 1*s.* 10*d.* *per* stone; barley about 42*s.* *per* quarter; oats from 28*s.* to 34*s.* *per* quarter; hay 5*l.* to 6*l.* 10*s.* a ton; straw from 2*l.* 10*s.* to 3*l.* 10*l.* *per* ton; coals at the pit 4½*d.* *per* 112 lb."

ROADS.—Speaking of waste lands, Mr. M. says, p. 48. "Some of the roads, being thrown out upon the inclosures thirty feet wider than is necessary, may almost be deemed waste. It is true the grass is eat up by sheep, &c. turned on for that purpose; but the value of it in its present state is very little to what it would be if taken into the adjoining fields, and cultivated in a proper manner. It is, besides, very inconvenient, and very unlike a good farmer, to have his

his cattle running about the high roads. Many score acres (taking the country through) are wasted owing to this slovenly practice."

The practice is certainly *slovenly*, but it is, unfortunately, *legal*, though very *unwise*.

Mr. Monk's strictures, on the *cross roads* of Leicestershire, are rather too severe. The practice of the County, in this respect, however, is (or was) no doubt reprehensible. I insert his observations the rather, as similar instances of negligence are to be seen, in other Counties of the kingdom.

P. 54. " There are many individuals, who have been at a great expence in repairing the cross roads through their estates; but in many parts of the county they are infamously bad. Indeed, great part of them are not to be called roads, for they are nothing more than passing through the different closes (fields) upon the turf, and in many of them not the least track of a wheel is to be seen for miles together. In riding a few miles, you have an intolerable number of gates to open ; and in most of the cross roads it is impossible to pass with a carriage.

" I viewed with regret a number of their pastures, most shamefully cut to pieces with waggons, &c. through which those (what are called) roads led ; for, when one rut gets rather deep, the carters immediately take a fresh path, and so on till the field is injured to a very great degree. There is a field near Leicester, and through it a road, or rather path, leading to a village, which is so shamefully cut up that it is of no use whatever as a pasture ; and what is still more extraordinary, this field runs parallel with the high road to a great length, and the passengers cannot possibly save twenty yards by going through it. This is by no means an uncommon thing. It is impossible to estimate the hundreds of acres spoiled by this shameful practice. Why not make proper roads ? I am certain it would be attended with much less expence to the landholder, and would be much more convenient both to the traveller and the farmer. The former would have the satisfaction of a good road, and and the latter the pleasure of seeing his cattle graze in sound pastures, undisturbed by passengers."

MARKETS.—The Reporter mentions, and has copied, some Resolutions that were entered into, by the occupiers of the Midland District, respecting the sale of produce, by *legal weights and measures*. The result, however, could not be well ascertained, at the time of making his Report ; as the Resolutions were not entered into, before the autumn of 1793.—See Mr. PITT's Report, ensuing, respecting those Resolutions.

SOCIETIES.

SOCIETIES.—P. 63 "There is a society which meets annually on the fourth Wednesday in October at Leicester. It consists of about one hundred members. The Earl of Moira is the President; William Pochin, Esq. M. P. and J. Peach Hungerford, Esq. Vice-Presidents. At the last meeting, an experimental farm was fixed upon, which they are about to take in Queniborrow lordship. This farm is to be under the direction of the first and most practical men in the county; and I have no doubt but that, in the course of a few years, many very valuable experiments will be tried, and much light thrown on the most important branches of agriculture."

RURAL ECONOMY.

TENANTED ESTATES.

MANAGERS.—P. 60. "Nothing has retarded improvements more than noblemen and gentlemen of large fortunes employing stewards who are ignorant of the principles of agriculture; they ought always to be men well versed in the science as well as practice of agriculture. This is not generally the case (I do not speak merely as to Leicestershire): therefore a spirited tenant, who would improve his landlord's property as well as his own, is prevented from exercising his talents to advantage. This is a subject of the utmost consequence, and cannot be too much attended to. Surely the barely receiving the rents, transmitting the same to the landlord, and keeping the accompts, are not all the requisites of an agent, where so much is at stake."

TENANCY.—P. 58. "Very few leases are granted, and those few decrease daily."

WOODLANDS.

ON this subject, I find little to extract. Leicestershire is not a wooded County. And, Charnwood Forest excepted, there are but few lands within it that are well suited to planting. Fortunately, therefore, the rage for planting sites which are fitted by nature for agricultural purposes, has not, I believe, wormed its mischievous way into Leicestershire.

Mr.

Mr. Bakewell's plot of *willows* are alone entitled to notice.—P. 45. "Mr. Bakewell has different small plantations of the *Dutch* willow in several parts of the estate, one of which he cuts down annually at seven years growth; they run very long, and some of them very large, and are split and made use of for posts, gates, rails, &c. for which they are very excellent. Mr. Bakewell uses no other kind of wood for those purposes; and several people, I observed, are following his ornamental and useful method."

AGRICULTURE.

FARMS.—P. 9. "The general *size of farms* is from 100 to 200 acres, though there are many much more extensive and many much under 100 especially in the neighbourhood of great market-towns, which are occupied by tradesmen or manufacturers. The greatest improvements are made on large farms, from 200 to 500 acres; many of which are occupied by the proprietors themselves, and chiefly in the northern part of the county."

Laying out Farms.—P. 45. "The size of the new inclosures depends a great deal upon fancy, and the size of the farms. They run from five to forty acres, but in general are from seven to ten or twelve acres. In the old inclosures they are of all sizes, from the half-acre homestead, up to one hundred acres. It is the opinion of the best farmers, that from eight to twelve acres is the best size, and the most convenient. Mr. Bakewell is certain, that fifty acres of pasture ground divided into five inclosures will go as far in grazing cattle as sixty acres all in one piece; this was the opinion likewise of several capital *graziers* I conversed with on the subject."—These remarks apply to *Grass Lands*, chiefly.

OBJECTS of HUSBANDRY.—P. 9. "The land is employed for the most part in pasture for sheep, dairies, feeding neat cattle, a considerable part for breeding horses, and a proportionable quantity in meadow for hay for winter use. The farms employed chiefly for dairies, of which there are a great number, have always land in tillage to produce straw, turnips, &c. for the cows in winter. A farm of 200 acres may perhaps have about thirty or forty acres of various sorts of grain, &c. Those parishes where the land is of an inferior quality, have a greater proportion of arable ground than where the soil is richer.

"About Ashby de la Zouch, and Loughborough, three parts in four are in pasture. Near Melton Mowbray, there is is very little arable, not more than one acre to thirty. Market Harborough has also very little arable. The pasture near Lutterworth is in proportion of eight to one. At Hinckley, five parts in six are in pasture."

These are appropriate remarks; as tending to give a *general idea* of the existing state of Agriculture, in a County or District; and to enable a reader to enter into *details*, with more pleasure and advantage.

P. 58. "From the best information I could get, I understood that not *one half* of the corn consumed in the county was cultivated in it."

PLAN of MANAGEMENT.—Having said a few words, on the "rotation of crops," Mr. M. concludes—p. 13,—"The above are the general rotations of crops; but in the practice of individuals they vary very considerably, and in no part of the country is there any regular system of cropping."

IMPLEMENTS.—In this Report, are inserted "descriptions of implements of husbandry made by Mr. Hanford of Hathern, Leicestershire," together with engraved sketches of some of them. But I perceive nothing of peculiar excellence, that is *new*, in any of them.

MANURES.—*Bones.*—P. 19. "Mr. Paget recommends, instead of being at the expence and trouble of grinding the bones, to mix them in a heap with lime, which will in a short time reduce the bones to powder."

Gypsum.—P. 19. Gypsum is found in great quantities in many parts of the county, and has been tried by several gentlemen for various crops; but, from the best information I could get, it is the general opinion that it will not answer."

CARROTS.—In the following notice, we find a few novel ideas, that may be useful to those who, on suitable sites, persevere in the carrot culture.—Who is Mr. Baker? What are *his* soil and situation?

P. 15. "*Carrots* are very little cultivated. Mr. Bakewell cultivates a few for his horses, &c. Mr. Baker used to cultivate them, but of late years has left them off, owing to the heavy expence attending them, by reason of his land running so much to weed. He is a great advocate for their culture upon land suitable. When Mr. Baker cultivated carrots, he used to cut the tops off the latter end of June, and make them into hay, which thought, I believe, is original. He informed me, that the tops of a good acre of carrots would produce *four tons* of excellent hay, (the trouble in making of which is little more than clover-hay), and that all kinds of cattle were very fond, and throve very fast on it. I objected to cutting off the tops, as it might tend to diminish the weight of the root (I know it will with potatoes);

potatoes); but Mr. Baker was not of my opinion, as he always observed the tops to shoot out very luxuriant immediately after they were cut over. The tops were *cut over* with a scythe, and care taken not to injure the crown of the plants by mowing them off too close. On mentioning this to a friend, who is curious in the cultivation of his garden, he is of opinion, that, instead of decreasing the weight of the root, it will increase the weight, as he always cuts off the top of his parsnips, for the very purpose of increasing the size of the root, which he always found to answer. He thinks the carrot and parsnip alike in point of growth.

"The carrot-tops must be taken off the ground to be made into hay. Mr. Baker *used* to give his carrots to all kinds of cattle, particularly horses, and found them very excellent for mares and foals. Mr. Baker preserves his carrots in the following manner: he digs a trench about three feet wide, and eight or ten inches deep. The carrots being dug up, and their tops (which are given to cattle, &c.) cut off, they are placed as close to each other (perpendicular) as possible in the trench. When the trench is full, they are covered over with straw, and over the straw the mould that comes out of the trench, by which means they are preserved from the frost, &c. By this method they are perfectly good till May or June. He informed me that his carrots had been viewed at different parts of the winter by Lord Winchelsea, who found them equally as good and juicy as when first taken up. If carrots are preserved in sand, Mr. Baker says, they will lose their juices, and become tough and stringy; and, if preserved in straw, they will generally rot. Care must be taken, when carrots are wanted for use, to stop the hole of the trench close from the weather."

GRASS LANDS.—A *new* species of grass land produce.—P. 57. "*Catsup.* I was informed, by some of the inhabitants of Market Harborough, that within these few years there has been an immense quantity of catsup made in the villages round that town; that the quantity of mushrooms in the old pasture-grounds was incredible; and that they were certain no less than 200 hogsheads had been sent from that town this last season."

LIVESTOCK. On this most prominent subject, in the Rural Economy of Leicestershire, it may *now* be said, very little that is new,—(either instructive or interesting)—appears.—Even at the time of reporting, nearly the same observation might have been truly made. The public being, then in possession of digested details of the improvement, and existing state, of the several species, by a *resident*,—

resident,—the loose memoranda of a *stranger* might well have been deemed too inconsiderable for publication.

CATTLE.—P. 29. "In conversation with Mr. Bakewell respecting Mr. Paget's bull having had but few cows, I was of opinion that if Mr. Paget had fixed his price at five or ten guineas a cow, he would have found it answer better than fixing so high a price as twenty-five guineas; but Mr. Bakewell says, the only way to improve the breed of cattle is to keep up the price; for, if the price is low, people send any kind of cows, and if the produce fails, the bull is blamed; but, if the price is high, they are particular, and send none but the very best, which is the only method to improve the breed. The same argument, he says, holds good with all other kinds of cattle."—that is to say,—livestock—domestic animals.

The following pleasant sort of chit-chat information may tend to show, either the extraordinary ignorance of the Leicestershire breeders, in general; or the *extravagant* ideas of the enlightened few;—or both.

P. 29. "To shew the difference of judgement in respect to the value of cattle, Mr. Bakewell informed me, that some years since he used to attend Loughborough Tup-market, where he had a ram which he let for twenty-five guineas. Soon after the agreement, another farmer wanted to purchase this ram, and Mr. Bakewell (in joke) asked him twenty-five shillings for it. The farmer offered eighteen; and at last they parted for two shillings. I myself saw a heifer sold at Mr. Pearce's sale, near Norhampton, for eighty guineas; and a few days after, as she was driven through Leicester, a party of farmers standing together valued her at about eight pounds. I was likewise informed, that Mr. Bakewell had let a bull to a gentleman for fifty guineas for the season. The gentleman dying in the interim, and the executors not knowing any thing of this transaction, sold the bull by auction with the rest of the cattle. When the season was over, Mr. Bakewell sent for his bull; and, after investigating the matter, found, to his great surprise, that the bull had been sold to a butcher for about eight pounds, who had killed it, and sold it for 2½*d.* *per* pound. Mr. Bakewell in course applied to the executors for the value, which was fifty guineas for the season (the stipulated agreement) and 200 guineas for the bull. The executors refused payment, thinking, 'that as the bull was sold by public auction before a great number of farmers, and many of them thought to be men of judgement, for only eight pounds, it was an imposition.' Mr. Bakewell was therefore obliged to bring an action for the amount; and people appearing as witnesses on the trial who were acquainted

quainted with this breed, and making oath that Mr. Bakewell had not over-valued his bull, a verdict was given in favour of Mr. Bakewell to the full amount, with costs of suit.

"The person that gave me this history disliked the long-horned breed so much, that he would not accept of Mr. Paget's bull (which was of the same breed, though it sold for 400 guineas) if he might have him for nothing."

P. 34. "The following are some of the particulars of Mr. Paget's sale, which will shew the high estimation this breed is held in.

"First day's sale, November 14, 1793.

		Guineas.
"Lot 8,	Short Tail, by Shakespear, bought at Mr. Fowler's	38
9,	Eyebright, by a Bull bred by Mr. Varnam	51
14,	Strawberry, by a Dishley bull	31
16,	Brindled Eyebright	33
26,	Penn	35
29,	Young Dandy	30
30,	Brindled-Finch-Tidy	29
	Bulls and bull-calves.	
34,	Shakespear (bred by the late Mr. Fowler), by Shakespear, off Young Nell. Whoever buys this lot, the seller makes it a condition that he shall have the privilege of having two cows bulled by him yearly	400
35,	Bull-calf, by Lot 34	23
37,	A ditto, by ditto	31
39,	A ditto, by ditto	31

"Second Day's Sale.

"Lot 45,	One three years old heifer	70
47,	One ditto	32
48,	One ditto	35
52,	One ditto	35
55,	One two years old heifer	25
57,	One ditto	60
58,	One ditto	84
60,	One ditto	29
61,	One ditto	25
64,	One ditto	27

"The whole of the foregoing heifers are by lot 34; and, together with the cows, have been bulled by him, except lot 52, which has been bulled by a son of Garrick, *off* lot 8."

DAIRY.

DAIRY.—P. 43. "In respect to the *grand secret* of making Stilton cheese, I should have left the county without acquiring the process, if it had not been for the politeness and attention of Major Cheselden, of Somerby, who, upon my acquainting him with my disappointment, kindly undertook to procure it for me from one of his tenants, who was among the first for making it. The following is the receipt.

"'Take the night's cream, and put it to the morning's new milk, with the rennet; when the curd is come, it is not to be broke, as is done with other cheeses; but take it out with a soil-dish altogether, and place it in a sieve to drain gradually; and, as it drains, keep gradually pressing it till it becomes firm and dry; then place it in a wooden hoop; afterwards to be kept dry on boards, turned frequently, with cloth binders round it, which are to be tightened as occasion requires.

"'N. B. The dairy-maid must not be disheartened if she does not succeed perfectly in her first attempt.'

"In the dairies which I visited, the cheeses, after being taken out of the wooden hoop, were bound tight round with a cloth, which cloth was changed every day until the cheese became firm enough to support itself; after the cloth was taken off, they were rubbed every day all over, for two or three months, with a brush; and, if the weather is damp or moist, twice a day (and, even before the cloth was taken off, the top and bottom was well rubbed every day)."—If Stilton cheeses are not *pressed*, in the vat or hoop, the Reporter, surely, should have said so.

On SHEEP,—even on "Leicester sheep"—either "old" or "new,"—I do not perceive a syllable that is entitled to extraction.

SWINE.—P. 37. "Richard Astley, Esq. has a very fine sort, which he sends to different parts of England. The boars serve sows at half a guinea each; and Mr. Bakewell, in order to make people particular in sending good sows, wishes Mr. Astley to increase the price to a guinea; the produce Mr. Astley sells (for breeding) at five guineas each, weaning old and barrow pigs at one guinea. They are very broad over the back, with very little offal, and have a great propensity to fatten."

"GENERAL VIEW

OF THE

AGRICULTURE

OF THE COUNTY OF

LEICESTER.

WITH

OBSERVATIONS ON THE MEANS OF ITS IMPROVEMENT.

PUBLISHED BY ORDER OF

THE BOARD OF AGRICULTURE

AND INTERNAL IMPROVEMENT.

BY WILLIAM PITT,

OF WOLVERHAMPTON.

1809."

THIS is a second Report of LEICESTERSHIRE, in which, however, are incorporated some extracts from Mr. MONK'S Report; so that, in this case, the matter of the "*original*" sketch would not have been, entirely lost to the public, as it would in other instances, without my assistance.

On Mr. Pitt's QUALIFICATIONS, as a Reporter of Rural Affairs, I have touched, in the first article of the present volume; and I have little or nothing to add, in this place.—His sentiments, as I have before intimated, are not always those of a maturely experienced practical husbandman. Yet we are assured that he has had "twentyfour years of experience upon a considerable scale."

The account given of his mode of survey, in this instance, is more satisfactory, than in that of Staffordshire. He had repeatedly *visited*, at least, the County of Leicester, from 1797 to 1807; and, in 1807, he would seem to have examined it, as a *tourist*, with some attention. He gives copious accounts, in the *journal* manner, of a variety of considerable farms; and has inserted *travelling notes* (in my own manner—see the EASTERN DEPARTMENT, for a specimen) on traversing different lines of road, in the County.

To

To the matter thus personally collected, Mr. Pitt has added extracts from the writings and the parole communications, of others;—chiefly, from those of three informants, whose ideas are nearly of equal estimation; although they appear to have been drawn from three distinct sources; namely, *reading*, *hearing*, and *imagination*.

Mr. AINSWORTH, who was formerly a gardener, at Little Glenn; but who, in 1807, had retired from business to Leicester, is evidently bewildered in the labyrinths of ancient lore, and modern philosophy.

Mr. FERRIMAN, in one place styled the *reverend*, but of what *church*, or where resident, is not said,—appears to have *assisted* at the *conversations* of the initiated, in the mysteries of breeding. And

DOCTOR DARWIN (long known in the Midland Counties, as a wit, and to the public, as a flowery poet);—who writes poetic imagery in prose; which Mr. Pitt, no doubt, quoted with a fellow feeling.

Judging from the selections which the Reporter has made, it really does appear, to me, that the quotees, here named, and incessantly brought forward, were equally deficient in practical knowledge, belonging to the subjects on which they were writing, or communicating *

Nevertheless, when men of superior natural abilities apply their talents, though it may be merely for amusement, to particular subjects, it is *reasonable* to *expect* that they should elicit some new or useful ideas concerning them. I will therefore pay the required attention to what Mr. Pitt may have drawn from the sources above mentioned; as well as to the more radical information which he has collected from practical men of the higher class, with whom he occasionally conversed.

With materials thus gathered together, and with extracts from Mr. MONK'S Report, and a few, from my MIDLAND COUNTIES (by way, it would seem, of preserving them †) Mr. Pitt has filled an ample octavo volume.

The following is Mr. P's own account of assistance received.—

* I think it right to take this peculiarly apt opportunity of intimating (what I have long been convinced of) that writers of this class, namely those who, with an easy confidence, and a plausibility of manner, deal out bold, unqualified, and uncorroborated assertions, on subject which they have not maturely studied,—are capable of leading others, who have no more experience than themselves, into errors of the most mischievous tendency.

† But as well, let it be put, might needles be preserved in a hay rick,—pearls in a shifting sea beach,—or diamonds in a mountain of rubbish.

ceived.—P. iv. "To the Agents of the Duke of Rutland and the Earl of Moira, I am much obliged for their liberality and candour: the latter Nobleman, who had been apprized of the business, had directed every assistance to be afforded, and I was attended by the farming Agent through the neighbouring part of the county; but his Lordship has, upon all occasions, encouraged and patronised every public and private proposal, having for its object the extension and improvement of the commerce, manufactures, or agriculture of the country.

"To Mr. Monk's Report I am indebted for such matter as it contained within the present plan, and to many other respectable gentlemen, for their communications; and have farther to express my acknowledgments for the liberality and hospitality I experienced in the county.

"From a gentlemen of the name of Ainsworth, who formerly resided at Glen-parva, and since at Leicester, I have received much valuable matter; and he deserves great credit for his ingenuity, public spirit, good intentions, and the labour he has bestowed, without expectation, or hope of reward. I have freely used his communications, and shall only premise, that he has not been a practical farmer but on a small scale, that he has had considerable experience in gardening, that his observations are freely made on objects as they strike him, without prejudice, and from his own conclusions; but where I think he has been carried rather too far by theory, I have endeavoured to counteract his observations by such remarks as have occurred to me on the particular subjects.

"To the Rev. Robert Ferryman I am also obliged for much information on the subject of live-stock, and other matters therewith connected, and for tracing the progress and means used in their improvement, which he was well enabled to do from a personal intimacy with the county, and with many active and respectable breeders and improvers of land and stock; upon the whole, the information obtained, and here detailed, has been the result of my own observations, or communicated from the most capable and respectable authorities; and I hope it may, in some degree, answer the expectation, and meet the approbation of the Board, of the spirited breeders and improvers of Leicestershire, and of others interested in the improvement of agriculture and live stock."

Touching the AUTHORSHIP of the volume before me, little of praise, and much of censure, attaches to it. Mr. P., it is true, makes an apology for its defects.—P. vi. "Some of the subjects are treated in a manner rather desultory

desultory and unconnected, for which I hope the Board and the public will accept of the following apology; the information was received, and the observations made, at different times, and committed to paper; sometimes when an article was supposed finished, fresh matter came forward, which was thought too important to be omitted, and this repeatedly; so, that to have made it appear regular and systematic, the writer might have had it to recast several times; he has therefore been obliged, in some degree, to sacrifice regularity and system to matter of fact and general utility."

This apology, however, (ingenuous and commendable as it is) only adds to the reader's apprehension, that a similar kind of laxity, and want of patient attention, and sedulous deliberation, which the digestion and revision of the materials have experienced, may have prevailed in collecting them.—The quotations are generally loose, and *slovenly* in the extreme. Even those that are intended to be literal, are often stumbling blocks to the reader. For although the commencement may be *marked*, their terminations are frequently not to be found;—the Reporter's own remarks, or those of some other hand being *confounded* with them.—The repetitions are numerous, and the typographical errors without number*. How disgraceful must such a publication appear, in the eye of the public, to the *administration* of the Board of Agriculture †.

On the whole, however, I have pleasure in saying—Mr. Pitt's Report of Leicestershire, and particularly his journals, whether of enquiry or travelling, will generally be found interesting, to those who read for *amusement*. His manner is superior to that of most of the literary corps of the Board. What his Report contains of *instruction* I will here *preserve*, for the use of the agricultural public:—such parts of it, I mean to say, as are not already before them, in a more detailed and digested form. The eastern and southern quarters of Leicestershire were less the subjects of my

* So very numerous, indeed, that I have not deemed them an object of correction.

† Mr Ainsworth's paper, on the principles of vegetation, which had evidently, and properly, been intended to appear as an *appendix* to the volume,—and, in the table of contents, is inserted as if it were, *there*, actually standing,—is found at its commencement; not only in the place, but under the title of an "*introduction*" to the work! while some preliminary "hints on vegetation," by the President of the Board,—intended, no doubt, to whet the appetites of Mr. A's readers,—stands like a portico without a temple, at the close of the volume.—*This*, surely, must have been done, *in sport*.

my own examinations, than the western and central parts of it; and; concerning the former, I shall *hope* to find, in Mr. Pitt's Report, much valuable matter for extraction.

The number of pages—four hundred and one.

A map of the County, and several engravings of implements, a farmyard, &c.

SUBJECT THE FIRST.

NATURAL ECONOMY.

EXTENT.—P. 1. "Its greatest length from the south of Lutterworth to the north part of the vale of Belvoir is 45 miles, and the greatest breadth from Netherseal in the west, to Wymondham or Easton Magna in the east, is upwards of 40 miles; its mean diameter is about 30 miles; and it contains about 816 square miles, and 522,240 acres."

SOILS.—P. 3. "This county has no surface soil that can properly be denominated clay or sand; it has no chalk; and its peat bogs having been long since drained, are now become a meadow soil, being a compost of peat and sediment; the peat originally formed by aquatic vegetation, and the sediment brought down by streams and rain water from the upland."

P. 4. "The nature of the soil is very liable to vary much in short distances, respecting its strong or friable qualities: from Tamworth to Market Bosworth, I found light loam on gravel and sand, then strong loam on clay; past Orton-on-the-hill, soil thin, poor, harsh and cold, then a deeper but harsh clay loam; Welsborough, high sound land; Bosworth to Hinckley, various, generally sound and good; about Hinckley, a good deep mixed soil, excellent for corn as well as grass; to Lutterworth and Harborough, the soil generally strong enough to build mud walls, for which it is often used; yet in many places excellent for turnips and barley; about Leicester, a light or mixed loam, generally on gravel; poorer and thinner soil about Mountsorrel, and various to Charnwood Forest; about Ashby, different varieties, sandy and gravelly loam to clay; Ashby Would, lately inclosed, in their natural state, harsh cold clay loam, but becoming more mild and friable by drainage, cultivation and using lime plentifully.

"About Odston the soil is a deep gray loam, sometimes moist and springy till drained; about Knighton it is a good deep gray loam; Scraptoft towards Bilsdon, a deep moist gray loam; about Melton Mowbray, and to a great extent, rich

rich sound pasture land abounds, but being a heavy loam upon clay, mixed with small fragments of calcareous stone, it is very wet in winter, and liable to tread with heavy stock: Melton towards Grantham, strong clay loam, road repaired with limestone; Waltham a sound gray loam; Branston towards the vale of Belvoir, a deep red or snuff coloured loam to some extent; Hathern, deep gray loam, roads heavy: this is the general characteristic of soil in the vale of Belvoir.

"Dishley Farm consists generally of a mild friable loam, of a good depth, on a clay or marl bottom: the meadow soil similar to that of the other low lands of the county.

"Charnwood Forest is generally a moist grayish loam, and in want of drainage and improvement; of which it is well worthy."

P. 7. "Respecting a plan of the county, Prior's, as a general one, is sufficiently correct; but to colour it, so as to distinguish the different soils with any accuracy, and so as to give any correct idea, is not easy, if it be at all possible. The change of soil is by imperceptible shades, and the distinction is less than in most counties, and the intermixture more varied with less distinctive difference; there is nothing that approaches the sterility of sand, or the harshness of clay: the margins of the rivers, brooks, and rivulets are natural grass lands, and the upland is in some places gravelly, but generally loam more or less tenacious, the strongest of which is in the vale of Belvoir."

No attempt is made to divide the County into *Districts*; but the Reporter has undertaken a more arduous task. For altho he justly observes, "the nature of the soil is very liable to vary much, in short distances," and notwithstanding what he appropriately says about their imperceptible shades and intermixture,—he ventures to set down, in figures, the number of acres of the several species which the County contains; and how they were occupied, in 1807:—a bold attempt, this, in a nonresident.—His statement, however, is short; and I will here find room for it.

P. 5. "The general characteristic of the upland soil of Leicestershire is, therefore, a grayish or brownish friable loam, of greater or less depth, upon an under stratum of clay, marl, gravel, or rock, and may be divided as follows:

	Acres.
"Strong clay loam 160,000 acres, one half only in occasional tillage - - - - - -	80,000
Milder friable loam in occasional tillage	160,000
Total occasionally in tillage	240,000

"Strong

	Acres.
"Strong clay loam in permanent grass	80,000
Natural meadows in permanent grass, upland pasture attached to farms and occupations, and near towns, parks, and pleasure grounds in permanent grass - - - - - -	160,000
Total permanent grass	240,000
Cultivated lands - - - - - -	480,000
Waste lands—Charnwood Forest, Rothley-Plain, and all other waste land in the county - -	20,000
Woodlands, plantations, roads, rivers, waters, towns, villages, buildings, gardens and yards	22,240
Total as before	522,240"

MINERALS and FOSSILS.—*Coals.*—P. 7. "There are coal mines at Cole Orton, and again at the Lount, and on Ashby Wolds; the two former are ancient works, and have been long in use; the latter has been lately established by the Earl of Moira, at a great expense, the coal being raised from a depth of near 200 yards, a three yard strata: it is of a good quality, and readily sold on the bank at 10*s.* per ton. The Ashby canal, which is close at hand, is ready to take off any quantity not wanted by the neighbourhood."

Ironstone.—P. 8. "*Ironstone* is found in great plenty upon Ashby Wolds, the property of the Earl of Moira. His lordship has erected an iron foundery at a great expense, by the side of the Ashby canal, where the ore has been smelted, and cast into pigs, as well as utensils for various purposes. The ironstone lays at from 5 to 8 yards from the surface, a three yard measure, but mixed with two-thirds of a rubbishy blue bind, or clay marl."

SUBJECT THE SECOND.

POLITICAL ECONOMY.

APPROPRIATION.—P. 174. "This county contains no moors, mountains, bogs, fens, or marshes, or at least none of any extent, or worth the least notice in a general survey: its only wastes of any account, are known by the names of Charnwood Forest, and Rothley Plain; they are both of them properly commons, or sheep-walks; the former is is said to contain 15 or 16 thousand acres, and the latter 5 or 6 hundred. Ashby Wolds, lately a waste, have been enclosed and cultivated within the last 6 years."

P. 68. "A very large proportion of this county has been enclosed in modern times, and within the last 30 or 40 years, under the authority of different acts of parliament; very little of the county now remains unenclosed, except the wastes: I suppose the whole county does not contain more than 6 or 8 open fields, dispersed in different quarters, and that their whole extent does not exceed 10,000 acres of land."

The following commonfield regulation I have not before met with.—P. 72. "The number of sheep kept in the common field system" (in the parish of Queensborough, the account of whose inclosure fills several pages) "was, 10 flocks, of 210 each; these were folded on the fallow field, counting in the lambs in May, when the culling ewes with their lambs were sold off in couples, and the whole stock reduced by sale to the above number; these were under the care of 3 public shepherds, at 30*l.* per annum each."

Speaking of the improvement of the Belvoir estate, by inclosure, Mr. P. says, p. 14. "These enclosures were managed with great economy, by often uniting two parishes in one Act," (?) "and under one commission; those expenses have not exceeded 10*s.* per acre, nor the enclosure, 3*l.* per acre, reckoning the same price for fence timber cut upon the estate, it could have been sold at. This is indeed great economy, and a credit to those concerned. I have in other counties, in more instances than one, been assured of solicitors and commissioners expenses, amounting to 3*l.* per acre, and the enclosure 5*l.* per acre more.

"A large tract in the vale of Belvoir was, before the enclosure, an open chase, or forest stocked with deer; the remainder open common field in the three shift system, of fallow, wheat, beans. The deer often committed depredations on the crops, and were at some seasons obliged to be watched by night."

P. 76. "This parish" (Glenfield) "has had no modern enclosure; its soil may be divided into 3 classes of management; 1, old enclosures near the village; 2, grass land, pasture and meadow; 3, tillage land.

"The enclosures near the village are of ancient date; the fences being full of timber trees, arrived at maturity, but in small proportion to the extent of the parish; they are divided into yards and small pastures: the grass land consists of head lands, and margins between the tillage land, including the low grounds, or vallies, to which is to be added a considerable tract of meadow and pasture on either side

side a brook which runs through the parish, and afterwards falls into the Soar."

This may be considered as a good description of a feudal township, in most parts of the kingdom.

P. 46. (Section "Tithes.") "The ancient enclosed land is generally titheable; the modern enclosures are as generally exonerated by an allotment of land, which is commonly about one-seventh part of the whole, in lieu of tithes; but I was informed by Mr. Graham, a resident farmer; that upon the enclosure of Queensborough, one-sixth of the land was given up in lieu of great tithes, which in the open field state had been collected in kind; besides which, a small allotment to the glebe in addition, and an annual money payment was given in lieu of vicarial tithes; the few remaining common fields are titheable. In the enclosures in the vale of Belvoir, the tithes are all exonerated, either by an allotment of land, or by a corn rent; in the latter case, commissioners name, or specify how many acres of corn ought to be cultivated, and the average price of wheat for 14 years past, and thence deduce a specific sum, to be in lieu of tithes annually: at the end of 14 years, this is liable at the instance of the parties to be renewed by a reference in the same way; the old enclosed part, of every new enclosed township, has also been exonerated; no instance but of one rectory in that part of the county."

P. 47. "Experience has already proved, that no evil or inconvenience can arise, from giving land to the rector in lieu of tithes. In the vale of Belvoir, the experiment has been made over and over again, to the mutual satisfaction of all persons interested. The rectory of Bottesford, upon the inclosure, being commuted for in land, is now worth upwards of 900*l*. per annum, in landed estate."

MANUFACTURES.—P. 323. "The principal manufactures of Leicestershire, are, wool combing, woollen yarn, worsted, and stockings principally or wholly of worsted, the manufacture of which employs a great number of people, not only in Leicester, Hinckley and other towns, but also in the principal country villages throughout most parts of the county."

"In the town of Ashby are considerable cotton works, erected and set on foot by the late Mr. Wilkes, which employ a great number of the industrious poor of all ages.

"In Hinckley and Ashby a good many hats are manufactured; in Castle Donnington and its neighbourhood, a great many of the female sex principally are employed in the manufacture of patent net lace, for lady's veils, &c. dependant I believe upon Nottingham and its neighbourhood.

"Mr. Monk

"Mr. Monk says, 'the manufactures of woollen yarn and stockings are lately much increased, and the landed interest much benefited thereby;' if so I met with many, who are insensible of benefits received. Mr. Watkinson informed me that poors' rates were enormously high in his neighbourhood, (but this was in 1801) which he attributed to the number of stockingers, who could not maintain their families; and were sometimes, when out of employ, set to work by the farmers; but he observed, they made but indifferent labourers. Mr. King also informed me, that upon the Duke of Rutland's extensive demesnes, poors' rates were low, as there were no stockingers, and care was taken that there should be none; the fact is, that with the increased population, occasioned by manufactures, poors' rates increased also, but the consumption of landed produce is thereby increased, and the price advanced in proportion."

P. 72. "The village" (of Queensborough) "contains a number of tenements occupied by stocking weavers, who frequently take apprentices, and thus make parishioners (this accounts for the high poors' rates;) when trade fails they apply to the parish officers, and if the farmers give them employment they make very indifferent labourers."—See also the next article.

Poor Rates.—P. 48. "The poors' rates in this county are very various: in many of the parishes merely agricultural, as in the vale of Belvoir, and in many other farming and grazing districts, that have kept clear of manufactures, the poors' rates continue low, not exceeding at the present, from one shilling and sixpence to two shillings in the pound, upon the real annual value of property.

"But in the manufacturing districts, and in some distressing seasons, the poors' rates have risen to an enormous height. In 1801, as I have been informed, the poors' rates of Barrow on Soar, containing about 3000 acres, amounted to 2000*l.* which is thirteen shillings and four pence per acre. The parish contains, besides farmers and their dependants, a good many lime men, and stocking weavers.

"Also Mr. Watkinson of Woodhouse stated to me, that poors' rates in his parish had risen within his memory, from 100*l.* to 1200*l.* per annum, at which amount they were in 1801, upon about 1200 acres, being full 20 shillings per acre: a good many stockingers reside in the parish."

P. 328. "Mr. Ainsworth says, 'in the parish I lived in, I served the office of overseer of the poor, more than once at one shilling in the pound; but in the year 1795, in consequence of the war, and the advanced price of necessaries of life, I had four shillings in the pound, and it did not do. I believe

believe in the county it may now average five shillings; in great towns six shillings, and I have just paid a poors' rate (in Leicester) at two shillings in the pound, for one quarter (the above are upon an estimated rental). Manufactures, he says, affect and raise the poors' rates; their employment is unhealthy, by too much sitting and confinement in one posture, and from the effects of confined air; this brings on consumptions and premature deaths, and poverty brings the wife and children to the parish.'"

"Mr. Ainsworth, who seems to have had experience on the subject, as well as to have studied it with some attention, observes, 'the situation of the poor is deplorable; and general as it is to exclaim against them, I am of opinion that encouragement would make them better; little noticed while they are wearing out their strength for a bare subsistence, left unassisted or scantily supplied under sickness or accident, so that they are depressed their whole lives after. In regard to sick clubs, some cannot be admitted through age or infirmities; some are prejudiced against them, and some to my knowledge cannot spare from their families the weekly subscription; and when their labour is totally over, they have no better prospect in view than the tyranny of overseers, a badge of disgrace, and the confinement of a workhouse, the entrance into which is to deprive them of the little property they had with hard labour attained by the sweat of their brow and pinching frugality; poor incitements these to care and industry. I could wish by no means to give offence to any, but as I am more conversant with the lower classes than gentlemen can possibly be, I honestly and conscientiously declare this picture is not exaggerated. Would to God it were! I fear it is not in the power of the philanthropic Board to give the spring of encouragement, to communicate the most extensive relief to them; if they could, they would bear the nearest resemblance to the source of all good, who showers his blessings with a liberal hand on all without distinction. If a large population be the strength of a nation, it occurs naturally that the lower classes of that population are entitled to legislative assistance, to ameliorate their condition; and as every one thinks that they have some natural right to the use of the ground, so most persons are willing to assist in harvest. Land originally was open and equal to all, and though one acre of land enclosed is worth more to the community than many acres in its natural state, yet when this appropriation first began, the poor were deprived of their egress and regress; to compensate them for this loss a public fund ought to be raised and supported by people of property, to pay annuity's to the aged, infirm, and those in distress, by which means the contributors

contributors would soon be gainers by abolishing entirely the poors' rate.'"

On this subject, we see Mr. A. writing as a *practical* man; and in his strictures we perceive his cast of mind, his good intentions, and humane disposition.

For other remarks on this subject, see the preceding article.—How nearly connected, and difficultly separable, are *poor rates* and *manufactures*.

TITHES.—See the article *Appropriation*, aforegoing.

EMBANKMENT.—The Reporter has thought fit to *dictate* on this valuable art; and has given us an engraved sketch, the better to convey his ideas. Nothing, however, of novelty or excellence appears in his strictures.

INLAND NAVIGATION.—This is a subject, as I have observed, aforegoing, p. 5, on which Mr. Pitt is particularly conversant.—He has not only given a satisfactory detail of the several canals and the river navigation of Leicestershire; but has made some judicious remarks on their execution.

P. 314. "The Ashby Canal is cut and navigable from Ashby Wolds to the Coventry Canal, near 30 miles in length, cut on a level without lockage; it was intended to have been continued to the navigable part of the Trent below Burton, and with that view was coustructed for barges of 60 tons burden; but the money to the amount of 180,000*l.* having been expended, the line to the Trent, on which is a tunnel, and considerable lockage, has been abandoned, and rail-ways substituted to the high ground."

"The whole expenditure upon the Ashby Canal and its dependences seems to have been a profusion of money. The late Joseph Wilkes, Esq. who was treasurer, from motives of liberality, patriotism, and public spirit, as a friend to commerce wished to see the barges of the Trent float over the hills of Leicestershire and Derbyshire, and taking an active part in the business had the canal constructed upon that scale; in consequence, by the extra expense of deep and wide cutting, wider and higher arches for bridges, extra backing up the avenues to such bridges, a tunnel upon a large scale, and the complete and spirited manner in which the works were executed, the money was expended before any of the lockage was constructed, and the communication with the Trent remains undone; that to the high ground is by means of the rail-ways above named, and the canal, is navigated by canal boats only, carrying from 20 to 24 tons instead of Trent barges of 60 tons, having no communication except with the Coventry Canal, which is constructed for such boats only."

How

How mischievous is genius, without judgement and foresight to direct it; especially when urged on by *wild* commercial, otherwise gambling, *speculations**.

P. 315. "LEICESTER NAVIGATION, on or near the line of the river Soar, sometimes along the channel of that river, in other places carried out by lockage into a new channel, the line is from Leicester down the Soar Valley to the Trent, with a collateral branch to Loughborough, and this latter continued over part of Charnwood Forest, by canal or railway, to Cole-orton colliery, and the Cloud hill lime work; this continuation, from some cause, at present 1807, of no use; the canal let dry and rail-ways not used, coals being to be had cheaper at the Leicester and Loughborough markets, from Derbyshire: I am informed, however, that the Leicester navigation altogether is a good concern; the trade of Leicester and Loughborough keeps it up, and it is said to pay 25 per cent.; it is constructed on a scale for the barges that navigate the Trent.

"The MELTON CANAL, from the Leicester Soar navigation along the valley of the Wreke, to Melton Mowbray, and continued to Oakham, and capable of being continued to Stamford, to the navigable part of the Welland.

"GRANTHAM CANAL, from the Trent along the vale of Belvoir to Grantham, with a large reservoir to collect winter water; has cost 100,000*l.* capable of being continued to the sea, at or near Boston; begins to pay five per cent. This canal is a great accommodation to the vale of Belvoir, where the roads in winter were dreadful, but now lime and coal can be conveyed there with ease at pleasure, as well as other heavy articles to and from Grantham: this is likely to become a good concern as the country improves, and which it will be a means of facilitating.

"UNION CANAL, from the navigable Soar at Leicester, by way of Harborough to the Nen at Northampton, and intended

* It was not in public matters, only, that the genius, above-named (a well intentioned good private character) failed for want of judgement and foresight. I recollect his building a range of cattle sheds, *on a grand scale* (calculated to hold fifty or a hundred head) at the foot of a slope; which were constructed merely of arches (each arch to receive two cattle) to be covered with earth, as a roof. But, for want of a firm buttress being previously placed, at each end of the range,—the whole, on being loaded with earth, fell, *of course*, flat to the ground.

This is not mentioned to harm the character of "departed genius,"—much less with a view to hinder *thought-less genius* from building "baseless fabrics" (as that were impossible); but to caution men of reason and common sense from being led into labyrinths of folly and extravagance; by the false splendor of its specious misconceptions.

tended to communicate with the Grand Junction Canal; but has been arrested in its progress by untoward circumstances, though some little progress is now making toward Harborough, and a good many workmen employed on it, August 1807, in constructing a bridge over the turnpike road, and extending the canal.

"Half a million or more has been expended on these speculations, without in general the expected profits: the Ashby Canal has yet made no dividend, though I understand it to be in the receipt of some thousand pounds a year in tonnage. These great public works are a convincing proof, and wonderful instance of the spirit of enterprize existing in the people of this country; a few projects of this kind having succeeded well, and turned out very profitable, roused forth a rage for canals, which has been carried to a greater length and extent than the nature of the case required. I should very much doubt the Ashby Canal becoming a fair concern, or paying reasonable interest upon the expenditure, unless it could be continued to the Trent, and thus be made a thoroughfare; in that case Lord Moira's iron would find a readier way to market.

"To supply the Ashby Canal with water, a reservoir has been formed upon Ashby Wolds, containing when full 36 acres of water; this is quickly filled by the rain and melted snows of winter, and dealt out gradually to supply the canal in summer: when I saw it in October 1807, it was reduced to a few acres only."

Railways.—P. 313. "Iron rail-ways have been formed in this county with great spirit, as appendages to the Ashby Canal: these rail-ways extend about 12 miles in length, from the Ashby Canal, to and by near the town of Ashby, thence to the Lount Colliery, and Cole-orton to Ticknall, and the Cloud-hill lime works. On these rail-ways there are embankments and deep cutting, to preserve the level, or a regular descent and ascent; also a tunnel of a quarter of a mile in length, with arched bridges for roads over the deep cutting leading to the tunnel in the canal style; these railway appendages to the Ashby Canal have cost thirty thousand pounds; it was the original design for these to have been continuations of the canal; but the money being expended, and the expense of lockage on these lines necessary, rail-ways were substituted, and they are, I believe, the best mode of artificial inland conveyance, for heavy articles next to canals; but the sum expended upon them seems to be enormous, in proportion to the length, and can only be accounted for by the tunnel, deep cutting, and embankments."

Roads.—Mr. Pitt, as Mr. Monk, speaks of the *concave* or *washway*

washway principle of forming them *.—Mr. P. appearing to have given it a degree of consideration, his ideas on the subject (of course, let me say) coincide with my own. His concluding remarks are these:

P. 313. "*Application of water.*—This as a means of mending roads is rather theoretical than practical. Where the road lies with a declivity, a sudden heavy shower may wash and clean it, but a perennial stream can seldom be applied to this purpose. I saw little or nothing of the kind in Leicestershire, in the summer and autumn seasons when I was generally there, and in winter frosts, it would be a great nuisance, by filling the road with ice; it may happen in local situations, where the road has a proper declivity, that it may be thus improved."

MARKETS.—See Mr. Monk's Report, p. 186, aforegoing.—The resolutions, there noticed, tho they appear to be judicious, and likely to have a good effect, did not avail. Mr. Pitt's Report of that attempt at improvement, made fourteen years after the resolutions were entered into, is the following.

P. 321. "Notwithstanding all this, I believe but little alteration has been made, the ancient custom of any particular market still remaining, and the buyer and seller understanding each other, make that the governing principle."

Query, was the failure owing, solely, to the obstinacy of custom, right or wrong? Or have buyers (corn dealers, maltsters, and innkeepers) an interest in purchasing by one measure, and selling by another? Their profits, by this complex mode of dealing, being the more difficult to ascertain.—The practice, however, now pretty generally adopted, by corn dealers, in this part of the kingdom (northeast Yorkshire) of buying corn, *by weight*, completely annuls that advantage (if any) and sets the silly custom of selling by illegal measure, at rest,—*in the country*. But, by the dealers who send their corn to the *London market*, and there sell, *by measure*, the juggle is still kept up.

Surplus produce.—P. 324. "This county is well accommodated with commercial conveniences, the Trent washing one of its borders, and the Soar, its own natural river, being rendered navigable into it, and for many miles through the county; this with other conveniences executed or on hand, give it a fair share of commercial advantages."

P. 325. "Of provisions, cheese is a considerable article of

* For a minute examination of this false principle, see my MIDLAND COUNTIES; especially the first edition, in 1790.

of export, not less than 1500 tons per annum, according to the best information; the produce of this county, going down the Trent for the metropolis, or the use of the navy; this at 60s. per hundred, amounts to 90,000*l*.

"Of sheep, a very large number bred in this county, are sold fat to London and Birmingham; half fat to farmers in adjacent counties to be finished on turnips, or in store condition, to farmers to breed from.—See the article Sheep. Of cattle a great many are also fatted in this county, more than it consumes, and sold to London, Birmingham, and the populous parts of Staffordshire; these are in part bred in the county, and in part bought in from elsewhere.—See the article Cattle.

"A good many excellent strong black draught horses, and some of the blood kind, are bred in, and sold from this county; in hogs and butter, I suppose it to be nearly in statu quo; respecting grain it has barley to spare, but certainly a deficiency of wheat, and its oats and beans are eaten by its own horses, as well as its green crops and hay, by other stock."

SOCIETIES—See Mr. Monk's account, p. 187, aforegoing.—Mr. Pitt having copied part of it continues, p. 354. "This society still continues, with the same president; but the vice-presidents and time of meeting are altered. The following is their last advertisement, 1807."

No mention being made of the *experimental farm*, noticed by Mr. Monk, this intended LOCAL INSTITUTE would seem to have become a mere *Premium Society*. Having however, been formed in the most enlightened district of the kingdom, in regard to livestock at least, and comprizing more objects, I apprehend, than most others of the numerous societies that have now been formed, in various parts of the kingdom, I will here insert the views and regulations of "the Leicestershire and Rutlandshire Agricultural Society." It will serve, at least, as a matter of history to future generations of agriculturists; who will thereby become acquainted with the taste of the present.

P. 355. "The following premiums are offered for the year 1808:

"To the person who shall produce the best estimate of the comparative advantage between the use of oxen and horses in husbandry work—25 guineas.

"To the person who shall make the best comparative experiment between the effects of fresh dung and rotten dung, arising from the same species of animal and forage, upon grass land within one year; the extent not being less than one acre for each kind of dung—10 guineas.

"N. B

"N.B. Dung not to be considered as fresh after the third day.

"To the person who shall, on the day of the annual meeting for 1808, produce a pen of five of the best fat shearhogs, to have been fed with grass, hay, or roots, and not to have had corn or cake—10 guineas.

"For the second best pen of the same—5 guineas.

"For a pen of five of the best 2-year old wethers—10 guineas.

"For the second best pen of the same—5 guineas.

"For a pen of five of the best fat shearhogs that shall have been bred and kept on natural grass alone, respect being had in this, as also in the preceding classes, to the quality and quantity of the mutton, as well as to the quality and quantity of the wool—10 guineas.

"For the second best pen of the same—5 guineas.

"For a pen of five of the best 2-year old wethers—10 guineas.

"For the second best pen of the same—5 guineas.

"For a pen of five of the best ewes, to be shewn at the annual meeting for 1808, which shall have produced and reared lambs at two years old, and the following year, the lambs not being taken from the dams until Midsummer (old stile) in each year, to have been fed with grass, hay or roots, but not to have had corn or cake—5 guineas.

"For a pen of the same number of ewes that shall have been kept on natural grass alone—5 guineas.

"For the best conducted experiment for ascertaining the relative profit of different breeds of sheep in wool and carcass, strict attention being paid to the quantity of food each breed has consumed; the weight and value when put up to feed, and when taken off, being specified, and to have been fed with artificial food, with the exception of corn and oil cake—10 guineas.

"For the second best experiment—5 guineas.

"For the best conducted experiment for ascertaining the relative profit of different breeds of sheep in wool and carcass, the same attention being used in this as in the last class, to ascertain the quantity of food consumed, the weight and value of the animals, when put to feed and taken off, to have been bred and kept on natural grass alone—10 guineas.

"For the second best experiment of the same—5 guineas.

"*Note.*—These premiums will not be allowed, unless the experiment in every case has extended to at least 5 sheep of some distinct breed.

"For the best ox under three years old, the time when calved being ascertained as nearly as may be—6 guineas

"For

" For the second best ditto—4 guineas.

" For the best ox under 4 years old—5 guineas.

" For the second best ditto—3 guineas.

" [To have been fed with grass and vegetables.]

" For the best ox that shall have been worked from 3 years old off, to 6 years old off, or longer, the age being specified—8 guineas.

" For the second best ditto—4 guineas.

" [To have been fed with grass and vegetables or oil cake, but in case the latter has been used, an account of the quantity consumed to be produced].

" To the person who shall make the best experiment and shortest report on the practical effects of lime upon the various sorts of land—20 guineas.

" To the person who shall state the best manner of forming compost dunghills, mentioning their materials, quantity, and place—5 guineas.

" For the best conducted experiment, ascertaining the relative advantages to be derived from soiling or grazing cattle in the usual way—10 guineas.

" The same experiment for sheep—10 guineas.

" To the person who shall have cleared not less than 5 acres of land from ant-hills, within one year, in the best and most effectual manner, the expense being stated to the committee, and it being understood that no premium will be allowed without proof of the efficacy of the measure for 3 years—20 guineas.

" The following premiums are offered for servants:

" To the person having had the care of sheep, to be exhibited for the premiums, that shall appear to have rendered the most effectual service to his master, in the capacity of a shepherd—3 guineas.

" The claim for this premium to be accompanied by a testimonial from the master, as to the good conduct of the man; which testimonial is to state the number of the sheep under such servant's care, the number of lambs reared, and other circumstances connected with such servant's duty, so as to enable the committee to form a correct judgment of his merit.

" To the man who shall make the experiment as to dung, for which a premium shall be obtained—1 guinea.

" To the servant that shall be employed in working of horses and oxen in husbandry work, on which a premium shall be awarded—2 guineas.

" To the man who shall cut, lay, or plash an hedge, in the best and most effectual manner as to the preservation of the quick, and for making it a fence, the same to be ascertained

ascertained by the owner and two of the committee, a premium of—3 guineas.

" To the person who shall, at the annual meeting for 1808, report the most satisfactory information, as deduced from actual experiments, of the soils and situations best adapted for orchards, and of the means used in their plantation and subsequent management—10 guineas.

" For the best cow that shall have produced not less than 3 calves, and shall be in milk at the time of shewing, the time of her last calving being ascertained by the owner—6 guineas.

" For the second best ditto—4 guineas.

" These premiums not to be given for any animals of mixed breeds, nor unless the particular breed is ascertained to the satisfaction of the judges.

" The following conditions are to be complied with by all candidates for premiums.

" Every candidate, or person appearing on his behalf, is to enter his stock or claim to a premium with the secretary, on or before the 1st day of September next, the stock to be exhibited at a time and place to be appointed by the committee. A certificate, in the following form, is to be delivered to the secretary at the time of entry:

" I, A. B. do certify, that the intended to be produced for the premium offered by the Leicestershire and Rutlandshire Agricultural Society in class is the property of

" [Here shall follow a statement of such other particulars as may be required by the terms of the premium, and for ascertaining the claim of the candidate.]

(Signed)

" The secretary is requested not to disclose the entries of claims for premiums until after the 1st day of September, 1808.

" All cattle shewn must be previously rendered tractable, in order to prevent accidents.

" No candidate to enter more than one lot in the same class.

" In every class where doubt shall arise, the committee is to decide.

" There shall not be more than three judges for each description of animal, and no person is to act in that capacity in any case in which he may be interested.

" *Instructions to the judges.*—You shall decide which is the best animal, or lot of animals, in the several classes, having a regard, in forming your judgment, to excellence and utility of form, quality of flesh, lightness of offal, propensity

pensity to fatten, and early maturity, as far as may be consistent with the special terms of the premium. Also in sheep, to quantity and quality of wool. Having signed your adjudication, you are not afterwards to propose any change, nor to mention your decision till announced by the committee. You are not to disclose the opinion of each other; and the decision of the majority is to be conclusive; and you shall number the lots in each class in the order of their merit."*

Village Libraries.—"A plan for village or parish libraries" is proposed, p 344; not by the Reporter; but by the Publisher; who has given a list of *appropriate* books; not to promote the art and science of practical agriculture; but to obtain a market for his publications.

SUBJECT THE THIRD.

RURAL ECONOMY.

TENANTED ESTATES.

ESTATES.—We have no estimate, or intimation, of the *Sizes* of estates, in Leicestershire.

TENURES.—P. 17. "*Tenures,* in this county, are principally freehold, with some little copyhold."

P. 18. "A very small proportion is church tenure, or held under life-leases, renewable between the parties, upon payment of a fine."

SODBURNING.—P. 187. "Paring and burning has been very generally and successfully practised in the improvement of Ashby Wolds, the soil being generally a cold clay or loam."

"Many persons attempted the cultivation of this waste by other means, but none answered in any comparison so well as paring and burning; which, therefore, became general once over."

IRRIGATION.—P. 77. (Section "Enclosures")—"A good portion of this meadow land was under natural irrigation when I saw it, the preceding days having been rainy, but no

* PREMIUM SOCIETIES in AGRICULTURE.—*Bull Shows* for *Premiums* originated, I believe, at DRIFFIELD, in the East Riding of Yorkshire, about the year 1792. See my YORKSHIRE,—edition 1794, Vol. II. p. 183. The first PETWORTH Meeting took place in November 1797.

no vestiges of any assistance from art, except the curvature of the water-course, which prevents the water from passing off too quickly. I have often supposed, upon viewing the curvature of water-courses, that the course was artificial, and a project of our ancestors to irrigate the land; who observing the fertility occasioned by an overflow of water, rather chose to submit to the inconvenience of floods, than be deprived of this advantage. I have no doubt, but the natural channel of a stream as formed by the current would be much more rectilinear, than they are commonly found; and when men found the necessity of a channel to keep the water from off their land, they cut one with a deviating course, to drain the land in common, and to water it in floods."

This is to me a novel doctrine. That the Reporter himself believed in it is plain, from his repeating it, in his section "Irrigation."—P. 200. "The irrigation or watering in this county, may be divided into natural and artificial; the natural irrigation comprehends, the fine meadow land upon the banks of the Soar and other rivers, and rivulets, which taken together amounts to a very considerable quantity of land here: as the fertility by watering became apparent, a necessity arose to confine the stream within due bounds, except in floods; and a channel for the main stream was consequently cut, and this is the origin of the channels of our rivulets, and minor rivers; and I can have no doubt, but the circuitous and zigzag course of many of them, was a work of design, to irrigate the land in floods, and prevent the water going off too fast."

No law of nature is more certain and obvious, than is that of running waters rendering their channels *crooked;* unless where rocks prevent them.—Were it at all probable that any man should carry this principle of irrigation into effect, through the suggestion here brought forward, it might have been prudent to *expose* its futility.

The Reporter has stained near a sheet of paper, and inserted an engraved diagram, by way of treating the subject in a *master-like* manner. Had not the art of irrigation been previously raised to a degree of science, Mr. Pitt's novitial strictures might have had their use. But seeing the different works, on the subject, which were, at the time he wrote, before the public, he might well have spared his own and his reader's time, by passing the subject in silence.

EXECUTIVE MANAGEMENT of Estates.—MANAGERS.—P. 13. "The great estates, as those of the Duke of Rutland, the Earl of Moira, and others of that class, are managed by resident stewards, who live either in the mansion, or in a separate dwelling in the neighbourhood; and this

this system becomes necessary for those whose high rank and connections in life require their attendance on public affairs; and in the management and improvement of a few thousand acres of land, it will well answer the proprietors end, in all cases where such proprietor cannot, or does not chuse to attend to his own affairs, to engage the whole time of a man of business, ability, and active mind, to study systematically, and put in motion the various improvements to be made on such estate."

Rent.—P. 45. "The rent of farms in Leicestershire may be reckoned from one pound to two pounds per acre, average 30 shillings; the rent of water meadow land, and good grass, and other land near towns, three pounds to five pounds per acre, and in some few instances higher; but this subject can only be stated in a general way, as minute inquiries of this kind are looked upon with suspicion, and considered as an over curious prying into private affairs."

Receiving Rents.—P. 46. "The credit given for rents is three months in hand; generally rents due Lady day, paid about Midsummer; and due Michaelmas, paid about Christmas; but with some variations."

Manor Courts.—P. 17. "Manor courts are pretty generally held, even where the copyhold tenure is extinct, and their utility is experienced upon many occasions, as the settlement of boundaries, and preventing of litigations, appointment of constables, &c."

Principles of Management.—P. 15. "A numerous and able bodied *peasantry* is here supported" (a translation, this no doubt from the Rusian); "no stockingers, or other manufacturers, and care taken that there shall be none; poor rents low, and rents well paid. Mr. King is aware, on behalf of the duke, (of Rutland) that the occupiers are rather farmers of the old stamp; but observes they are gradually improving, and some of the rising generation, as they grow up, are for striking at new improvements. He believes the estate produces as much nett income as it might do in abler hands at greater rents, as much polish and change in building at great expense, would be wanted. Something of this kind, however, is intended, and even set a going, to be brought about by degrees."

WOODLANDS.

P. 169. "This is by no means a woodland county, and therefore, without any particular established systems of managing coppice woods; the timber is cut down promiscu-

ously

ously at the pleasure of the owner, and meets with a ready sale, for the various purposes for which it is adapted. On the Belvoir estate is plenty of timber and plantation, and Donnington park has all sorts of timber trees, and of every age, from the young plant to a state of decay. About many other of the gentlemens' seats is plenty of timber and plantation, and I particularly observed upon the Beaumanor estate of William Herrick, Esq. an abundance of ripe well grown oak, carefully preserved in a maiden state, and now so ripe as to be fit for any use to which oak is applicable."

P. 170. "There is very little timber on the Melton Mowbray side of the county, till you reach the Duke of Rutland's estates, where there are very extensive plantations of oak and other forest trees, which as they grow up will be a great ornament to the country."

"But little or no great supply for ship building, or naval purposes, must be looked for here, although Lord Moira has a profusion of timber of every kind in Donnington Park, of between 4 and 500 acres; oaks of all ages, from the young sapling to the old venerable oak, that has stood the blasts of 4 or 5 centuries, now past maturity, and verging to decay. I cannot help thinking but it would be a rational, desirable, useful, and much to be wished for triumph of utility over taste, if the great land proprietors would permit these to be culled out and sent to market, before they were too far decayed; their places might be supplied by fresh plantations; and interest, profit, and personal advantage must strongly second the proposal; many of these would now in a mild and moist spring yield a good deal of bark (an article now of high price and in great demand) and some might produce useful timber, but many of them I fear are too far gone. A considerable quantity of excellent and capital oak is also there to be found, in high perfection and maturity, growing almost close to the Trent; and dispersed all over the park, is elm, ash, lime and beach in great plenty, and of every stage of gowth.

"Lord Moira has annual falls of timber and sales, in South Wood, Ashby old Park, not by auction, but upon the following liberal principle: the timber is cut down by his lordship's agent, and the bark and appendages sold; it is then marked and valued by a proper judge, tree by tree, and the value entered in a reference book: an agent attends at stated times, and sells to any one who applies, farmer, dealer, or tradesman; whatever he fixes on, whether on one or more trees at this valuation, no abatement is made or advance put on. Mr. Dawson, his lordship's steward, thinks more money might be made by auction, but the tenants

tenants and the country are thus accommodated for their own consumption.

"The price and value of the different kinds of timber in the Midland counties, I have been well acquainted with, for about 40 years, the first 20 years of which, it underwent but little advance; but within the last 20 it has advanced considerably: the following are the Leicestershire prices, at two periods of time.

"*Price of Timber in* 1786, *from Mr. Marshall.* *Price in* 1807.

	S.	D.		S.	D.	S.	D.		S.	D.
Oak in the round, per foot - -	1	6	to	2	0	2	6	to	3	0
Ash, ditto - -	0	9		1	0	1	6		2	0
Elm and Beach, ditto - -	0	9		1	0	1	8			
Poplar, ditto - -	0	8		1	2	1	6			
Inch Oak boards, per square foot				0	3	0	6			
Elm, ditto - -				0	1½	0	2½	to	0	3
Ash, ditto - -				0	1½		ditto			
Poplar, ditto - -				0	1½		ditto			
Ash Axle-trees - - -	3	3	to	3	6	4	6	to	5	0
Six-inch felleys, a trine of 13 -	12	0				16	0		18	0
Narrow, ditto, ditto -	8	0				12	0			
Elm Naves, per pair - -	4	0				7	0		8	0

"The value of growing oak, coppice timber, with the bark and all appendages, seems to be doubled within the last twenty years; the timber itself is advanced rather more than as two to three; but the value of oak bark in that time is advanced more than four-fold."

AGRICULTURE.

FARMS —*Sizes.*—P. 28. "The farms of Leicestershire are of various and almost all sizes. In the vale of Belvoir, and in many other parts of the county, as upon the Beaumanor estate, belonging to William Herrick, Esq. are a great many farms of from 80 to 100 acres; here the occupiers put their own hands to the plough.—A more general size of farms is from 100 to 200 acres, and from 200 to 500 acres are in the hands of many of the principal breeders and graziers, and in some instances occupied by the owner. On farms of this larger size the greatest improvements have been struck out, and established, which have often been adopted by the smaller farmers: some few occupations are larger still, and much more is kept in hand by some of the great land proprietors."

P. 29. "His Grace the Duke of Rutland (as I was informed at Belvoir Castle) has in hand 2000 acres of land and upwards of all descriptions, including pleasure grounds, plantations

plantations, meadow, arable, and lay land, where stock is taken into keeping."

"At Donnington Park, the Earl of Moira has in hand, besides the park of 450 acres, a regular farm of about 370 acres, making in the whole about 820 acres."

Mr. Pitt, in continuation of the above, proceeds "to detail particulars of some of the principal occupations, from minutes or memorandums made on the spot, in various and different tours through the county." p. 29.

The Farm of Dishley (formerly Mr. Bakewell's, now Mr. Honeyborn's) has engrossed the principal share of Mr. P's attention. Those of Odstone (Mr. Astley's), Knighton (Mr. Stone's), Woodhouse (Mr. Watkinson's), and a detached farm of Mr. Stone's of Barrow,—are more slightly noticed.—And in another part of his book, Mr. P has described some "New Farms," on Ashby Wolds.

In these minutes, the amateur, who has not trodden the classic ground of Leicestershire, may find *entertainment*. But altho Mr. Pitt has brought down the history of Leicestershire farming, eighteen years lower than my account of it reaches*, I perceive nothing in the journals, now under notice, that could add to the *practical information* already registered. It is, indeed, a matter of some astonishment that so few *alterations* in *practice* should have taken place, in so considerable a length of time.

HOMESTEADS.—P. 27. "Price of Building Materials, and Labour.

	"*From Mr. Marshall, in* 1786.				*Price in* 1807.						
	s.	*d.*	*s.*	*d.*	*£.*	*s.*	*d.*		*£.*	*s.*	*d.*
Bricks at the kiln, per 1000	16	0			1	5	0	to	1	7	0
Laying Bricks, per 1000	4	0			0	6	0		0	7	6
Bricklayer, per day	1	10			0	3	0		0	3	6
Carpenter, per day	1	10 to	2	0	0	3	0		0	3	6
Building timber, per foot -	1	6			0	2	6				

"The advance in lime in this period, is about as 2 to 3, that in bricks and timber rather more; and in labour quite as much: the general advance in the expense of building is therefore within the last 20 years, as two to three nearly, or in some places rather more."

COTTAGE GROUNDS.—P. 134. "The uses of potatoes as food for mankind are well known; and they are so important a part of the subsistence of a labourer's family, and so

* Namely, from 1789 (when I examined the practice of *Leicestershire*, in particular) to 1807.

so wholesome and generally acceptable to children, that nothing but the greatest cruelty and absurdity in our rural economy can prevent (and nothing ought to prevent,) every industrious labourer resident in the country from having as much land for potatoes as he can well cultivate, without loosing his daily labour, which ought to be as much as will produce a peck a week for his family, and twice the quantity for his pig, making in all about 40 bushels per annum, which may be grown upon one-eighth of an acre, in the rotation of potatoes and wheat alternately, which, with other vegetables, would require at least one-third of an acre; and this quantity of land at least ought to be laid to every country cottage, at the same rent it is worth for agricultural uses; which would, perhaps, be the cheapest and best relief that can be given to the poor in the country."

OCCUPIERS.—P. 216. "In their corn cultivation, they are perhaps but little above mediocrity;* in that of green crops, as more connected with live stock, they rank higher; their pastures and grass land, aided by a fertile soil, are so managed as to be productive, though not always neat or agreeably picturesque;" (!) "but in their live stock, taken generally, they have surpassed every other county in the kingdom, and I suppose every country in the universe.

"The spirit of emulation for improving every kind of live stock, and which is now so widely spread, was first raised by Mr. Robert Bakewell, of Dishley Farm, near, Loughborough, in this county, who was a man of great enterprize, and of sound and acute judgment, and he entered upon business with many advantages: his father had long been in possession of a small freehold estate, and the well-conditioned farm of Dishley, held on lease, at an easy rent; and through the whole of a long life he maintained the character of a respectable and upright man, and of being the most skilful grazier in that part of the country. The late Robert Bakewell was bred to his father's business, and his early genius for selecting and improving stock was encouraged by his father, beyond all parallel, and without limitation; and it may be truly said, without partiality, that he has done more than any other man who had lived before him."

PLAN of MANAGEMENT.—P. 87. "The tillage land in Leicestershire is much less in proportion than that of most other counties. In the south, east, and middle of the county, are many instances of farms and occupations, without any tillage land whatever."

P. 92.

* In Mr. P's travelling notes, many instances are observable of their being *beneath* mediocrity.

P. 92. "The favourite course of crops of the Leicester shire grazier, breeder, or principal farmer, upon all mild, moderate, or friable loams, is a five tilth system, as follows: 1, oats, or wheat, or sometimes, but more rarely, barley; 2, a green crop, turnips, Swedish, or cabbages, or cole-seed; 3, barley, with seeds, viz. red and white clover, trefoil, and ray-grass (and at Dishley a few pounds of burnet have lately been added for experiment); and 4 and 5, pasture and clover mown: I believe this course will include half the tillage land of the county, or 120,000 acres." (?)

P. 14. (Vale of Belvoir) "Here the course of Agriculture has since the enclosure been turned topsyturvy, the richest land in the vale, formerly tillage, has been laid to grass; and the poorer land up the hills, and the skirtings of the vale, formerly a sheep walk, have been brought into tillage. Any land is permitted for tillage, whose staple, in the opinion of a proper judge, is not worth more than a guinea per acre; but rich deep soil, exceeding that value, is compelled to lay at grass."

WORKPEOPLE.—P. 305. "Prices of various kinds of labour in this district, at two periods of time.

"*From Mr. Marshall.*	*Prices in* 1786				*Prices in* 1807.			
Servants.	L.	S.	L.	S.	L.	S.	L.	S.
A waggoner - - -	8	8 to	10	10	12	0 to	14	0
Maid - - - -	3	3	5	5	4	4	6	6
Youth - - - -	4	4	5	5	4	4	6	6
Lad - - - -	2	2	3	3	3	3	4	4
Day Wages.	S.	D.			S.	D.		
Labourer in winter - - -	1	2	beer		2	0		
Do. Hay-time - - -	1	6	ditto		2	0 to 2 6		
Do. Harvest - - -	2	0	and ditto			and beer		
Women in common - -	0	6	ditto		0	8		
Do. Hay-time - - -	0	9	ditto		0	10 and ditto		
Piece Work.								
Threshing wheat and binding the straw - - - -	0	4 to 5 pr. bus.			0	7		
Do. Barley per quarter - -	1	4	1	6	2	6 to 2 9		
Do. Oats ditto - -	0	8 to 0	10		1	6		
Thresher extra, for foddering in the yard, Sunday included -	1	0 per week						
Reaping wheat by the thrave -	0	4 to	6 beer		0	6		
Mowing, sheaving and raking oats	5	0 per acre						
Spreading dung from small heaps	0	1 per ct. load						
Threshing beans per bushel -	-	-	-		0	4		
Iron Work.								
Common iron work per lb. -	0	4			0	5 to 6		
Horse-shoe - - -	0	5			0	6		
Remove - - -	0	1½			0	2"		

MANURES.—*Food of Plants.*—Mr. Ainsworth's paper has been mentioned, p. 195, aforegoing.—In the following extract

extract will be seen Mr. A's manner of treating the subject; and the pith and marrow, or shall we say, the quintessence, of his principles of vegetation!

P. xv. "It may seem assuming in an obscure individual to attempt to decide in a question of such great importance, and upon which the learned have been so divided in opinion, and which is not yet ascertained, or by any means settled; but every man has a right to enjoy and to propagate his own opinion, till convinced by fair argument, just reason, or experiments, of his error; and it may be observed, that printing was found out by an obscure German, the use of gunpowder by a solitary Monk, ærostation by a French paper-manufacturer, and inland navigation by a millwright's apprentice, &c.; but as was before observed, what this food of plants is, neither cultivators nor philosophers have as yet perfectly agreed upon.

"The learned Boyle says, that in the chemical pursuits he made after it, he had often lost sight of it, and, Proteus like, it had changed its figure during the time of his operations upon it; yet that, at the last, he found it in the same quality again.

"Helmont says, that water is the food of plants; but the celebrated Mr. Tull is confident that earth is the food of plants; some say that oil is, some that salt (or nitre); but the author of an excellent Treatise on Agriculture, printed at Edinburgh in 1762, infers, from various observations, that it is compounded of some, or all of them. But there is one element (if I may be allowed the expression) not yet mentioned, wherein some plants, such as the tree sedum, cabbage, onions, &c. The former for years, suspended in the air, will put forth roots, without the assistance of any of the other principles, though there are none that will live in any of the other without the assistance of air. Some plants will live in water, but the particles of that fluid being globular, the cavities are pregnant with air. The great Dr. Franklin has proved, that a considerable quantity of air is contained in water, which it obstinately retains, so that it cannot be deprived of it, either by boiling, or by the air pump, or by any other known means than a long continued agitation in vacera.

"But I beg leave to have it understood, once for all, that what I mean by air in this sense is thlogisticated with its burthen of effluvia of all corrupted and putrefied bodies of animals and vegetables, the steam of dunghills, of earths, of waters, the smoke of cities, towns, &c. the breath of animals, &c. &c. &c. which arises so plentifully in the air, and which, if it did not return again to the earth, this terrestrial planet would long ago have been involved

involved in total darkness, but which floats on the globe in the night, or when the air becomes dense, till interrupted by the often and newly pulverized soil, which greedily devours it, but passes over (as it were in silent contempt) the lands of the sloven, until it finds a better reception. And this attraction of the earth accounts for the cause that a country becomes more healthy when in a cultivated state than in its natural one. Corruption is the life of vegetation, though destructive to animals.—But, to return from this digression. Too much nitre or other salts corrodes a plant, too much water drowns it, too much heat burns it, too much earth smothers it, but too much air a plant never can have."

And, after many an *ingenious argument*, and *quotings* of GREW, PRIESTLY and INGENHOUZ, the Essayist has gained confidence enough to draw his conclusion.

P. xxiv. "From what has been observed, we may, I trust, safely infer, that the phlogisticated air is the food or fabulum of plants, and from this principle, every problem in agriculture may be solved."

After a few more theoretical wanderings, he proceeds to the application of his new principle,—to *drilling*.—But of this in its proper place.

That an *ingredient* of atmospheric air is friendly, and perhaps essential, to the growth of plants, would seem to have been sufficiently proved, by Dr. PRIESTLY, several years ago.—But let not this lull the husbandman into a state of indifference, about MANURES! If he is desirous of full crops of corn, let him trust to the dungcart, and lime furnace, rather than in the plausible saying of aerial phylosophers.

'What has been *vegetable*, may be vegetable'—is a maxim I laid down, some thirty or forty years ago; and, in my extended practice, during that length of time, I have never found occasion to doubt its accuracy.—All *animal* matter has been vegetable, and may be said to be vegetable matter refined.—It is well known to practical men to be the first of manures.—*Calcareous* matter, if not in reality animal matter, so much resembles it, as to operate, on soils, in a similar manner.

LIME.—P. 195. "The advantage of using lime upon the late enclosed waste of Ashby Wolds lime has been decisively apparent, and nothing has been done there to advantage without it. Mr. Ingle, of Ashby, assured me, that wheat he was employed to value there upon some occasion was, after paring, burning, and fallow, only worth £5 10*s*. per acre; but after paring, burning, and fallow, with six tons of lime per acre, in the same field and season,

and

and land the same, it was worth £13 10*s.* per acre."—This, among millions of others, is a sufficient evidence of the efficacy of calcareous earth, as a *manure.*

SEMINATION —*Drilling.*—Mr. Ainsworth's application of his phlogistic principle of vegetation, is mentioned above.—Were there not ample evidence, in his paper, of his uprightness and integrity of intentions, he might have been suspected of interested and sinister views, in drawing it up ;—for his *extravagant* praises of drilling and drill-makers, read so much like a *puff*, that it is difficult to get rid of the aukward idea.

How, it may be asked by those who have not read Mr. A's paper, can phlogistic air act upon corn, in rows, more beneficially than on that growing, at random. Why, because—" When plants are sown at random, and too thick, the air stagnates, and prevents the current of air from conveying them any phlogistic, and the stems and leaves of the plants are depraved, or rather destroyed, as may be perceived by their turning yellow instead of being green ; the consequence is, they do not die, because they receive half their food from the soil, but they become weak and sickly ; and this may account for the degeneracy of our present sample of grain. But when plants are sown in parallel lines, there is a free current of air in the intervals, and the plants being then in the rows, each one absorbs a sufficient quantity of phlogistic as it passes by them, and they become healthy, strong, and vigorous."—p. xxxvi.

If the wind were invariable ;—constantly blowing from the same point ; and if rows of corn were directed to that point ; there might, or might not, be some truth in the above conception. But seeing and feeling, as every man must, that nothing is more changeable than the wind,—the idea dissolves in air :—Unless, indeed, Mr. A. or his friends, could contrive to hang corn fields on pivots, as weathercocks are now properly hung. But, until such an invention be brought to light, the evanescent theory, here examined, cannot be entitled to a moments consideration. Its author, surely, never saw four or five quarters of wheat an acre, grow up to perfection, and afford a goodly sample, without intervals to conduct " phlogistic."

In an observation attached to Mr. Ainsworth's " Introduction"! (query, by the Reporter?) we perceive much good sense, reason and truth ;—well agreeing with what we daily see in the field of practice, in every quarter of the island :—a contrast to Mr. A's introduction.

P. xxxix. " I have the pleasure of observing, that both in Leicestershire and the neighbouring counties, the practice of drilling here alluded to, and the use of drill machines, is considerably

considerably increasing; few arable farms of any considerable importance, but have now drill machines; but the great advantage to be derived from them, must be principally in the tillage or culture preparatory to that operation; the drill husbandry naturally implies land well cleaned and highly cultivated, or the drill cannot be used to advantage; and in this preparatory culture the improvement chiefly consists, for in many experiments in well cultivated land, no difference has been perceptible.

"At the same time it must be admitted, that the drill husbandry is a neater mode of culture; it comes nearer to the garden stile, and gives a better opportunity of hoeing out weeds, but these should be principally destroyed in the preparatory tillage, for the hoe is not sufficient to destroy the couch grasses, colts-foot, docks, and other hardy and tenacious root weeds, without more labour and expense than can generally be bestowed; these should therefore be extirpated by the plough and other implements in the tillage."

These remarks, though the writer of them sets out as a friend to drilling (being perhaps ashamed or afraid to do otherwise) place the practice of drilling in nearly its true light. I of course register them, here, with peculiar satisfaction*.

ARABLE

* THE EARLY MORNING AIR.—Having considered it a duty to endeavor to place Mr. Ainsworth's theory, concerning the food of plants, in its true light, and in strong coloring;—lest, from the conspicuous place it fills, in a public report, a state paper!!! it might, in these talking, frivolous times, become *fashionable;*—it would be a want of candor not to bring before my readers a *new idea,* I believe, thrown out by Mr. A. which does his philosophical ingenuity great credit. The alchemists, though they failed in their main design, made some useful discoveries.

P. xxxvii. "We are told by mariners, that in the calmest weather, and perhaps in all parts of the globe, there is a land breeze that will generally fill their sails soon after Aurora makes her appearance; this is attributed to the sun; but if so, why not a sea (where there is no obstructions) as well as a land breeze? and why not follow the course of the sun? as this is, according to Dr. Ingenhousz, the exact time that plants begin to emit the pure air. Query, whether it is not the perspiration of the infinite number of plants united, that puts that tremulous elastic fluid in motion! If so, this will account for that hour being the most salubrious and pleasantest of all the twenty-four; according to my poor judgment, I have not the least doubt of it, as I have taken the opportunity, since writing this Essay, for numbers of mornings together, and always found the plants begin to wave at that time."

Hence, shall we say, the WHOLESOMENESS of EARLY RISING?—which it would be difficult, perhaps, to account for, rationally (if really a fact, I mean) on any other ground.

ARABLE CROPS.

IN the close of the Reporters section, "Course of Crops," we find the following, statement of the species, and extents of the several arable crops, that are grown in Leicestershire. —It must of course be, in a considerable degree, conjectural.

	Acres
P. 96. "The wheat grown in the County may be estimated at - - -	25,000
Barley, about - - - -	40,000
Oats on turf, or after wheat, or on strong land instead of barley - - -	30,000
Beans 10,000 acres, pease and vetches 5,000	15,000
Green crops, turnips, cabbages, coleseed, potatoes, &c. - - - - -	40,000
Arable land, at or under clover or artificial grass - - - -	85,000
Fallow for wheat or barley -	5,000
Acres	240,000"

These crops are separately spoken of; but seldom in a way that can claim particular notice, in this register of matters of superior intelligence.—In examining the several articles, with attention, I have, I find, marked very little in them, as being proper for extraction.

BARLEY.—P. 104. "Barley is generally supposed to be adapted only to light land, where green crops may be grown, yet Mr. King assured me, that the greatest part of the vale of Belvoir (although strong land) will bear barley, and in great crops when clean fallowed, though unfit for turnips."

Good crops of barley may, under such management, be *grown* on strong lands. But I have rarely seen *fine malting barley* produced on soils of that description.

BEANS.—P. 112. "The county of Leicester was formerly much more famous for beans than at present. About the middle of the last century, when one-half of the county was in the common field culture, it is very probable that one-half of the land of the common field parishes was in the three-shift system of fallow, wheat, beans; this would give 40,000 acres of beans, the same quantity of wheat, and an equal quantity of fallow, supposing the practicable land of the county, as stated in Chap. i, to be 480,000 acres; but it appears from the rotation of crops, that the beans now grown in the county, do not exceed 10,000 acres.

"In all the ancient accounts of the county, beans are named

named as one of its staple productions, but I do not think they are at all famous for them at present."

What is here said, of Leicestershire, is applicable to most or all of the strong-land districts of the kingdom, that have been inclosed from the commonfield state.—Formerly, horses were fed, and swine fatted, with beans;—practices that have declined with the inclosure of common fields.

POTATOES.—P. 133. "The disease in potatoes, called the curl, is now very happily extinct, and is known to have been caused, by the particular variety being worn out, by long continued lateral reproduction, which being but elongations of the original plant of that sort, must, in length of time, perish from age; the remedy by sexual reproduction of new varieties has been successful, and plenty of healthy varieties are now in culture. The curl in potatoes, as well as the canker in fruit trees, are hereditary diseases, and show that the original plant, with all its lateral reproductions, are worn out from age; new varieties of potatoes raised from seedlings do not blossom for some years, which is analogous to fruit trees raised from the pippin or kernel."

The Reporter is here repeating what I advanced, many years ago; while the disease was in force. It has, since, abated; and through the means, I trust which I suggested. But it has not, yet, in *this* part of the island, quite disappeared.

P. 135. "Dr. Darwin says potatoes which have undergone a certain degree of heat, contribute more to fatten animals, because the acrimony of their rinds is destroyed by the heat, and their austere juices converted into mucilage, supposes them best boiled in steam."

Is the above an ascertained fact? or is the whole a mere matter of *supposition?* Query, does a certain degree of warmth induce the saccharine fermentation? Are potatoes *maltable?*

CABBAGES.—P. 128. "Cabbages are supposed to be less casualty as a crop than turnips, and to be in less danger of being destroyed by the fly, or insects; the greatest danger they have to contend with is from drought at the time of planting, as a large quantity cannot well be watered; when the roots have taken to the ground they will do pretty well."

A few years ago, I constructed a watering cart, to guard against drought, at the time of transplanting cabbages, or bulbous rape, or sowing the latter and common turnips, when grown on ridges, in the Tweedside manner. Not to spread the water *over* the ridges; but to deposit it *within* them; through the means of hollow coulters, similar to those which I formerly used, in drilling beans. See Minutes of Agriculture.

For the mode of construction, the method of using it, and its effect, see my WEST of ENGLAND, Minute 64. See also the NORTHERN DEPARTMENT of my present work, p. 80.

BULBOUS RAPE.—P. 117. "In my tours through the county in 1807, I estimate, that between Leicester and Loughborough, and in many other of the best parts of the county, from two to three acres of Swedish turnips are sown for one acre of the common turnip, and probably near two acres to one the county through." Can this estimate be near the truth?—For modes of consumption, see the article, *Sheep*, ensuing.

COMMON RAPE.—The subjoined practice, though not peculiar to the Dishley farm, is in many cases, eligible; and is therefore entitled to a place, here.

P. 126. "Stubble cole, is sown upon the ploughing up of an early stubble, generally oats; and if this can be done about the middle of August, and showers succeed, it is almost equal to summer cole. At Dishley, Mr. Honeyborne informed me, they gather and bind their oats, and set as many lands in a row as they can in shocks, and then immediately plough the cleared lands and sow coleseed, without waiting for harvesting the oats, and afterwards plough and sow the lands occupied by the shocks of oats; dispatch in this business is the great object; a day or two, if a shower occurs, being of great importance; and when the month of August is past, it is too late to sow coleseed on stubbles to any advantage."

GRASS LANDS.—*Meadows*.—P. 148. "The natural meadows on the banks of the rivers, brooks, and rivulets of this county, are very considerable in extent, and many of them of excellent quality: on the banks of the Soar, near Leicester, is a considerable tract of excellent meadow land, which seems formed by the deposition of sediment of that river, through a long course of succeeding ages; in some places large breadths are formed as level as a sheet of water, and as rich as can be conceived: this fertility is kept up by the river, by the process of natural irrigation. Excellent meadow land continues on the banks of that river, down through Quorndon and Barrow, and to its junction with the Trent; these meadows are occasionally subject to inundation, by which, their fertility is preserved, and is, perhaps, increasing; but this river having its source in a level country, without receiving any considerable supply from hills or mountains, is not very subject to sudden or summer floods. The meadows on most of the other considerable rivers are similar."

Grazing

Grazing Grounds —P. 151. "In the south and east of the county is a considerable breadth of rich old feeding land, which is often unsightly, from abounding in ant-hills; these are, however, generally removed by the neatest and best managers, but a good many still remain."

P. 157. "*Breaking up grass lands.*—This is not often done in Leicestershire, at least not old grass lands; the farmer is generally too fond of turf to do this if he had permission, and the covenants or customs or all occupations forbid it; it could, therefore, only be done by special agreement between the owner and occupier. Meadow land that will mow a ton of hay per acre, or more, and rich old pasture land should never be broken up; if such wants improvement, it is best done by draining, watering, and top-dressing. The opinion of the principal graziers and breeders of the county is, that rich old feeding land broken up and converted to tillage, could scarcely be brought to recover its former fertility and nutritive qualities in 40 years, and that therefore it should not be broken up on any account."

LIVESTOCK.

ON this important branch of the Rural Economy of *Leicestershire*, Mr. Pitt has drawn together an ample store of matter; which, if the subject had not been previously treated of, in a fuller, more regularly detailed, and digested form,—might have been deemed a valuable acquisition to the public.—Whatever I may have left behind me, in the field of useful information, and which Mr. Pitt has gleaned up, after me, I will here deposit, as an addition to my own collection. And what I may find of improvement, or alteration, since the time I wrote, I will carefully register; as an enrichment of my own account. To do more would be a waste of "paper and print," and an unecessary load on the shelves of agriculture;—already bending under the weight which has recently been placed upon them.

HORSES.—The subjoined anecdote in the history of the *Dishley breed*, is new to me.—P. 283. "In company with Mr. G. Salisbury, he" (Mr. Bakewell) "went through Holland and part of Flanders, and there purchased some West Friezland mares, which excelled in those points wherein he thought his own horses defective, from which with great labour, expense, and judgment, he produced some capital horses."

MULES.—P. 294. "These are a species of stock which have long been in use in this county. When Ashby Wolds was in its waste state, I have seen a good many mules grazing thereon; and at Lord Moira's, when I was there, were half a dozen mules, got by his own stallion asses;

they

they are used either for draught or the saddle; two were sent with a caravan to Scotland with domestic articles; they are capable of travelling any length, being possessed of more hardiness, patience, and perseverance, than horses, and can subsist on much coarser food; their duration and longevity is surprising: they will begin to work at three years old; are in their prime at thirty, and are said to live to sixty or seventy, and to be then useful; they have been used in the plough, as well as other draught; and they make very hardy and useful hacknies."

ASSES.—P. 293. "Asses are used in many parts of the county for carrying burdens, and have been lately introduced as farmer's stock: at Lord Moira's two or three are constantly kept for carrying turnips, cabbages, or other green food, for the supply of live stock; they are worked by boys, or superannuated old men, or by women, and are, perhaps, the best stock that can be employed for clearing green crops from strong land in wet weather; their step being light, and not poaching the land; they will easily carry two hundred weight; and an ass has been known to carry 40 bricks, of 8lb. each, as its common burden, and will thus do a great deal of work by perseverance, with the assistance of those who are too weak to manage horses. Some have the paniers constructed to open at the bottom, to let out a load of turnips at once, spreading them afterwards; and this stock is approved by all who use them.

At Lord Moira's are also two very stout stallion asses, of 14 or 15 hands high, for getting stock; they are, I believe, of the Spanish kind; one of them was offered to sale by auction when I was there (one being thought enough to keep); the price offered for him was 38 guineas, but he, being valued at 50 guineas, was bought in, and they both remained in hand; they cover at one guinea each mare, and half-a-crown the groom."

CATTLE.—*Breed.*—P. 216. "The *natural* breed of cattle in Leicestershire, is *now* the long-horn."

P. 217. "What was the particular breed of cattle in Leicestershire before the middle of the last century, about which time Mr. Bakewell began his exertions, it is difficult to determime."

On the eastern side of the County, on the borders of Lincolnshire, the short-horned, or a mongrel sort, might be the *natural*, or let us say the *established*, breed; but on the western, and in the central parts of it, the same breed which has inhabited the Midland Counties of Stafford, Warwick, and Derby, time immemorial (I believe) were doubtlessly in possession of Leicestershire.

The

The Reporter attempts a history of the improved breed; but it only tends to mar that which the public previously possessed.

On the *breeding*, *rearing*, or *fatting* of cattle, I perceive not a line that can claim a place, here.

The Dairy.—*Sizes.*—P. 154. "In various parts of the county good dairies are kept, the business well understood, and large quantities of cheese produced, particularly upon Lord Moira's estate to the north-west of the county, adjoining Derbyshire; also in the neighbourhood of Appleby, Snareston, Bosworth, and Hinckley, are dairies of from 12 to 25 cows each, universally of the long-horn breed. In the vale of Belvoir are many dairies, but the Holderness, or short-horn cattle, are kept, as well as the long-horn."

Produce of Cows.—P. 224. "Mr. Ferriman, who has given much vuluable information to the Board concerning live stock, has, in some degree, impeached the skill of the dairy women of this county, and I suspect either from inattention or mis-information has done them great injustice; he says, 'making good cheese is but little understood in Leicestershire; the ground indeed is unfavourable to dairies, the skill of the dairy women is still worse, notwithstanding Stilton cheese is chiefly made in this county.' If this were correct, whence comes the very great quantity of cheese, and of excellent quality, which is found annually in Leicester fair, on Oct. 10, in the very centre of the county, and which cannot come from out of the county without being brought near 20 miles, though I believe some little is brought both from Warwickshire and Derbyshire, but not at all superior to the cheese of the county; this cheese may be somewhat inferior in staple and appearance to the best Gloucester, but is nevertheless a very good and useful article, of a moderate size, from 6 to 9 or 10 to the hundred weight of 120 lb. in part coloured with anatto, and in part of its natural colour.

"The late Joseph Wilkes, Esq. who dealt largely in this article, and whom I have more than once seen very busy in this fair, who sometimes bought up large quantities of cheese for the navy, the capital, or other places of great consumption, would have borne ample testimony to the industry and good conduct of his countrywomen in the management of the dairy, and with many of whom he was personally well acquainted. I have been informed by Mr. M. who was some years out-rider and clerk to Mr. Wilkes, who bought many thousand tons of cheese for him, and whose knowledge of the Leicestershire dairy is accurate as his veracity is unquestionable, that in no country do they know how to make more cheese from their quantity of milk, and in few countries

tries how to manage it better. The quantity of cheese generally produced from a cow, is from three hundred weight and a half to five hundred weight per annum, average four hundred weight."

This is considerably above the average of the cheese districts of the kingdom; and is rarely, it is more than probable, produced in Leicestershire.

Produce of the *County*, &c.—P. 228. "By information from a very intelligent cheese factor who attended Leicester fair, Oct. 1807, I was informed, that the quantity of cheese generally sent there amounts to about 200 tons; the general price this year from 58*s*. to 60*s*. per hundred plain, and to 62*s*. or 63*s*. best coloured; general average about 60*s*. for new milk cheese; skim or two meal cheese of course lower.

"By the same person I was informed, that the quantity of cheese annully sent down the Trent from the counties of Leicester, Nottingham, Derby, and the north of Staffordshire, considerably exceeds 5000 tons; this may be considered as the surplus of those districts over and above their own consumption: the place of destination being the metropolis, and for victualling the navy. Of this, Leicestershire produces at least 1500 tons."

Stilton Cheese.—P. 159. "The following is given as the best receipt for making it:

"Take the milk of seven cows, and the cream of the same number; heat a gallon of water scalding hot, and pour it upon three or four handfuls of marigold flowers, that have been bruised a little; then strain it into a tub to your milk, and put some rennet to it, but not too much, to make it hard: put the curd into a sieve to drain, it must not be broke at all, but as the whey runs from it tie it up in a cloth, and let it stand half an hour or more; then pour cold water upon it, enough to cover it, and let it stand half an hour more; then put half of it into a vat, six inches deep, and break the top of it a little to make it join with the other; then put the other half to it, and lay a half hundred-weight upon it, and let it stand half an hour; then turn it and put it into the press, and turn it into clean cloths every hour the day it is made; the next morning salt it, and let it lie in salt a night and a day; keep it swathed tight till it begins to dry and coat, and keep it covered with a dry cloth a great while. The best time to make it is in August."

Age of a *Cow*.—P. 243. "Mr. Watkinson at Michaelmas 1796, sold a cow for 18*l*. 7*s*. 6*d*. that was full twenty years of age; for near seventeen years in the milking season, this cow had given from ten to twenty quarts of milk per day; was

was in moderate condition when taken up, and only six months in fattening." *

SHEEP.—*Breed.*—Origin and rise of the "new Leicester."—P. 248. "The origin of this breed has been variously traced and accounted for, but all agree in allowing the principal merit of its production to Mr. Bakewell, of Dishley. Mr. Ferryman, who has conversed on this subject with many of Mr. Bakewell's contemporaries, says, that he had formed in his own mind an ideal perfection, which he endeavoured to realize; and that with this view he, with unwearied perseverance, year after year, and at something more than a market price, selected from the flocks around him such ewes as possessed those points, which were most likely to produce the animal he wished for. The sheep of the old enclosures before that time were flat-sided, long legged, and somewhat coarse in their offals. To correct these defects was Mr. Bakewell's object. The idea thrown out by some, that this was done by crossing with the Wiltshire or Ryeland breeds, seems totally erroneous, fanciful, and void of foundation.

"Mr. Ferryman says, about the year 1747, there were a succession of wet seasons, which occasioned a great rot in the rich deep clays, and in a short space swept away whole flocks. Some of the small and indigent farmers were ruined; but the more opulent and enterprizing resorted to the high grounds near Fridaythorpe, in Yorkshire, where they purchased some neat small sheep, which, crossed with the few that remained in their own fields, produced some very useful animals. As the numbers bred for a long time afterwards were not equal to the demand, they sent year after year to the same market. Jobbers were established, who employed themselves in purchasing sheep on the Yorkshire wolds, for the use of the Leicestershire farmers and graziers. Mr. Bakewell engaged these jobbers not to offer their sheep to public sale till he had seen them, and had taken out such as he thought would best serve his own purpose."

This is another anecdote concerning Mr. Bakewell's extraordinary improvements of livestock, which escaped my notice, while I was resident in the Midland Counties. But whether the idea it conveys is not equally "erroneous, fanciful, and void of foundation," as others that have been held out, with equal confidence, may be doubtful. Seeing, as those did who had the good fortune to be well acquainted with

* This extraordinary notice I insert, here, on Mr. Pitt's authority.

with that extraordinary man, how cautious he was, in his communications; and how dexterous, in leading his hearers away from truths that he wished not to be known,—the whole of what has been said about his improvement of sheep, may be little more than conjecture.

It would be very desirable to possess the real history of the improvement of the Dishley breed; not merely as a matter of gratification; but for the purpose of prosecuting, with greater facility and certainty, other improvements of a similar nature. The reality of the improvement itself, is, however, fully established, and more or less known, in every quarter of the kingdom; and the breed may be said to be now assimilated with most other breeds of longwooled sheep within it; tho not with equal propriety.—See EASTERN DEPARTMENT,—*Secretary's Lincolnshire.*

P. 247. "Mr. King, who is the Duke of Rutland's steward, and very intelligent, gave me a variety of information respecting sheep and other matters: he says, the distinction, old and new Leicester sheep ought to cease, as every intelligent sheep master keeps that sort which best suits the land he occupies, and therefore very few but what have crossed accordingly; that the true distinction now ought to be, to call one the strong and heavy, and the other the fine and lighter breed; that upon all the stout rich deep clay feeding soils, the strong heavy breed succeeds well, and will make the most profit; that upon such lands, weight of mutton and weight of wool, are material objects for profit, and that both these objects can be well supported upon the richest and best soils; and that no grazier who has land capable of supporting heavy stock would benefit by introducing lighter, but that even upon such land where the stock was grown too heavy and coarse, much advantage has been derived from crossing with the Dishley breed, by obtaining that form and those points that have in that breed so well succeeded.

"That upon the inferior gravelly and shallower soils, of weaker staple, or inclining to sandy or lighter land, the lighter and smaller boned breed is incomparably the best; upon such land this breed will load itself with fat, and grow to a great weight, whilst the heavy great sheep, with long wool, would not do at all.

"That in the account given by Mr. Young, in his survey of Lincolnshire, of those townships which are stocked with the heavier breed, and those with the lighter, it almost universally occurs, that the former are upon the richer stouter lands, and the latter upon that of inferior staple, where the heavy sheep would not so well succeed."

This perfectly coincides with the opinion I formed on them

them, twentyfive years ago; and I am much gratified in finding a man of Mr. KING's good sense and extensive knowledge of rural concerns, strengthening my opinion.

Letting Rams.—After inserting a sort of broken transcript of my account of prices, from the first letting, in or about 1750, to the year 1789,—Mr. Pitt brings them down to 1807. For which he has my thanks.

P. 257. " From that time to the present, 1807, the numbers have encreased much more than the prices, but the spirit of enterprize amongst the breeders remains undiminished, and their connections are much more widely extended; from 60 to 100 guineas has, to my certain knowledge been repeatedly given for the use of a ram one season, into Staffordshire and Worcestershire, by farmers who have found their account in so doing, by the great improvement made in their flocks. Numbers of rams are now sent from Dishley, and by Mr. Stubbins, Astley, and others, annually into Ireland; in Sept. 1806, six of the Dishley rams, with the shepherd attending them, were unfortunately shipwrecked on their passage to Ireland, in the King George packet, and all lost. Messrs. Honeybourne, Stubbins, Astley, and others, now make regular annual excursions into Ireland on the above speculations.

" The following particulars and facts respecting sheep, were given me by Mr. Astley, who is himself an eminent breeder, upon an extensive occupation, and whose veracity is far above suspicion: That in 1795, he (Mr. Astley) gave 300 guineas for the use of a ram, distinguished by the name of Magnum bonum, being a shear-hog sheep, the property of Mr. Breedon of Ruddington, one of the Ram Society, and had twenty of Mr. Breedon's ewes with him, the serving of which was valued at 120 guineas; total value of the ram for that season 420 guineas; that, in 1796, Mr. Astley gave for the use of the same ram 300 guineas, and had forty of Mr. Breedon's ewes with him, the serving of which was estimated at 200 guineas; total value of the ram for this season 500 guineas. He was this season judged capable of serving one hundred ewes; the year before, when a shear-hog, he was allowed no more than seventy ewes.

" In 1797, this ram was let elsewhere at 300 guineas, and twenty ewes sent with him, the serving of them valued at 100 guineas, and confined not to exceed sixty more; value for this season 400 guineas; thus this ram has made in three seasons, the enormous sum of 1300 guineas.

" In one of my excursions into Leicestershire, Mr. Astley shewed me forty ram-lambs, got by this ram in one season; they had been all reserved, and were kept in pasture, in lots of of ten each; many of them were expected to make capital first rate rams.

"Mr. Astley has since then offered 400 guineas for the use of a ram to Mr. Stubbins, which was refused: I saw Mr. Stubbins's letter, in which, in the most decisive terms, he refused to take less than 500 guineas, and in consequence Mr. Astley resolved to use two of his own shear-hogs instead, which he could have let at 150 guineas each. I was afterwards informed by Mr. Astley's bailiff, that Mr. Astley having a little set his mind upon this ram, had sent him to make the best bargain for him he could, which he had concluded by agreeing to pay 400 guineas down, and to take twenty of Mr. Stubbins's ewes with the ram; the serving of which, and eighty of Mr. Astley's, was estimated at 500 guineas.

"Mr. Astley informed me, that he had rather give 500 guineas than a less sum for the use of a ram which he thought deserving of it; also, that those who have given the highest prices for the use of rams, have generally made the most profit by letting; and also, that no ram has been yet produced that has been thought perfect in all points; yet so nicely and critically similar are the ideas of different breeders, that from a number of ram's, the same individual one has been selected as the best, when separately examined one by one, and without comparison, by a number of judges, and that in a great many instances; yet the similarity and analogy is so close, that without the nicest skill both of eye and hand, no difference in point of merit could be observed.

"The terms of the connection between the Society of Rambreeders and Dishley, which is still looked up to as the fountain head of the breed, is kept a secret; but I have been informed, that the said society for the choice of a given number of rams, and upon the conditions before named, pay 3000 guineas per annum; after which they are at liberty at Dishley, complying with the conditions, to make what they can by ram-letting in common with others."

This society was formed, or forming, at the time I wrote; and I register the subjoined account of it, with further acknowledgement to Mr. P.

P. 255. "Mr. Ferryman gives the following account of the Ram Society and the Associated Breeders: 'I find that there is but very little knowledge to be drawn from them, and even that little must be admitted with extreme caution, for they are divided into two parties, each jealous of the others, but still more jealous of the public; the allowed beauty of their sheep, the symmetry of their parts, the quietness of their dispositions, and their aptitude to lay fat upon the

the most profitable points have gained them such a degree of celebrity, as to enable their possessors to exact from the public large sums annually for the use of their rams. A certain number of these breeders have formed themselves into a society, or rather entered into a combination, and bound each member, by heavy penalties, to the observance of such rules as they imagine will maintain the superiority of their breed, and continue to themselves the advantages of it unrivalled and undivided.'

"'The late Mr. Bakewell bound himself, and his successor, Mr. Honeybourn, binds himself, not to engage nor show his rams to any person, till the members or the society have seen them and are supplied, and not to let a ram to any person within fifty miles of Leicester for a less sum than fifty guineas, for which, and other privileges, the society pay a large annual sum; and Mr. Honeybourn, as well as every other member of the society, confine themselves not to sell, nor to let their ewes at any price, nor to show their rams at any public fair, nor at any other place than their own houses, and that only at stated times, from the 8th of June to the 8th of July, and again from the 8th of September till the end of the season; with several other regulations of a similar tendency.*

"'The opposite Society profess openly to disapprove of these principles, as illiberal, tending to impede the progress of universal improvement, and, of course, as injurious to the welfare of the country. There are indeed some gentlemen of liberal minds, and independent fortunes, who are above rule, and by whose assistance I am enabled to communicate the particulars herewith sent, and which are interspersed in the Account of the live Stock of the County.—R. F.'"

Food of Sheep.—Bulbous Rape.—P. 270. "Another principal resource for the rams early in spring is the Swedish turnips, which are then washed clean, and cut in slices by Hanford's machine, and thus given in troughs, to rams, or other prime stock. Mr. Stone's shepherd informed me, that three bushels per day are thus given to 10 sheep; they are very nutritive, and keep the sheep in good condition, at this scarce time of food."

P. 271. "Mr. Honeybourne a few days ago turned 100 lambs at large into a piece of Swedish turnips, to eat off their tops, which they are doing without touching the roots; the

* Speaking of Mr. Stones's farm p. 43, Mr. Pitt says—"Mr. Stone had nine capital rams, making off for the butcher, having so many above his number. By a rule of the Ram Society, no individual is to let out more than 30 rams in one season."

the tops afford a great deal of keep, and he supposes the roots will receive no injury, and send out fresh shoots; he is thus saving his pastures against winter.

"He sometime ago turned a lot of lambs at large into a piece, containing summer cole, Swedish turnip, cabbages, and common turnip alternately; they began, 1, on the cole; 2, on the tops of the Swedish turnip; 3, on the cabbages, and at the end of three weeks had not touched any part of the common turnips, nor the roots of the Swedish."

P. 39. "Mr. Stone grows coleseed, cabbages, the common turnips, and Swedish turnips in the same field, for the support of his capital store sheep stock, which he disposes of in the following manner: 1st. The summer, or fallow cole, is brought into use; it is generally mown, and carried to turf land for the rams and ram lambs; the store ewes and ewe lambs being seldom indulged with any, and the wether stock being elsewhere. The turnips and cabbages are next brought into use; and lastly, the Swedish turnips. This plant answers the best for supplying the vacancy of sheep-keep, which has often occurred in the month of April, as it preserves its juices completely, and sheep will even eat it from choice after they are put to grass and clover; at which time they reject the common turnip."

Kept Grass.—P. 271. "*Kept grass,* has been named as a food for sheep, and it is a practice with the best managers, to shut up in September a piece or two of pasture land (being then eaten down level and bare) to the spring following for ewes and lands; or if for cattle until the first shoots of grass, mingling with the autumnal herbage, is found to render the whole more wholesome and nutritious to stock, than either of them would be separately; and this preserved pasture is more to be depended upon, as a certain and wholesome supply of early spring food, than turnips or cabbages; though the Swedish turnip from its certainty of standing the winter, has rendered a less quantity of kept grass necessary."

Water for Sheep.—P. 272. "Mr. F. says, 'providing water for sheep does not appear to bave been sufficiently attended to, it is every where believed to be necessary in hot weather for all sheep, particularly those which suckle lambs.'"

An instance lately came to my knowledge of a ewe with two lambs, which had been shut up in a small inclosure of dry land, in hot weather, tho with a sufficiency of grass, but without water,—dying, it was believed, from attendant circumstances, through the want of it.

Shepherding.—P. 275. "Mr. Frisby, of Waltham, recommends, and practises, the dipping of lambs in arsenic water,

water, to kill lice, and prevent the attacks of the fly; a pound of arsenic is boiled well, and dissolved in soap suds and water, then poured into water in a tub, and farther diluted with water, to a proper warmth and quantity, so as to be sufficient for twenty lambs; in this solution the lambs are immersed singly, and laid in a rack on their backs over the tub to drain, squeezing the moisture out of the wool by hand; two or three persons will dip thirty in an hour: the proper time immediately after shearing the ewes; one dipping destroys all their lice or ticks, and generally preserves them through the summer from the fly or the maggot; this account was corroborated by two or three of his neighbours, who are in the same practice. I believe care should be taken not to dip the lamb over head, so as to swallow the solution."

The same objection lies against this practice, as against that of steeping seed wheat in arsenic water; namely that of accidents being liable to arise from it.

Diseases of Sheep.—P. 276. "Mr. Ferryman states, that two spoonfuls of spirits of turpentine to each sheep were given by Mr. Woodroffe of Leak, to part of his flock, which he thought were in danger of suffering from bad weather, and unwholesome keep; many of those which had not the turpentine died of the rot; all which had it escaped."

That turpentine has extraordinary powers, as a medicine, would seem to be fully ascertained; and its efficacy in this almost hopeless disorder, ought certainly to be tried; both as a preventive and as a remedy.

P. 278. "The red water" (query the blood, black water, or braxey of other districts)—"is believed to be owing to the extremes of keep, from very good to very bad, but most frequently when changed from bad to good, and it is thought here incurable. Mr. Watkinson has used a preventative for thirty years, and during the whole of that time he has not lost a single sheep by that complaint, though it was very fatal to his flock before the use of the medicine, which is as follows:

"Two ounces of myrrh, boiled in 60 table spoonfuls of ale; he gives three table spoonfuls to each lambs about Michaelmas, and never repeats it."

At the close of his section, "Sheep," Mr. Pitt places the following *calculation;* which is the result of some pages of figures. Mr. P. modestly acknowledges that "these calculations are clearly uncertain." Nevertheless, I insert their result, as it may lead those who may have more leisure, than Mr. P. would seem to have (from the unfinished state in which he has ushered into public notice the volume under considerations)—to endeavor to bring them nearer to certainty.

P. 282.

P. 282, "From the above data the produce of mutton per acre may be thus calculated, 10 acres gives 8 shear-hogs, at 25 lb. the quarter average. - - - - - - -	800lb.
And, 8 ewes, or theaves, at 20 lb. the quarter, ditto - - - - - - - -	640
Total	1440

"Which is 144 lb. weight of mutton, bred and fatted per acre."

SWINE.—P. 295. "The improvement of hogs in Leicestershire has been attended to with the same care and success, as that of other live stock. At Dishley, some years back, a fine-boned sort, of small dimensions, had been carried to great perfection: I have seen there a hog of small size, when lean, fatted to 20 score weight, or more; his length, height, and thickness, being nearly equal; belly touching the ground, the legs being enveloped in fat, and the eyes scarcely to be seen for fat, the whole appearing a solid mass of flesh. I have measured a small hog, killed there, 13 inches and a half through the chine.

"Mr. Astley, at Odstone, has a very capital breed of swine; they are rather of more bone and larger make than those mentioned above, and will either ripen into good pork or bacon, of moderate size, or may be fatted to a great weight; they are always in good condition with any kind of food."

P. 297. "Very little pains were taken in breeding of swine in Leicestershire, till within these few last years; but Mr. Honeybourne, of Dishley; Mr. Buckley, of Normanton; and Mr. Astley, of Odstone, have now a breed, that are capable of being made wonderfully fat; whilst lean, their frames are gaunt and narrow; but when fat, their backs are broad and straight, bellies light, legs, head, ears, and tail, very small, generally blind with fatness, and their bodies almost without bristles; Mr. Honeybourne's seem to have a cross of the wild boar, both in shape and colour; Mr. Astley's are said to be bred between the Chinese and Berkshire."

"Mr. Ferriman details the following method of preserving brewers' grains, as being practised by a gentleman of great observation, who informed him, that he has for some time been in the practice of keeping brewers' grains in a large cask, with fine holes at the bottom to drain of the moisture; the grains are put into the cask in layers of about one foot thick; salt is put between each layer; they are pressed hard together to force out the moisture, and kept covered

covered to guard them from dust; they are cut out with a knife in small parcels, as wanted, and are thus good food for hogs, or other stock."

PROFIT.—P. 52. "Mr. Marshall complains much of the precarious nature of farming, and thinks the profits more uncertain than even those of the merchant, who depends upon wind and weather, as he can insure against losses; 'while the farmer is left at the will of the elements, without any surety;' and gives instances of stock starving, and crops failing from drought. However, I am of opinion, and always was, that from attention and experience, the profits of farming are but little affected by the seasons; if the weather be wholly favourable, universal plenty must insure low prices; if excessive drought, or excessive rains occur, they are public calamities, and their consequences must be born by the public; and if such be general, high prices are sure to ensue. A difficult or critical season opens a field for activity and exertion, and those whose management has been, and is above par, will generally be gainers by it. In 24 years experience, upon a considerable scale, I always made the most money in difficult seasons. I state these circumstances, as a stimulus to exertion and improvement. Land the most improved, is the least injured in inclement seasons."

These remarks are scarcely entitled to my particular notice; as they allude, chiefly, to the *profession* at large; mine to *individuals*, only. There has rarely happened a more striking instance of their truth, than what now (October 1812) presents itself in this neighbourhood; where the crops of many individuals are rotting on the ground; while those of the more southern and major part of the kingdom, have been well harvested, and now lie securely in the stack or barn. This difference has not been owing to any want of "activity and exertion" (in which Yorkshiremen, to a proverb, are not apt to be deficient); but to a difference in *climature* and a *wetness* of *season*, which *happened* to take place, in this quarter of the kingdom, at the time when the crops became ripe. So far, indeed, from "exertion and improvement" being always a safeguard against the "will of the elements," it not unfrequently happens that forward crops are caught in a wet season, and those of less active managers, are, afterward, well harvested. Much depends on FORETHOUGHT, and much on HAZARD. Mr. Pitt is a *lucky* man.

RUTLANDSHIRE.

RUTLANDSHIRE.

THIS least of English Counties is intimately joined with Leicestershire, and may be considered as a natural portion of it. The western side of the County, which borders on Leicestershire, is a continuation of the cool grassy swells of the latter:—a billowy sea of grazing and breeding grounds.

The eastern side of Rutlandshire, however, bears a different character. It is mostly in a state of aration. The soil, principally, is a redish coloured gravelly loam:—a pleasant sort of soil to cultivate.

The Vale (as it is called), or rather the Bason, of Catmos, which is situated in the center of the County, is a singular passage of land:—a *level* of rock, covered with rich soil,—of a depth sufficient for profitable cultivation; and surrounded by bold swells,—chiefly or wholely of a cool earthy nature. In the middle of this salver, Oakham, the County town is situated.

"GENERAL VIEW

OF THE

AGRICULTURE

IN THE COUNTY OF

RUTLAND.

WITH

OBSERVATIONS ON THE MEANS OF ITS IMPROVEMENT.

By JOHN CRUTCHLEY,

OF BURLEY, IN THE COUNTY OF RUTLAND.

1794."

OF THIS intelligent Reporter, or of his QUALIFICATIONS for the task he undertook, not a syllable is to be found, in the sketch with which he has favored us;—saving what appears in the title page; and excepting what his few succeeding pages evince, as to his general knowledge of rural affairs, and his intimate acquaintance with those of Rutlandshire.

In twentysix pages, only, his observations are comprized Yet we find more appropriate Report, and more practical information,

information, compressed within that small compass, than is to be met with in some *volumes* of the Board's *publications*. Nevertheless, this remains an "original Report," that has never been "reprinted," and, of course, never *published!*

NATURAL ECONOMY.

SURFACE.—P. 7. "The face of the county is much diversified, by small and gently rising hills, which run east and west, with vallies intervening about half a mile wide."

CLIMATURE.—P. 12. "The harvest in this county, is generally later than in the counties both north and south of it, owing I apprehend, in a great measure, to the late sowing:"—together with, shall we say, the coolness of its substructure.

WATERS.—P. 7. "It is well watered by rivulets."

SOILS.—P. 7. "The soil is generally speaking fertile. It varies very much, the east and south east parts, through which the great north road runs, being in general of a shallow staple, upon limestone rock, with a small intermixture of cold woodland clayey soil, and the other parts of the county, being made up of a strong loam, of red land, and of a cold woodland clay; the red land, is a rich sandy loam intermixed with *keal;*" (?) "iron stone is also found amongst it; this soil is esteemed most fertile."

SUBSTRUCTURE.—P. 7. "The under stratum of the whole county, at different depths, is a very strong blue clay."

POLITICAL ECONOMY.

APPROPRIATION.—P. 30. "About one third of the county is uninclosed."

P. 31. "In regard to that important question, whether inclosures have increased or decreased population, I am of opinion, when the first great run of inclosures took place (which was about the year 1760) that in several new inclosed parishes, the laborers wanted employment, therefore were obliged to take shelter in other parishes, or get other em-employment. The reason was obvious. The farmers at that time, laid a considerable part to grass, and the remainder was kept in the same course of crops; and nearly in every respect the like management, as in the open field state. But since better modes of cultivation have been adopted, which are still improving, I have no scruple to say inclosing increases population."

EFFECTS of APPROPRIATION.

All *general* remarks on the EFFECTS of "INCLOSURES," in regard to POPULATION,—must necessarily be inconclusive. Appropriating *Common Pastures*, and completing the appropriation of *Common Arable Fields*,—distinctly considered,—will ever, in their opposite tendencies, have a contrary effect. Common pastures, mostly, and frequently common mowing grounds, are broken up for a succession of corn crops; and of course give employment to numbers, where little or none was required, before. Whereas newly inclosed *arable fields*, especially those of a deep fertile soil, which they mostly are (the best of the lands of a parish or township having almost invariably been set apart for that purpose) are frequently laid down to grass:—permanently, perhaps, if of a cool, deep, rich quality; or, for a length of time, proportioned to their specific natures. Hence, in this case, after the draining, fencing, and roadmaking are finished, fewer hands are required to manage them.

But, as in all open townships, no parts of which have been previously appropriated, there are, necessarily, common pastures, and common mowing grounds, as well as arable fields;—and not only will the appropriation of such townships require additional labour, in the first instance; but, from an increase of exertion, afterward, in proportion to the quantity of land, employed in aration, will necessarily continue to increase population:—as far, I mean, as laborers in husbandry promote it. And hence, on the whole, the effects of appropriation and inclosure on the population of the nation at large, must necessarily, and in defiance of any *calculations* that can be made on *particular townships*, be very considerable. Calculations founded on arable fields, alone, without including the pasture and meadow grounds that inseparably belong to them, can only proceed from gross ignorance of the subject, or some less excusable source.

These things appear to my mind so self-evident, that I think it was ill judged in the Board, to cramp their Reporters with the question.

For the practice of Rutlandshire, in the business of appropriation, regarding *Tithes*, see that article, ensuing.

PROVISIONS.—P. 20. "Corn is something cheaper in Rutland, than in the adjoining counties, (though something dearer than in London) which is principally owing to the want of water carriage; beef, mutton, and pork, are nearly the same as in the neighbouring districts, and as near as can be ascertained about one penny per pound cheaper than in London; but when it is considered, that the prime meat is sent to London, or sold at distant fairs, the price paid for the inferior sort is high."

These

These are appropriate remarks; considerate Report.

MANUFACTURES.—P. 22. "No manufacture is carried on in this county of any account; the want of water, and scarcity of fuel, are the only reasons, and not want of inclination, spirit, or property in the people of the county."

POOR RATE.—After speaking of "friendly societies," Mr. Crutchley informs us—p. 23, "there is also another society established in this county within these few years, which has been of infinite service in promoting industry, amongst the children of the laborers, and the good effects of it have already been felt by the poor rates having been lowered since its establishment, instead of having risen; which I believe to be the case in most counties in England, during the same period; but were the poor rates to stand at the same sum they did some time ago, it might fairly be called a lowering of the rates, because the price of several articles which the poor use, has since the establishment of this society, been raised, and the rental of the county has increased, consequently less per cent, out of the produce, is paid to the rates, supposing the sum of money, in the rate, to be the same; but here the sum itself is lowered, which no apparent cause has so much contributed to, as the institution of this *society of industry*, for which the county is indebted to the zeal of the public spirit of the reverend Mr. Foster of Ryall; he proposed it, and has taken, and continues to take infinite pains in promoting it, and by him I have been favoured with the following account of the establishment of the society, and of the proceedings in it, which, I think useful to add, being convinced that it cannot be too publicly made known, or too generally adopted."

SCHOOLS of RURAL INDUSTRY.

Mr. FOSTER's beautifully simplex plan is seen in the following short extract.—P. 25. "1. That the overseers of the poor of each parish, do immediately provide such raw materials, as wool, woollen yarn, hemp, and flax, as also wheels, and other implements for the employment of the poor of every denomination, as shall be necessary to enable them to do such work, as they are capable of performing, either by spinning, knitting, or any other employment which the overseer may direct; and that the overseers do make complaint, before a justice of the peace, of those who refuse to work, or who wilfully spoil the raw materials given them; and that the overseers shall in the several respects above mentioned, act according to the direction of the nearest justice.

"2. That no person be allowed any relief, till they have done such work as they are capable of.

"3.

"3. That from and after the 1st day of January then next, no person be allowed any relief, on account of any child above six years of age, who shall not be able to knit.

"4. That no person be allowed any relief, on account of any child, above nine years of age, who shall not be able to spin either linen, or woollen.

"5. That the *overseers* of the poor of each parish, shall meet, at the least, once every month, in the church of their respective parishes, upon the Sunday, after divine service; there to consider of the best course and order to be taken and made in the employment of the poor."

This is, in truth, a plan for CULTIVATING INDUSTRY,—raising it from the root. By some it may be thought too severe. And so may almost any wise regulation, or law, when carried to the extreme. But, under the superintendence of magistrates, it might, I conceive, be productive of much good. The principle of it is excellent, and the thought enviable.

Had a plan of this sort been thought of and adopted, half a century ago, during the happy age of VILLAGE MANUFACTURES, it could not have failed of producing great benefit;—not to the *industry*, only, but to the *morals*, of cottagers.—The modern practice of spinning by machinery (a most unfortunate, and, to the rising generation of this island, a most ruinous invention, I fear)—militates, however, against the plan.—The wives and daughters of farm laborers, in agricultural districts are already become almost entirely destitute of employment; unless in the summer months:—habits of idleness and immorality are the natural and much to be lamented consequences.

Mr. Crutchley brings forward another plan for the propagation of industry (p. 26): on principles, however, widely different from the above. This plan we are informed was "proposed, and with great success carried into execution, by the Rev. Mr. BOWYER, in the southern district, in the parts of Linsey, and the county of Lincoln."—This, likewise, was adopted by "the owners and occupiers of lands and tenements, in the county of Rutland, at a meeting holden at Oakham, in September, 1785."

This plan is formed on *Subscriptions* and *Premiums*:—the latter (p. 27.) chiefly "consisting of cloathing, given from the said subscription, to such children of certain ages and description, as in a given time, shall have produced the greatest quantity of work, of different kinds, and of the best quality."

Those two plans appear to me to have nearly opposite tendencies.—The former to secure a succession of moral, industrious farm workpeople;—the latter, to lead away the

the children of farm laborers from their *native* and appropriate habits, to manufactures, and other comparatively useless arts.—The one is raising plants in the natural soil,—the other in a hotbed.

Honorary rewards, especially to children, and, most especially, *distinctions* of *dress*, instead of enuring the plastic minds of those who receive them, to patient industry, tend to implant in them *exotic* ideas, that are unfriendly to the laborious line of life, by which, only, the children of laborers in husbandry can fill, with due effect, that station in society, which is to be desired, by "the owners and occupiers of lands."

On the contrary, children being early induced to assist in *maintaining themselves*, with *their own labor*, merely, without any foreign inducement, or temptation thrown out, to inveigle them from that humble, but indispensible station, would, I conceive, be the best initiation they could possibly receive, to render them useful to society; and most especially, to "the owners and occupiers of lands."

It belongs not to the *landed* interest to throw temptations in the way of the children of farm laborers (of whom, only, I am now speaking or ought to speak here)—which may lead them away from the paths of their parents, or render them dissatisfied with their condition in life.—Trials of power and skill momentarily induce extraordinary efforts; —rouse the energies of *adventurers;—amuse* the *multitude*, for a *while;*—and vanish.

I cannot quit this interesting topic without reverting to Mr. FOSTER'S PLAN.—The principal objection to it appears to lie in the increased attention and attendence which would thereby fall on the overseers of the poor. But if any employment for laborers' children, in the winter months, can be discovered, during the overbearing sway of pesthouse manufactures, might not village school-masters and mistresses be appropriately employed as their assistants? Might not READING, WRITING, and the HABITS of INDUSTRY, be acquired under the same roof;—the teachers' reports of the abilities of the children, to assist in their maintainence, being a warrant to the overseer, and the magistrate?

TITHES.—P. 7. "Nearly one third is subject to tithes, which are usually compounded for. Upon inclosures, land is generally allotted in lieu of tithes. The common proportion now given is one-fifth of the arable land and one-ninth of the greensward."

INLAND NAVIGATION.—P. 7. "At present there is no navigable river or canal in the county, but an Act passed last Sessions of Parliament for extending the Melton Mow-

bray

bray canal to Oakham, the centre of the county, which it is hoped will be of great benefit to it; and if carried to Stamford would be of the greatest advantage, not only to this county, but to the community at large, by uniting the Trent with the Welland, which runs through all the fen county to Boston, and would be the best means of supplying the manufacturing part of the kingdom with corn."

ROADS.—P. 21. "The parochial roads are mostly ill formed, being raised too high before the materials are laid upon them, and the materials are laid on too large; therefore must remain in a bad state, until a better mode is adopted, and parish officers are more attentive in enforcing parochial duty, which is very much neglected.

"A custom prevails, which I hope will soon be removed, that is, parishes not assisting one another with materials; for without this friendly aid, in the parish which unfortunately has no materials of its own, the roads must still remain in that bad state, and be perhaps reproached by their neighbours who should assist them; this custom of each parish, reserving its materials to itself, is carried so far, that even upon the turnpike roads, notwithstanding the turnpike acts are perfectly explicit on this head, the surveyor never thinks of taking materials from any adjoining parish, if the land owners (which is too often the case) make any objection to it.

"The turnpike roads, like the others, have been badly formed and not in good repair; the materials for repairing them, which are stone in general, are laid on in the autumn and winter, instead of the spring; levelling the sides of the roads for the carriages to pass upon, in the summer, would be of great benefit to the roads, and pleasure to the traveller; but this is neglected, which ought not to be, as by this method the roads repaired, would have a long time to settle, and be in good order against the winter."

Yet, unaccountably strange, as it may appear, this plain obvious improvement (after having been thought of and *known)* of the PLAN OF PUBLIC ROADS, which I have been repeatedly recommending, for more than twenty years,—remains, to this time, without general adoption. See my GLOCESTERSHIRE, district *Cotswold Hills*,—first published, in 1789.

RURAL ECONOMY.

TENANTED ESTATES.

IMPROVING FARMS.—P. 32. "Where ploughed land is let upon leases, great care and attention should be taken, in in making covenants between landlord and tenant applicable to the soils; but the great business is, to see them afterwards enforced; for want of this, I have often seen farms greatly injured by the tenants, while the landlord thought himself perfectly secure, by the covenants having been judiciously drawn, but to his great surprise, at the expiration of the term, he finds his farm worse by fifty per cent. When this is the case, the landlord not knowing what to do with his land in this ruinous state, is induced to let it to a monied man at a very low rent, to improve, and on his own terms; this seldom or ever succeeds; the tenant knows well how to manage these terms to his own advantage; and it is more than ten to one, but that the farm is left in as bad, if not worse state, than when he entered upon it.

"Most gentlemen of landed property, have farms upon their estates in this ruinous state, and which must fall into their own hands, or be let at so low a rent, that it becomes comparatively speaking, no estate: when this happens, it is the landlord's interest to take such a farm into his own hands, and put it under the best management possible for four or five years, or until it is got in so good a state, that a responsible tenant will gladly take it upon the landlord's terms: this will be giving an example to others, and satisfaction to himself in seeing his land in a good state of cultivation, and his tenant going on well and following a rotation of crops, by which he will be ultimately benefitted, and the land kept in good condition. This makes the interest of landlord and tenant unite in the same cause, upon which the happiness of both so much depends, that it is much to be regretted when either deviate therefrom.

"Besides, if gentlemen were regularly to take farms into their own hands, that are badly cultivated, and as regularly let them again, when put into proper order, it might be the means of promoting, a great spirit of improvement and good management among the farmers.

"I am sure every good tenant will agree with me in what I have suggested, when he considers, how exceedingly hard it is, upon every industrious occupier of land, to have one or more farms in his parish, so reduced by bad management as to be let, and consequently rated, at half the rent it had been let for, and was fairly worth, at the commencement of a lease; by which means, an additional burthen, (it may be of one half the parish levies, which had been before equal,) is, by bad managers and reduced rents, thrown on the industrious tenants, whose farms are well and properly managed and cultivated. This is only a private injury 'tis true, but I hope it is sufficient to apologize for what I have advanced."

These

These are sensible observations; and show that Mr. Crutchley is acquainted with the management of tenanted estates. In SCOTLAND, this plan of management is not only practicable, but is practised, frequently, on a large scale; and, often, with the most beneficial effects. But, in ENGLAND, where men of large landed property, speaking generally, are themselves less practically acquainted with the means of improvements of that nature, and where proper agents are more difficult to be met with, than in Scotland,—the plan becomes, in a considerable degree impracticable; tho it may be frequently, in itself, perfectly eligible.

In England, I have ever found that when a farm has been let down, by neglect, into the ruined state described by Mr. C. it is generally most adviseable to let it to an industrious tenant, at a fair rent (when restored) and allow him the first year's amount of it (more or less as the case may require) to enable him to bring it up again to a profitable state; he being of course bound, by proper conditions to keep and leave it, in that state.

Most agents, even of large estates (practising lawyers always excepted) have leisure, and ought to have exertion, sufficiently to superintend the *management* of its *tenants;* tho quite unequal, perhaps, to the task of *executing* large *improvements;* scattered, in different and distant parts of an estate.

I perfectly and cordially agree with Mr. Crutchley, in his concluding remarks.—P. 34. "The spirit of improvement has encreased very much of late years, among the occupiers of land in Rutland. The best and surest method to excite that spirit, is to set the farmer a good example, and this can only be done by Gentlemen of property, whose interest is more than equally concerned with the tenant; the advantage to the former being permanent, whilst that of the latter is of a more temporary nature. I think, upon every estate, that the owner should sacrifice a few acres of land, to the trial of every useful experiment, for if the tenants see any advantage resulting from them, they will be sure to follow."

TENANCY.—P. 22. "The greatest part of the land is let to tenants, from year to year."

Covenants.—P. 22. "The covenants between landlord and tenant are in general the same now that have existed a long time back; a few new ones have of late been introduced, namely.

1. "That of only taking one crop of white corn before a fallow.

2. "The tenant not living in the farm house to pay an additional rent of ten pounds a year.

3. "The

3. "The tenant not keeping the buildings and fences in good repair, and after three months notice, neglecting or refusing to repair them, the landlord to have power to enter and do the same; and for the amount of the expences to have the same remedy as for rent. Seven, fourteen, and twenty-one years, are the usual terms of a lease. The tenant not to mow the same grounds two years together, nor twice in one year, but to mow one year and graze the next."

WOODLANDS.

TIMBER.—P. 20. "Oak timber is not much raised in this county; and there is but little fit for the navy. The best sort is used for building, and of late for the canals and navigations; the coarser sort, which is not used for fences, &c. is made into gates, hurdles, &c. and sold at Spalding and Peterborough fairs, and carried into the fen country."

COPPICE—P. 20. "Underwood is cut from twelve to sixteen years growth; some woods are good; others not so good; owing to their having been cut too high from the ground, and not early enough in the season. All underwood should be cut as soon as the leaf is off, and not more than four inches above the ground, which would greatly invigorate the spring shoots; and I am of opinion that wood so cut and managed, in the course of twelve years, will net more by two pound an acre, than if cut high. *Drawing*" (draining) "of woods is another improvement; much benefit would arise by making open grips to carry off the water, which should be opened every third year at furthest."

AGRICULTURE.

FARMS.—P. 8. "The farms are not in general very large; greater in the inclosures than in the uninclosed parishes, but not rising to the great amount they do in some counties; three or four hundred pounds a year is esteemed a large farm; there are a great many very small ones."

HOMESTEADS.—P. 21. "The houses are generally speaking good, but inconveniently situated, being mostly in towns; whereas if they were built upon the farms, it would make them more valuable both to landlord and tenant; the

the offices are not well constructed, there are too few of them, and they are mostly badly connected."

COTTAGE GROUNDS.—P. 8. "There are a great many cottages, by which I mean, occupiers of small portions of land just sufficient to enable them to keep one or two cows, without preventing them from working constantly as day labourers; this custom does not prevail in all the parishes, but wherever it does, the benefit of it is felt by the cottagers themselves in the greatest degree, and by the proprietors and occupiers of the lands in the lowness of the poors rates, and in the industry and good order of that description of laborers. These small portions of land are generally well managed, and made the most of."

On this subject, I have repeatedly spoken my sentiments, in prosecuting my present work. I am not surprized to hear it mentioned, in favorable terms, in Rutlandshire; especially by a resident at Burley.

P. 19. "I think every laborer should have a good garden to his house; the comforts they derive from it are innumerable; it greatly assists him in keeping a pig, and there the poor man, who has only a scanty allowance of meat, must find the deficiency greatly filled up, with a variety of vegetables to eat with it: generally speaking, the farmers in this county, are well disposed to the poor, and if they were to indulge their laborers with sowing potatoes in the angles of the fields which cannot be ploughed, it would be of great support to them in winter. I know several farmers do this, but it is not a general practice."

These would seem to be Mr. Crutchley's *own* sentiments.

OCCUPIERS.—P. 8. "Several gentlemen farm part, and some the whole of their land, and certainly may be considered as the best managers in the county."

PLAN of MANAGEMENT.—P. 8. "*Arable open Field Land.*—All the open fields are under the old course of two crops and a fallow; upon most of the light soils, a great improvement has taken place within these few years, by turnips being cultivated upon part of the fallows, and fed off upon the ground by sheep, that part is then sown with barley, and the dead fallows with wheat; pease and beans intermixed, are usually the second crop upon the clayey soils, and pease alone upon the lighter soils; sometimes white corn is sown after wheat instead of beans or pease, but this is reckoned bad management.

"In some open fields in the eastern part of the county, the following is the course of crops: After fallows, barley, and broad clover sown with it; the second year, the clover is is mown; the third year (being fallow) the clover is fed with sheep, then it is broken up and sown with wheat.

"The manure is always laid upon the fallows, the fallows are never stirred till spring, winter ploughing being deemed hurtful to the land; the whole is sown broad cast. No crop but the turnips, is ever hoed, the red lammas is the species of wheat cultivated; the crops, after the fallows, are generally good and clean, the second crop very much otherwise, particularly upon the light soils.

"Long beam swing ploughs, with four or five horses in length, are in common practice."

P. 10. "*Arable Inclosed Land.*—This is almost entirely confined to the light soils, grass lands meant to be improved by ploughing for a few years after draining, and now and then a small piece of land near a grazier's house for the convenience of straw, being the only strong land that is in tillage. Of the light soils there are two sorts, the red loam, and the lime-stone soil; upon the former, two different modes of culture are adopted; the one according to the *Norfolk* rotation:

"The first year turnips;

"The second year barley, sown down with clover;

"The third, clover mown;

"And the fourth year wheat upon the clover lay.* The other course is, on breaking up clover, to have two crops of spring corn; the third year turnips, the fourth year barley, and sown down with rye grass and clover, and in that state the land is kept for three or four or more years, mowing it seldom, but being grazed principally by sheep, then broke up and sown as before. The turnips are in all cases fed off upon the ground by sheep. Both these methods have their advocates. In the former, excellent crops of wheat are procured. In the latter, a great quantity of sheep-stock is kept, and the crops of spring corn are very large."

P. 11. "Light single wheel and two furrow ploughs are much used upon this sort of land," (light) "and two horses frequently work abreast without a driver."

For a *bad* plan of management, see *Grassland*, ensuing.

IMPLEMENTS.—See the last head.

MANURE.—*Lime.*—P. 10. "This manure has been introduced of late years, and the use of it is now well understood, it being always applied to the fallows, precedes the sowing of the grasses; eighty bushels of lime to an acre is the usual quantity."

ARABLE

* No. That is *not* the *Norfolk* rotation. See EASTERN DEPARTMENT.—*Secretary's Lincolnshire, &c. &c.*

ARABLE CROPS.—P. 11. "I cannot pretend to form a calculation of the crops in the open field lands, as they are very uncertain, it is more easy to guess at them in the inclosed lands, and I should think upon the *red land* four quarters of wheat," (?) "four and a half of barley, eight of oats thirty-five of potatoes, three and a half of pease, and five of beans, about the average quantity per acre; and upon the *lime-stone* soil, three quarters of wheat, three and a half of barley, four and a half of oats, and two and half of pease upon an acre. About two bushels of wheat, two and half of barley, three of pease, four of oats, three of beans, are commonly sown upon an acre; oats are generally sown from the beginning of February to the end of April, pease and beans in February, and barley in March, wheat in October; when land is broken up late for oats, it is even sown as late sometimes as new May-day, and where barley and seeds are sown after turnips, which are fed off late, it is sown as late as May, which is not a good practice."

P. 10. "The wheat is in great repute, being sold into Leicestershire at an advanced price for seed. The sort, the red lammas: other species of wheat are but little known, and consequently not so much esteemed."

GRASS LAND.—P. 12. "Of the inclosures, about three fifths are *permanent grass*, and the other two fifths are *convertible land.* Of the grass land, about one half is good feeding land, the rest of an inferior quality, and used as store land: in general the ground is healthy for sheep and cattle; the land has been almost all laid down with too high ridges, by which means the furrows are frequently wet, and unproductive, and the grass on the tops of the ridges at the same time burnt up: this is an old bad custom, and I am sorry to say, that in the latest inclosed lordships, it has not been corrected. The land is much over-run with ant-hills, and in many places; in want of ponds, rivulets or waterings; draining the sides of the hills, which in general are full of water, would, in many places, remedy this inconvenience, by affording an ample supply of water, for all purposes, and be a great improvement, by laying the land dry below those springs."

Mowing Grounds.—P. 14. "They are chiefly upland meadows; the only meadows which are ever naturally flooded, are those by the side of the Welland, Gaush, and Calmose rivers. Those by the side of the two last are but little flooded, except in heavy rains, when great quantities of water are collected in them, and the water goes off very quick; the Welland river having but little fall, and the meadows by the side of it being very flat; the water goes off slowly, and continues so long upon the land it floods, as to to make the pasturage unwholesome, and frequently rots the sheep."

Breaking up Grass Land.—P. 13. "Some clayey grass land, much over-run with ant-hills, have been ploughed as the quickest and cheapest method of getting rid of them, but the remedy has in general proved worse than the disease; for although we have a great many good farmers upon the light soils, the management of the plough upon heavy lands is little understood. This sort of grass land, though wet and spungy, is frequently broken up without being previously drained, is never winter fallowed, or cross ploughed, and after being repeatedly cropped with white corn, is laid down again to grass, with the ridges in exactly the same state as before ploughing, and the lands impoverished. I speak of the general practice, to which there may be, and certainly are, many exceptions; but I may venture to assert, that four out of five fields of strong clayey grass land, which have been ploughed, have been injured essentially by bad management."

HORSES.—P. 16. "Some tolerable good black horses are bred, but not the very best."

CATTLE.—*Breed.*—P. 16. "Very few cattle are reared, and those few of no particular breed; in general bad ones. A few of Bakewell's breed of long horns, and some of the Devonshire breed, have been lately introduced with an intention of rearing."

DAIRY.—P. 16. "The dairies are very few; except for family use; grazing is the principal object."

Grazing Cattle.—P. 16. "The cattle most in request are the Irish and small Scotch. The Irish have not been known in this country a great while, but they are now bought in preference to the Welch, Shropshire and large Scotch, which were formerly grazed here. The graziers say the Irish are very cheap in comparison to the others. They vary much, some being very good, others as bad; they are all long horned, and by all accounts have been much improved by bulls sent to Ireland from Mr. Bakewell. In general they are, after one summers grass, sent to London; stall feeding being little practised: now and then hay is given in the fields to some of the best, to keep them till after Christmas. Barren cows are frequently grazed."

Store Cattle.—P. 16. "Short horned heifers of the Durham breed, are bought in, at two years old, and sold when three years old in calf to jobbers, who take them to the dairy countries, or to London."

SHEEP.—*Breed.*—P. 14. "The sheep of this country are all of the polled long wool kind: in the open fields they are

are of a very inferior sort, and little pains taken about them. In the enclosures, the breed has been always more attended to, and lately much more than formerly. The breed is in general of the old Leicestershire, but in part of the country near Lincolnshire, the Lincolnshire breed prevails. The prices given for rams are low; from two to five guineas may be called the usual price. The new Leicestershire, or Bakewell's breed of sheep, has, however, of late years, found its way into the country, and as much as fifty guineas has been given for the hire of a ram: some people are very partial to this breed, and all to having some cross of it in their stock. The reason assigned for not liking the intire breed is, that it does not produce so much wool as the old Leicestershire sort; the superiority of it in form of carcase, and inclination to fatten, is universally allowed; and as a proof of the estimation in which it is held, it is certain, that all the ram merchants who profess dealing in the old Leicestershire breed, have had a cross of this breed: the great prices of the rams is the chief reason of its not being generally adopted."

P. 15. "Where there are a number of flies, they" (the Dishley breed) "suffer very much from them. I have seen sheep of this breed quite ruined by the flies, and Welch sheep in the same fields not at all affected by them."

Management of Sheep.—P. 15. "They are sold at two years old from turnips, and two and a half from grass: very few are sheared three times."

Disease of Sheep —P. 15. "The sheep are subject to a disease called the foothalt, which is thought to be catching: paring the feet, and applying the butter of antimony, is the remedy."

Markets for Sheep.—P. 15. "The fat sheep are sold at London, and at Melton Mowbray to go North."

I cannot lay aside this morsel of Report, without expressing my approval of it. I have rarely found so much useful information comprized in so small a compass. Had the materials been better digested, my labor would have been less. But this I freely give when matters that are worthy of attention come before me

GENERAL

"GENERAL VIEW

OF THE

AGRICULTURE

OF THE

COUNTY OF RUTLAND;

BY RICHARD PARKINSON.

1808."

MR. PARKINSON is known to the Public by his different Works on Rural Economy; his remarks not being confined to English husbandry, but are extended to that of Ireland, and the continent of America. His American book I have seen; and read with considerable interest.

Mr. P's MODE of SURVEY of the County of RUTLAND is similar to that of Mr. VANCOUVER, in viewing *Cambridgeshire;* (see Mr. V's CAMBRIDGESHIRE, ensuing; also the EASTERN DEPARTMENT); namely that of going over, or at least visiting, each parish of the County, separately; and endeavoring to obtain, by observation, or enquiry, or both, information relative to certain heads, previously chosen, as the groundwork of Survey.

Seeing the small extent of Rutlandshire, which contains only "fiftythree parishes and four hamlets," and Mr. P's method of obtaining information being directed, it would seem from the matter collected, to *enquiry*, rather than to *personal examination*,—the task might be less laborious than, on first thought, it may appear.

Mr. Parkinson's manner of COMMUNICATING the information collected, differs essentially, however, from that of Mr. Vancouver; who gave *progressively*, and at some length, the observations he made, in *each parish*, under its respective head. Whereas, Mr. P. has *digested* his items of information, in short memoranda, or in tables, under his several *heads* of *enquiry*.

Some of the particulars of these heads are reduced to the table form; and lie in a small compass. But, mostly, they

they are given in *detail*; and swell out pages, where nothing, perhaps, but the *results* were required.

What forcibly arrests the attention of the reader in passing over Mr P's statements, is the minuteness with which he has set down quantities; particularly those of admeasurement. Not only is the extent of each parish, and each hundred, but that of the County itself, given to a perch! even the aggregate quantities of each crop, in a parish, is not unfrequently shown, in acres, roods and perches; and this without explaining the way in which he was enabled to ascertain them. In church briefs and official estimates, it is common to come down to fractions,—to pence and farthings; tho the sum total may amount to millions. This is well understood, I believe, by the initiated in those mysteries, to be done on the *principle* of what, in slang language, I understand, is termed "gullaby:"—a principle, this, on which I cannot, as a brother author, bring myself to conceive, Mr. Parkinson could be induced to act.—If he has approached within one tenth of the truth, in those things, his industry, at least, has great merit.

Another matter of some surprise, in studying Mr P's Report, is excited by not finding Mr CRUTCHLEY'S Report once noticed, *by name!*—tho numerous extracts from it have been taken, and incorporated with that which is now under review; as if they were *this* Reporter's *own!*

Regarding his *real* sentiments, opinions and positions, which are dispersed in his Report, (volume it cannot properly be termed, it being "done up" with Mr. Pitt's Leicestershire) it may be said (without intending any direct offence) they, in matter as well as manner, much resemble what we hear, from the more *eloquent* in *conversation*, at a market ordinary, or other meetings of disputants in agriculture:—that is to say, many good practical ideas, mixed up with a certain quantity of strong prejudices, and ill conceived, unfounded notions; by which, before the argument be ended, the better parts of it are obscured by the worse; and the hearer rises not a whit the wiser than when he sat down.

That Mr. Parkinson was bred a farmer, and has seen some service, in his profession, is undoubted; and he may, for aught I can possibly know to the contrary, be an accurate manager; tho I have rarely known a man of *eloquence*, in any art or science, who could either act in it, or write upon it, with due effect.

In a prefatory "address to the reader," the author's own general remarks on his work are seen.—I give them entire.—P. iii. "Though I have had frequent opportunities of hearing the public opinion, on the Reports already published

published by the Honourable Board of Agriculture, during my journey, in the collection of materials for the following Report, and frequently heard much censure passed on the Reporters for the insertion of opinions so much at variance, even in the same parish, many of which it is asserted, are too absurd and ridiculous for insertion. I have, nevertheless, pursued the same plan, being (independent of my Orders from the Board) well convinced of its utility; for many systems, which have at first been considered as improper or absurd, have at last proved much to the contrary. Besides, from difference of opinion, something useful may be gleaned, and from the comparison of systems in their various stages, every one can chuse that which he thinks best. In drawing up the following sheets for the consideration of the Board, not one parish is omitted, the information being drawn from gentlemen to whom I was recommended,* and whatever I could collect laid down in such a manner as will, I hope, meet with their approbation; having endeavoured to place every thing in so clear a light as to enable any one, in possession of the Report, to gain a knowledge of any part of the county, adequate to buying an estate † or taking a farm. It now only remains for me to observe, that wherever, my own opinion is given, I have endeavoured to steer clear of giving any one offence, as far as is consistent with what I conceive to be the duty of a Reporter, and have endeavoured to give such a general opinion for the improvement of the Agriculture of the county, as seemed to my judgment best adapted to it; in which, should I have erred, I hold myself accountable for such error, observing that, in a *general* opinion error is very liable to creep in, as even on *one field* very different management, from its variety of soils may be necessary, how much more then upon a review of a *parish* or *district*."

The number of pages—one hundred and eightyeight.

Five engravings of cottages, a sheepwash, &c.

An unstained map of Rutlandshire, is joined with that of Leicestershire.

SUBJECT

* A list of those who assisted him is given in the Appendix. Not less than fifty in number.

† The Reporter would here seem to have forgot that he was writing for the *public*; not for land jobbers.

SUBJECT THE FIRST.

NATURAL ECONOMY.

EXTENT.—P. 1. "It is of small extent, being but 48 miles in circumference, and is divided into five hundreds, containing 91,002 acres and 29 perches, which are applied in its several parishes to the uses expressed in the following Table."

These uses are *pasture*, *meadow*, *arable*, *common*, *waste*, *plantations*, *woods*, *water*.—The quantity of each of these, in every parish of the County, is inserted. The totals will be given under their respective heads.

CLIMATURE.—P. 10. "For the quantity of rain fallen for the following eight years, I am indebted to Samuel Barker, Esq. of Lyndon, who formerly kept an accurate account, but has now discontinued his journal." (The years are those of 1791 to 1798.) "Mean of eight years 24.61; but, as the year 1792 is a very large one, the average, probably, should not be more than 24 inches" p. 11.

WATERS —P. 19. "This county is, generally speaking, well watered; the rivers Eye and Welland are its south-west and south-east boundaries; its two principal rivers are the Guash and Chater, with a great number of rivulets, and numberless springs."

The Reporter next proceeds to inform us how each parish is watered:—whether by "springs" or "ponds," or both. But we are not told whether the springs overflow, and cause rills, thereby forming chains of watering places; or whether the ponds are natural or artificial.

The *extent* of water (of what description is not mentioned) is set down at 44 A. 0 R. 22 P.

SOILS.—P. 11. "Under this head will be shewn the number of acres of the different soils in each parish, as near as could be computed throughout the county,* in alphabetical order.

ASHWELL, - - 600 acres of red land, 600 acres of good clay, and 600 acres of poor clay.

AYSTON, - - 590 acres of red land, 298 of white clay.

BARLEYTHORPE,

* In p. 16, it is said "as near as could be computed from the best information which I could obtain."

BARLEYTHORPE, - 250 acres of good clay, 500 acres of poor clay, 250 acres of hazel earth.

BARROWDEN, - - 150 acres of red land, 750 of white stony land, 600 of black clay.

BELTON, - - 485 acres of good clay, 242 of poor white clay, 243 of gravelly clay."—And so of the rest; without calculating the quantity of each,—in the County at large.

P. 16. "The soil of this county is, generally speaking, fertile, varying, as I have shewn above, very much; the east and south-east parts through which the great north road runs, being in general of a shallow staple, upon limestone rock, with a small mixture of cold woodland, clay soil. The other parts of the county are composed of a strong loam, red land intermixed with keal; (iron-stone is found amongst it.) This soil is esteemed most congenial for convertible tillage crops."—No map of the soils of Rutlandshire.

FOSSILS.—P. 18. "There is nothing worthy of remark in this county under this head, except that at Ketton there is a kind of stone very proper and famous for buildings. There is also in many parts stone for lime, consisting of a soft and hard species."

SUBSTRUCTURE.—P. 17. "The understratum of the whole county, at different depths, is generally a very strong blue clay."

SUBJECT THE SECOND.

POLITICAL ECONOMY.

APPROPRIATION.—P. 111. (chapter "Wastes") "To the honour of this county, I have to observe, with the greatest satisfaction, that there is no land in it which can be thus denominated."

Nevertheless, at the foot of the column, headed "Waste," (in the table of "Extents,") we find thirty acres; and at that of "Commons," 693.

In a section, entitled "Divisions" (p. 5.) Mr. P. has given an alphabetical list of parishes, as they are comprized within each division of the County; mentioning their several states of "Inclosure:"—not merely in regard to appropriation; but

but noting the sorts of fences (as hedges, walls, &c.) and the species of hedgerow timber.—The *commonfield parishes* appear to have been, at the time he wrote, only eight in number.

FUEL.—P. 153. "Coals are now the general fuel of this county, which are brought up by the canal to Oakham—They are however mostly used with wood; and there are, from my information, four or five parishes where wood is still the principal material for fuel."

MANUFACTURES. (P. 159.)—Under this head, Mr. P. has inserted a literal transcript of Mr. CRUTCHLEY's remarks on the subject, without the least acknowledgement; and those, only. See p. 244, aforegoing.

POOR RATES.—After giving, in detail, the rates of each parish, which vary from 1*s.* 6*d.* to 5*s.* in the pound; and after transcribing Mr. C's observations on Cottages (without acknowledgement) see p. 251, aforegoing, the Reporter says, p. 34, "The average of the poor's rate through the county, is to" (two) "shillings and seven pence per pound;" but without explaining any one circumstance which causes the disparities.

Again, in another section, entitled "Poor,"—*this* Reporter has availed himself of Mr. Crutchley's account of the SOCIETY of INDUSTRY formed in Rutlandshire. But, extraordinary, as it certainly is, after giving the origin of the institution (in Mr. Crutchley's words) to Mr. FOSTER, and saying (in Mr. C's words) "*I have* been favoured with the following account," leaves out, entirely, Mr. F's plan; and proceeds to copy the account of the meeting, at Oakham,—relative to the adoption of Mr. BOWYER's plan!

But this aukward suppression may have been done (by some one) lest any plan, bearing the impression of nature, reason, or common sense upon it, should tend to show, in too conspicuous a light, the reigning *taste* of the times, and the consequent *aim* of the literary Manager of the Board. So obvious an act of suppression, by an *agricultural* conductor, could not, I conceive, be well accounted for, in any other way.

The public are indebted to Mr. Parkinson, himself, for bringing down (by adding to Mr. Crutchley's tables) the progressive state of Mr. *Bowyer's Society*, from 1794 to 1806; when it appears to have been in a *flourishing* state.

TITHES.—Mr. Parkinson's account of those of Rutlandshire, corresponds pretty nearly with that of Mr. Crutchley (see p. 246, aforegoing). Having noticed the circumstances of each parish, in regard to tithes, Mr. P. says, p. 32, "It may be observed, that the greater part of the parishes are exonerated from tithes, either by modus or being made free

free. This desirable object has been attended to in all the recent enclosures, and the greatest advantages in every respect have been the happy consequence to both the clergy and the laymen."

There were, it is probable, more tithefree parishes, in 1806, than in 1793: owing to the appropriations which probably took place, during that period. This being as it may, Rutlandshire may be said to be happily circumstanced, in regard to this *now* impolitic and irrational impost.

Mr Parkinson, in enumerating the " obstacles to improvement," speaks, at some length, on the impolicy of tithes. His leading remarks show sufficiently his general sentiments concerning them

P. 171. " Tithes are, in so many lights or points of view, such obstacles to improvement, and so universally declared to be such, not only in this county, but in all counties that ever I was in, that it may perhaps, be deemed superfluous for me to dwell longer on the subject than merely to say, I found them a severe preventitive to improvement in agriculture, in the county of Rutland, and also to the increase of population; and that, therefore, it were most earnestly to be wished, that some *equitable* means could be devised for their commutation. Many hundreds of acres are kept in grass, carrying only one ewe and a half, (to raise lambs) per acre, when in pasture; and producing, if in meadow, about one ton of hay per acre; which, were they exonerated from tithes, would be pared and burnt, and brought into tillage, not only producing many valuable crops, but from the straw being properly made into manure and compost, and laid on the land, would be much improved, at the same time, that the community would be largely benefited both by the production of large crops of grain, and *more stock* also, being kept per acre, and where only one man and two boys had been employed, there would be one hundred people comfortably maintained and employed."

INLAND NAVIGATION.—The remarks, under this head, are copied from Mr. CRUTCHLEY; with, however, the following additional observations.—P. 158 " The canal is frequently defective in the summer season, from the very scanty supply of water. From my view of the county and the hills which surround the canal, I am of opinion, that an able engineer would obtain by Elkington's System of Drainage, an ample supply of water; should this, on trial, prove to be the case, the advantages would be immense, not only to the canal, but to the lands below those hills, which are very wet: thus two birds would be killed with one stone, and the expense could by no means be equal to the advantage."

ROADS

ROADS.—After giving a sketch of the state (as to good or bad) of the roads of each parish of the County, Mr. P. proceeds to transcribe the whole of Mr. CRUTCHLEY'S observations; excepting those relating to the raising of materials (see p. 247, aforegoing). Hence, let us hope, the injurious practice, there spoken of, has been rectified.

In elucidation, it would seem, of Mr. Crutchley's remarks on Parish Roads, Mr. P. favors us with a *picturesk* description of the bye roads of Rutlandshire. I transcribe it the rather, as it will convey to my readers a tolerably fair specimen of Mr. P's manner of writing.

P. 155. "I observed, that where enclosures had taken place, and new roads had been formed, especially if it happened to be over ridge and furrow, that the greater part of the land allotted for the use of the road was rendered *useless;* for though there were 40 feet appropriated for the purpose of a road, yet, from their method of making the road, which is by raising a very high bank in the middle, with two steep sides, leaving on each side a space like unto a fence ditch, and betwixt each of these spaces and the outside boundary of the road, is left a high narrow ridge, entirely useless to the road; the middle part not more than from nine to ten feet in width, is the only space out of the forty feet which is usable; this space is covered in a flat manner with large stones; a track, or hollow place, is soon formed on the top or middle of it, by the horses in carts, &c. and ruts of considerable depths on the sides, so that it is impossible to quarter with a single-horse chaise, but the traveller must keep the wheels of the vehicle in the ruts, by which both he and his horse are thrown and tost about in the most horrid manner imaginable; a chaise and pair has much greater difficulties to encounter, for as the horses cannot quarter, they go jostling one against the other, and keep slipping into the deep ruts, and are thus liable to fall every step they take, at the imminent risk of breaking the carriage, harness, &c. &c. By what I have stated, the reader will easily picture to himself the hazard there is in one carriage passing another on such roads, for, from the steepness of the sides of the bank I have already described, it is impossible to travel on them; but on meeting any other vehicle, each traveller is obliged, at the risk of being overthrown, to draw out of the ruts, which is not effected without difficulty, and give way by drawing partly on the slope, whence the water is prevented from draining off into the side drain, by those ridges on each side of the road, which are also too narrow for any carriage to pass upon; and even if a horseman attempts to go upon them, from there being hollow bad places in them, and if he once gets on on them, he cannot easily get off again; he is in more danger than though he were to leap over the side ditches into the fields on each side; on the whole, a worse system could not be pursued."

This description reminds me of the roads of the Vale of Pickering, some twenty or thirty years back, when I described them (in my YORKSHIRE). I am happy in being able to say, however, that the absurd practice, there censured, is no more.

SUBJECT THE THIRD.

RURAL ECONOMY.

TENANTED ESTATES.

ESTATES.—In the section, "Estates and Management," the Reporter has merely inserted the *names* of the principal proprietor, or proprietors, in each parish in 1806.

TENURES.—P. 23. "These consist of freehold, leasehold, and copyhold; but are chiefly freehold, as will appear by the following accurate account"

Then follows a list of the parishes, with the tenure, or tenures, prevalent in each.

IRRIGATION.—I may be censured for inserting, here, the subjoined extraordinary and *unfashionable* strictures on watering lands. But it is well to hear evidence on both sides of a case; and the sentiments they contain, may enable us to form a right judgment of the writer's specific character (if one may so speak with due respect of an author) as a public writer on rural practices.

P. 114. "As this practice has long been held up as very advantageous, I am aware, that I tread on tender ground when I venture to assert, that the contrary has been generally proved to be the case; though I assert this from experience, could I not bring forward facts in support of my assertion, I believe I might not have ventured it. The system has been pursued by a gentleman in this county, of the first respectability, in a most correct manner; he has now discontinued the practice. The following is an extract from a letter with which he was so obliging as to favour me since my departure from Rutland: 'In my opinion 'watering renders the quality of the herbage and *the land* 'the worse for the process. Where land is tolerably productive,

'ductive, and in a situation where a quantity of grass food 'is not required, I should certainly not advise it: I think 'the land may be turned to better account without it. 'But I think there are many situations, particularly on 'gravel, sand, or open soils, where it may be very advan'tageous; the produce, by such means, is certainly much 'increased, and, in some instances, rendered larger when 'very little otherwise would be produced.' Though the produce is encreased, yet it becomes in time, in a few years, of so coarse a nature, and mixed with rushes and water plants, that cattle frequently refuse to eat it, and when it is eaten, the appearance of the cattle proclaims it far from being of a nutritious nature. I was formerly an advocate for irrigation, and am still on such soils as are described in the above extract; but having had since opportunities of viewing several water meadows which have been of long standing, which have operated to the disadvantage of both the herbage and the land, I have been obliged, in a great measure, to alter my opinion."

In treating of the watering of lands, there are three ESSENTIALS to be considered:—the nature of the *land;* the specific quality of the *water;* and the *method* of using it. But, in the above *decisive* remarks, one of the three, only, is brought forward.

TENANCY.—Having mentioned a few farms that were let on lease, being the whole, perhaps, he heard of in the County, Mr. P. says, p. 34,—"the greatest part of the land, it will therefore appear, is let to tenants from year to year."

RENT.—At the foot of a table of rents, payable in each parish, showing, it may be presumed, the average rent of each, is this entry,—P. 31. "The average rent of this county is about 21s. per acre."

WOODLAND.

WOODS.—In the general table of *Extents*, the total of the column "Woods," stands 2815 A. 2 R. 34 P.

PLANTATIONS.—And at the foot of the column "Plantations," we find 65 A. 2 R. 0 P.

HEDGE TIMBER.—It is mentioned, above, that, in a section entitled "Divisions," the Reporter has mentioned the sort, and given, in general words, the quantity, of timber, in the hedges of each parish of the County.

Mr. Parkinson is friendly to trees in hedges. and so am I. But our attachments have arisen from somewhat different

ferent motives. The following are Mr. P's opinions on the subject.

P. 108. "I have every reason to *believe* that where land is well enclosed by good thorn-hedges, with timber trees in the rows, the soil is made more fertile, and that were any given number of acres to be enclosed in fields of from 20 to 15, or 20 acres, with those *shadowy* fences, and a like quantity of acres, of like quality, but only enclosed by post and rails, that the part which had the *shady* fences would, in process of time, be far superior to the other in fertility; and although there should be some loss in produce by the sides of those fences," (where only the shaddows fall!) "that the middle parts of the fields" (where no shaddow could fall!!) "would, by their produce, more than compensate for such partial loss, which would be owing to the *shade* and warmth produced by the fences."

That hedges promote the growth of *grass*, no one of experience, I believe, will doubt:—not by the *shade*, I conceive, but the *warmth*, they occasion. But Mr. P. is a SHADDOWIST (an original character),—a friend to *shade* rather than to *sunshine*. He speaks of the use, even, of large *ash* trees in the fence of an *arable* inclosure!

P. 108 (In continuation of the above)—"I am also of *opinion*, that the mildew would partly be prevented by the fences, from an instance which I noticed in a crop of wheat of my Lord Winchelsea's, which was affected by the mildew; there being on the west side a plantation, it was clearly discoverable to the exact distance which the sun was prevented shining upon it, that the wheat looked much whiter, and was not so much affected by the mildew. There were several large ash trees in the east side, and as far as their shade extended, the same effects were very visible."

I have repeatedly given my sentiments on the subject of trees in hedges; more particularly in the MIDLAND COUNTIES.—It would be time ill spent to comment on the above remarks.

AGRICULTURE.

FARMS.—This being one of Mr. Parkinson's heads of enquiry, in making his parochial survey, he has set down the scale of sizes, and frequently the number of farms, in each parish; without any further notice of them, than what is contained in the subjoined extract: which, it may be seen in page 250, aforegoing, is nearly a literal transcript

script from Mr. CRUTCHLEY'S Report; to which this circumstance is highly creditable; in showing that it is able to stand the test of a parochial survey.

P. 30. "By the foregoing account it will be seen that farms are by no means large in this county, and never rise to the great amount they do in some counties, three or four hundred pounds a year being esteemed a large farm; there are a great many very small farms."

HOMESTEADS.—*This* Reporter,—having formed a table of the number of "farm houses," "dwelling houses," "cottages," "repairs," and "by whom done,"—inserts, at the foot of it, a literal copy of Mr. CRUTCHLEY'S remarks. See p. 250, aforegoing.

COTTAGE GROUNDS.—I am happy in fully agreeing with Mr. Parkinson, on the subject of the following remarks.

P. 27. "The rent of cottages varies very much; in some towns in the county, a comfortable house with a good garden is let at 1*l.* per annum; these are hired of gentlemen; but in some towns where the cottages are let at second-hand, high rents are paid for them, and frequently as much as 2*l.* given for a bad house without any garden. The comforts derived from a garden are so many, that I think it very proper that every cottage should have one: the poor man would thus be enabled to keep a pig; and from the variety of vegetables and roots which he could by this means raise, would fill up the deficiency of a too often scanty portion of meat. I have in general, however, found the farmers well disposed towards the poor; and were they more generally to allow to their labourers to plant with potatoes the angles of such fields where the plough cannot be used, it would be attended with very beneficial consequences, and the produce be of very great support to them in the winter."

P. 104. "At Oakham three acres of ground are yearly taken from the bean field in the occupation of farmers, and divided into 24 gardens, for the use of the labouring people, for which they each of them pay 5*s.* per year to the farmer from whom the land is taken. At Hambleton, in like manner, a 3½ acres close is divided into 14 gardens, and the like rent paid. Half of this quantity being sown with barley, and the other half with potatoes."

These are admirable regulations, where cottages are destitute of garden grounds.

PLAN of MANAGEMENT.—Mr. Parkinson's section, "Course of Crops," is the longest in his Report. The subject, indeed, is endless, and allows of indefinite space, for opinion and argument.

Mr. P's account begins with his parish memoranda; in which his list being alphabetical, the *commonfield* management

ment is mixed with that of the *inclosed lands ;* and this without any explanation, or remark, concerning the various and miscellaneous courses there exhibited ; the remainder of the section being filled with a dissertation on manures (rather than on the course of crops) ; and with disputations between the Reporter and Mr. Hinton, about whether one or two "white crops" *(corn* crops) ought, on the lighter lands, to precede the turnep crop. A rencounter which turns out to be nothing more than an indecisive skirmish.

Were it not odious to draw comparisons, I would here say, that, in the two short extracts inserted aforegoing, p. 251, there is more intelligence, more useful information, and estimable Report, than in the sheet of letter press, now under review.—*There*, the general management of the *common fields*, and that of the *inclosures*, are separately and clearly stated. The student who has not yet passed his novitiate, may read and understand them, at sight.

MANURES.—In Mr. P's parish register, concerning this "main spring of husbandry" (as Mr. P. justly terms them) we observe but little variety, in Rutlandshire. *Yard dung*, as in other recluse districts, is the prevailing species. In the Stamford quarter of the County, *town manure* is in use. Some little *sheepfolding* is done. But even *lime* does not seem to have become general, in 1806. See p. 252, aforegoing.

On the *management* of *dung*, we find extraordinary strictures. Not under the head "Manure," only, but under that of "Course of Crops."—In these, we hear of the "old practice," the "present practice," and the "improved method."—The first, which this Writer *praises*, is the slovenly practice of letting the winter's dung lie, undisturbed in the yards, until wheat seed time ; and, then, plowing it into fallowed ground, for wheat,—long or short as it may happen to be.—The second, which this Writer *condemns*, is that of turning it up, in the yard, or carting it into the field, where it is to be used ; and there piling it for turneps, or other fallow crop ;—a practice which is now pretty generally pursued, by superior managers, in every quarter of the kingdom. The last, is that of forming yard dung into compost ; which this Writer *extols*, as if it were something new ; or an improvement of his own invention. But, perhaps, he means only to intimate (for he does not directly express it) that he has found out a new method of making "compost dung." He does not, however, divulge it.

The *principle* on which his *reasonings* turn,—that is to say, in other words, his *theory* of *manures*,—is such, "I will be bold to say," as no student can understand.

P. 90.

P. 90. "By the *old* practice, more salts were retained in manure by carting it away, as the cattle, &c. made it, and laying it on the land in its long state, and ploughing it in, and when it is laid in the fold-yard, by being continually trodden down, it became firm, and did not lose so much of its virtues by exhalation; nor did it ferment so much, or was there an opportunity for the salts to drain away from it so much as they now do By the *present* practice of turning the manure in the fold-yard, or of carting it out and laying it in hill, although it is made shorter, or more sightly thereby, and spreads better on the land; yet the strength of the manure is diminished, by reason of the turning it, causing such a fermentation to come on, as is sufficient to carry off by evaporation some of its most saline nutritious qualities, without being the cause of destroying the seeds of weeds, and further, by laying it up in that light state, the rains penetrate in such a manner, as to carry off much of its strength in copious and repeated discharges of *black water*; and it may be seen to operate in these two ways, in every succeeding rain for some time, until, I have but little doubt, nine-tenths of its valuable particles are drained and evaporated away."

P. 51. "By the present system under turnips, barley, clover and wheat, the land gets so much reduced from being only dunged once in four years, and then too frequently with a little light strawy sort of dung, which, were a cart load of it reduced into mould, would but consist of about eight bushels, therefore twelve loads would but be ninety-six bushels per acre in four years, when, in the course of that period, by the method I prescribe, 720 bushels of good fertile earth would be laid on the land per acre.* The salts would also be retained in a much greater proportion, bushel for bushel, in the latter than in the former; indeed I have some doubts whether any salts remain in the manure at all, under their present management of it."

Speaking of the sweepings of the streets of Stamford he says, p. 93, "These sweepings, &c. are best when taken up after heavy showers of rain, which wash the tops of the houses and the channels, &c. and bring down quantities of soot, urine, &c. which get mixed with the finely pounded soil in the streets, and are then laid amongst stable dung, &c. on a hill. The rains which fall do not wash away the salts, as this sort of town dung absorbs them, and keeps them

* That is to say, seven or eight times as much. Yet not a word about the *quality* of this earth before fertilization, otherwise *salination*; nor how, nor where an indefinite *quantity* of it is to be found.

them in."—It surely must be *salt unique* which "heavy showers of rain" are unable to "wash away," when exposed, and thinly spread, on a pavement.

P. 92. "On reference to my first edition of The Experienced Farmer, and to my Farmer's Tour in America, it will be found I strongly recommended the use of *compost dung.* Since that time, from *a few chemical ideas* and actual experience in *Ireland,* have had reason, still more strongly, to recommend the making and using compost. For at Slane, from 100 loads of straw dung which had been but two months in making with cattle, horses, and pigs, made made up into a hill of compost, I carted out 242 loads of compost, which being laid upon a piece of land worn out and exhausted, by having had eight successive crops taken from it, and no dung during that time, caused it to produce four very extraordinary good crops, viz. turnips, barley, potatoes, and wheat—(See this fully described in my English Practice of Agriculture in Ireland, page 29). It is plain, that the wonderful increase in the manure arose from the salts of the raw dung having been absorbed by the earth, and thus acting like yeast put to flour, and that its *strength* did not arise from the quantity of strawy matter, but from the *salts* contained in the *straw.*"

The modern philosophers of Ireland, I trow, will not thank, the Reporter for holding this out as *Irish chemistry.*

As to what SPECIES of SALT the Writer is speaking of, throughout those recondite remarks, and in which the entire virtue of dung would seem to reside, the reader is uninformed;—nor does the Author explain to him how *any salt,* in *any quantity,* can fertilize a soil in the "wonderful" manner described.

TILLAGE.—*Plowing.*—Mr. Parkinson has registered the plow team of each parish; which varies greatly; accordingly, no doubt, to the soils, as has been noticed by Mr. Crutchley. Mr. P. appears to attribute it, solely, to another cause.

P. 42. "How to account for the very injudicious method of ploughing, which is practised in this county, I should have been at a loss, or for what reason, from five, to six, seven, and eight horses, and three men, could possibly be employed with one plough, had I not witnessed what gave me reason to suppose it originated from the time of the year the fallows are made. I saw, whilst in the county, ploughing, if it might be so called, (as in some places the earth was absolutely torn up as deep again as it ought to be, and in other places entirely missed) performed in the month of July, to the greatest distress of the number of horses I have above-mentioned, and the destruction of the ploughs and harness

harness, I could then nc longer be at a loss for a reason why such numbers were employed."

This was the practice of feudal occupiers, I believe, throughout the kingdom; and, on strong soils, which, when finely pulverized, and freed from vegetable fibers, are liable to flux, or run by heavy rains, into a state of mud,—the practice of breaking up summer fallows, after the spring crops were sown, and it is more than probable,—grew out of experience.—See my MIDLAND COUNTIES, &c. &c. on this subject. Also Mr. CRUTCHLEY'S Report, p. 252, aforegoing; where he says—" The fallows are never plowed till spring; winter plowing been deemed hurtful to the land;"—and I do not perceive how the land could be injured by autumnal and winter plowing, unless by its being thereby rendered too pulverous, and fluent, by the frosts of those seasons;—and thus being rendered more liable to *suffocate* the tender wheat plants, in early spring; by the incrustation of the mud, and the consequent deprivation of air from their roots.

Fallowing.—Another section of parochial memoranda is set apart for this process; and, in the close of it, Mr. Parkinson censures, in more direct terms, the practice under view. But he appears to be there censuring a slovenly method of pursuing the practice, rather than the practice itself. One is lead by his strictures to conceive that he has neither made, nor seen the effects of a clean summer fallow.

ARABLE CROPS.—Mr. Parkinson has formed a Table of the quantity of seed, and the acre produce, of each grain crop of the several parishes of the County. The averages are, as follow.

Wheat, ...	Seed 3	bushels	Produce 22¾
Barley, ...	—— 4	——	—— 32½
Oats, ...	—— 5½	——	—— 42¼
Pease, ...	—— 4	——	—— 24¾
Beans, ...	—— 4¾	——	—— 23¾

After this Table, each crop, with a sort of synopsis of its cultivation, appears in a separate section. But no distinctions being made, as to the specific natures of the different *soils*; or whether they lie in the state of *common field*, and of course liable to parochial regulation; or in a state of *inclosure*, under unrestricted management; much practical instruction cannot be expected, from the details.—Nevertheless, as there is something new, in the arrangement;—the materials having the merit of being concise; and some of the sections being interspersed with incidental items of information;—I think it right to insert here, the more important of those crops.

WHEAT.

WHEAT.—P. 66. "1. Preparations, by two or three ploughings. 2. Manure, with yard dung, and some lime. 3. Season, in October. 4. Putting in, by the plough on fallows, by one ploughing, and the seed harrowed in on clover leas. 5. Seed. 6. Steeping, in brine strong enough to bear an egg; by some only in pure water, merely as a washing. 7. Sort, Red Lammas. 8. Depth, from 3½ to 4 inches. 9. Drilling, not a practice. 10. Dibbling, not practised, except by Lord Winchelsea. 11. Water furrowing, nothing particular as to system, but generally practised. 12. Hoeing, by the horse hoe, but only by Lord Winchelsea. 13. Feeding, some little eaten off by sheep. 14. Reaping, &c. by the sickle; shocked, but not capped. 15. Distempers; but very little affected by the mildew this season; by the smutt, a great many; crops by burnt and red gum, none; cockle eared and root fallen very little 16. Stacking; common methods in long and round stacks, foundations on timber, or stone pillars and caps. 17 Threshing, by the flail. 18. Price, 75*s.* to 84*s.* per quarter. 19. Grinding, paid by toll, at the rate of 2 in 24, for grinding, cadging, and carrying. 20. Bread, nothing worthy of observation. 21. Stubbles, these are mown, by some for thatch, others for litter; and by some farmers are not mown at all."

BARLEY.—P. 67 "Is ploughed once, harrowed, and rolled. 1. Put in without ploughing, none; and none scarified. 2. Manuring, none applied to this crop. 3 Drilling, only practised by Mr. Wright, of Pickworth, whose crops were very thin. 4. Time, in April. 5. Sort, long eared, a little of the sprat, and a small quantity of big of the four sided kind; some barley sown by Earl Winchelsea for the winter, for sheep-feed during that season; and some (one acre) eaten off by way of an experiment, as late as May, which proved as good a crop as that from whence the sheep were taken off a month earlier, only later in harvest. 6. Seed. 7. Depth, one inch and a half. 8. Rolling, by the common wood rollers. 9. Harvesting, mown and cocked. 10. Produce. 11. Straw, given to cattle in the winter. 12. Awns, broke off by some only with the flail, by others with an iron chopper, which process is termed faltering. 13. Malt, made as by act of parliament directed. 14. Price, of barley, per quarter, 38*s.* to 42*s.* of malt, 74*s.* 15. Bread, raised with yeast, salt, &c. and laid in sponge.* It is a practice to eat off

* "This county" (Note, p. 17.) "produces barley of a very superior quality, so that the inhabitants call it *corn*, calling other grain by its name, such as wheat, oats, &c."

Does not this serve to show that *barley* was formerly the *bread corn* of Rutlandshire? In Scotland, *oats* are termed "corn;" and, in Wales, *barley*; which is, there, the ordinary material of bread.

off turnips very late, so that barley and seeds are not sown often until May; this is a very bad practice: indeed all their harvests here are later than in the counties both north and south of them, which in a great measure is to be attributed to the very late sowing."

OATS.—P. 68. "As to tillage, the ground is ploughed once, harrowed, and rolled; no seed put in without ploughing, nor any land scarified. 2. Manuring, little or none applied. 3, and 4. Drilling and dibbling, none. 5. Time, from the beginning of February to the end of April. 6. Sort, potatoe, Irish blue, Poland, and short smalls. 7. Seed. 8. Depth, one inch and a half. 9. Rolling, same as in the barley. 10. Weeding, by the spud or hook. 11. Harvesting, mown and cocked into small heaps, of about a fork full. 13. Straw, eaten by the cattle in the winter. 14. Application, chiefly given to horses and cattle; none made into bread, but small part manufactured into oatmeal for domestic uses. 15. Price, 30*s.* per quarter."

PEAS.—P. 68. "1. Tillage, ploughed once, harrowed to a fine mould, but very seldom rolled, though a good method at this time; none put in without ploughing, nor any scarifying or manuring. 2. Drilling, by very few. 3. Dibbling, very seldom done. 4. Time, from February to the end of April. 5. Sort, the Marlborough and common gray; Lord Winchelsea has tried the pearl, or black eyed pea, and found it to answer well; and also another kind of white pea, a good looking pea, recommended by a seedsman; but the crop was not so good, nor was it so early in harvest. 6. Seed. 7. Depth, one inch and a half. 8. Rolling, none. 9. Podding, for market, none. 10. Hoeing, none practised but by Lord Winchelsea, who uses the horse hoe. 11. Weeding, by the spud. 12. Harvesting, mown, and put into small heaps, about half a fork full in each heap. 13. Produce. 14. Straw, eaten by horses and cattle. 15. Application. for fattening pigs. 16. Stubbles none left but the weeds, scattered peas, &c. eaten by sheep and pigs. 17. Price, none quoted. 18. Bread, none made of this grain in this county."

BEANS.—P. 69. "1. Soil, chiefly clay. 2. Tillage, ploughed once, harrowed to a fine mould; rolling seldom done, though beneficial, without ploughing, none; scarifying, none practised. 3. Manuring, seldom any applied, though it would be much better to apply it on this crop, than (as is practised at present) on the fallow. 4. Drilling, by very few. 5. Dibbling, not much practised. 6. Time, February. 7. Sort, large horse and pigeon. 8. Seed. 9. Depth, when harrowed, in one inch and a half; when ploughed, in three inches, and sometimes deeper. 10. Rolling, none.

11.

11. Harrowing, none. 12. Horse hoeing, none. 13. Hand hoeing, some little. 14. Weeding, by the spud and hook; some little by sheep. 15. Distempers, the black fly and green louse. 16. Cutting green, some done, and said to answer well. 17. Harvesting, mown and cocked. 18. Produce. 20. Application, for sale pigs, horses, &c. 21. Stubbles, sheep turned on them. 22. Price, 42*s.* to 52*s.* per quarter. 23. How used as food, no way that I could hear of."

POTATOES.—P. 84. "This crop is only raised in this county on a very small scale, and with no other view than for domestic uses."

TURNEPS.—P. 72. "1. Soil, red or keal land, lime-stone or creech land. 2 Tillage, ploughed three or four times, harrowed and rolled. 3. Manuring, chiefly by yard-dung, in rather a long light state, 12 to 20 loads per acre; and lime on the red or keal lands, but not approved of on limestone land. 4. Time, July. 5. Drilling only practised by Earl Winchelsea, whose crop was beautiful. 6. Sort, white Norfolk tankard. 7. Seed, 2½ lb. per acre. 8. Rolling, by a plain wooden roll. 9. Harrowing, none. 10. Fly preventatives, none particularly used. 11. Hoeing, done by hand two or three times over."

To the *consumption* of turneps, the Reporter assigns a separate section.—P. 73. "Chiefly by sheep: 1st. drawn; some few; 2d. fed on the land. This practice chiefly followed. 3d. Hurdling, common to all parts of the county."

He speaks, at large, on the benefits arising from "*hurdling*" them off; as if it were a new thing, in Rutlandshire, and required enforcing by argument. He is still a more strenuous advocate for folding them off with *two flocks* of sheep; or what, among sheep farmers is usually termed "fat sheep and followers;"—a practice that is highly proper; and is common, where sheep are reared as well as fatted, on the same farm.

His objections to *drawing* them are these.—P. 74. "Turnips, when fast in the ground, are in a better position, and, of course, more firm to the bite of the sheep, and are thus nearly scooped out, 'ere they are dragged and given to the incoming store-sheep. By the turnips being thrown into a cart promiscuously, they are all daubed with dirt, and are by no means so fresh and pleasant to the sheep as they are whilst growing in the field. For as gooseberries are more pleasant to the palate, when gathered one at a time from the tree; so it is with turnips to sheep. And a grazier or feeder of sheep, &c. cannot attend too minutely to such circumstances."

The

The latter part of this argument, I conceive, is somewhat theoretical. All graminivorous animals affect soil. It is probably congenial, or necessary, to their health. Hence the small quantity of it which adheres to the smooth rind of a turnep, may be grateful, rather than offensive, to them. And hence, between a dirty turnep for sheep, and a dirty gooseberry for their shepherd, there appears to me to be little or no analogy.

When the soil is tenacious, the season wet, the sheep to be fatted bear long wool, and where a dry grass ground is situated at a moderate distance from the turnep field, drawing them will be greatly preferable to folding them off.

The rest of the lengthened section, "Consumption," is occupied with observations on "the fly in turneps:"—not, it would seem, the "Fly," as it is called, or small beetle, which preys on the *seedlings*;—nor that which produces the caterpillars that are, some years, so destructive to the *tops* of larger plants;—but the parent of the grub, which, in some districts injure materially the *roots* of turneps; and, in Rutlandshire brings on a disease called "fingers and toes."——All that I can say concerning the Reporter's diffuse wanderings, on this subject, is, that he recommends, very properly, perhaps, clean tillage, and compression of the lighter lands, as a preventive of this disease.

SAINFOIN.—P. 85. "1. Soil, creech or lime-stone. 2. Manure, none. 3. Tillage, sown with the corn crops. 4. Seed, four or five bushels per acre. 5. Time, April. 6. Drilling, none. 7. Application.—1. Hay, mown, for this purpose generally. 2. Seed, some little. 3. After grass, depastured with sheep.—8. Duration, for five or six years. 9. Harrowing, none. 10. How broken up, by the plough, and generally for oats or peas. 11. How soon renewed; the sowing of sainfoin in this county is too new a practice to obtain an answer to this question."

Seeing the shortness of its duration, on lands which the Reporter says are "remarkably well calculated for its production," it is more than probable that its *management* is not sufficiently understood. It certainly is not by the Reporter, at least; who treats of the subject in a didactic way, and recommends eating off the "eddish" (doubtlessly the growth after mowing,) in July. His words are —(p. 86.) "The eddish will be ready at a time when the other artificial grasses are going off; and the lambs might then be taken off from the ewes in the month of June or beginning of July: this would give the ewes a great opportunity to get in good condition against the winter, thus enabling them to stand the winter much better. The corn stubbles

stubbles would be ready by such time as the best of the sainfoin eddishes were over, upon which the ewes or lambs, or both, as occasion required, might be turned."

Under treatment, such as this, it is a matter of surprize how the duration is protracted, even to five or six years.—The land must be peculiarly well adapted to the crop.—In the best management of sainfoin, in this kingdom, the lattermath, or second crop, is never suffered, by superior managers, to be bitten, until it has done, or nearly done growing. October and November are the months most proper for depasturing it.—See my Glocestershire,—District, *Cotswold Hills;* and SOUTHERN COUNTIES, *District* of *Maidstone.*

GRASS LAND.—The extent of grass lands, in Rutlandshire, appears, in Mr. P's general tables of extents, to be—of *pasture* 34,861 : 0 : 1. and of *meadows* 9,956 : 0 : 0; together 44,817 : 0 : 1.

Regarding the information found in *this* report, concerning the *meadows* and *ordinary pasture grounds*, nothing appears sufficiently estimable to require particular notice, here; excepting what has been copied from Mr. CRUTCHLEY'S; for which see p. 253, aforegoing.

On grazing grounds, the following observations are entitled to a place in this register.—P. 95. "The management of grazing lands is much better understood in this county than in many others. There is less waste of grass, and the ground is generally stocked with an equal and proper proportion of cattle and sheep, with a small quantity of horses, so that the sorts of grass suitable to each of the different palates of those animals, are all taken off."

How far *horses* are eligible, as grazing stock, the opinions of graziers differ. The reported practice of Rutlandshire is what I am, here, considering. The remark upon it, in this place, reads well. But when applied to *horses* and *sheep*, in the same pasture, it is, I believe, in great part theoretical. —*Horses* and *cattle*, in a hard stocked pasture, certainly clear the ground, more evenly, than either of them, alone; owing to the well ascertained fact that each will bite nearer the dung of the other, than either of them will, near their own.—Horses *after* cattle and sheep, will clear the ground more effectually.

P. 97. "The average stock kept, is one ox and one sheep on two acres of land in summer, and one sheep, or one sheep and a half in winter.

"It is the opinion of the graziers, on calculation, that from 40 to 50 stone of flesh is *sent off* per year, from an acre.

acre.* There are no dairy grounds. The sheep pastures are various; but in summer, upon the best breeding land, about 4 or 5 old and young sheep are kept per acre; and one beast to four acres; and in winter, about 1½ sheep per acre."—Here, the horses are shut out.

P. 96. "The thistles are mown; and most of the pastures of the richer quality are hobbed:"—the plots and tufts of stale, uneaten herbage mown off.

Common Cow Grounds.—P. 100. "There is a cow pasture at Hambleton for the cottagers, containing 114 acres, which is divided into 91 pastures, and let partly to farmers and cottagers, at 30s. each, yearly. It is stocked as follows: One cow, or four barren sheep, or three ewes and lambs, from old May-day to old Michaelmas-day, and from old Michaelmas-day to old Lady-day, with 2½ sheep, or 3 lambs to each pasture. The land is not stocked from old Lady-day to old May-day.

"At Egleton the cottagers have a cow pasture, containing 35 acres, which is stocked with 28 cows, or four barren sheep, or three ewes and lambs, from old May-day to old Michaelmas-day; the remainder of the year it is stocked and managed as at Hambleton. The price of a common, as it is termed, is 1*l.* 16*s.*

"At Greetham the cottagers have a cow pasture, containing 67 acres, which is stocked with 29 commons, at 30s. each. The land is stocked with cows from old May-day to Candlemas-day, and is not stocked for the remainder of the year. The cottagers have also from six to eight acres of arable land, which is in this state, on account of its being too shallow of earth for pasture; on parts of which they cultivate sainfoin and clover for winter fodder.

"At Burley the cottagers have two closes containing 12 acres each, which is divided into eight commons, each ground or close being mown alternately. There is a cottage hovel between the two grounds, which contains the eight cows; the stock kept here is eight cows and three sheep in the summer, and six sheep in winter to each common."

If it be right that mere day laborors should keep cows, this mode of providing for them appears to be, by far, the most rational and eligible. Letting them detached grounds is assuredly wrong.—See EASTERN DEPARTMENT,—*Secretary's Lincolnshire.*

LIVESTOCK.

* We are not informed what portion of that quantity is *sent on.*

LIVESTOCK.

Mr. Parkinson has executed the laborious task of tabling the several species of domestic animals;—setting down the number of each description, in every parish of the County.

HORSES.—P. 136. The number of "*horses, mares,* &c. 2118,—of *foals,* &c. 339."

P. 138. "The horses which are bred in this county, taking them in the aggregate, are the most unprofitable sort I ever saw for sale, considering, that they are chiefly raised on enclosed grounds, which, from their quality, are capable of raising horses of great value, whether hunters, roadsters, coachers, or for the dray."

CATTLE.—P. 115. The numbers, in 1806, were—of *cows* 2,729—*calves* 1244—*store cattle* 700—*fatting cattle* 2,775—*sucklers* (?) 332—total 7,780.

After the intelligent, yet brief, account of the cattle of Rutlandshire, inserted aforegoing (p. 254,) from Mr. CRUTCHLEY'S report (every line of which is copied into that under review, without acknowledgement) I perceive not a syllable in *this*, though of ten times the length, which would add to the value of my abstract.

SHEEP.—The *number* of sheep, in Rutlandshire, in 1806, appears in a table of parishes to have been—of *old sheep* 57,830—*lambs* 23,316—total 81,146.

Breeds of Sheep.—Every thing of real consideration, respecting the breeds of sheep in the county of Rutland, to be found in *this* Report, appears at p. 254, aforegoing. But Mr. Parkinson being an ANTI-BAKEWELLIAN, it will be right to pay some attention to the *original* matter of his section, concerning this subject.—Volumes have been *written* in *favor* of the Dishley breed; but, much as has been *said against them*, little of the obloquy which has been vociferated has, I believe, reached the *press*. And it might be wrong to lose a favorable opportunity of recording some *written evidence against* the Bakewell breed of sheep.

In copying Mr. Crutchley's observations, Mr. P. has stopt short at the "old Leicester sort;" leaving the remainder of what Mr. C. has said, in the same paragraph to sink into oblivion, no doubt, with the other untranscribed matter of Mr. C's report.

Catching at a real defect of the "new" breed, as properly held out by Mr. Crutchley, Mr. P. says, p. 129,—"This is well authenticated by Mr. Godfrey, of Wardley, who is a very correct good grazier, and has been in the habits of buying the best year old sheep that could be met with at the fairs in this county: he shewed me his todd bills for the last 20 years

years; and, by way of substantiating the actual decrease in the weight of wool, he permitted me to take an account of two year's weight of wool 10 years ago; and for the last two years he has sold his wool." The result stands thus:—P. 130. "By the above account it appears, that wool has nearly declined in weight one-fourth."

Laying hold, likewise, of another defect pointed out, by Mr. C. this Reporter says, p. 131.—"The sheep are very tender, suffering very much in the winter from the cold, and in summer from heat. They are in a state of continual torment during the latter season, from the flies, if they have not caps on their heads, and if they have not jackets after clipping, the sun burns them in such a way, that the pelt, or outward skin cracks, like to the outside of a roast pig, and becomes very sore. The clothing for the sheep is a continual expense, and a very unnecessary one, as there is a sort to be found which have no occasion for cloathing, having a natural preservation against the heats of summer and the inclemency of the weather in winter; for no artificial means can preserve the frog-eyed sheep in that season, whilst the sheep which is thus protected by nature, will be found to be of a much better sort, of a fattening kind, thriving in all seasons, and having much more wool upon them. The frog-eyed sheep, which are thus called on account of their eyes being large and wide, and appearing to stand out of their heads, are a kind of dunk sheep, very bad feeders, and, although there are parts about them which would induce one to suppose them to be of a fattening kind, yet there are such decided marks about them to the contrary, that this supposition is but short lived, for their heads are short, a bad indication in many other fattening animals, foreheads broad; and their ears, though thin, are very often broad and shaped like the aspen leaf; their crag thin, with little or no flesh upon it, and extending from the head to the shoulders; their *tails small*, which is an indication of there being but little useful flesh along the *back*, that is to say, from the thick or upper part of the *neck* to the *loin*," *(!)* "which is certainly the best flesh about a sheep."

Having still, perhaps, some qualms of judgement hanging about him, our Reporter sets out on a journey (pilgrimage it could not, perhaps, be strictly termed) to Dishley and the hallowed land of Leicestershire; but returned, alas! the very *infidel* he was "ere" he set out;—as the following account plainly testifies.

P. 134. "Having on my view of almost every flock in this county, both good and bad, but particularly every one said to be good, and seeing so many defects even in those best

best flocks, and that there were really more of those dunks in the best flocks than in the inferior ones; I paid the more attention, on my going into Leicestershire, to viewing both the rams and breeding ewes of the first ram breeders in the county, and was sorry to observe many of those defects amongst them which I have described in the county of Rutland. So true it is, that in all things various fashions have their turns, and thus it happens that the breeders having got too much in the extreme, have got wrong: as I have before observed, like will, in a great measure, get like; it therefore seems very strange to me, that when a breeder wants a ram to get sheep of 28lb. per quarter, with 14lb. of wool, that he should chuse a ram which would not weigh more than 18 or 20lb. per quarter, and has not more than 5 to 7 lb. of wool on him; or how, with the sort of keeping he means to give, the produce he can expect to accomplish the object he has in view. A ram breeder is like any other man who sells wares, and cannot be expected to depreciate his own stock, but, on the contrary, will do his endeavour to persuade the buyer it is the best; it only astonishes me, that he has power of persuasion over the buyer, or hirer, or against conviction."

Trusting that my readers have, by this time, made up their minds, about this disputed point of *faith*, pass we on, in search of less doubtful ground to proceed upon.

I search in vain, however, in the volume before me; for I have examined, and, I trust, duly estimated, every topic it contains;—excepting the most disputable and difficult one to settle;—that of

PROFIT and LOSS.— Mr. Parkinson treats the subject, table-wise, or in the ledger form, in two separate statements:—one of them "according to the present method," the other "under an improved system." The latter is, *of course*, the more profitable.—I put little trust, however, in arbitrary calculations, on this most abstruse problem of AGRICULTURAL ARITHMETIC;—well knowing their deceptious tendency. See the former volumes of my present Work.

I WILL close my remarks on this most extraordinary performance, by saying (what I have repeatedly intimated, on other occasions) that the sentiments of a *known public Writer* indispensibly require to be more cautiously, examined, and his errors in judgement (if any) to be more forcibly drawn forth and corrected,—than those of a man who has not a public character, to aid in giving currency to dangerous ill founded doctrines.

WARWICKSHIRE.

WARWICKSHIRE.

THIS County is, wholely, and inseparably, a portion of the MIDLAND DEPARTMENT. It is, almost throughout, an extension of VALE LANDS; among which, however are interspersed some heaths and other insulated under-productive passages; but they are nowhere divided by extended ranges of hill and dale. Aggregately, Warwickshire may be termed a rich and beautiful County.

"GENERAL VIEW

OF THE

AGRICULTURE

OF THE

COUNTY OF WARWICK,

WITH

OBSERVATIONS ON THE MEANS OF ITS IMPROVEMENT.

BY MR. JOHN WEDGE.

1794."

THIS is an "original" and *unpublished* Report; and the only one of WARWICKSHIRE, which (to my knowledge), has yet (November 1812) been even "announced."

It was, I believe, understood, at the time this Report was written, that Mr. WEDGE was steward, or estate agent, to the EARL of AYLESFORD. The Report itself, indeed, evinces this; and moreover shows, pretty plainly, that Mr. W. is a native of the County.—See the head, *Elevation*, ensuing.

It

It also appears as if Mr. Wedge wrote from his own previous knowledge of the County, rather than from a SURVEY of it, for the special purpose of making up a Report. By a very copious enumeration of "improvers" (N. p. 11), it would seem, however, that Mr. W. had a general acquaintance with its principal occupiers.

The number of pages, including an Appendix, sixty.

Four sketch Maps of draining.

SUBJECT THE FIRST.

NATURAL ECONOMY.

EXTENT.—P. 7. "In regard to its extent, by the best information I could procure, it contains about 618000 acres."

ELEVATION.—P. 7. "The woods near Lord Aylesford's, and at Corley, have been supposed to be higher than any other land in England." (!) "From this elevated ridge, the water runs on one side into the Avon, and so on to the Bristol Channel, from the other side into the Tame, which empties itself into the Trent and Humber, at Hull. As Packington and Corley are near the center of England, the supposition seems to be well founded; but, however that may be, the situation is not colder, nor the air more sharp, than in other parts of the county; owing, perhaps, to the vast quantity of timber and woods, with which this high ground abounds, and is sheltered."

CLIMATURE.—P. 7. "Its situation, near the center of England; the mildness (comparatively speaking) and salubrity of its air are so well known, that it will be unnecessary for me to say more on that subject."

Time of Harvest.—P. 15. "July for pease, and the beginning or middle of August for most other crops: but it is no uncommon thing to see wheat, oats, and barley, not cut in October and November, and beans in the fields so late as December; owing to late sowing in *bad seasons*, and to other bad management. Yet the great bulk of corn harvest, in this county, is housed in August, and the first week of September."

WATERS.—P. 7. "Its principal rivers are the Avon and the Tame. The Avon rises a few miles east of Rugby, and runs in a south west direction through Warwick, to Stratford on Avon; and leaves the county, after having crossed the Ikenild street, at Bitford: and in its course receives the Sow,

Sow, the Leam, the Stour, and a great number of other small streams, which make it imperfectly navigable to some distance above Stratford on Avon. The Tame rises N. W. of Birmingham, and running through the N. W. corner of the county, receives the Rea, the Cole, the Blythe, and other streams of less note, and leaves the county at Tamworth."

SOILS.—P. 8 " There are not any fens in this county; and much of the wet and swampy lands are drained; though on almost every farm there is some land in want of that most essential improvement."

" The soil of this county varies much ; and abounds in almost every kind, except those which have chalk or flint as their basis: but, although the soil, extending from Atherston on Stour, to *Stratford on Avon*, Alveston, Wellsbourne, Charlcot, Snitterfield, Barford, *Warwick*, Radford, Cubbington; Kenelworth, Stonely, Baggington, Ryeton, Wolston, Binley, *Coventry*, Allesley, Meriden, Packington, *Coleshill*, Castle Bromwich, Birmingham, and to many other adjoining villages, amounting to about one fourth of the county, is chiefly a fine dry red loam, or good sand ; yet in many of those parishes, strong clay, or barren sand, are more or less intermixed.

" The south east part of the county, which is bounded by Oxfordshire, Northamptonshire, and the Wattling-street, extending to the Roman Fosse-way, (which passes through this county) is also about one fourth part of the whole. It consists of good strong clay-land, and other rich pastures of a mixed nature; where great numbers of fine sheep and cattle are fattened, for the consumption of the country; but chiefly for the London market. In this tract, also is some sand and gravel, and almost every species of limestone, or other cold clay-land to be found. A less proportion of land is in tillage in this division than in any other.

" The north-east end of the county, which is in part bounded by the Wattling-street-way, extending from High Cross to Withy-brook, Bulkington, *Bedworth*, Burton Hastings, *Nuneaton*, Weddington, Ansley, *Atherston*, Baddesley, *Polesworth*, Newton Regis, Seckington, Amington, Wilncot, Baxterley, Whitacre, Astley, &c. contains about one other fourth part, and is good strong clay and marl land, with such exceptions as have been mentioned before. This tract has a considerable quantity of land used for grazing cattle and sheep, but has much more ploughed, than the south east quarter.

" The remaining one-fourth, or western side of the county extending from Sheldon, near Birmingham, to Elmdon, Solihull, Barston, Balsal, Packwood, Lapworth, *Henley*

in

in Arden, Morton Bagot, Aston Cantilow, Alcester, Bitford, &c. &c. is principally marl, clay, and other cold land, with such exceptions as have been before noticed. This land is mostly in tillage, and a much smaller proportion of sheep are kept, than on the other parts of the county, partly from the nature of its soil, and partly from the neglect of its occupiers, in not draining."

MINERALS.—P. 9. "There are considerable coal mines worked about Bedworth, Griff, Chilvers Cotton, Oldbury, and extending in the same line, near to Atherston, Polesworth, and Wilncot. They are of a sulphureous quality, but make durable hot fires, and are sold from three pence to five pence per hundred weight, at the pits. Some *lime* is also *found* in that neighbourhood, and worked."

SUBJECT THE SECOND.

POLITICAL ECONOMY.

APPROPRIATION.—P. 37. "The waste lands in this county, including the roads, I have estimated at 120,470 acres."

After mentioning some of the larger commons, Mr. W. says, p. 39. "These commons, and those in other parts of the county, have a large proportion of land, which, under proper cultivation, would become very useful for the purposes of tillage, grazing, &c."

P. 20. "About forty years ago, the southern and eastern parts of this county consisted mostly of open fields, which are now chiefly inclosed, at an expence, on the average, of about 45*s.* per acre, when frugally managed; which, in many instances, was not the case; and, from the best information which I can obtain, these inclosures have produced an improvement of near one-third of the rents, after allowing interest for those expences, and, in many instances, much more, upon a twenty-one year's lease. There are still about 50,000 acres of open-field land, which, in a few years, will probably all be inclosed. Many of the open fields, which have been inclosed, are converted into pasture, particularly in the southern and eastern parts of the county, which are let at high rents, (from 15*s.* to 35*s.* per acre) and on which a much improved breed of cattle and sheep are kept and fattened. If the increased produce of these inclosures, and of those in the neighbouring counties, be taken into consideration, and also the advanced price of butcher's butcher's meat, it seems to prove, that either population or luxury (or perhaps both) must, on the whole, be immensely increased. These lands, being now grazed, want *much fewer hands* to manage them than they did in their former open state. Upon all inclosures of open fields, the farms have generally been made much larger: from these causes, the hardy yeomanry of country villages have been driven for employment into Birmingham, Coventry, and other manufacturing towns, whose flourishing trade has sometimes found them profitable employment.

"It may be granted, that the fewer men and horses any given tract of land requires for its proper management, the greater will be its produce for market; and that the supernumerary labourers, which must have been fed and employed in the cultivation of small open field, and other small farms, are employed, with much more advantage to the public, in the different manufactories of this county; but if trade in general should, for any great length of time, continue bad, the Board will be much better able to judge of the consequences than myself, and will also see how much the peace and prosperity of this country depends on its trade, in the train in which things now are."

MANUFACTURES.—P. 20. "Commerce and manufactures have been carried on to a great extent in this district: the toy and hardware trade, &c. of Birmingham and its vicinity, and the ribbon and tammy trade, &c. of Coventry and its neighbourhood, are well known. The good or bad effects which commerce and manufactures are likely to have on the agriculture of this district, depends on many circumstances; but their effects have hitherto, in my opinion, been good, by furnishing manure, such as soot, horn-dust, malt-dust, rags, soap ashes, coal-ashes, the refuse of dyers, &c. and all the varieties of putrid manure for the improvement of land, by consuming its produce, and by giving employment to superfluous hands."

P. 21.—See the last article.

P. 22.—See *Canals*, ensuing.

P. 23.—See *Workpeople*, ensuing

P. 24.—See the next article.

POOR RATES.—P. 24. "The poor's rates, and other parochial payments in this county, vary much, and, on the average, amount, I guess, to about 2*s.* in the pound on the rents. In Birmingham, Coventry, and other manufacturing places, they are from 10*s.* to about 5*s.* in the pound, as trade is better or worse; and, in many of the adjoining parishes, they are very greatly oppressed with poor's rates, particularly at Foleshill, near Coventry, where they are, this year, 12*s.* in the pound. The rapid growth of manufactories in

this

this county, the greatly decreased value of money, and a continual increase of poor's rates, are incontestible facts: but I am inclined to believe, that the latter does not arise, in country villages, from any want of industry or effort in the labouring poor, but that they receive from parish officers only what they ought to receive in *wages*. If it be admitted, that the value of money is less now by one half than it was one hundred and fifty years ago, that the wages of agricultural labourers are not, on the whole, advanced, since that time, much more than one-fourth, and that their wages at that time were not more than sufficient to support themselves and their families, it follows, that such a deficiency (of about one-fourth) must have greatly added to the burthen of the poor's rates: that those rates may still continue to advance, from the same and other causes, the following considerations will, I think, render probable; a vast number of those who are employed in manufacturing towns, are parishioners to different villages, (particularly those in their vicinity); whenever infirmity, old age, or a check in trade, happens, these men are not supported by those who have had the benefit of their labour, but are sent for subsistence to their respective parishes; which seems an hardship that I hope the wisdom of the Board will find some means to lessen or remove."

TITHES.—P. 39. "Having spoken of waste lands, it may be proper to mention tythes in kind, as a great, and, in some cases, an insurmountable obstruction to their effectual improvement. It is but justice to the clergy, in this county, to say, that, *on the whole*, they are more reasonable in their demands for tythes in kind, than the lay-impropriators; and, where lands have been regularly and well cultivated for a great length of time, there is no great hardship in the occupier paying them, as, in that case, it is chiefly a tax on the land-owner, originating in custom or title, prior to that by which the estate itself is held;* but, where much improvement is wanted, and especially in the cultivation of all fens, bogs, and other barren *unproductive* waste lands, the matter is widely different; for, in such cases, almost the whole value of the land depends on personal labour, skill, industry, and the advance and risque of private property: therefore, something seems necessary to be done to remove so great a bar to the improvement of *such unproductive land*."

PUBLIC DRAINAGE.—The following statement shows how very beneficial would be a GENERAL LAW of DRAINAGE.

P. 17.

* In this position, there is some truth and much theory. I have never yet known a land valuer make a suitable distinction between titheable and untitheable lands.

P. 17. "It may not be improper here to mention, that all the different rivers, and smaller streams, in this county, have been *very much neglected*, by permitting the accumulation of soil, roots, &c. deposited by floods to remain unremoved; and by a mercenary principle of the land-owners, or tenants, planting on each side, poplars, and other aquatic plants. These rivers, &c. are consequently become so narrow, and so full of shoals, and the meadows are so often overflowed in wet seasons, as to be *very much reduced in their value* by rushes, coarse grass, and the hazard of floods.

"Lord Aylesford, observing this, is now clearing out the river Blythe, which runs several miles through his estates; and I have authority to say, that the soil dug out from that river will, as manure, be worth more than the whole expence of widening it, which is about one hundred pounds per mile. If the method pursued by his Lordship in this business, was to take place generally on the other rivers of the county, the improvement would be immense; the meadows would become sound, and summer floods, which frequently carry off, or spoil the whole crop of hay, would seldom, if ever, happen. Mr. Moland, at his much improved place of Springfield, has also opened a part of the same river."

Canals.—P. 26. "The canals that pass through this county, are, one from the Wednesbury and Dudley coal and lime works to Birmingham, and from thence to Fazeley and Fradley-Heath, to join the Staffordshire grand trunk, from Fazeley, to Atherstone, Bedworth, and Coventry; one extending from that at Longford to Braunston and Oxford; one from Birmingham to Worcester; one branching out of the Worcester, one way to Dudley, &c. and the other way to Stratford on Avon; and one from Birmingham to Warwick."

P. 21. "It seems fortunate, at this period," (1793 4) "that the creation of a new kind of property gives employment to so many thousands of the laborious poor; I mean inland canals, by which, on the return of peace, commerce will no doubt be considerably increased, the cultivation of waste lands be promoted, and manufacturing towns flourish. We may then think ourselves happy, that Birmingham and Coventry are within this district; and, on the whole, find advantageous employment for an immensely increased population."

For canals being favorable to working *cattle*, see *Working Animals*, ensuing.

Roads.—P. 28. "The turnpike roads through this county are tolerably good; some of the private roads are well managed, and in good repair: but most of them very bad, from a scarcity of materials, and from a considerable neglect,

lect, or injudicious application of the statute duty, occasioned by want of skilful permanent surveyors being appointed."

The Reporter, then, enters largely into the breadth of wheels, the weight of carriages, and the form of roads. But he does not appear to have sufficiently studied the general subject to have gained clear notions of it; so as to convey new, or superiorly useful information concerning it. Having caught the idea of WAGGON PATHS, which are admirable in *private* roads, for agricultural purposes (and for bye roads, in a deep country) he would seem to have generalized them, to *public*, and even to "turnpike roads, where there is a sound middle tract only" (p. 30.) and this, without any expedient to permit carriages, travelling in contrary directions, to pass each other.

ACCUMULATING AGRICULTURAL INFORMATION.—P. 49. ("Appendix") "Warwickshire, like the other counties in England, being divided into hundreds, and having, in the whole, nineteen chief constables, who issue precepts, and collect the county-rates, &c. from the petty constables in each parish or constablewick, some of which are not extensive; if the Board were to obtain a Report from each of those chief constables, the particulars of which would be furnished by the petty constables in their respective parishes, at a small expence, conformable to printed Queries, to be delivered to the chief constables, the *exact state* of agriculture and breeding, and their progressive and particular improvements, not only in this county, but in every district of the kingdom, might be annually and accurately known. Papers, which I gave to Mr. Cruchman and Mr. Slater, two of the chief constables, in part filled up, one of which is hereunto annexed, may best explain my ideas on that subject. The expence attending the procuring of this information being trifling, each county might easily defray it, without any charge to the Board of Agriculture.

"The following are the Queries drawn up for that purpose, and a copy of the Return by Mr. Slater, one of the chief constables of the hundred of Kington."

This is a thought which does Mr. Wedge's mind much credit. But it was too simplex, and, to common sense, too obviously capable of being made useful (under proper regulations and management) to be adopted by minds of a different cast:—*by men of ingenuity!*

Chief constables are, or should be (but unfortunately are not always) chosen from among the yeomanry or principal occupiers of a hundred, or other juridical division of a County. But, what renders Mr. Wedge's plan, in some degree, defective,—*petty* constables are generally appointed from

from among the least informed class, in a parish or township. Were *church wardens* (mostly better informed men) and *road surveyors* (whose office leads them over every part of the districts under their charge) united with them,—something nearly bordering on accuracy might be attained.

What renders the idea of collecting agricultural information, thro the medium of CHIEF CONSTABLES (duly chosen) peculiarly eligible, is the circumstance of their being amenable to the magistracy of the districts, in which they severally act; who, jointly and separately, have interests in bringing such information to the required degree of perfection; by examining, correcting, and improving, the accounts of the several parishes in their respective neighbourhoods; and reporting them, at their sessions or other meetings.

The subjoined extract shows the outline of Mr. Wedge's plan.—P. 50. "*Queries proposed to be sent to the Chief Constables of each hundred, in order to obtain the necessary information from the petty constables of each particular constablewick.*—What are the parishes or hamlets in your constablewick, and how much in the pound are the poor's rates?

"What is the quantity of common or waste land, exclusive of roads?

"What is the length, and in what repair are the turnpike roads?

"What is the length, and in what state are the private or bye-roads?

"What is the quantity of open field land?

"What is the quantity of meadow-land? And what the quantity of grazing-land?

"What is the quantity of land which is alternately ploughed for grain, and sown with grass-seeds, and what is the course of husbandry?

"What is the quantity of wood-lands?

"What are the proportions of sand, loam, clay, and other soils?

"What is the number of each sort of horses, cows, oxen, sheep, hogs? And are any ox-teams used?

"Who are the graziers or farmers most remarkable for their improvements in the breed of cattle and sheep, or for their improvements in agriculture?

"Would carriages, with wheels nine or six inches broad, drawn with horses geered double; or would those with six-inch wheels, drawn with horses geered single, be most useful in your parish, on the public and private roads, taking into consideration the use of carriages for the purposes of agriculture?

"Is your parish tythable, or tythe-free? And are those tythes

tythes in the hands of lay-impropriators, or the clergy? And what is the compensation paid for them?

"What are the improvements that have taken place, or are now going forward?

"What are the rivers and other streams?

"What water-meadows are there, what is their produce, and how are they managed?

"What are the towns, the number of houses occupied by gentlemen and tradesmen, the number of inhabitants. and what are the trades carried on, &c.?

"What are the different manures made use of?

"What are the green foods, how are they cultivated, and how used?

"What is the state of cottages and of the poor? Are there any clubs or friendly societies for their support?

"What is the average produce of the different sorts of grain and green food per acre?

"What are the parks, forests, or chases, and their quantity?

"What are the canals?

"Are there any mines of coal or lime, &c? And to what extent are they worked or sent, and at what price sold?

"What fuel is used, from whence brought, and at what price?

"What is the whole rent and land-tax of the parish?"

Mr. Slater's return is made tablewise. Several of the columns, however, were unfilled up, at the time when Mr. W's Report was printed. But this is no disparagement to his general plan; whose fulness of good is not to be produced in a day or a year. That part of the table which appears to have reached a degree of fulness, or fulness itself, is here subjoined.

P. 52. "CONSTABLEWICKS

"CONSTABLEWICKS OR PARISHES.	Quantity of land.	Waste and roads.	Open field land.	Grazing land.	Meadow land.	Arable land, that is, up and down.	Wood land
Illmington, - -	2500	—	—	400	100	2000	—
Compton Scorpion,	650	—	—	350	150	150	—
Whitchurch,	2500	200	1800	—	200	300	—
Atherstone, - -	750	—	—	—	50	700	—
Eatington, - -	3370	300	2200	400	350	20	100
Whalcot, - - -	1130	80	970	—	80	—	—
Oxhill, - - -	1830	80	1300	300	150	—	—
Tysoe, - - -	2700	200	2200	—	320	—	—
Radway, - - -	1030	10	—	500	300	190	30
Kington, - - -	1800	30	—	520	250	1000	—
Chadshunt, - -	1450	6	—	824	260	330	30
Combrook, - -	1305	5	—	320	80	900	—
Gaydon, - - -	1380	10	—	600	260	500	10
Compton Verny, -	840	10	—	500	200	80	50
Lighthorn, - -	1620	30	—	300	80	1200	10
Buttlers Marston,	1505	5	—	300	150	1050	—
Halford, - - -	905	25	—	100	60	720	—
	27265	991	8470	5414	3020	9140	430"

The other columns of the table are headed.—" Number of ox teams."—" What is the length and state of the turnpike roads."—" What is the length and state of the private roads.—" What are the poor rates in the pound."—"Tithable or tithe free."—" Number of broad wheeled carriages."—" Number of narrow wheeled carriages."—" Horses drawn double or single."—" Are cattle or sheep chiefly kept."—" What is the proportion of light, strong, and other different sorts of land."

Nor let Mr. Wedge's plan be condemned, or thought meanly of, because some of his Queries may not favorably meet the ideas of every man; or because they may not be thought to comprize every useful enquiry, regarding Rural Economy. The principles and outline of the plan are, in the first instance, the points of consideration.

SUBJECT

SUBJECT THE THIRD.

RURAL ECONOMY.

TENANTED ESTATES.

ESTATES.—P. 10. "The land in this district is possessed by many of those who occupy their own estates; by the considerable tradesmen and manufacturers of Birmingham, Coventry, and other towns: but principally by those of large estates, namely, the Dukes of Buccleugh and Dorset; the Marquises of Buckingham and Hartford; the Earls of Aylesford, Clarendon, Spencer, Warwick, Denbigh, Northampton, Abergaveny, Hertford, Plymouth, and Coventry; the Lords Craven, Middleton, Willoughby de Brook, Bagot, Digby, Dormer, Wentworth, Lifford, and Clifford, the Lord Bishop Cornwallis, Sir John Mordaunt, Sir G. A. Shaukburgh, Sir Robert Newdigate, Sir Robert Lawley, Sir H. G. Calthorpe, Sir H. Bridgman, Sir Thomas Gooch, Sir Thomas Biddulph, Sir R. Throckmorton, and many other respectable gentlemen."

IMPROVEMENT of Estates.—For a general intimation respecting improvements, see *Occupiers*, ensuing.

Draining Estates.—Mr. Wedge, in the Appendix to his Report, has inserted a Paper, and four descriptive Plans, concerning his own practice in Draining; chiefly it would seem, on the estate of Lord Aylesford.

This Paper, considering the *then* infant state of drainage, in the MIDLAND COUNTIES, (see its history in my Register of the Midland Practice) is highly creditable to Mr. Wedge's good sense and perseverance.—For admitting that "Old SAMUEL of FAZELEY" (see as above) and Mr. ELKINGTON, might have the merit of leading Mr. W. into the field of practice,—he is entitled to much praise in assisting to explain, and convey to the inexperienced, what might, in them, be termed the INTUITION of PRACTICE.

But, at this time, when the theory and practice of draining has been raised to a degree of science, which, I will presume to suggest, few, if any, of the rural arts have attained,—I perceive nothing in Mr. Wedge's Paper, which could, *now*, be of sufficient value to the public, to warrant my inserting it, here. Indeed, without the sketches, it could avail nothing.

RENT.—P. 12. "If I had been able to ascertain with more certainty these proportions," (see Plan of Management, ensuing)

suing) "I should here have attempted to calculate the rental and produce of the whole county, by entering minutely into the particulars of each article; but at present, I shall only suppose the average price of land, exclusive of waste, to be 18*s*. per acre, which amounts to the yearly rent of 448,200*l*. exclusive of houses; and that the produce is three times that sum, or 1,344,600*l*."

WOODLANDS.

WOODS.—P. 40. "There are large woods and much timber in the county of Warwick, particularly in what was formerly called the Forest of Arden, extending through a large portion of the middle part of it, which consists of almost all the different kinds of forest-trees, but more especially of oak. The woodlands of this county, are, in general, kept under a regular system, the underwood of which is cut down every ten or twelve years, and converted to various uses, such as rake, mop, and broom-stails, faggots, brooms, hoops, &c. Hurdles (seven feet and a half long and three feet and a half high) are made by being wattled round nine upright stakes, which are sharp at the bottom, to assist in fixing them as a temporary fence; for eating off turnips, and other uses, for which they make an excellent fence, during three or five years, if properly taken care of, and are sold at 5*d*. each. The white poles (which are twenty-four years growth) are converted into rails, ladders, hoops, and various other articles, by cloggers, brush-makers, turners, &c. Much of the value of our underwood depends on a proper selection of plants at each fall to be set up, and continue growing for white poles, particularly ash and oak: and this is best done by those who fall and convert their own woods; for it is evident, that those who buy them for a round or two, (as it is here called) will pay more attention to their own profit than to the future value of the woods, however they may be restrained by any agreement. The price of these woods is from 3*l*. to 8*l*. per acre, in proportion to the value of the land, as there are more or less of white poles, and the quantity of oak timber set up.

"But those woods which grow oak well, answer best by being gradually converted into groves of that timber, which has been done in this county, by setting up oaks, either from maiden-plants or stubs, and by previously dibbling in acorns where wanted. By this means the underwood will be reduced in its value, after two or three falls. In woods which are brought under this management, great care is necessary

necessary in *pruning* and training the oaks when young, during the three falls here alluded to; for, if not properly pruned when *young*, all that can with safety be done to the branches of an oak, when the heart is formed in them, is to restrain their growth at some part where they divide into a fork."

AGRICULTURE.

FARMS.—*Sizes*.—P. 10. "The land in this county, from an average of the large and small occupiers, may, I think, be considered as being in middle sized, or rather small farms, about 150 acres each, perhaps less; and the average size of the new inclosures about 15 acres, and those of the old inclosures about 10 acres."

OCCUPIERS.—P. 10. "There are many opulent farmers and graziers in this district, who occupy large tracts of land, who, for the management of it, and judicious care in breeding cattle, sheep, &c. are equal to any others in the kingdom, and who are able to judge of the practicability of those schemes or improvements made on a small scale, in gardens, on rich lands highly manured, or under other circumstances, which, however laudable in those who make them, are sometimes delusive, and not found to answer on a larger scale of practice."

OBJECTS of HUSBANDRY, and PLAN of MANAGEMENT.—P. 11. "I have estimated the whole county at 618,000 acres; of which, about one-fourth, 154,530 acres are constantly under a successive round of tillage, and such grass seeds as will be hereafter mentioned. In every course of tillage, consisting of two, three, or four crops, a summer fallow for turnips or wheat, well manured, is generally made. Of this 154,530 acres, about one-sixth, 25,700 acres may be every year wheat; about 30,000 acres every year fallow; of which 30,000 acres, about 15,000 acres may be turnips and vetches; about 41,500 acres every year, barley, oats, beans, &c. and the remaining 57,330 acres of seeds, the greater part of which are grazed with cattle and sheep; perhaps 45,000 acres grazed, and the remainder mown. The remaining 463,470 acres I suppose to consist of gardens, meadows, pasture, woods, water, open fields, waste lands, and roads. Of gardens, (to about 24,000 houses) about 4000 acres; of meadows 82,000 acres; of pasture and feeding lands 150,000 acres; of woods, canals, and rivers, &c. 50,000 acres; of open field land 57,000 acres; and of waste lands and roads 120,470 acres."

P. 12.

P. 12. "The *system* of husbandry, in Warwickshire, varies much on the same sorts of land. Many of the best managers avoid taking two white straw crops in succession, but there are greater numbers of occupiers who do not attend sufficiently to that circumstance, who are, in other respects, good managers."

WORKPEOPLE.—P. 23. "The price of labour is in some degree governed by the Birmingham and Coventry trade in the vicinity of those places, and is there, generally speaking, one-fourth more than in the remote villages. In those country situation, in harvest, labourers have 1*s.* per day, and victuals; and, if extraordinary hands are wanted for the harvest months, or indeed at any other time of the year, their wages depend on the necessity of the work, their skill in particular undertakings, and sometimes on the goodness or badness of trade. At other times of the year, labourers have from 4*s.* to 5*s.* per week, and victuals; and from 6*s.* to 8*s.* per week, without them; but sometimes with, and sometimes without, an allowance of small beer."

For sensible remarks on the overlowness, or inadequacy, of wages, see the head *Poor Rates*, p. 285, aforegoing.

WORKING ANIMALS.—P. 25. "Ox teams are used in some parts of this county; but in a very small degree, compared with the almost general use of horses: and this arises from prejudice, which may probably be removed by the Board. In the management of farms, lime, coal, &c. must generally be drawn along hard roads, to a considerable distance, and their produce be conveyed to market by the same means, which is certainly best done with horses. I am, therefore, apt to believe, that few farmers can use oxen advantageously, except those who want the labour of more than *seven or eight horses*; but all team work, beyond that, would, I am persuaded, be highly profitable to the farmer, and greatly beneficial to the public, if done with oxen. My reasons for fixing seven or eight horses as necessary to be kept on the larger farms, are these: many of the greater works in husbandry, are done (in harvest, &c.) with two *going* and one *standing* waggons or carts, (according to our phraseology) which will employ that number of horses, as will also a nine inch wheeled waggon for lime, coals, &c. &c. Lord Aylesford keeps fifteen working oxen, (three teams), for home work, which are supported at *half* the expence of an equal number of horses. It may possibly happen in particular situations, which have the advantage of canals, that both the large and small farmers might do their whole business with oxen; because, in those situations, not any team work on hard roads, or to great distances, would be wanted."

This is a valuable suggestion. Canals and railways are friendly

friendly to the working of cattle in husbandry. And cattle, properly bred for the purpose, would be equally eligible as horses, to be employed on either of these species of public roads. The tracking paths of canals, and the drawing paths of railways being usually (or might readily be made in most situations) soft and pleasant to their feet.—And with what an inconsiderable portion of the millions that are annually squandered, in ruinous profusion, over the face of the earth, might the latter be extended across every district of the island; and thus lessen, incalculably, the labor of carriage, and the present *extravagant* number of horses of draft; and the consequent *waste* of HUMAN FOOD.

IMPLEMENTS.—P. 27. "The larger occupiers of land, and public carriers, have, many of them, six and nine-inch wheeled waggons for the road; but those most generally in use for harvest work, and employed by the smaller farmers, have narrow wheels. The carts most commonly used for husbandry, have wheels of six or nine inches broad."

MANURE.—*Lime.*—P. 45. "I shall here beg leave to say something on the subject of *lime*, because its use is much, and very expensively mistaken in many parts of this district; vast quantities being every year used improperly, where it seems to have no other effect than assisting to impoverish the land on which it is spread. I shall endeavour to explain its real use, by reciting some experiments, which I made a few years since, in order to ascertain the most speedy method of bringing barren waste-land into a productive state of cultivation.

"Some years ago, Lord Aylesford having enclosed and drained Meriden Heath, (and settled the vicar's claim by a *corn rent)* sixty acres of it were ploughed up, in the winter months, and in the spring following, well harrowed, to close the furrows, and in that state left to rot till the following autumn. The whole was then cross ploughed and harrowed. In order to pulverize ten acres of the best of this land, I had a roll made *five feet and a half long*, surrounded by five strong sharp plates of iron, so that the sharp edges of the plates of this roll, when loaded, and drawn by six horses, cut through the whole surface as deep as the plough had gone at the first ploughing; and by repeated harrowing, and the operation of this roll, the land had the appearance of being sufficiently well pulverized for a crop, except only, that by those repeated operations a great quantity of moss, and the roots of different coarse grasses, &c. were brought to the surface: these *we* collected into heaps, burnt, and spread the ashes, which produced a good dressing. The land was sown with oats, in March, and seeded down with clover and rye-grass the oats, when cut and housed, the next autumn, did not

not produce so much as had sown the land, nor any seeds worth saving.

"Three other parts of the same piece (ten acres each) were pulverized, and the roots, &c. burnt in like manner, at the same time. One part was treble folded with a flock of one thousand sheep; one part was well dressed with good rotten dung; and the other part was well limed. These three pieces were also sown with oats, clover, and rye-grass. That which was folded, had not a bag of oats on an acre, nor were the seeds, worth saving; that which was dunged, succeeded very little better; and that which was limed, produced a most excellent crop of oats and seeds.

"Another piece of ten acres, prepared in the same way, was marled, and produced a tolerable crop of oats and seeds.

"The remaining ten acres were limed, prepared, and sown with rye, at Michaelmas; and the spring following, seeds harrowed in, which produced a very fine crop.

"Upon the future management of this land, that part of it which was before limed, continued constantly productive; and the other parts not so till they were limed; the piece that had been marled only excepted, which, from its calcareous quality, I consider as having the same effect on vegetable substances as lime, with the addition of earth of such a quality, as, uniting with loose peaty soils, makes an excellent manure for them.

"From these experiments, and from many others which I have made with *lime*, both on cultivated and uncultivated lands, I am clearly of opinion, that the chief use of lime, perhaps the only one that can answer the expence at which, in some parts of this county, it is brought home (three pounds for a common waggon load) is in the cultivation of heath, peaty or common lands; I might say of all *other* lands, where the parts of vegetables have from time to time been permitted to fall on the surface of the earth, and there, by long accumulation (not being of themselves capable of rotting) to produce a variety of coarse surface, sometimes strongly matted with roots, and sometimes a light, and, as it were, a frothy surface, &c. Lime in such cases will seize on all those imperfect vegetable substances, and by its *septic quality*, convert them into *vegetable mould*, in which all kinds of grain and grasses grow luxuriantly.

"In well pulverized *light soils*, where the turf, and other vegetable substances, have been well rotted before using it, I never could perceive that lime was of any use."

These remarks are not inapplicable to different parts of the Midland Counties; and may have had their use, where lime was fetched twenty miles or more; and of course at an

expence

expence which might not *answer*—But they will not hold equally good, in the kingdom at large. The writer of them, it would seem, had not been sufficiently *travelled*, at the time he wrote, to decide *generally* on this subject. Lime has been of long continued use, in various parts of the island; where the rental value of lands and their produce, of course, have been greatly increased by it, during half a century, perhaps; and where they still continue to receive essential benefit from its application. Thousands, tens of thousands, of acres, of "light soils" (which in general are most sensible to its virtues) have been converted from *rye* lands to profitable matrices for *wheat;* and still afford, occasionally,—and principally, I believe, through its use,—valuable crops of the latter grain.

That lands may be, and have been, satiated with, or "tired" of lime, appears to be well ascertained. (see NORTHERN DEPARTMENT,—District, *Cleveland.*) But this may have happened through an immoderate, and of course an *improper use of it.*—And so it has ever been with marl.—Further;—lands are liable to be "tired" of clover, and of turneps, by too frequent use of these crops. This, however, ought not to be a bar to their cultivation *.—If we yet (November 1812) know any thing of the PRINCIPLES of VEGETATION, and the FOOD of PLANTS, lime—calcareous earth—is a favorite food of arable crops†.

Sheepfold.—P. 31. "Folding sheep is here but little practised, and seems not to be well understood; *perhaps* our long-woolled sheep are not so proper for that purpose as those which have shorter wool."

SEMINATION.—*Time* of *Sowing*.—P. 15. "Wheat is sown early in September, and so on till December: beans, vetches, and pease, in February, March, and April; vetches for green food till the latter end of May; and Flax in April. Early sowing seems to gain ground, and generally secures an early harvest."

Drilling.—P. 42. "The drill husbandry is practised with Mr. Cook's machines in this county, to the south of Warwick, by

* FOOD of PLANTS. For a striking and very extraordinary evidence of land being saturated, satiated, or "tired," even of the DUNG of CATTLE! see my NORFOLK: *Minute* 32; on the Bullock Hill of St. Faith's; the largest cattle fair in Norfolk.

But this well authenticated fact, perhaps, only tends to show, that MUCILAGE, *alone*, is only an *ingredient* of the food of plants.—The Minute referred to was made in 1781.

† The above was verbally written, nearly twelve months before I read the LECTURES of Sir H. DAVY, (I never heard them); and I am glad to find that we accord in *this* particular.

by Mr. Moor, of Charlcot; Mr. Thomas Jackson, of Alvaston pasture; Mr. Boot, of Atherston on Stour; Mr. Bolton, of Wellsbourne; Mr. Chandler, of Kington; and by some others in various parts of this district. On loamy and other rich soils, the drill husbandry may be found to answer, if the system of *making good turnips follows* is adhered to; but not otherwise, except in particular situations, where the soil is uncommonly rich, or where great plenty of *putrid* manure can be obtained. But the opinion of the greater part of the farmers in this county is in favour of the broad-cast practice, and more particularly so respecting barley and oats, with which grass seeds are generally sown. Mr. Boot, of Atherston on Stour, has been longer, and more largely in the drill husbandry, both on strong and on excellent light land, than any other person in this part of the kingdom. On looking over his farm, I find nothing to recommend the practice either in his fields (turnips excepted) his rick yards, or his barns; but the reverse. The former are poor, and full of couch-grass; and the latter scantily filled. His rotation of crops on the light lands is wheat, on clover lay a fallow for turnips, and, previous to those turnips, vetches, as soon as the wheat is housed, on such of the land as is clean; after the turnips barley seeded down, and those seeds grazed, or mown one year; then wheat, &c. as before. As he constantly drills his strong land, and as wet seasons have oftentimes prevented him, by that method, from cropping that strong land, it sometimes lies fallow for *several* years together, and no specific course of cropping has been pursued upon it, as I was informed by his neighbours, (for Mr. Boot was unfortunately from home, when I called there); nor has his produce, by about *fifteen years drill husbandry*, been nearly equal to that of his predecessors in the broad-cast way. Some of my information on this subject may, it is possible, have been given with prejudice."

Arable Crops.—Produce.—P. 13. "On loam or good sandy soils is, about 24 bushels of wheat; 40 bushels of barley; 45 bushels of oats; 30 bushels of pease; 20 tons of turnips; 1½ ton of clover (or seeds, &c.); and 35 stones of flax on an acre."

P. 14. "*Of good strong land*"—"is about 35 bushels of beans; 28 bushels of wheat; 30 bushels of barley; 40 bushels of oats; 40 stones of flax; and 2 tons of clover, on an acre."

"Of *poor lands*, *poor clay*, and *other cold land*—is about 24 bushels of barley; 28 bushels of oats; 24 bushels of rye; 16 bushels of wheat; 18 bushels of beans; from one, to one and a half ton of clover; and 15 tons of turnips, on an acre."

P. 15

P. 15. Of *commonfield lands*, "the produce of open fields is about 20 bushels of wheat, and 24 bushels of barley, oats, and beans, per acre. The average rent of open fields is about 10s. per acre; the rent of same kind of land, when inclosed, about 18s. per acre."

GRASS LAND.—Mr. Wedge's Report is very defective on this important subject, in a country which abounds with it. I find no notice of it; excepting under the head, *Soil*; which see in p. 283, aforegoing.

CATTLE.—On this prominent article of production, in a country abounding with grass lands, Mr. W's Report is almost equally deficient.—Neither on the breed, the rearing, the management, nor the grazing of cattle, in Warwickshire at large, can I find a line that is entitled to extraction.—Mr. Fowler's stock is noticed; but not in a way that is *new*.

The Reporter is a friend to *crossing*; but judging from the little he has said on the subject, he had not, at the time he wrote, gone beyond a *first* cross; which will frequently produce a *mule* of a superior quality.

DAIRY.—P. 34. "There are fine dairies of cows in almost every part of this district, and much excellent cheese made; but I am of opinion, that many of what are called the better bred cows, are but indifferent milkers; and that the average produce of each cow is not more than three hundred weight of cheese in a season."

SHEEP.—*Breeds.*—P. 30. "There are, generally speaking, two sorts of sheep bred in this county; a larger or polled sort for pastures, which weigh from sixteen to forty pounds per quarter, some more, when fat; and cut from six to fifteen pounds of wool each. The average size of this kind of sheep, when sheer-hogs and fat, is about twenty-two pounds per quarter, and their fleece weighs eight or nine pounds: the wool of the former is combed for Jersey, the latter for hosiers, and used by clothiers."

P. 31. "A smaller sort, some with black and some with grey faces, are also bred for commons, open fields, and inferior pastures, which weigh from *eight to twenty-five* pounds per quarter, when fat, at two, three, or four years old; and cut from one to five or six pounds of wool each, which is used by clothiers; some with and some without horns.

"Some few Wiltshire sheep, and others of mixed breed, are also bred. Great numbers of sheep are every year bought from distant counties; ewes for making fat lamb, and wethers for feeding."

"There has also been lately introduced to this county a kind of sheep called the *new Leicestershire*, which are much lighter

lighter in their bone, offal, and wool, than the old Leicestershire, or Warwickshire breeds; they are neat animals, and much resemble the better kind of Wiltshire sheep,* in their legs, wool, and faces; but have no horns. Such has been the reputed excellence of these sheep for becoming fat, with a much less proportion of food than any other kind, that rams of this new breed are said to have produced a profit of 1000 guineas a year to their owners, and exorbitant prices from that sum downwards."

After speaking with indignant warmth on the *combination* of *rambreeders,* Mr. W. continues, p. 32,—" As opposition sometimes brings on useful discussion, I shall, on this ground, remind those breeders, that, about twenty years since, they recommended, in the strongest possible terms, a breed of sheep almost totally covered with wool, and that were, in appearance, dwarfs.† These sheep, they asserted, bad also the gift of becoming fat, with very little food; and, as they are now totally out of use, I cannot place so much confidence in the assertions of those breeders as I otherwise should have done; but yet it must be admitted, that the new Leicestershire breed are greatly preferable to those which they *formerly recommended,* and for some lands a valuable breed of sheep. As it is the business of a quack to conceal the composition of a nostrum by which he fills his pockets, so also has it been the practice of those ram-breeders, to conceal the manner in which their *new kind of sheep* have been bred: on that account I shall endeavour to explain what their owners have, with so much care, endeavoured to keep from the public. I have called them a *new breed of sheep,* because that fact they (the breeders) have laboured hard to establish: and, taking that for granted, it establishes, beyond contradiction, another fact, viz. that this *new breed* of sheep must have been a *cross* from some others.

" From the similitude which these sheep have in their wool, and in other particular points, to the better sorts of Wiltshire, and from their similitude also to the better sorts of old Leicestershire and Warwickshire sheep, I have little doubt but that a cross, or crosses, from those kinds, has produced the new breed of sheep in question. In this opinion I

* In my eye, no two breeds of English sheep (mountaineers excepted) are less alike. This I speak from an extensive, and long-continued acquaintance, with the Wiltshire breed.

† I recollect passing a flock of this sort, slowly travelling toward Smithfield. The sight was interesting.—They resembled fleeces of wool moving along the road, as by enchantment.—Not a leg, scarcely a hoof, was discernable.

I am confirmed by my own experiments, and by the judgment of others; and I have here sent a sketch of a sheer-hog bred in that way."

That the Wiltshire breed might have been employed *to lengthen the legs* of the first short-legged variety, is not improbable. But the idea that the present breed were produced by a cross between the Wiltshire and the old Leicestershire and Warwickshire sheep, has always appeared to me to be void of probability.

By Mr. W's *manner* in speaking of the "new breed of sheep," he would seem (and I do not wonder at it) to have been annoyed by the offensive importunities of ram breeders of the then new school,—until he was disgusted, not only with the men, themselves, but with their breed of stock.

RETROSPECTIVE OBSERVATION.

Mr. WEDGE's Report was evidently done in haste. It was among the first that were sent in to the Board; being printed in January 1794. This circumstance shows that if Mr. W. had had more time to study and write, he would have produced a valuable work, on the Rural Economy of Warwickshire. And it is to be regretted that the Board did not, or could not, prevail upon him to furnish a more ample account of it.

It appears to me most extraordinary that the Reports of Messrs. WEDGE (brothers I believe) Mr. DAVIS, Mr. MAXWELL, Mr. CRUTCHLEY, Mr. DONALDSON, and others of the original Reporters,—men whose abilities as writers on Rural Economy would outweigh the rest of the Board's *Authors*,—should not have been permitted to meet the public eye.

As yet (November 1812) nearly twenty years after the establishment of the Board, WARWICKSHIRE is without a *published* Report!

" GENERAL VIEW

"GENERAL VIEW

OF THE

AGRICULTURE

OF THE

COUNTY OF WARWICK,

WITH

OBSERVATIONS ON THE MEANS OF ITS IMPROVEMENT.

BY ADAM MURRAY,

LAND-SURVEYOR AND ESTATE-AGENT.

1813."

THIS is the *last* Report from the MIDLAND DEPARTMENT.—It is *dated*, May, 1812.—Some month's ago, it was "announced" in a list of "publications by the Board:"—not as being *in the press;* but as being *then published!*—It was not, however, *to be had* until the middle of this month; November 1813.—Such is the *deliberate* and *regular* mode of proceeding, observed by the literary manager of the Board.

Mr. MURRAY'S *profession* appears in the title page *. By the evidence of his book, he is familiarly acquainted with the husbandry of SCOTLAND;—and he speaks of different districts of ENGLAND; but not with intimacy.

The MODE of SURVEY adopted by Mr. M. is seen in the subjoined extract, from a prefatory letter, addressed *to* the right honorable, the President of the Board,—and, judging from its style and manner, it would seem to have been *from* the right honorable pen of the same.

P. viii. "That I might do justice to the mission in which I was engaged, and that I might give due attention to

* At the close of his thin volume, Mr. M. furnishes a CATALOGUE of IMPLEMENTS, headed thus:—" A Catalogue of Scotch Agricultural Implements, sold by Adam Murray, Surveyor and Land-agent, at his Repository, No. 61, St. Martin's Lane, Charing-Cross; who also provides Noblemen and Gentlemen with Scotch Stewards and Baliffs, free of Expense."

to every object deserving remark or enquiry, from the moment of my approach to the County till the period I quitted it, I never entered a carriage or crossed a horse, but walked every step; considering this mode of travelling (though attended with much bodily fatigue and no small expense) as best calculated for procuring information."

But neither the *period* of this pedestrian missionary's *approach*,—nor the years, months, or days he was *engaged* in his mission,—is handed down to posterity.

Mr. Murray's *own* manner is mostly plain, intelligible, and well adapted to the business of Report.—It is not, however, a little extraordinary that the ORIGINAL REPORT, by Mr. WEDGE, is not directly noticed by Mr. M. He speaks repeatedly of "Mr. Wedge of Packington," as one of his *informants!* and in a way which would have conveyed the idea that he was not aware of the existence of such a Report, had he not *borrowed* from it.

The number of pages one hundred and eightyseven.

A Map of the County. One other engraving; and an intelligent Index.

SUBJECT THE FIRST.

NATURAL ECONOMY.

EXTENT.—P. 2. "The county contains, by Cary's Map, 597,477½ acres, at the calculation of 80 chains statute measure to a mile."

ELEVATION.—Mr. Murray adopts Mr. WEDGE's mistaken idea, about the *Warwickshire mountains.*—P. 23. "The woods near Lord Aylesford's, and at Corley, have been supposed to be higher than any other land in England. From this elevated ridge, the water runs, on one side, into the Avon; and so on to the Bristol Channel; and from the other side into the Blythe, Tame, Trent, and Humber, at Hull. As Packington and Corley are near the centre of England, the supposition seems to be well founded."

CLIMATURE.—P. 13. "The most general winds are from the south-west, and are usually accompanied with rain; but not unfrequently, the effects of an easterly variation are felt to the middle of May; and it scarcely need be remarked, that vegetation must, in consequence suffer severely. Warwickshire, upon the whole, however, is not to be considered as subject to any particular excess of damp or frost."

WATERS.

WATERS.—See Mr. WEDGE'S account of them (p. 282, aforegoing); which Mr. Murray gives his readers, "with additions and emendations;" but none that requires to be mentioned, here.

SOILS.—P. 13. "It would require much time, and very minute observation, to describe exactly the extent of each different sort of soil in the county under review; indeed it would be a task hardly possible to effect, for the soil varies so much in all the districts of the county, (two or three different kinds of soil being often found in the same field), that any exact description cannot be expected."

Nevertheless, a *painting in water-colors* of "the soil of Warwickshire" is prefixed to the volume. By whom it was *designed* is not declared.—How disgraceful are such proceedings, *to some one*.

Mr. M. it is true, gives itinerary notices of the soils he happened to travel over, in his walks along different lines of the County. But they convey nothing satisfactory regarding the soils of the County at large.

Yet in the map, we see large plots firmly outlined; and distinguished by different colors; as if an actual survey of the County had been taken, and extensive tracts of uniform soils had been found,—in flat contradiction of the above printed and published Report of it. If such a survey has actually been made, the circumstance ought to have been mentioned; and the person or persons, by whom it was executed, to have been named. How mysterious are the ways of *im*providence.

FOSSILS, &c.—P. 19. "The minerals and fossils in Warwickshire, are coal, limestone, freestone, iron, blue flagstone, marl, and blue clay; also a clay, having some of the properties of soap, is found on the estate of the Earl of Warwick; but it has not yet realized the sanguine opinion once formed of its value. Considerable quantities of coal are wrought at Bedworth, where the seam of coal runs from three feet to three and three quarters, and in some places to four feet in thickness, and the quality is considered the best in the county. The coal sells at the pit at 11*s.* 8*d.* to 12*s.* per ton. At Griff-hollow, Chilvers-cotton, Nuneaton-common, Hunts-hall and Oldbury, there are considerable quantities of coal also wrought.

"The seam at Oldbury is about 40 yards in depth, and from three feet to three and a half thick. The quality of the coal is inferior, being only fit for burning limestone, and in consequence sold at the pit at 9*s.* per ton. This vein of coal extends by Merevale, Polesworth, and Wilnecote. I was informed that Mr. Dugdale, one of the Mem-

bers

bers for the County, had sunk several shafts, but the success had not been completely ascertained.

" *Limestone.*—The county abounds with limestone in many places. Extensive quarries are wrought at Bearley, Grafton-court, Stretton, Princethorpe, Ufton, Harbury, Wilnecote, Bitford, Newbold-on-Avon, and in many other places; sold in shells at the kiln from 2*s.* 6*d.* to 3*s.* per quarter, or 43*s.* to 45*s.* per waggon load."

P. 21. " *Freestone.*—There is abundance of freestone rock about Warwick, Leamington, Kenilworth, Coventry, and many other places in the county. Where the soil is a light sand, freestone rock will in general be found below; the use of which is not so general as it was in earlier times, when all buildings were of stone; now brick is substituted, as being dryer and cheaper, yet much stone is still used, particularly in all public buildings.

" *Ironstone.*—There is ironstone at Oldbury, and at Merevale, which was formerly wrought near Oldbury, in a wood called Iron Wood; and this stone runs all the way to Mr. Dugdale's house at Merevale.

" *Blue Flagstone*—Is found in many places in the county: considerable quarries are wrought in the neighbourhood of Bitford and Wilnecote, and used for paving and flooring.

" *Marl.*—The western district of the county abounds with marl, of different colours and qualities; a great proportion of which is of a very strong and excellent nature"(?); " but I did not see much of it dug and used, although the advantage of mixing it with native earth is so well known and acknowledged.

" *Blue Clay*—Is found in great abundance in the eastern districts of the county: it has been analysed, and found to contain alkali," (?) " and other ingredients used in making soap; and it was supposed this earth might be made to answer all the purposes of soap; but either the expense was too great, or the opinion proved not to have been justly formed, as the continuance of it in the Navy seems to have been abandoned; and for general domestic uses, it would I fancy be very difficult to introduce it, even if its qualities were really all that were supposed."

SUBJECT THE SECOND.

POLITICAL ECONOMY.

APPROPRIATION. P. 62. " The extent of commons and unenclosed land in Warwickshire, is much less than

than is to be met with in most counties in England. The spirit for enclosing has been pretty general through the county, and in my opinion, if the example were followed up in every other county, commons would be a rare thing to be seen.

"About fifty years back, the south-eastern part of the county was very much in common, but is now all enclosed and subdivided. The only common I met with, of any considerable extent in that quarter, is at Long Compton, and an Act has been since obtained for enclosing it. There are small commons still remaining in different parts of the county, the greater part of which would not pay the expense of obtaining a bill for enclosing them. Although the expense of enclosing is very great, yet the beneficial effects resulting from enclosures, are generally felt throughout the county. With regard to an increase of produce, *that* is evident to every person, for it must be admitted, that the land that formerly kept a few half-starved sheep, is now yielding abundance of both grass and corn."

P. 144. "The quantity of waste land, including roads, but not including the common-field land, in the county of Warwick, was estimated about ten" (twenty) "years ago by Mr. Wedge, of Packington, at 120,470 acres, and of commons and common-field at 57,000; but since that period, a great many Acts of Parliament have been obtained for enclosures, which have reduced the quantity of commons into a small compass, when compared with other counties. It is lamentable to observe with what slowness and supineness, the enclosing, draining, and bringing into cultivation the commons in almost every county in England is carried on, when the country is so much dependant on foreign supplies of grain, and that grain paid for by draining the nation of its coin and bullion. This indifference is truly astonishing, when we consider that the cultivation of all the commons and wastes capable of being cultivated, would be a certain means of diminishing, if not altogether removing, this dependance, and would increase the comforts and riches of the community."

P. 145. "The great expenses attending the procuring an Act of Parliament, prevent a great number of small commons and wastes from being taken in, and on that account, enclosures only become an object where the quantity of land is great. A General Act of Enclosure can alone effect the enclosing of the small commons and wastes; and until that shall take place, they must remain in their present miserable and unproductive state."

And see the article, *Tithes*, ensuing.

Manufactures.—P. 176. "Manufactures of different descriptions

descriptions are carried on to a great extent in the county of Warwick. At Birmingham, all kinds of hardware goods are made, and in the vicinity a very extensive trade is carried on by Messrs. Bolton and Watt, in the manufactory of all kinds of plated goods, coinage for Government, and making steam engines, not only for the supply of almost the whole of the Empire, but sending immense numbers to every part of the civilized world. The steam engine first constructed by that great and ingenious mechanic, Mr. Watt, has stood the test, and proved to be superior to any yet invented; as is most clearly proved by the house of Messrs. Meux and Co. brewers in London, who have tried a great variety of engines of different constructions, which were constantly going wrong, and who, therefore, were under the necessity at last of having only Messrs. Bolton and Watt's engine, which they find to answer their full expectations.

"There is a very considerable nail manufactory carried on at Bromwich, by Messrs. Whitehouse and Co.; but since the non-intercourse with the United States, the principal trade carried on at Birmingham and the vicinity is the manufactory of muskets for Government: six thousand are sent weekly to London.

"At Coventry, are very considerable manufactures in the silk and ribbon weaving, tambouring, &c.

"At Kenilworth, there is a considerable manufactory for horn-combs of all descriptions.

"At Warwick there is a very considerable manufactory established and carried on by Messrs. Parkess, Brookhouse and Compton, for worsted for the hosiery trade: from four to five hundred people are constantly employed in combing and spinning long wool, and in other branches of this manufacture.—Also one for weaving calicoes and other cotton goods, of yarn spun at Manchester and the neighbourhood: at this factory about two hundred people are employed by Messrs. Parker. About the same number of people are employed by Mr. Benjamin Smart: about a mile and a half from Warwick, Mr. A. Emscot has a mill on the river Avon, for spinning cotton yarns. All these manufactures were erected and established about fifteen years ago.

"At Alcester, there are very considerable manufactures for needles; about six hundred people are employed in this branch, by different persons.

"At Berkswell, Balsall, and Tamworth, there are considerable flax manufactures, and a good deal of linen yarn spun."

PROVISIONS.—See *Markets*, ensuing.

FUEL.

FUEL.—P. 171. "COALS are in general use throughout every part of the county, which is well supplied, not only by means of the coal-mines wrought in different parts of it, but in a great measure also from the coal-mines of Staffordshire, which are of a much superior quality, and are conveyed into all parts of the county by means of canals. The price of them varies, according to where they are delivered; but at Birmingham, the great mart for coals, they are sold at 11*s.* to 12*s.* per ton, and at Bedworth and Griff, and other collieries, they are sold at the pit-mouth at 11*s.* 6*d.*, 11*s.* 8*d.*, and 12*s.* per ton.

"Faggots and bavins are used in heating ovens, and for brewing; and in some parts of the county, cord-wood is used, especially when there is any grubbing of underwood going on; but coal-fires come cheapest in the end."

POOR RATES.—P. 38. "The poor's-rates in the county of Warwick vary much in different parts of it; I should suppose the average about 5*s.* 6*d.* in the pound on the rents. At Warwick, Coventry, Birmingham, Alcester, and other manufacturing towns, the rates generally run high; from 10*s.* and 12*s.* to 15*s.* in the pound, which becomes a very great cess upon the landed property of the country."

P. 178. "In so large a manufacturing county as Warwick, it must be expected that the poor's-rate runs high, the manufacturers drawing together a large population, who, through sickness, disease, intemperance and other causes, become a very heavy burthen on the parishes for support. This throws a heavy cess on the landed property, which does not derive a benefit bearing any proportion to that of the trading interest."

TITHES.—P. 37. "The farmers in Warwickshire complain of tithes, as in other districts, and wish that they could be converted into a corn rent, or some fixed payment; but their complaints are more generally directed against the lay impropriators than the clergy, the former being more rigid in their exaction than the latter. Most of the old enclosures through the county are subject to tithes, which in many instances are compounded for, at the rate of from 6*s.* to 12*s.* per acre on the tillage land; on the meadow and pasture lands from 1*s.* to 5*s.* 6*d.* per acre; and lately, as high in some places as one seventh of the rent. Enormous as this is, some are not satisfied with it, but collect their tithe in kind.

"The new enclosures are exonerated; where they take place, a proper proportion of land is set off in lieu of tithes. It would be a great national advantage, if the proprietors of landed property throughout the kingdom, had an opportunity of purchasing their tithes; the amount of the purchase

chase money to be invested in the funds of the nation, as ecurity to posterity for the principal."

CANALS.—P 173. "The canals that pass through the county, are one from Dudley to Birmingham, and from thence, the Wigginshall, Birmigham, Fazeley Canal, and from Fazeley, the Coventry Canal, to Atherstone, Chilvers-Coton, Griff, Longford, and Coventry; a branch of the Ashby-de-la-Zouch Canal, and another to Marston and Griff; the Oxford Canal, which joins the Coventry, near Longford, to Brinklow, Brownsover, and Brawnston, where it joins the Grand Junction, and from them proceeds by Lower Shuckburgh and Merstondale, and leaves the county near Wormleighton to Oxford; one from Birmingham to Worcester; one branch to Stratford-on-Avon, called the Stratford-on-Avon Canal, and one branch from it to Tamworth, and another to Grafton Lime works; one from Birmingham to Warwick, called the Warwick and Birmingham Canal, a branch near Lapworth-street, which joins the Stratford Canal; and one from Warwick, that joins the Oxford Canal about two miles east of Southam, called the Warwick and Napton Canal.

"All these canals join, and are of immense benefit to the county, both in an agricultural and commercial point of view; and still there might be branches from these canals that would benefit the county much, by bringing coal and limestone to centrical situations in different districts, to lessen the land carriage, which would tend greatly to improve every part of the county to the highest pitch of cultivation, would increase the value of property amazingly, and at the same time better the circumstances of the cultivators."

ROADS.—P. 172. "It certainly would be of very great advantage to the community at large, if all the public roads through the kingdom were made broad enough to admit of an iron rail-way at each side, and to reduce the size of the wheels, and the tracts or treads to one standard. The great facility and dispatch in the conveyance of all kinds of commodities, would in a very short period defray the expense of making the rail-way, and the saving of horses and labour would be immense."

This, surely, must have been written, without due consideration. The *present roads* of England, speaking generally of them, cross hill and dale; whereas *railways* require a level, or nearly a level line.

MARKETS.—P. 170. "The great facility in the intercourse between one part of the kingdom and the other, by means of canals, railways, and good roads, and the reports of the clerks of the markets being regularly made public, has

has the effect of keeping the price of grain pretty equal through the kingdom; and the prices now are very much regulated by the prices given in the London market. The consumption for stock, cattle, sheep, lambs, pigs, &c. is certainly great at Birmingham, Coventry, and Warwick; still a great deal is drove to Smithfield, for the supply of the London market; and at any time there is not more than 1*d.* to 2*d.* per pound difference between the prices in London and at the above places, and often the same. It would be difficult to state the exact average price of grain and stock, except I was in possession of all the weekly returns, and even then perhaps it might not be correct."

SUBJECT THE THIRD.

RURAL ECONOMY.

TENANTED ESTATES.

ESTATES.—*Proprietors.*—The following detail of proprietors, many of whom have residencies in the County, exhibit, a *richness* and *elevation* of *neighbourhood,* which no other portion of the island of equal extent, I believe, can furnish.

P. 25. "The state of property in Warwickshire, may be considered as very unequal in its division: the most extensive estate is that of Stone-Leigh, possessed by the Rev. Thomas Leigh, supposed to contain upwards of 25,000 acres; a great proportion of which is very excellent land. There are other proprietors possessing great extent, in the county, namely, the Dukes of Buccleugh and Dorset; the Marquisses of Buckingham and Hertford; the Earls of Aylesford, Clarendon, Spencer, Warwick, Denbigh, Northampton, Abergavenny, Plymouth, and Coventry; the Lords Craven, Middleton, Willoughby-de-Broke, Bagot, Digby, Dormer, Wentworth, Lifford, Clifford, Calthorpe, and Bradford; the Bishop of Lichfield and Coventry (Cornwallis), Sir John Mordaunt, Sir G. A. Shuckburgh, Sir Roger Newdigate, Sir Thomas Gooch, Sir Theophilus Biddulph, Sir John Throckmorton, Mrs. Leigh, Mr. Legge, Mr. Bromley, Mr. Dilke, and many other respectable gentlemen; whose example, and whose liberal encouragement to their tenants, has contributed so much to the improvement of the agriculture of the county."

TENURES.

TENURES.—P. 26. "The greater part of the county is freehold, though there are many copyholders of some extent; and their tenures, as in all other counties, vary much; but as these are unchangeable, it would avail little to enter into a detail of them. The following instances of their absurdity may be worth noticing.

"At Hampton-in-Arden, if a man possessed of an estate marries, and has several children the issue of that marriage, he cannot give it away by will, without his wife's consent, nor does it descend to his children; but the wife, after the death of her husband, has *then* the absolute power to give it to the children of another person, or to whom she pleases." (?) "In another manor in the same parish, if a widow marries, without having put her finger into a hole in a certain post, and there craved the consent of the lords of the manor, she forfeits her estate. It is much to be re gretted, that such remnants of feudal absurdity cannot be done away.

"A very considerable extent of land is held of the Church, principally of the Cathedrals of Worcester and Lichfield. About 500 acres on the south side, adjoining the city of Coventry, the property of the Marquis of Hertford, is Lammas or common, from the 13th of August to the 13th of February; and the quantity of land in the county of Coventry subject to this right of pasturage, is estimated at 3000 acres; a right enjoyed only by the Freemen of the City of Coventry, and not transferable."

IRRIGATION.—P. 157. "Irrigation is practised in the neighbourhood of Birmingham, Castle Bromwich, and many other parts in the county, but only on a small scale, and is executed in a very slovenly manner. The watering of grass lands appears not to be properly understood. There are many places well situated for irrigation, which, if judiciously performed, would effect a wonderful improvement on all the meadow land susceptible of the operation. Water that flows from calcareous substances, is considered best for this purpose, and in many parts of the county, there are numerous springs of water that flow from limestone and marl, which might be converted to this use with very great advantage."

Mr. Murray, I believe, is the first of the Board's Reporters who has adopted the truism, that *calcareous* waters are the best (of *clear* waters incomparably the best) for the purpose of irrigation.

TENANCY.—On *leases* Mr. M. has written some pages. But his strictures belong to *general dissertation*, rather than to *provincial report*. They convey what, in the writers opinion, *ought to be*, rather than the *practice* of *Warwickshire*.

shire. He enumerates, however, several heads of leases, which he understood to be in use, in Warwickshire. But I perceive none that requires transcription; excepting what appears in the section "Repairs."

P 30. "It is customary for the landlord to allow the tenant rough timber, and other materials, for making repairs, the tenant being at the expense of carriage and workmanship."

RENT.—P. 36. "If we except that part of the county of Warwick which lies in the immediate vicinity of Birmingham, Warwick, and other populous towns, the rents of this county are *low*, considering the generally excellent quality of the soil, and its local advantages for the export and consumption of its produce. The best grass land for pasture, lets from *2l.* to four guineas per acre; the arable land from 18*s.* to 25*s.*, 30*s.*, 42*s.*, 50*s.*, and some at three guineas per acre; the meadow land from *2l.* to *5l.* 10*s.* to six guineas per acre: accommodation land near the towns, lets from four to six guineas per acre; garden-ground as high as *10l.* to *15l.* per acre.

"In many parts of the county the rents are very much under what I have quoted; I suppose the average rent of the whole county would amount to 29*s.* per acre."

Are those low rents!—Would arable lands at six guineas, pasture grounds at eight guineas, and meadows at twelve guineas, an acre, be reckoned low rents in Scotland? See *Donaldson's Northamptonshire*, ensuing.

CHOICE of TENANTS. *Capital.* P. 43. "It is necessary in the first place, to ascertain, as nearly as possible, the expense of stocking a farm in Warwickshire; or the gross sum that it will take, per acre, and which a farmer ought to have, before he enters on a farm; but this circumstance depends greatly on the state of cultivation that the farm is in when the tenant enters; if in a good state of culture, it will require much less; in a bad, it will require considerably more. The farmer should not only have what will purchase his stock, and carry on the expense of labour until he receives the new crop, but he should have a year's rent at command, to prevent any sacrifices being made in his property for want of money, for necessary demands that may arise.

"The following calculations, show nearly the expense attendant on entering on a farm of 200 acres in Warwickshire.

"*Expense*

" *Expense of stocking a Farm of* 200 *Acres*, Clay Soil, *and managing it, paying for keep of the House, and paying One Year's Rent.*

	L.	*s.*	*d.*
Ten work horses, at 40*l.*	400	0	0
One riding ditto, ...	40	0	0
Two large four-horse waggons, at 55*l.*	110	0	9
Five two-horse carts, at 20*l.*	100	0	0
Three ploughs, at 4*l.* 4*s.*	12	12	0
Ten harrows, ...	15	15	0
Harness, cart, and plough, ...	50	0	0
Two rollers, ...	12	0	0
Drags, rakes, forks, dung drags, fans, barn implements, sacks, and sundry other things, ...	30	0	0
Labour, ...	320	0	0
Maintenance of horses, ...	330	0	0
Seed, ...	180	0	0
Rent, at 40*s.*	400	0	0
Tithe rates, king's taxes, &c.	160	0	0
Keep of the family, ...	200	0	0
	L. 2360	7	0

" On this statement, it would require 11*l.* 16*s.* per acre; but as the prices vary in general so much in different districts, we may fairly conclude, that upon an arable farm, according to the system practised in the county, it would be more desirable than otherwise, to have 13*l.* to 14*l.* per acre, to do the farm justice."

I insert the above calculation and remarks as Mr. Murray's; and not as a standard of capital, for men of fortune or their agents,—whereby to make choice of tenants. If a man of well known *skill*, *industry* and *moral character*, can show that he is possessed of capital, equal to ten pounds an acre, in ordinary cases, or a less sum in others, it might be imprudent to refuse him, on that account. In cases where much draining is required, or where irrigation, extraordinary manuring, or tillage, is necessary, —let the landlord *improve*, or *allow* for improvement; and fix the rent, accordingly; namely, at what the land will be worth, when improved see p. 249, aforegoing.

WOODLANDS.

WOODLANDS.

WOODS.—P. 140. "That district of Warwickshire which contains the largest woods, is what was formerly called the forest of Arden, extending through a great part of the middle of the county. I have heard it mentioned by some of the old people, that this forest of wood or timber trees stood so thick at one period, that a squirrel might leap from one tree to another, nearly the whole length of the county. The middle, western, and northern districts of the county, appear to abound most in timber, and in these districts there is a great quantity of most valuable oak, admirably adapted for ship-building, and other purposes.

"The estate that is considered to possess the largest quantity of oak timber in the county, is the Leigh estate: I was creditably informed, that the quantity that is ready for cutting upon this estate, if sold, would exceed the sum of 150,000*l.*; I was sorry to observe a great deal of timber decaying on this estate.

"Almost every nobleman and gentleman in the county, possess a considerable quantity of valuable oak timber on their estates; but the finest and best grown oaks I observed in any part of the county, was on the estate of Mr. Dugdale at Merevale. The trees standing near his house are remarkably tall and stately; and I do not consider I exaggerate when I say, that a great many of them will measure from 1 to 250 and 300 cubical feet: they appear to be at maturity, and if it were not for the present ornament, and an idea of their original grandeur, it would be much better that they were cut down, and converted to the purpose of ships for the Navy.

"The Marquis of Hertford's estate at Ragley, also abounds with oak timber of very large dimensions; but I understand no consideration would induce his Lordship to fell any quantity of it."

COPPICES.—P. 142. "Copse woods, consist of oak, ash, hazel, alders, birch, and beech, which are managed, and trained up in the usual method as in other counties. The quantity to be cut annually, is allotted according to the extent of the wood, which is divided into falls of one, two, three, four, five, six, seven, eight, nine, ten, and sometimes eleven and twelve years' growth, which come in regular succession for one fall yearly. The wood is converted into various uses; into hurdles for folding sheep, hoops, faggots, rails, rake and broom stails."

AGRICULTURE

AGRICULTURE.

FARMS.—P. 33. "The size of farms in Warwickshire, from what I could learn, runs from 50 to 500 acres; very few exceed that extent, and many containing not more than 50, 100, 150, 200, 250, and 300 acres. Mr. Wedge at Packington," (!) "who from his long experience must have had opportunities more favourable than most people, for ascertaining the truth on this head, reckons that 150 acres are about the average of the county; the average size of the new inclosures about 15 acres, and the old about 10 acres.* In the eastern district of the county, the farms are large; in the west, and north-west, in general small."

Farm *Gates.*—P. 65 "I am persuaded, if a light, well-constructed cast-iron gate were introduced into the county, that could be furnished for two guineas each, it would be found to be not only of great utility, but in the end attended with a great saving."

I insert this as something new. Cast-iron carriage gates may, or may not, be found eligible on a farm.

Farm *Cottages.*—There is much truth and good sense, in the subjoined sentiment, relating to the residences of farm workpeople.

P. 31. "The servants of farmers are so valuable a class of people, that their comfort should in all respects be considered; and in none is it so essential as the providing them with comfortable cottages on the farm. These may always be built at a small cost, and being under the eye of the farmer, the conduct and morals of his servants may be expected to be better. They will not, as now is too much the case, be driven into towns and villages far from the farm, for a residence, where, having ready access to public-houses, they are apt to spend both their time and money, be led into dissipation, often abandon their families in consequenee, and thus increase the poor rates in a high degree. Whereas, were cottages always provided on a farm, these evils would in a great degree be prevented; and a farmer would have a controul and command over his servants' time and conduct, that he cannot possibly have, when, the moment their day's labour ceases, he sees them no more until they return to it."

In

* The above is nearly verbal quotation of Mr. Wedge's original Report !! See p. 294, aforegoing.

In Scotland, as well as on the English borders, the regulations that are here recommended, are not only practicable, but universally (it may be said) practised;—for reasons already explained*.—In England, at large, they partially exist. And, in many cases they might be extended; more especially on detached farms, where there are not a sufficiency of cottages, *ready built,* in their neighbourhoods.

Occupiers.—The following relation is too tempting a morsel to forego. It shows the disadvantage, if not the danger, attending the collection of the existing state of agriculture, in a County, by *enquiry.*—The character, here brought forward, was comparatively, an *honest man.* For another, more artful and mischievous than himself, might have readily filled up the blanks of the Tourist's query paper, with *false information.*

P. 34. "The character of the farmers in Warwickshire, like other counties, varies as much as the size of the farms. There are to be found in the more remote parts of the county many small farmers, who are exceedingly shy and jealous in communicating their modes of farming, although it is very evident there is nothing new to be learned from them, even if they were communicative. The only information required, is, the facts as to the present state of agriculture, which there is hardly a possibility of getting. Even in the very best district of the county, farmers of the same description are often to be met with; and I wish I could say that this jealousy was confined to the farmers only. It is to be regretted, that sometimes people of large property and liberal education are unhappily the dupes of those about them; and though perhaps willing of themseleves to afford information, are biassed by their bailiffs, and act contrary to their own original good intentions.

"In confirmation of this remark, I beg leave to state a fact which happened to myself. In the prosecution of this Survey, I waited on a clergyman, a gentleman of good property, and producing my credentials from the Board, requested his assistance in furnishing me with any information in his power, so as to enable me the more perfectly to draw up my Report. He received me very politely, and seemed willing to further the object I had in view: he said that he knew very little about farming himself, but would send for his bailiff, who was an intelligent man, and could give me a great deal of information, not merely concerning his own extensive property, but the properties adjoining; and in the meantime he would write a letter to one of his tenants, whom he

* See Northern Department, district *West Yorkshire,* p. 370

he conceived very competent to afford me the details of the system of farming in his district. However, the bailiff arrived before the gentleman had well begun his letter, got closeted with his master, over whom he had an unbounded influence, and persuaded him that it would be a very dangerous measure to give me any information; and that instead of giving me a letter to his tenant, it would be much better for him to go with me to him, for fear, as I supposed, that he should be too communicative in telling me the rents they paid, which were a mere feu-duty, only 16*s.* to 18*s.* per acre, for some of the best land in the county of Warwick. My suppositions were well-founded; for when we arrived at the tenant's, the bailiff made his way into the house as quickly as he could, got closeted with the tenant, and no doubt communicated to him his apprehension of the danger that might attend his giving me any information: that the rents would be raised, and every thing would be against him. The consequence was, that the tenant was alarmed by the misrepresentations of the bailiff, and immediately on my being introduced to him, he at once told me he did not see any advantage the county of Warwick would derive from such a Survey; that it must do a great deal of hurt instead of good; and that such being his opinion, he declined giving me any information on the different heads of queries I meant to put to him. If it had not been for the ignorance, or mischievous interference of the bailiff, I have no doubt I should have derived much valuable information from the tenant, who, I was informed, was a man that stood as high in his profession as any in the county. From motives of delicacy I decline mentioning names; but I vouch the fact."

For the required *capital* of an occupier of farm lands,—see *Choice* of *Tenants*, p. 314. aforegoing.

Plan of Management.—P. 74. "In Warwickshire, where the soils vary considerably in every district, and where the farmers practise different systems, and follow different plans of arranging and cropping their lands, it is hardly possible by any general remarks to give a correct idea of the rotation of crops followed through any particular hundred. From the remarks I could make, and from what information I could obtain (which, I am sorry to say, was very limited), the farmers through the county are in the practice of taking two white crops running. They have what appears a strange practice to a person coming from the North, of sowing pease and beans on clay lands broken up from old grass, and some sow wheat. On good dry loams, wheat from old grass, if clean; and fallow for turnips, if foul, is a general maxim among them."

Notwithstanding those forbidding circumstances, the Reporter

porter has thought it right to enter largely upon the subject; charging a succession of pages with "courses of crops,"—nearly forty in number—which he learned were in use in Warwickshire, together with recommendatory remarks thereon.

WORKPEOPLE.—P. 167. "Wages from 2*s.*, to 2*s.* 6*d.*, 3*s.*, and 3*s.* 6*d.* per day, with an allowance of small beer; women from 1*s.* to 1*s.* 6*d.*"

P. 168. "*Hired Farm Servants.*—The wages given to ploughmen, and waggoners, boys, &c. differ in different parts of the county; but in general, they run from 12, 14, 16, and some as high as 20 guineas a year, and their board. Boys, five to six guineas a year, and their board. Hours of labour from six o'clock to two, or from seven to three, in the summer, and afterwards clean down their horses, and procure meat for them: clean out the stable, and any other thing necessary to be done; in winter about six hours."

"The principal animal food used by labourers is pork or bacon, boiled or broiled, which is cut in slices, and with an onion eaten on a piece of wheaten bread, and washed down with water, when they cannot procure beer; but in general, they have as great a respect for beer in this county as any in England, and if it is possible to procure ale, they will not want it, if their wives and children should go naked."

WORKING ANIMALS.—See *Horses,* ensuing.

IMPLEMENTS.—On this subject, seeing that Mr. Murray is a disseminator of implements (see N. p. 303, aforegoing), his observations are commendably brief; evincing a degree of moderation and becoming modesty.—I perceive nothing in his chapter of the Implements of Warwickshire, that requires to be noticed, here.

TILLAGE.—*State of.*—P. 66. "Warwickshire farmers are far from being neat in ploughing their land: the strong clay land is ploughed in large, crooked ridges, gathered very high, with a small ridge between them; and a great deal of the light land in a similar manner. I did not notice in any part of the county, half the labour bestowed on the land, as is customary in the Lothians and Berwickshire. The light sandy soils bore the appearance in many places of great slovenliness; for they were completely choaked with couch and other noxious weeds. The country from Stratford to Warwick appeared to be the best cultivated part of the county."

Ridges.—P. 68. "The general breadth of the ridges on the clay land in this county, is about 30 feet, with a small ridge between, about 10 to 12 feet broad, which formerly used to be generally in grass, but now remains in

that

that state only in the common-field land; in the enclosed land it is cultivated in the same manner as in the other parts of the field."

After recommending fifteen feet ridges, the Reporter informs us,—p. 69,—that, "upon wet lands, narrow ridges will not keep the land so dry as ridges of the dimensions before described, well rounded, so as to throw off the rain that falls."—Now this, I will venture to say, is practically erroneous.

Fallowing.—Mr. Murray is decidedly a fallowist, and speaks at some length on the subject. But nothing new is said in favor of the practice. The advantages of it, to strong, tenacious, moist soils, have been, again and again, sufficiently shown.

MANURES.—*Species.*—P. 149. "The manures principally made use of in the county of Warwick, are, dung, urine, soot, horn-scrapings, lime, marl, soap-ashes, and compost. The quantity of dung made at Birmingham, Coventry, and Warwick, is very considerable, and is generally consumed, and made use of in the neighbourhood of those towns; very little is drawn above ten miles, except soot and horn-scrapings, which are carried to a greater distance for top-dressing of wheat, being found to answer extremely well for that purpose.

"The price generally paid at Birmingham, where the greatest supply is to be had, is 8*s.* to 9*s.* per ton for good dung; at Coventry, and Warwick, it sells at 9*s.* 10*s.* 6*d.* to 12*s.* per ton, which is a high price, and precludes it's being carried to a great distance."

Lime.—P. 152. "This is obtained in many parts of the county by burning the limestone. Considerable quantities are burnt at Grafton-Court, Bitford, Wilnecote, Bearley, Billesley, Ufton, Harbury, Stretton, Princethorpe, Newbold, and in many other places. There is great abundance of limestone along the borders of Oxfordshire, and Leicestershire, and very considerable quantities of lime are brought by the canals from Staffordshire and Leicestershire, for use in this county. There is more than a sufficiency of limestone for the consumption of the county, if it were quarried and burned in kilns of a proper construction; this is not the case, for they are very badly contrived, and the process of burning is both tedious and expensive. If they were built on the plan I before noticed, ten times the quantity of lime might be burnt, with a great deal less labour, and a very considerable quantity of fuel saved."

In one who has examined, he believes, every species of lime furnace, in *England*, it may surely be allowable to exclaim, on reading the above passage, *can this be true!* I have

have often been *paused* by the Board's Reports. Here, I am *stunned*. In a lime kiln, properly constructed, *one tenth* more of lime may certainly be burned, than in one of a less perfect construction. But who can believe that a kiln may be so situated and constructed that *ten times* more shall be burned in it, than in ordinary kilns. The subjoined is the Reporter's incomprehensible description of his wonder-working kiln.

P. 20. "A lime-kiln should be placed in an open situation, where the air has full power; the walls of the kiln should be at least 22 to 24 feet in height, and should have a good inner coat of the best fire bricks, and a cast-iron horse with a strong grate at the back, for the small lime to go through; there should be four eyes, three for drawing the shells, and one at the back of the kiln, for carrying away the small lime, &c.; an arch should go through the back part, and the eye for drawing the small lime at the middle, or half way through the arch. A kiln, if constructed in this way, and well managed, would burn and draw 500 bushels per day, of good and well-burnt shells, and would also save a great deal of time."

What is the capacity and internal form of the kiln which is calculated to burn "five hundred bushels" (nearly sixteen chaldrons) "per day"?—If the height of the walls rise "twentytwo to twentyfour feet," above ground,—how are the stones and coals got within them? And what is their *thickness*.—But enough.—The whole reads (in the loose unintelligent language in which it is written) so much like a hoax, I repent, almost, that I did not pass it as such.

But having said this much, I think it right to add, that, if the kiln of *Scotland* is really capable of saving even *one tenth* of the expence which is at present required to burn lime in the *best* constructed kilns of *England*, the Board of Agriculture will be doing the latter more service, than all they have hitherto done it*,—by furnishing the several limestone districts of England with accurate WORKING MODELS of the SCOTCH KILN:—The *iron horse*, and *back eye*, may have their use.

MARL.—P. 156. "Marl is to be found in many parts of the County; that of the best quality lies under the strong clay land; marl that is wrought under light soils," (?) "is of a very inferior quality. From the number of pits that are

* Saving and ever excepting the ASSISTANCE they have afforded me in COLLECTING MATERIALS for the purpose of REGISTERING the RURAL ECONOMY of ENGLAND, at the commencement of the nineteenth century.

are to be seen in every district of the county, it would appear that marl was formerly in much greater use than it is at present. Since the practice of burning lime commenced, the use of marl has diminished yearly, and the effects of lime have been found from experience so infinitely superior to those of marl, that the last will in a short time cease to be used at all."

SEMINATION.—*Drilling*.—P. 69. "The drill husbandry is very little practised in Warwickshire, only by a few individuals."

BARN MANAGEMENT.—P. 169. "The following is a comparative statement between thrashing grain with the flail and with the thrashing-mill; supposing a good, well-constructed thrashing-machine of four-horse power, to thrash 30 quarters of wheat per day, and 50 quarters of oats.

"*Statement of the Expense of Thrashing Thirty Quarters of Wheat with the Thrashing-Mill.*

	£.	s.	d.
"Four horses one day, at 6*s*. per horse, ...	1	4	0
One man or boy to drive them, ...	0	2	6
One man to feed into the mill, one day, ...	0	2	6
Two women to give up the wheat, and bring it forward, ...	0	3	0
Two men to take away the straw, one day, ...	0	5	0
One man to riddle and clear the fanner, one day, ...	0	2	6
Tear and wear of the machinery, oil, &c.	0	5	6
	2	5	0
Thirty quarters of wheat thrashed by the flail, at 5*s*. 4*d*.	8	0	0
Cleaning thirty quarters, one man and three women; two days, man at 2*s*. 6*d*., six women at 1*s*. 6*d*.	0	14	0
	8	14	0
Balance in favour of a good thrashing-mill,	5	9	0

"The

	£.	s.	d.
"The mill will thrash fifty quarters of good oats in one day, with the same expense,	2	5	0
Fifty quarters of oats, thrashed with the flail,	5	0	0
Cleaning fifty quarters with the fanners or winnowing-machine, one man and three women; two days and a half of one man at 2*s.* 6*d.*, seven days and a half of three women at 1*s.* 6*d.*	0	17	6
	5	17	6
Balance in favour of the thrashing-mill,	3	12	6

"In wet weather, in winter, when a farmer's horses are idle, the corn may be thrashed at less expense. In the above, I have charged the labour of both man and horse as high as it is before stated."

See the REPORT of CAMBRIDGESHIRE, on this subject,—ensuing!

ARABLE CROPS.—Mr. Murray has appropriated forty pages, to their cultivation in Warwickshire, and his own observations on the same. The whole of the chapter, "Arable Lands," may be said to be a sort of *mule* production, between the Scotch and the Warwickshire practices of husbandry. It cannot reasonably be supposed (we are obliged for lack of explicit information to raise conjectures) that Mr. M. as a professional man, and moreover an implementarian, could spare any length of time for his walk through Warwickshire. And, it is more than probable, as nothing appears to the contrary, that it was performed in some one particular season of the year. But to enable a Writer to make out a sufficiently accurate Report, from *his own examinations*, of the culture of arable crops, in their several branches, he must necessarily *reside* in the district of survey, *one whole year, at least.* We may therefore, I think, fairly conclude, that the principal part of Mr. M's knowledge of their culture and management, in that county, was obtained through *enquiry**. And, seeing, as we have been shown, the cautiousness of men who are most able to give

* Those remarks apply, not to Mr. Murray alone; but to every ENQUIRING TOURIST,—who attempts to give detailed accounts of the various operations and processes in husbandry, which take place in succession, throughout the several seasons of the year, in a County or District.

This, a weak man, or a wicked one, might say, is striking at the vitals of all the touristical books that now load the shelves of libraries. The

give authentic information, concerning the best practice of the district, in which they are the leading practitioners, it might be pardonable in Mr. M. and fortunate, perhaps, for the farmers of Warwickshire, to fill up deficiencies from his own knowledge, or opinion, of what *ought* to be the practice of that County. He not unfrequently, indeed, brings forward, in a didactic way, his own sentiments; especially on the general subjects of ARATION. I will quote, as a specimen, the opening of his section.

WHEAT.—P. 87. "There is a great deal of land in Warwickshire well adapted for the cultivation of wheat; and the culture of that valuable plant might be considerably increased, if a different system of husbandry were practised. In the south-east part of the county there is much strong good clay land in grass, that has apparently been laid down in very bad order, and is now full of pernicious root-weeds and ant-hills, that require very much to be broken up, and brought into a state of cultivation. After a crop of oats being taken, if well summer-fallowed, cleaned, limed, and sown with wheat, you might insure a great crop. There are also in the north-east and north, and south, and south-west parts of the county, a great deal of good strong land, admirably suited for the cultivation of wheat. On the best clay soil, you may have wheat after a summer-fallow, dunged and limed; again after clover, and again after drilled beans; so that by this rotation you have three crops of wheat in the six years, from manuring once. On the poorer clay soils, wheat after summer-fallow, dunged and limed; again after clover. By this rotation they might have two crops of wheat in four years, from manuring once; whereas by the present practice of the county, on the best clay soils under tillage, they have only two crops of wheat in the six and seven years; and on the poorer clay soils, only once in four and six years.

"I am certain, that the system I have pointed out for the management of these strong clay soils, will yield three-eighths" (a nice calculation) "more produce than what is now obtained, and the lands be always in better condition than under the system at present adopted."

Mr.

The reply, in that case, would be apt. There are many things, as I have repeatedly shown, even in agriculture, which a traveller may note down, in passing through a country, and publish, with propriety for the information of others. He may describe the operations belonging to arable crops which happen to be going on, at the time of his tour, or during the short stay he may make in a district. But he must necessarily leave it, in perfect ignorance, regarding those which are performed, in every other season of the year; unless he have recourse to *enquiry.*—It is the *agricultural* tourist of whom I am particularly speaking.

Mr. Murray then enters upon the task of giving, in detail, the Warwickshire practice of cultivating wheat, on different soils in the county;—and proceeds, in like manner, to describe the cultivation of its other arable crops. But, in consequence of the foregoing reflections, and by reason of my perceiving nothing, in the details drawn out, that indispensibly requires either praise or censure,—I will pass over, in silence, the remainder of the chapter, "Arable Lands," which is extended over sixty pages (nearly one third of the volume) without farther observation or extraction;—saving the subjoined passage.

P. 116. "Every farmer who sows Swedish turnips, should be very particular in the selection of the seed; for there is more spurious seed of this root, than of any of the other kinds; he who cultivates them extensively, should raise all his own seed, and raise it only from the turnips he can select that are well-shaped, and of a small stem."

BULBOUS RAPE is doubtlessly liable, (like other *forced* or *selected varieties* of vegetables and animals), to revert, through negligent management, to its original state of nature.

GRASS LAND.—*Extent.*—P. 128. "It is supposed the extent of land in permament meadow and pasture grass in Warwickshire, amounts to 235,000 acres, and the quantity in artificial grass to about 60,000 acres, making together annually in grass 295,000 acres. Out of this quantity, it is supposed 80 to 85,000 acres are meadows, and mown for hay annually; and of the artificial grass about 10 to 15,000 acres are cut green, for horses and other cattle, and made into hay: the remaining 195 to 205,000 are pastured with sheep and cattle. The eastern district of the county appears to be more in permanent pasture than any other part I observed. At Radway, Warmington, Avon-Dassett, and along the Buckingham road, right and left, to near Gayden-Inn, is very rich pasture grass; but the defective manner in which a great deal of it has been originally laid down is truly lamentable, for the loss to the grazier, and consequent injury to the public, must be very great, owing to the unevenness of the surface, and especially so in wet seasons; for the spaces between the high ridges being mostly level, must be rendered nearly useless, from the quantity of water that lodges on them, and which produces a great number of sour grasses. From Rugby, all along the borders of Leicestershire, there is also a great deal of very rich land in permanent pasture, the greater part of which is nearly in the state just mentioned. Indeed many parts of the county abound in old pasture grass; and on each bank of the Avon, until it leaves the county, there are considerable ties of rich meadow and grazing land."

Meadows.

Meadows.—P. 132. "The most valuable part of the meadow land in Warwickshire, lies along the banks of the different rivers that run in the county; still there is an extent of meadow land scattered over different other parts of it. The produce in favourable seasons, upon the richest meadow land, is from two to three tons per acre; on less fertile, from one to two tons per acre."

Pastures.—P. 133. "The greatest extent of pasture laying together, is in the eastern districts of the county. With respect to the mode of management, it is principally grazed with cattle and sheep: the quantity of stock, per acre, depends upon the goodness of the pasture, and quality of the soil, and on the kind of stock put upon it. Good rich pastures will keep from six to seven sheep, or a good sized ox, per acre. Some farmers stock with sheep altogether, and others with cattle and sheep; when together, one ox or cow, and three sheep, to two acres. If the season be favourable, it will keep them from the month of May till November, and after that, winter one sheep to each acre.

"With regard to dairies, many farmers have given them up, finding they can make more of their pastures by feeding cattle and sheep, than by keeping cows for making cheese and butter, and rearing young cattle. The graziers stock the pastures with all kinds of breeds of cattle, preferring those they think will pay them best, according to the soil, and circumstances of the pastures. Of the female kind, they prefer the long-horned heifers and cows; and of the ox, they like the Scotch and Hereford; but they make great complaints, of the very high price the Scotch cattle stand them in now.—The sheep are generally the New Leicesters, which are preferred to others."

Horses.—P. 164. "The horses generally used in the county of Warwick for farm purposes, are heavy black horses; which are much improved by the fine stallions that are sent from Leicestershire every year. There are also a great many riding, hunting, and coach-horses, bred in the county, the prices of which run very high; thirty, forty, fifty, and even sixty guineas, are given for good work-horses for farm purposes; but the general prices are from thirty to forty pounds: good riding horses sell from fifty to one hundred guineas; and for hunting horses, more is paid from fancy, than for the real value of the animal."

Cattle.—P. 159. "It has been already noticed, that many of the farmers in the county have given up keeping dairies, and that the breeding of cattle is less followed than what it used to be formerly, the grass lands being appropriated to feeding" (fatting). "Farmers and graziers buy in whatever kinds of store cattle will pay them best; and by this means the county abounds with many different breeds. The kind of cow that is bred in this county, is mostly the long-horned, which, from the appearance of their shape and size, seem to have been originally brought into the county from Lancashire. Considerable pains have been bestowed by many of the breeders, to improve the breed; but I could hear of none who had bestowed so much attention, and improved them so effectually, as Mr. Webster, of Canley, near Coventry, and Mr. Fowler, of Rollewright, on the borders of the county; the stock of the latter gentleman was particularly admired by most people, and sold at greater prices than ever were known before."

DAIRY.—Not many years back, laborers of every discription, in London and its neighbourhood, might be said to live (at least to *dine*,) on "Warwickshire cheese;" and Mr. WEDGE makes no mention of the decline of the Warwickshire dairy. Yet, by the notices, above transcribed, the only one regarding it that I have found in Mr. Murray's Report, it would seem to have been in 1812, takeing its leave of the County.—See *Grass Land* aforegoing.

I am disappointed in not finding, in either of the Warwickshire Reports, an intelligent account of its practice, in regard to this article of its produce.—It is, I believe, of long standing; and has therefore, it is probable, some valuable particulars of management belonging to it.

SHEEP.—*Breeds*.—P. 161. "There are several sorts of sheep bred in the county. The large polled sheep, or ancient Warwickshire; the New Leicesters; the Wiltshire; a small sort, some with black and grey faces, bred on the commons; the South Down; Welsh; and of late the Merinos. The large polled sheep, or old Warwickshire, breed by Mr. Palfrey at Finham, near Coventry, and several other eminent breeders, when very fat, will weigh from 40lb. to 48lb. per quarter, and shear from 9lb. to 16lb. of wool each. The average size of this kind of sheep, when hogs and fat, is 23lb. per quarter, and their fleece weighs from 6lb. to 9lb."

P. 162. "Of the Wiltshire sheep, very few are bred in the county. Lord Aylesford has a considerable flock for folding, being more adapted for that purpose than the long-wool breed; the ewes are considered good mothers, and make very fat lambs, and the weathers for feeding.

"The sheep that are found on the commons and open fields, some with black and grey faces, and bred there, are a very mixed breed; the best of them, when fat, at three years

years old, will weigh from 18 lbs. to 23 lbs. per quarter, and shear from 4 lbs. to 6 lbs. of wool each; the inferior sort will weigh from 5 lbs. to 10 lbs. per quarter, and cut from 1 lb. to 3 lbs. of wool, which is used by the clothiers for making coarse cloths.

"The South Down sheep have been introduced into the county by Lord Hood, on his estate near Coventry: they answer the purpose of folding much better than the long-woolled sheep, being more active, and less liable to injury from driving about."

P. 163. "The Spanish Merino sheep have been lately introduced into the county, and bred by Lord Aylesford at Packington, and Mr. Thomas Jackson at Alveston Pastures, near Stratford-on-Avon, whose flock is about 600; which number may be considered as sufficient for making a fair trial of their success or failure."

SWINE.—P. 165. "There are many different breeds of pigs in the county; the large white pig, the black and white spotted, the grey-coloured, and the dark brown. The large white pig grows to the greatest size, and will weigh, when fat, from twenty to forty score each; but they are not considered so profitable as those of a less size. The Berkshire pig is reckoned as profitable as any that has been introduced into the county. Fewer pigs are now kept, since the dairies have decreased."

POULTRY.—P. 165. "The county of Warwick abounds with poultry, owing to the prevalence of small farms. At several places, I counted 50 and 60 full grown turkies walking by the side of farmers' rick-yards, and at Coombe Abbey near Coventry, the seat of the Earl Craven, I saw several hundreds of fine full grown turkies, and other fowl in abundance. Great quantities are sent to London, but the principal market for them is Birmingham."

GAME.—P. 166. "There is great abundance of pheasants, partridges, and hares, in the county of Warwick; the protection of them is particularly attended to by many of the noblemen and gentlemen; but where the pheasants and hares are so very much encouraged to breed, and remain unmolested, they become a great pest to the farmers, and in many instances are very destructive indeed to the corn-fields contiguous to these preserves. The injury done by the pheasants is so very great, that I have understood the damage sustained by some farmers so situated, has been equal to 150*l.* and 200*l.* some years;—a consideration of no small magnitude."

PROFIT of FARMING.—P. 43. "There is very great difficulty in obtaining the truth on this head: farmers, like other people in business, are shy in laying open their affairs

to

to any one, and now more so than ever: in the first place, for fear their landlords should get hold of it, and thus be the means of an advance in their rent the first opportunity; and, in the second place, for fear the Commissioners of the Income Tax should be made acquainted with it, and raise the duty on them. Farmers in general keep no books in a minute or regular manner; it is not therefore in their power to give the particulars of their expense and profit correctly, only in a rough way."

To make up, however, for the want of replies, to aukward questions asked, Mr. M. enters upon a series of speculative calculations (in imitation, no doubt, of others) in order to make out the expence and profit arising from the cultivation of different soils. The subjoined are the calculator's retrospective remarks.

P. 54. "These calculations no doubt will appear to leave a high profit on the grazing land; but the grazing system being much better understood than the corn farming, it appeared to me, in going over the different districts of the county, that the grazing farmers must be much better paid than the corn farmers. These calculations must not be considered as the real average of the county, for to obtain it exactly, is next to an impossibility: the rent stated is low; for of such soils laying locally," (?) "and in a good climate, if managed on a different system, the rent would advance greatly. It should be remembered, that no degree of certainty can be attained on the head of real expense and profit; whoever is acquainted with the management of land, must perceive it, for a great deal depends on the seasons, and also on the activity and judgment of the husbandman."

In these remarks there is much good sense; which amply makes up for the lack of it, in the calculations.

NORTHAMPTONSHIRE.

NORTHAMPTONSHIRE.

STILL we are treading the widely extended billowy surface, which characterizes the MIDLAND DEPARTMENT. Northamptonshire may vie with any other part of it, in *natural richness;* and equals, or excels, every other County, which it comprizes, in point of *ornament;* tho not in *agricultural produce.* It is marked by its forests, and private woodlands, that are ornamentally, but, in many instances, unprofitably, scattered on its surface. In this particular, forming a contrast with Leicestershire.

"GENERAL VIEW

OF THE

AGRICULTURE

OF THE COUNTY OF

NORTHAMPTON.

WITH

OBSERVATIONS ON THE MEANS OF ITS IMPROVEMENT.

DRAWN UP FOR THE CONSIDERATION OF

The Board of Agriculture and Internal Improvement.

TO WHICH IS ADDED,

An APPENDIX, containing a Comparison between the ENGLISH and SCOTCH Systems of Husbandry, as practised in the Counties of Northampton and Perth.

BY JAMES DONALDSON,

DUNDEE.

1794."

BY the addition to the author's name, in the title page, it would seem that the Reporter of Northamptonshire is the author of the *present State of Husbandry in Great Britain;*

tain:—a work which I have not seen; but which is mentioned, with some warmth, by the Reporter of the *West Riding* of *Yorkshire;* while dwelling on the subject of leases.—See NORTHERN DEPARTMENT.

Whether Mr. Donaldson was merely a *literary surveyor*, in Northamptonshire, or whether he also appeared in the character of an *improver*, at Boughton (a seat of the duke of Buccleugh) where much of his information appears to have been collected,—and where he speaks of some experiments with shell marl, as his own,—is not, as it might well have been, mentioned.

By the following extracts from this Report, it will be seen, that its author has an extensive knowledge of rural affairs, especially those of Scotland; and that his manner of writing is well adapted to his subject; showing how well Mr. Donaldson was calculated to have given a more enlarged view of the agriculture of Northamptonshire, in a "reprinted report;" the work before me being one of the unpublished sketches which the Board style "original reports."

The subject of the Appendix is a "comparison between the English and Scotch systems of husbandry, as practised in the Counties of Northampton and Perth."—A few particulars of that comparison will be transcribed and incorporated with the valuable parts of the body of the work.

The number of pages, in this, sixtyeight:—in the Appendix, nineteen.

Printed in Edinburgh. No map, or other delineation.

SUBJECT THE FIRST.

NATURAL ECONOMY.

EXTENT.—P. 5. "Its greatest breadth from Higham Park on the east, to Stanford on the west, is 32 miles; but its mean breadth may be reckoned at 14 miles, making a square superficies of 910 miles, or 582,400 acres."

SURFACE and APPEARANCE.—P. 5. "The surface of this county is as peculiarly advantageous for cultivation, as it is delightful and ornamental. In no other part of the kingdom, perhaps, are more agreeable and extensive landscapes to be seen Here, there are no dreary wastes, nor rugged and unsightly mountains, to offend the eye, or to intercept the view. The surface is no where so irregular, but it can be applied to every purpose of husbandry and tillage. Every

hill

hill is cultivated, or may be kept in a profitable state of pasturage, and every inequality in the surface contributes to its ornament and beauty."

CLIMATURE.—P. 6. "The climate of this county is very favourable both to health and vegetation, and this may be accounted for from its situation and other natural advantages.

"It is abundantly supplied with excellent water. The surface of the ground is no where so elevated, as to confine the foggy and unwholesome vapours (which at times arise in this and in every country) from being speedily dispersed. As there are no high hills here, it is in a great measure exempted from deep falls of snow, and long continued rains, which are so injurious to farmers in the vicinity of mountainous regions; and as the seasons change gradually, the health of the inhabitants is little affected by them, and the operations of husbandry are seldom long or unexpectedly suspended by the inclemency of the weather."

App. P. 6.—"Periods at which seed-time and harvest commenced in the different counties, for the six preceding years, from 1788 to 1793 inclusive.

NORTHAMPTONSHIRE.

THE periods at which seed-time and harvest commenced on a particular farm in this county for the six preceding years, from 1788 to 1793, will be found in the following tables:

Years.	Wheat.	Spring Corn.	Barley.	Harvest commences.
1788.				4th Aug.
1789.				18th ditto.
1790.				16th ditto.
1791.	5th Oct.	5th Mar.	11th Mar.	8th ditto.
1792.	6th ditto.	1st ditto.	15th ditto.	13th ditto.
1793.	27th Sept.	28th Feb.	21st ditto.	1st ditto.

PERTHSHIRE.

Below is an account of the periods at which seed-time and harvest commenced on a particular farm in the Carse of Gowrie, from 1788 to 1793, inclusive.

Years.	Wheat.	Spring Corn.	Barley.	Harvest commences.
1788.	11th Sept.	7th April.	6th May.	25th Aug.
1789.	11th ditto.	6th ditto.	9th ditto.	27th ditto.
1790.	13th ditto.	3d March.	6th ditto.	27th ditto.
1791.	14th ditto.	7th ditto.	4th ditto.	18th ditto.
1792.	4th Oct.	9th April.	7th ditto.	29th ditto.
1793.	10th Sept.	25th Mar.	3d ditto.	28th ditto."

WATERS.

WATERS.—P. 7. "There are perhaps few districts better supplied with water than this, while the inconveniencies which so often happen from enjoying that advantage, are here felt but in a very inconsiderable degree. In almost every part, it abounds with fine springs, which being very plentiful in the upper part of the county, form numerous small brooks and rivulets, several of which uniting in their course towards the sea, at length become navigable rivers." See *Inland Navigation*, ensuing.

SOILS.—P. 6. "There is great variety in the soil of this district, and several very distinct kinds are found in almost every parish or lordship. These may be classed as follows:

1st, Strong, deep stapled soil, chiefly consisting of clay, free from any mixture of stone or gravel.

"2d, Light, thin, reddish soil, chiefly consisting of loam 6 or 8 inches deep, on a bed of stone, here called Kealy, or Scaley rock.

"3d, A rich loam of 8 or 10 inches deep, with a mixture of gravel, the under stratum being clay, mixed with small pieces of red or white stone.

"4th, A thin, staple, light clay, very retentive of water.

"5th, Fen and meadow land."

SUBJECT THE SECOND.

POLITICAL ECONOMY.

APPROPRIATION.—This is a topic to which Mr. Donaldson has paid peculiar attention. In his Appendix, he speaks, comparatively, and intelligently, of its progress in England, and in Scotland.

App. P. 1. "In order to form a correct idea of the rural economy of the two districts, prior to the introduction of improvements in the modes of Agriculture in either, it may be proper to observe, that previous to the year 900, the state of society in England and Scotland, appears to have been pretty much the same.

"About that period, King Alfred divided the kingdom of England into tithings and hundreds; and the honest inhabitants of every village or township, became by that law answerable, in their own private fortunes and property, for all the house-breaking, robberies, and other depredations, committed within their respective districts, and were also bound, to associate with their neighbours in arms, in order to repress every act of violence, and to maintain peace and public order. In Scotland, before the laws came to be properly

properly respected, or the executive government possessed that power and authority, necessary to prevent the great feudal Barons, and their dependents, from harassing and distressing their less powerful neighbours, it was common for the farmers, who then lived in villages, to enter into an agreement, called a *bond of good neighbourhood*, in which all acts which could be construed into bad neighbourhood were narrated, and certain penalties annexed to the commission of each, and from the joint manner in which they occupied the lands, (which was the same as is still practised in the open field parishes in England), as well as from the conditions contained in these bonds, they were induced to turn out in arms, on any general invasion of their property.

"This being the ancient state of both countries, and it being well known that a regular Government, together with the arts and habits of civilized society, and improvements in Agriculture, were much earlier introduced into England than into Scotland, it may appear difficult to account for the manner in which both countries are now inhabited. In England the farmers still living crowded together in villages, as in former times; whereas, in the cultivated parts of Scotland, ever farmer lives in the centre of his own farm, as if the feudal system had never existed. But that difficulty will be removed, when, on the one hand, the manner of cultivating the open field lands in England is considered, and that inclosing has only come into general practice of late years; and, on the other, that there does not appear to have been any commonable lands in Scotland; that since the year 1560, the payment of tithes in kind (except in a very few instances, and these where the tithes are in the possession of lay proprietors) have been abolished, and that the lands were in general possessed by great proprietors, who, when ever they were inclined, had it in their power, for the reasons just now mentioned, to divide their lands, and make such arrangements with their tenants as they judged most likely to promote the improvement of their estates; and that where a township was possessed by two or more proprietors, in place of a tedious negotiation with the Clergyman, and those having right of commonage, and an expensive application to Parliament for an inclosing bill, which is the case in England, the division of such lands, was effected by an action or process before a Court of law, (which was attended with little expence), or amicably settled, by a reference to some man of respectable character in the neighbourhood."

In the body of the work, Mr. D. mentions its existing state, in Northamptonshire, at the time of his survey — P. 24. "There are 316 parishes in the district, 227 of which

which are in a state of inclosure, and 89 in open field; besides which, there are many thousand acres of woodlands, and a large track of rich valuable land, called the Great Peterborough Fen, in a state of commonage; so that supposing the inclosed part of the county at present under the most approved modes of management, there is above one third of the whole, by no means in the best state of cultivation of which it is susceptible."

"Perhaps one half of the inclosed parishes, may be denominated old inclosures, at least that proportion may be said to be occupied as grazing farms, which is the use to which old inclosed lands in this county is generally applied."

P. 29. "Though there is not one acre of waste lands in this county, properly so called, yet there are many thousand acres in the open field lordships in a state of common pasturage, which, under proper management, might be made to produce abundant crops both of corn and grass, while at present they do not yield pasturage, which can at the highest computation be estimated at 5s. the acre. Indeed, if the calculation was fairly made, the occupiers are not benefited to the extent of half that sum, as the stock which they send to depasture upon these commons, is liable to so many diseases and accidents, as one year with another, nearly counterbalances any advantages which can be derived from possessing this right."

Of these commons the Reporter particularizes *Peterborough Fen*, only.—This valuable tract of land (recently appropriated) lying within the natural limits of the EASTERN DEPARTMENT, has been there noticed.

In prosecuting my present undertaking, I have embraced every favorable opportunity of registering the information collected by different Reporters, relative to the FEUDAL ARRANGEMENT of LANDS, in distant parts of the kingdom;—as materials of Agricultural History, when those arrangements shall no longer remain a disgrace to British legislation; and a bar to the productiveness of the Country.

P. 58. "The management of the open field farms is governed by the established customs which have prevailed in the parish for ages. An open field parish may be classed into three divisions, *viz.* tillage, meadow, and pasturage.

"The tillage lands are cropped in the manner before mentioned, and the several occupiers must conform to the ancient mode of cultivation of each division or field in which their lands are respectively situated; from which it will appear, that one obstinate tenant (and fortunate must that parish be accounted, where only one tenant of that description is to be found) has it in his power to prevent the introduction

introduction of any improvement, however beneficial it may appear to the other inhabitants of the parish. The tillage lands are divided into small lots, of two or three old fashioned, broad, crooked ridges, (gathered very high towards the middle, or crown, being the only means of drainage that the manner in which the lands are occupied will admit of), and consequently the farmer possessing 100 acres, must traverse the whole extent of the parish, however large, in order to cultivate this small portion. The great additional expence of cultivating lands, so situated, must be obvious to every farmer of common understanding; while the never-ending rotation of corn-crops, to which the lands are subjected, must render them incapable of producing any tolerable returns.

"The meadows are kept in a state of common pasturage from the time the hay is carried off till Lady-day, by which means the crops of hay are very indifferent, compared with that on inclosed lands properly managed.

"The leys are generally divided into three fields; one is allotted for the pasturage of the sheep, another for the cows, and, on the third, the shameful practice of *tethering* the horses is still continued. And by every information that could be procured, it appears the stock is not kept with a view to any profit that can possibly arise from the sales, but merely as the means of cultivating and manuring the soil. Indeed, long experience has evinced, that any species of stock kept in these open fields cannot be carried to market on terms nearly so advantageous to the farmer, as those of their neighbours, who occupy inclosed lands; nor is it to be supposed, considering the manner in which the stock is treated, that the owners will pay much attention to the improvement of the different breeds. While the numerous inconveniencies attending the occupation of land, so dispersed and intermixed, as open field lands always are, will remain for ever a bar to the introduction of any improved system of husbandry. The greatest, indeed the *only* objection against inclosing is, the depopulation of the parish, which, it is said, generally takes place in consequence thereof."—In the deeper better soiled townships this *may* be the case. But see p. 243, aforegoing, on this subject.

PROVISIONS.—P. 47. "The price of provisions are as follow:

Beef and mutton, 4½ *per* lb.	A goose, 3s.
Lamb, 5d. to 6d. *per* do.	A turkey. 3s. 6d.
Veal, 4d. do. do.	A duck, 1s.
Pork, 4½d. do. do.	A hen, 1s. 3d.
Butter, 8d. to 10d. do.	A chicken, 6d.
Cheese, 4d. to 5d. do.	Eggs, 6d. *per* score."
Bread, 1½d. do.	

MANUFACTURES.

MANUFACTURES.—P. 10. "The principal manufactures carried on in this district, are, shoes, bone lace, and woollen stuffs, principally tammys, callimancoes, and everlastings.

"In Northampton, and some of the neighbouring towns, upwards of a thousand hands are employed, in making shoes for the supply of the army and navy, and the shops in London, and also for exportation to different parts of the world. About 7000 or 8000 pairs are manufactured weekly in time of peace; but at present, (July 1794), in consequence of the war, from 10,000 to 12,000 may be manufactured in the same period."

"In Wellingborough, and the neighbourhood, and towards the south-west corner of the county, from 9000 to 10,000 persons, mostly young women and boys, are employed in lace making."

"All the thread of which the lace is made, is imported from Flanders, and the goods, when finished, are partly exported to America, the West India islands, and Ireland, but by far the greater proportion is used in Britain.

"The woollen" (worsted) "manufactory is principally confined to Ketteering, and its neighbourhood. This manufacture was in the highest perfection it has ever attained at the beginning of the present war. A very considerable number of persons were employed, in the different branches of it, at that time. It is difficult to form any probable guess at the number; but perhaps from 5000 to 6000 would not be an extravagant calculation. At present, not more than one half of the number of persons are employed in it."

TITHES.—The inclosed lands Mr. D. says, p. 14. "are generally exempt from tithes" which "may be reckoned at from 3 s. to 3 s. 6 d. *per* acre over the whole open field farm, including even that part of it which is annually under fallow."

I insert the following sentimental remarks;—not as being new; but as coming from one whose feelings of personal interest could have no share in dictating them.

P. 61. "The collecting of tithes in kind is very generally complained of, and in those parishes where that mode is adopted, it certainly operates very powerfully against the introduction of improvements in husbandry; while at the same time it is attended with very disagreeable consequences, both in a religious and political point of view, as it is often the means of creating such divisions between the clergyman and his parishioners, as renders the religious instructions of the former of little avail, while it loosens that chain of intercourse and connection which is considered of so much importance to keep united."

INLAND NAVIGATION.—P 7. (see *Waters* aforegoing) "The

" The *Nen* is the most considerable of these rivers. After taking its rise, as above mentioned, it is quickly joined by a number of other small streams and brooks in the vicinity of Daventry, and continues its course from thence to Northampton, where it becomes navigable, and forms a considerable river, extending its course along the east side of the county, it passes Wellingborough, Thrapston, Owndle and Peterborough, and from thence, by a new cut, (called Morton's Leam), to Wisbech, below which it discharges itself into the German Ocean.

" The *Welland* takes it rise near Hawthrope, in the hundred of Rothwell, and winding along the north boundary of the county, it passes by Rockingham and Stamford, where it becomes navigable ; from thence to Spalding, below which place it communicates with the sea.

" The *Ouse*, which is one of the principal rivers in the kingdom, takes its rise from a spring called Ouse-well, near Brackley, in the hundred of Sutton. It quickly leaves this county, and after taking a circuitous course through part of Buckinghamshire, touches again upon it at Stoney Stratford ; from whence it passes to Newport-pagnel and to Bedford ; from which last place it is navigable to the sea at Lynn."

Bridges.—P. 48. " There are few districts which can boast of a greater number of handsome, well built stone-bridges; every brook and rivulet is made passable by means of a stone arch ; and the bridges on the larger rivers do credit to the public spirit of the inhabitants."

Roads.—P. 48. " It is to be regretted, that as much cannot be said in respect to the roads. These, it must be acknowledged, display no great ingenuity either in the engineer who planned, or in the undertakers or overseers who executed the work."

P. 49. " Particularly in regard to the private or parish roads, which are in many places in a very ruinous situation, and, in general, so narrow as to admit of only one track. It is true indeed, that the country is but indifferently supplied with metal proper for road-making, the stone being very soft, and apt to grind into powder;—but it is equally true, that, in place of breaking the stone properly, and laying it on carefully to a proper depth, it is generally laid on the roads in the same state in which it is raised out of the quarry ; and in place of being broke with hammers, that operation is only performed in the course of time by the cart-wheels."

This is a hard blow—a home stroke—at English stone roads; many of which are *still* under shameful management.

Markets.

MARKETS.—*Surplus Produce.*—P. 47. "The quantity of wheat and flour which is annually exported from this county is very great, though it was not possible by any means to ascertain the amount, as the greatest proportion is transported by land-carriage; the wheat is sold by the farmers to the millers in their neighbourhood, who convert it into flour, and dispose of it in the neighbouring counties of Leicester, Nottingham, and Warwick, and great quantities are annually sent down the Nen to Wisbech. A great proportion of the barley crops is made into malt, and consumed in the county. The oats, and a great part of the beans, are consumed by the horses; a small quantity of beans are, however, annually exported to Wisbech and other places."

SUBJECT THE THIRD.

RURAL ECONOMY.

TENANTED ESTATES.

ESTATES.—P. 12. "There are many very considerable estates in this district, and by far the greatest part of the landed property is in the possession of noblemen and gentlemen, who reside at least some part of the year in the county.

"There are few estates, the rentals of which exceed 10,000*l.* *per annum*; there are a great many others under that sum, down to 1000*l.* a-year, and the remainder of the property is either possessed by those whose rentals amount to from 500*l.* to 800*l.* or by that respectable class of men who have been long known in England under the denomination of *Yeomanry*, who either occupy their own estates, of the value of from 100*l.* to 300*l.* or who, besides their own estates, rent extensive farms from the landlords in their neighbourhood."

TENANCY.—P. 13. "This county may be said to be principally occupied (with a very few exceptions indeed) by tenants at will, the few leases that are granted are of no longer endurance than for 7, 14 or 21 years; and the general conditions contained in them are, that the tenants shall pursue a certain rotation of cropping; that they shall not break up any old pasture ground; that they shall not dispose of hay or straw off the farm; and that they shall keep the houses, buildings and fences in proper order."

App. p. 3. "In this county, there are scarcely any lands

lands held by tenants under leases, except those granted by the Bishop, Dean, and Chapter of Peterborough, which are for 21 years, renewable every 7.

"The tenants, in general, possess their farms only from year to year. There are, however, written agreements entered into between the landlords and tenants, in which the mode of cropping the lands is specified.

"The farm-house and offices, are generally kept in repair, at the joint expence of the parties; though, in a great many instances, the whole expence rests with the tenant.

"The tenant, is, on all occasions, expressly debarred from breaking up any old pasture-grass, and from selling hay or straw.

"The term of entry, to a grazing farm, is at Lady-day, and to tillage lands, at Michaelmas."

P. 63. ("Obstacles to Improvement")—"next to the modes of culture, and the management of stock, which *must* according to the present system be universally practised in the open field lands, and the collecting of tithes in kind, nothing can operate so powerfully against the spirited exertions of farmers, in regard to the introduction of better modes of cultivation, and greater attention to the improvement of the different species of stock, than the *want of leases*.

"Every farmer who possesses a farm from year to year, must feel *that kind of dependence* which must tend in a greater or less degree to damp his spirit for improvement, and must prevent him from doing that justice to his farm, which would enable him to pay the highest possible rent to his landlord, or to procure that extent of *fair profit to himself*, to which the extent of capital sunk in carrying on the operations of the farm, and his own industry, are entitled.

"In such a situation, the *prudent* farmer must be restrained from any spirited expenditure, however much he may be satisfied that the improvements which might thereby be introduced, would, under other circumstances, prove beneficial both to his landlord and himself."

The Reporter, in this place, continues to reason on the indispensibleness of the proprietors of Northamptonshire, granting leases to their tenants; and catches at any opportunity, throughout his work, to enforce that favorite idea. But, even at the time he wrote (1794) the recommendation came too late; for, should any of them have followed it, they are now, probably, receiving not more than one half of the present rental value of their lands.—*Now*, (November 1812) leases of length are become mere *gambling contracts*,

tracts, which may tend to the embarrassment of landlords, *or* the ruin of tenants; as the value of the circulating medium, and the prices of produce, may *happen* to rise or fall.

In the former volumes of this Work, the subject of leases, I trust, has been sufficiently discussed to render any further remarks, in this place, unnecessary.—See NORTHERN DEPARTMENT, *West Riding of Yorkshire*; EASTERN DEPARTMENT; *Kent's Norfolk*, &c. &c.

RENT.—P. 14. "The average rent of the inclosed lands, which are generally exempted from tithes, may be accounted at 20s. the acre, that of the open field lands, which are subject to the payment of tithes in kind, may be reckoned at 8s."

App. p. 4. "The rent of inclosed lands, runs from 17s. to 25s. *per* acre, exclusive of tithes, from which the inclosed land is generally exempted. The average may be reckoned at 20s. to which may be added 3s. in the pound for poor-rates.

"The open field lands run from 6s. to 10s. *per* acre, medium about 8s. besides about 3s. 6d. *per* acre for tithes; the poor-rates the same as above mentioned."

"The rent of lands in the Carse of Gowrie is from 30s. to 45s. *per* acre, average about 35s.

"For lands in the open field state, from 10s. to 16s. medium, about 13s."

App. p. 5. "The difference of rent in favour of the Perthshire proprietor, may appear surprising to those, who do not know, that in Scotland there are no tithes, poor-rates, or other taxes which affect the tenant in his character of farmer."

Add to these valuable advantages, the comparative *cheapness* of *living*, among the farm workpeople in Scotland (see *Workpeople* ensuing) together with the great saving (in comparison with Northamptonshire) by *plowing with two horses*, instead of four or five (see *Tillage*, ensuing) and the surprize at the comparatively high rents, in the former, vanishes. Yet how long have we heard this comparison spoken of, exultingly, by the *improvers* of Scotland, and laid hold of, under a less amiable impulse, by *rackrenters*, in England*.

TIMES of REMOVAL.—P. 13. "The terms of entry are either at Ladyday or Michaelmas, the former being the period

* See NORTHERN DEPARTMENT, *Brown's West Yorkshire*,—where the disparity appears to be nearly as two to one; and that proportion is corroborated by the above remarks.

period for entering upon a grazing farm, and the latter on an arable farm."

RECEIVING RENTS.—P 13. "The rent is paid half yearly, and in equal portions. The first payment is usually made twelve months after the term of entry, and so on half yearly during the currency of the lease."

WOODLANDS.

THE following accounts of the forests and other extensive woodlands of Northamptonshire are highly interesting and valuable; in as much as they convey to us, before it is too late (while a few remnants of folly and mischief are left) some ideas of the evils, which heretofore harrassed the cultivators of lands in the neighbourhoods of forests and chaces, in various parts of the kingdom. The information concerning them appearing to have been obtained through respectable channels, and to have been reported with due thought and consideration,—it is the more particularly entitled to a place, in this register.

P. 32. "There are several very extensive tracks of woodlands in this district; they consist either of forests, chaces, or purlieu woods. The most considerable forest is that of Rockingham, which is situated in the northern parts of the county, beginning near the village of Wansford, on the great north road from London to Edinburgh, extending for near 20 miles towards the centre of the county, and forming almost a continued chain of woodland country: There are two other extensive forests, *viz.* Whittlebury and Salcey, lying towards the south border of the county; the chaces are those of Geddington and Yardly; the former in the neighbourhood of Rockingham forest, and the latter in the vicinity of Salcey forest.

"The purlieu woods, are both extensive and numerous, particularly towards the lower parts of the county, and upon the borders of the forest of Rockingham; and besides these, there are several small tracks of woodlands, very advantageously and ornamentally situated, in many other parts of the county.

"The whole of what are now considered to be forest woods, are subject to the depasturage of the deer, and at a stated time of the year, to the depasturage also of the cattle belonging to those who reside in the adjoining townships, and who claim to be possessed of a right of commonage; on these accounts, the profit arising to the proprietors of these woods, from the cutting of the timber, and underwood,

wood, is small, compared with that arising from regular well managed purlieu woods, which are not subject to the annoyance of the deer and cattle

"The underwood in the forests and chaces, principally consists of black and white thorn, ash, sallow, maple, and a small proportion of hazle. They are generally cut at from 12 to 18 years growth; the different woods are divided into as many parts or sales, as the number of years growth at which the underwood that is cut may amount to, so that a regular rotation in cutting takes place every year.

"The proprietors of the underwood in the forest woods, are empowered by the ancient laws and customs of the forest, to fence in each part or sale, as soon as it is cut, and to keep it in *band*, as it is here termed, for 7 years, except against the deer, which are let in at the expiration of 4 years; but the cattle belonging to the commoners, are not let in till the end of 7 years from the time of cutting; so that there are always 7 parts or sales constantly in *band*, and in which the cattle of the commoners are not permitted at any time to depasture. But from the depredations to which the young underwood is subject, by so early an invasion of the deer and cattle, even at the regular and stated times before mentioned, besides the great damage frequently sustained from inattention to the repairs of the fences, during the time it should be kept in *band*; the heavy expences attending the making a new fence in the first instance, and the continual expence incurred in keeping it in repair, during the time it should stand, make the profit arising from the underwood, very inconsiderable to the proprietor, compared with any moderate rent that might be expected from the land. The forest underwood, through the whole *sale*, or part which is cut, does not in general bring above 4*l.* the statute acre, though sometimes it is sold as high as 6*l.* the acre upon an average of the whole sale; but this depends entirely on good management in keeping the fences in proper repair, so as to prevent the deer and cattle from breaking in before the limited periods, as well as in suffering the underwood to stand to a greater age than usual.

"At the time the underwood is to be cut, it is parcelled out into small regular sized lots, generally consisting of about a statute rood of ground; the divisions of the lots are made by cutting a number of small passages or openings called trenches, which intersect each other at regular distances, and these trenches are just cut wide enough to admit of a passage between each lot; the underwood is valued and sold standing, and the purchasers cut it and carry it away at their own expence. A considerable part of it is made into hurdles for folding sheep on turnip; the remainder

remainder is applied to other purposes, and used as firewood, there being no coals in the county, but what are brought up the rivers *Nen* and *Welland*.

"A fall of oak timber * is generally made at the proper season in that part, or *sale*, in which the underwood has been cut; and this fall consists of the most unthrifty and unimproving trees, but the quantity and description of timber, must depend of course upon the state of the wood, as to the stock of timber.

"It is a general custom in the forest-woods, to value and sell the trees standing. Distinct and separate valuations are generally put upon the timber, the top, and the bark respectively. And it sometimes happens, that these three articles are sold to three different purchasers; but it is more usual to sell the tree and the top together, reserving the bark, which is sold to one purchaser, previous to the fall of timber being made. The conditions and prices vary in different parts of the country; they run generally, however, at from 7s. to 9s. in the pound of the value of the tree.

"The Prices of Timber in this District are as follow:

Oak,	from	1s. 4d.	to	2s. 6d.	*per* foot.
Ash,	from	10d.	to	1s. 6d.	*per* ditto.
Elm,	from	9d.	to	1s. 4d.	*per* ditto.
Poplar,	from	6d.	to	1s.	*per* ditto.

"Every other kind of white wood, such as beech, chesnut, lime, &c. sell at something more than the price of fire-wood.

"It is a certain truth, and well worthy of the serious consideration of Government, that the depredations committed in the extensive forests and chaces in this county, by the deer and cattle, in destroying the young trees at a very early period, prevent the possibility of obtaining any considerable succession of oak-timber, as scarce any saplings or young oaks are to be seen, although there are undoubtedly a great number of seedlings produced by the falling

"* There is a very small quantity of the oak timber taken out of the forest woods consumed in the country. It principally consists of timber of a large size, and more fit for the use of the navy than for country purposes It is therefore generally bought in large bargains, by contractors for the navy, who come into the county regularly every year, during the season for felling the oak timber. But if no speedy and effectual means are taken for the better management and preservation of the forest woods, in order to procure a regular succession of oak timber, the navy will, in a short time, be deprived of this valuable resource."

falling of the acorns; yet, when the number of destructive enemies, to which they are exposed in their infancy, is considered, it is a wonder how any of them escape their devouring jaws.

"If the forests in the other parts of the kingdom are under the same management, there is no man who wishes well to his country, but must be alarmed at the prospect of the deficiency, which, in process of time, must take place in regard to that valuable article, oak-timber, for the supply of the navy of this kingdom. The evil certainly requires a speedy and effectual remedy to be applied. What that may be, the wisdom of the Legislature can best determine; but, as particular attention was paid during the survey on which this report is founded," (?) "to the state of these forests and chaces, compared with those woods which are private property, it may be proper to add, that the difference is obvious to the most cursory observer. In the one, a young thriving oak-tree is scarcely to be seen, whereas, in the other, a regular succession appears in every quarter. The miserable state of the Royal Forests does not originate from any want of public spirit in those who have at present the charge of them, but necessarily arises from the errors of an ancient system, which had in view more the preservation of deer than of timber; and consequently sacrificed the preservation of the latter, for the purpose of securing food for the former.

"Perhaps the best plan that could be adopted, would be to disforest all these woodlands, under severe restrictions however, in regard to certain proportions of them being continued as forests for the production of oak timber. Those having right to the timber and underwood, being also bound to give a compensation in land to the commoners, having a right of commonage in these forests and chases, and according to the nature and extent of their different rights. Were some such plan adopted, certain considerable portions of these forests and chases, might be devoted solely to the purpose of growing oak-timber, and one person only having interest in them, there is no doubt proper attention would be paid, in order to bring on a regular succession of timber, which could be effected, whilst at the same time, a considerable improvement might be made in the growth and value of the underwood."

P. 37. "I am indebted to Mr. Edmonds of Boughton-house, for the following very interesting Observations, and for many other scattered in various parts of the Report.

"*Purlieu woods* are those woods which are situate immediately in the vicinity of the forest, and which, at one time formed a part of it; but the respective owners having at at some former periods, obtained grants and permission from the Crown to disaforest them, and to consider them as their own private property, they are not now subject to any of the laws and regulations to which forest-woods are subject.

"MANAGEMENT OF PURLIEU WOODS.

"The management of what are called purlieu woods in this district, differs materially from those of the chase and forest woods. These woods being entire property, of course there is no obstacle to prevent the proprietors of them from pursuing the best mode of cultivation and management in their power; but this advantage has been in very few instances taken; and little improvement towards rendering them more productive and profitable to the respective owners has been made. The underwood in these woods principally consists of hazle, ash, sallow, white and black thorn, and some maple; it is generally cut from 11 to 14 years growth, when the season for cutting arrives, which is as soon as the leaves are completely off. That operation is performed under the direction of the owner of the woods or his agent. The part intended to be cut is parcelled out for the convenience of the purchasers into regular sized lots, consisting of 20 statute square poles each. The whole of the underwood growing upon each lot is indiscriminately cut, and laid in one direction, on the ground from which it is produced; and in some instances care is taken to select such ash poles, as are of a larger size and proper to be converted to more valuable purposes, than those which are indiscriminately sold with the underwood. So soon as the operation of cutting is completed, and the wood parcelled out as above described, a valuation is put upon each lot or parcel, according to its quality, and what it may consist of; and the whole is then sold to such persons as may be inclined to purchase the respective lots or parcels, who, over and above the price of the underwood, repay the expence of cutting it, which is proportioned at so much *per* pole upon each lot according to its quantity. Such as the present mode of management is in these woods, their produce is much more considerable to the proprietor than forest or chase woods; but it is believed it is by no means equal to the produce of well cultivated woods in other parts of the kingdom. The average price of underwood, cut from 11 to 14 years growth, is about 6*l.* *per* statute acre; but it is sometimes sold so high as 8*l.* *per* acre.

"The underwood of the purlieu woods, as well as of the other woods in this district, (the management of which is exactly

exactly the same as that of the purlieu woods), is principally bought by bakers, who consume it as fuel. A considerable quantity of the smooth wood is manufactured into sheep-hurdles, which are used for temporary fencing: but in all cases, a reservation is made by the purchasers of the ash and sallow poles which are used for various useful purposes in husbandry. A fall of oak timber is usually made in that part or quarter from whence the underwood is cut; the quantity of which, of course, depends upon the state of the wood, as to a stock of timber.

"The oak timber in the purlieu and private woods, on account of there being so good a succession, as well as on account of there being a great deal of underwood, seldom attains to so large a growth as that found in the forest and chase woods; it is therefore much more fit and convertible for country uses, and for all purposes of building and husbandry, and is principally bought by carpenters, joiners, wheelwrights, and other artificers in the neighbourhood.

"*Chase Woods.*—There are two chases in the county, *viz.* Geddington and Yardly. The former was once a part of Rockingham forest; but permission was given by the Crown many years since, to the ancestors of the Montagu family to disforest it, and to convert it into a chase; the latter, it is presumed, was once a part of Salcey forest, and has been disforested likewise."

The management of *chace* woods is similar to that of the forests.—I cannot, however, pass over, unnoticed, the following sensible remarks, on the mischiefs arising from those remnants of feudal tyranny, and the intolerable folly, or neglect, of more "enlightened" times, in suffering them to remain, as unprofitable encumbrances, on the face of the Country.

P. 39. "Although there is at this time a valuable stock of oak timber in this chase, principally consisting of trees of a large size, and which have been the growth of ages; yet perhaps this extensive and valuable track of woodland exhibits at this moment the most striking and lamentable instance of the evil and pernicious consequences that must inevitably attend property circumstanced as the forest and chase woods are. The depredations and ravages committed by the deer and cattle upon the young sprigs and coppices, at so early an age, not only prevent even the smallest possibility of obtaining a regular succession of oak timber, but cause a daily diminution in the growth of the underwood. The injury sustained by the deer being admitted into the young spring wood in the first instance is very considerable; but that injury is small indeed, when compared to the destructive havock made by the devouring jaws of a herd

herd of hungry cattle, admitted into the young coppice, just as the leaves have begun to appear, and at a season of the year when it some times happens they have just survived a state of famine, the consequence of a want of sufficient fodder, in a hard and severe winter. All the townships using a commonage in these woods (except one) are in an open field state, and no attention is paid by the occupiers to the description of cattle bred and reared, which are of the most inferior kind, and which, in consequence of the inability of the occupier of an open field farm to procure a sufficiency of food for their support in the winter season, are reduced to an extreme state of leanness and poverty at the time they are turned into the woods, when whole herds of them rush forward like a torrent, and every thing that is vegetable and within their reach, inevitably falls a sacrifice to their voracious and devouring appetite. Under these circumstances it is not at all surprising that contagious maladies are frequently the fatal consequence; to which cause a considerable number of cattle fall victims, and the loss sustained by the owners not only deprive them from receiving any profit or emolument from those that are fortunate enough to survive the malady, but prevent their deriving any advantage from the commonage that year, and probably for many years to come. Such are the inconveniences which must ever attend property held under a mixture of interests so extremely inimical to each other, as those of the commoner and the proprietor of the timber and underwood are in woods of this nature."

Mr. Donaldson concludes his valuable strictures, on the woodlands of Northamtonshire, by offering his advice (as others have done, without effect) to "the wisdom of the legislature."

AGRICULTURE.

FARMS.—*Sizes.*—P. 13. "There are no very large farms in this county; for although great progress has of late years been made in inclosing the open fields, yet the lands have been in many instances parcelled and let out again to the former tenants, who occupied them in the open field state, and to such extent as it was supposed their abilities and circumstances would enable them to manage properly; so that it is only in the old inclosed parishes, where there are farms of any considerable extent; and even there, the rent of one farm seldom exceeds 500*l.*

500*l.* a year. In the new inclosed parishes, the farms are generally from 100*l.* to 300*l.* *per annum*, and in the open field lands, the rents run from 50*l.* to 150*l.*"

HOMESTEADS.—P. 38. "In this county, as well as in the greater part of England, the farmers still live crowded together in villages, or townships, as was the practice in the most remote ages, and when the system of open or common field husbandry universally prevailed. Though these crowded situations might no doubt be attended with considerable advantages in ancient times, and though the system of open field husbandry, where practised, precludes the possibility of placing the farm-houses in centrical situations; yet it appears surprising that the buildings belonging to the farms in a state of inclosure, should still remain at such a distance from the farms; there being but very few instances where the houses are properly situated in the centre of the farms."

Here, it may be proper to remark, that the Reporter appears not to have well considered the subject on which he was writing, or did not recollect that he was speaking of the rural concerns of England.

It is only where the FEUDAL ARRANGEMENT of lands, heretofore, took place, and where parishes or townships were laid out into *common arable fields*, with *meadows*, and *pastures* necessarily attached to them, that farm homesteads are now found in villages. Where the lands have been inclosed from the state of *woodlands*, as they evidently have, in various parts of the kingdom; or from that of stinted pastures, or *hams*, as in the West of England;—there, we find, farm houses and offices standing conveniently within the farm lands. But, wherever the lands have been parcelled out, in small lots, scattered over the area of a township, and those allotments have become the *property* of *numerous individuals*, each having his dwelling house, barns, and other substantial *immoveable buildings**, situated in the *original feudal villages*; and, especially, where such allotments have been inclosed, by piecemeal, by the several small proprietors, as was formerly the practice;—it is scarcely possible that any thing but another invasion, similar to that of William the Norman, can do away the inconveniencies complained of, by the Reporter whose work I am now appreciating.

In more recent time, when the common field townships have been inclosed, by statutes of parliament, the commissioners

* Which are spoken of, by the Reporter, as being very large in proportion to the farms, p. 43.

missioners have (or ought to have) done every thing in their power to rectify those inconveniencies,—as far as given circumstances would permit. Where one or more considerable properties occurred in a township, farms of some size have been laid out, on the commons and stinted pastures; but rarely in the arable fields; unless the whole belonged to one, or a very few proprietors. But, where the the property was found to be vested in *numbers*,—as it mostly was,—that desirable measure was of course impracticable.—In this case, impartial justice required that each proprietor should have a portion of land situated near the place of his *fixed residence*, and other parts at a less convenient distance from it; without having it in their power to form entire farms, within the areas of the commonfield lands, of a size sufficient to admit of suites of farm buildings in each.

Hence, unless in the awful event alluded to, above, or in cases of accumulation of property in particular townships, or by friendly exchanges, AGRICULTURAL VILLAGES of FEUDAL ORIGIN, will probably remain, in ENGLAND, until civilized society therein shall be no more.

But not so, in SCOTLAND, where the feudal system was continued in its pristine state, by the clanships of that division of the island, for several centuries, perhaps, after arbitrary dominion was fractured, or wholly broken, in England.—*There*, at the time of inclosure, *no small proprietors* could claim scattered allotments; the whole being occupied by *tenants*, of LARGE PROPRIETORS, who could, without hindrance, lay out their lands into farms of size, and erect buildings within their respective areas*:—The turfen huts of the petty tenants being profitably spread over the land, as manure.

Mr. Donaldson may be assured that I have not thus interrupted the regular course of my labor, for the vain purpose of cavaling at his observations; but to endeavor to place in the true light a circumstance which is commonly misunderstood, not by strangers, only, but by natives who inhabit the parts of England which have been inclosed from the woodland and grassland state, without having been subjected to the feudal plan of aration.

PLAN of MANAGEMENT.—P. 28. "It may be proper to observe here, that no general rotation of cropping is established in the county, each landholder or his agent, fixing

* The above was written, before I had examined the Appendix to the volume; in which Mr. D. conveys the same idea. See *Appropriation*, p. 333, aforegoing.

ing on that, for which the soil and situation of the farm is considered as best adapted."

Nevertheless, Mr. Donaldson gives what may be termed the general economy and plan of management of farms of different descriptions; namely common field, old inclosure, and new inclosure.

P. 29. *(Common Field)* " PARTICULARS of a Farm in the Open Field State, containing 100 Acres arable, 20 Acres Meadow, and 150 Acres Ley or Pasture.—Rent, 118*l.* —Tithes payable in kind.—Poor-rates, and other Parish-taxes, 5s. in the Pound of Rent.

" ROTATION OF CROPS.

1st year, fallow, part turnip, the land dunged or folded with sheep.
2d year, wheat, barley after the turnip.
3d year, beans, and a few acres under oats.

" SERVANTS.

2 men.
2 boys.
2 women servants.
1 shepherd takes care of all the sheep in the parish.

" STOCK.

7 horses.
9 cows.
6 or 8 horses.
130 sheep of all ages."

P. 27. *(New Inclosure)* " In what is called the new inclosed townships or parishes, a system of alternate corn and grass husbandry is adopted; a certain portion of meadow is generally allotted to each farm, where it is practicable; and some particular fields are kept in constant pasturage."

The management of *old inclosures* (chiefly grass lands) will be seen in the ensuing articles,—*Grazing Cattle,*—*Dairy,*—and *Grazing Sheep.*

WORKPEOPLE.—P. 44. " As there are no large manufacturing towns situated in this district, the variations in the price of labour are not considerable; and it is, upon the whole, more moderate than could well be expected.

" The wages of a ploughman by the year, are from 8*l.* to 10*l.* with board and washing.

" A young man or boy, from 4*l.* to 5*l.*

" A female servant, about 4*l.* 10*s.*

" A labourer in summer, receives 1*s.* 4*d.* without board, and in winter 1*s.*

" In hay-harvest, a man earns from 9*s.* to 10*s.* *per* week, and a woman 4*s.* without board; though each is allowed a certain quantity of beer. " In

"In corn-harvest, a man hired by the month, receives about 2*l.* 10*s.* besides board; a woman is paid at the rate of 1*s.* the day without board."

P. 45. "The maintenance of the servants is here a very expensive article to the farmer. The breakfast consists of cold meat, with cheese, bread and beer. For dinner, roast or boiled meat with pudding, and tor supper the same as at breakfast; and besides ale that they are allowed on extraordinary occasions, they have small beer at command at all hours. The luxury in which this class of people live, accounts in a great measure for the necessity of levying such immense sums annually for the support of the poor in England. While it is perfectly certain, that a person living in Northumberland, or North Britain, on ordinary fare will do fully as much work, and to as much purpose, as a Northamptonshire ploughman, who is maintained at a much greater expence."

In the Appendix, we find the subjoined particulars, relative to the diet, or mode of living of farm servants, in Perthshire.

App p. 11. "When servants are boarded in the farmer's house, the ordinary fare is for breakfast and supper *pottage* made of oatmeal, salt and water, which is eat with milk. For dinner soup, or, as it is provincially called, *broth*, made with pot-barley, vegetables, and butcher meat. But the more general practice is to give each ploughman a certain allowance of oat-meal, (about 36 ounces a-day), and three pints of sweet-milk, or double that allowance of butter-milk. They lodge and eat in a house disjoined from the farm-house, and cook their own victuals."

Mr. D's compararative statement stands thus.—App. p. 12. "A Northamptonshire farmer considers 6*s.* *per* week as a reasonable allowance for the board of a ploughman, which, for 52 weeks, amounts to - £. 15 12 0

"The Perthshire farmer furnishes his ploughman with that quantity of oat-meal, which, on the average price of meal for a number of years, amounts to 2*s* *per* week, to which, if 10*d.* *per* week is added for milk, makes the whole expence for the year - - £. 7 7 4

"For coals, bed-cloaths, &c. &c. may be added, - - - 0 9 8

——— 7 17 0

———

£. 7 15 0"

Thus it appears that farm servants, and, we may say, farm workpeople in general, are maintained at one half of the expence, in Perthshire, which the same description of persons cost the occupiers, in Northamptonshire.

WORKING

WORKING ANIMALS.—P. 51. "The horses used in the operations of husbandry, are for the most part purchased in the counties of Derby, Lincoln, and York; they are bought in at two or three years old. The object of the Northampton-shire farmer being to purchase horses, which are likely to answer either for the coach, the army, or large waggons, he keeps them two, and sometimes three years, and generally disposes of them at a profit of from 7*l.* to 10*l.*"

P. 52. "There is nothing, perhaps, that would tend more to the general improvement of this species of stock in the county, than if a number of the proprietors were to purchase some of the best stallions that could be found in the neighbouring districts, so that the tenants might be accommodated without any great expence or trouble. It was by this means that the breeding of blood horses came into such general practice here."

This recommendation is not new. But it is not, in itself, the less valuable on that account. On a large property, divided into small farms, the principle might well be extended to every species of domestic animals.—Among a number of small proprietors, the plan is not equally practicable.

P. 25. "A few young horses are generally reared."

For articles of *food* of working horses, see the head, *Oats*, ensuing.

IMPLEMENTS.—P. 44. "The principal implement, the plough, is a clumsey, piece of work, with a long massy beam, and an ill formed timber mould-board, better adapted as a machine for 4 or 5 horses to pull along, than for the purpose of turning over a neat clean furrow."

Northamptonshire, I am sorry, and almost ashamed, to say, is not the only County of England, in which such an *extravagant* implement *still* remains in use.—Let men of fortune, or their managers, look to it.

MANURES.—*Lime.*—P. 21. "This county abounds with limestone in almost every corner, and considerable quantities are manufactured for the purposes of building, yet very little is used as a mean of improving the soil; although, where it has been properly applied, its effects have been abundantly conspicuous. One great reason why it has not come into more general use, may be owing to many injudicious experiments having been made, where the quantity used has been too small to produce any beneficial effects."

Shell Marl.—P. 21. "*Marl* is not used here as a manure, though there is rich shell-marl in different parts of the county, particularly on his Grace the Duke of Buccleugh's estate of Boughton, and Sir George Robinson's estate of Cranford. The effects of this manure, in producing great crops

crops both of corn and grass, are well known in many parts of Scotland, and it would no doubt operate as powerfully here, if properly applied."

N. p. 22. "The marl which has been discovered upon the Boughton estate, was found in a low, and, rather wet situation in Boughton-park, at about 20 inches from the surface, which consists of a dark rich loamy soil ; a white loamy earth presents itself, mixed with a great quantity of fine small shelly substances, which, when perfectly drained and dried, either by the sun or fire, adheres together in lumps, and becomes extremely light. Upon immerging a piece of it in common vinegar, it causes a great effervescence. The shelly particles in a great measure dissolve, and the whole soon becomes a smooth liquid plaster. This stratum of white earth is from 12 to 18 inches in thickness, when another stratum is found, consisting of a darker coloured earth, with a large mixture of blue clay, and a much smaller quantity of shells than the white kind. This last stratum continues about the same depth as the former, when the strong clay makes its appearance.—The following valuable information, respecting this marl, has been given by an ingenious and learned chymist in Scotland.

"'I have assayed the two marls; one of them is almost white and chalky; the other, of a yellowish colour, and darker, and more plastic, like clay. The first is as rich a marl as ever I assayed. It is, when perfectly dry, very nearly equal in value to the first chalk, or best limestones; the difference is not more than 2 or 3 *per cent.*'"

"'The yellowish and more clayish marl is of little value in comparison with the former. It contains only when perfectly dry, one part of calcareous or lime earth in ten of marl; the nine parts being clay and sand.'"

"The same stratas" (strata) "of earth here mentioned having been found, by digging in many other places, near to which this has been discovered. White earth of the same kind, has been found at the bottom of a pond in a low wet part of the park, at the distance of near 300 yards from the first situation, from which it is conceived, there must be a continuation of the different stratas of earth before described."

N p. 14. "Dimensions of the ordinary dung cart.

Length at top,	7 feet 6 inches.
Ditto at bottom,	5 feet 9 inches.
Breadth at top,	3 feet 9 inches.
Ditto at bottom,	3 feet.
Height of sides,	2 feet."

Tillage.—P. 14. "In every part of this district, plowing is performed by a man and a boy, with 3, 4, and sometimes

times 5 horses in a single length; and though the soil (as has been already observed) is of very different qualities, yet the same expensive mode of plowing, with a few exceptions, universally prevails."

In his appendix, Mr. D. gives, very properly, and with good effect, a comparative statement, between plowing with four horses and a driver,—and two horses with whip reins.

Northamptonshire.

App. p. 13. " Ploughman's wages,	£. 10	0	0
Boy's wages, - -	5	0	0
Boy's board, at 4*s.* *per* week,	10	8	0
Maintenance of 4 horses, at £. 15 each, - -	60	0	0
	£. 85	8	0

Perthshire.

" Ploughman's wages, - - -	£. 10	0	0
Maintenance of 2 horses at £.15 each,	30	0	0
	£. 40	0	0"

Here, we see a saving of *more than half* by proper management; and this in the heaviest expence that belongs to cultivation.

It is to be observed in this place, however,—as Mr. D. does not appear to be, and others may not be, fully aware of it,—that the practice of plowing with two horses, guided and driven by the plowman, has been customary, in England, time immemorial; particularly in Norfolk; also in Essex, I believe, during ages past. In Yorkshire, and generally speaking, in all the agricultural districts of the north of England, it has been prevalent for half a century.

When the practice of plowing with two horses without a driver commenced, in Scotland, we are not informed.

Formerly, in the *Highlands* of Scotland, three or more small horses, *abreast*, (with a driver, we are told, walking before them,—some will say, walking backward, and urging the horses forward, by beating them on the forehead;—but that can scarcely be true of *Scotsmen)*—was, I have been I believe well informed, the common plow team;—and was not, twenty years ago, entirely in disuse, in the more recluse parts of the central highlands.

Whether the practice of plowing with *three* or *more* horses, *abreast*, was ever prevalent, in the *low lands* of Scotland, I have no certain information. But this being as it may,—it is a firm, strong, eligible draught, in breaking up stubborn ground, in a dry season; and is in use, on such occasion,

occasion, in the part of Yorkshire, in which I am now writing; the three being guided and driven, with reins, by the plowman.

It will be further proper to remark, here, while the subject is interestingly in view, that there are cases in which *two* horses, *abreast*, are *very improper*; namely that above noticed; and on tender soils, in a wet season; especially when laying up ridges, for a crop; and most especially while " making up the furrows;" when they are quite ineligible; tho commonly used. In this case, one, two, or three horses, *at length*, (agreeably to the nature and state of the soil, and the power of the animals) are necessary to accurate management.

HARVEST.—App. p. 17. " In this county the wheat is reaped with sickles, and the barley, and oats, and beans are mowed with the scythe, and after being turned over are put up in coles in the field, like hay, where they stand some time, and are afterwards carried home, and either put into the barns, or built and thatched in the stack-yard.

" The wheat is cut very high from the ground, and being bound up in sheaves, is allowed to remain in shocks in the field till it is ready to be housed; and after that is done, the stubble is cut with scythes, and carried home to the straw-yard, where it is either used for litter, or for thatching houses."

The Reporter's lengthened " observations," on the Northamptonshire method of cutting barley, with naked sithes, show, that his knowledge of agricultural practices, in England, was, at the time of writing, narrowly circumscribed. Not only the " bow," or " bout," which he speaks of, as a desideratum that has recently been found out (a mean contrivance that has probably been in use, for centuries past, in most districts of the kingdom) but the " cradle," a more efficacious addition to the naked sithe, where the crop remains upright (which is perhaps of nearly equal origin) is capable of " laying the corn from the sithe in such a manner as that it can be bound up into sheaves;" and has, for a length of time, perhaps unknown, been in common use, for that purpose, in Yorkshire; and, with peculiar efficacy, in Kent, and other parts of the southern Counties.

The *works* of *harvest* having no place, in the *plan* of the *Board's Reports!!* I have the more readily taken this singular opportunity of explaining the above important particulars, in practical agriculture.

ARABLE CROPS.—Prices of *Produce*.—P. 47. " Having been favoured with an account of the prices at which the bushel of wheat, barley, oats, and beans was sold on a particular farm in this district for the last six years, it is here

ere subjoined, and may be depended upon as correct."

P. 48.	1787.		1788.		1789.		1790.		1791.		1792		General average.	
	s.	d.	s.	d.	s.	d.	s.	d.	s.	d.	s.	d.	s.	d.
" Wheat,	5	5¾	5	8½	6	4½	6	6½	6	3½	5	10¾	6	0½
Barley,	2	6¾	2	6¾	2	7½	3	3	3	1½	3	4½	2	11
Oats,	2	0¼	1	10¾	1	8¾	2	4	2	5½	2	6¾	2	2
Beans,	3	7½	3	8¾	3	6	3	11	3	10½	4	1½	3	9"

App. P. 8. " Produce, in the same years.—

" Years.	Wheat	Barley	Oats	Beans	General average by the acre of all these grains.
	Bush.	Bush.	Bush.	Bush.	Bushels.
1787.	28⅔	28⅔	43⅔	20	30¼
1788.	28	29	33	21	27¾
1789.	21⅔	34	53⅓	26	33¾
1790.	22⅔	35⅔	48	22⅔	32¼
1791.	22⅓	31⅓	39	20⅓	28¼
1792.	28⅔	27⅓	35	20	27¾
Div. by 6.	152	186	252	130	180
General average,	25⅓	31	42	21⅔	30"

WHEAT.—P. 14. " A certain proportion of the tillage lands is regularly under wheat, perhaps about one third of the whole. It is generally sown in the open fields after fallow, but on the inclosed farms also, after beans or clover stubble."

BARLEY.—P. 16. " *Barley* is cultivated nearly in the same proportion with wheat. It is generally sown after turnip."

OATS.—P. 15. " There is but a small quantity of oats cultivated, compared with the other species of grain ; not so much indeed as is sufficient for the consumption of the ordinary working cattle," (Horses) " which are principally fed with beans."

BEANS.—P. 15. " *Beans and Peas* are generally cultivated separately, the former in considerable quantities. They are commonly sown after wheat."

POTATOES.—P. 17. " *Potatoes* are not cultivated here to any extent, the quantity necessary for the consumption of the inhabitants being very trifling, and the distance from the London

London market too great, to allow the farmers to send them there with advantage."

TURNEPS.—P. 17. " *Turnips* are cultivated in considerable quantities on every farm under tillage. The land is generally plowed four times; the first time, after harvest; the second time, in April; the third time, in the end of May, or the beginning of June; and the land being then manured, they begin sowing turnip in the end of June and finish about the middle, or end of July. The seed is always sown broadcast, and very soon after the turnips appear with the rough leaf they are handhoed, by way of thinning them, which operation is repeated once, or oftener in the course of the season, as occasion requires. The turnip-crops are always eat off by sheep, and principally by lambs; though a great number of wedders are fatted for home consumption, and for the London market, particularly about Northampton, and the higher parts of the county."

CULTIVATED HERBAGE.—*Rye.*—P. 16. " *Rye* is seldom cultivated here as a crop, though frequently as spring food for sheep; it is generally sown after oats or barley; the land is plowed, and the seed sown immediately after harvest, and the sheep are folded upon it about Lady-day. This is considered, and justly, as a great improvement, as the rye is ready to be folded upon by the time the crop of turnip is eat off, and the sheep by this means are kept on in good order, till the beginning of the grass season. It may also be observed, that it is an additional crop gained, because the rye is eat off in such time as to give an opportunity to prepare the land for a turnip-crop; indeed, all the preparation necessary is plowing, as in consequence of the sheep folding, the field must be well manured for the succeeding crop, whatever it may be."

Rape Herbage.—P. 16. " *Rape* or *Cole* is also cultivated as winter and spring food for sheep. The land is plowed three times, and generally manured before the last plowing with yard-dung. About one-eight of a bushel of seed is sown on the acre. The time of sowing is in the month of June, or the beginning of July. The sheep are folded in the same manner as on rye or turnip, and continue till about the end of February; and if the winter is favourable, and not very wet, the cole is sometimes allowed to stand for seed, when 30 bushels on an average is produced from the acre. This article varies very much in price, from 18*l.* to 35*l. per* last."

SAINFOIN.—P. 19. " Saintfoin is sometimes cultivated, but not generally."

How much useful information we find compressed within those few short extracts, concerning arable crops;—they being

being equally creditable to the occupiers of Northamptonshire, and the Reporter of their practice.—They are concise, yet clear.

Grass Lands.

In Mr. Donaldson's statement (see *Appropriation*, p. 334, aforegoing)—there would seem to be upward of one hundred of what may be termed grassland parishes, in Northamptonshire.

For the method of *stocking* those lands, see the heads, *Cattle*, *Dairy*, and *Sheep*, ensuing.

Of the *specific quality*, or the *mode* of *management* of the *grazing grounds*, and other *pasture* lands, *themselves*, no mention is made; and all that I find registerable, here, regarding the *meadow lands*, is comprised in the subjoined extract.

P. 18. "There is a very great extent of meadows in this district, not less than 40,000 acres. They are in general of a rich fertile nature, owing to the frequent overflowing of the waters, and possibly, no artificial means, in the present state of matters can be devised for their improvement. Indeed, the system of watering meadows, or any other kind of land, is seldom practised here; and it is but in very few instances, except along the banks of the rivers, where the lands are capable of that improvement. The most considerable track of meadow is that, on each side of the river *Nen*, beginning several miles beyond Northampton, and, extending down to Peterborough, which, from the circuitous direction, and various windings of the river, between these two points, may be supposed to pass through a country of more than 60 miles in extent."

Livestock.

On this subject, we find Mr. Donaldson more intelligent.—P. 49. "On the first view, it will appear surprising, that, in this district, where so great a proportion of the lands are in a state of pasturage, little or no attention has been paid till of late, to the improvement of the different kinds of stock; yet, when reference is made to the manner in which the farms are occupied, as before mentioned" (see the last references); "and when the vicinity of the great London market is considered, it will not be thought extraordinary. Of late years, indeed, the improvement of the breed of sheep has become an object of the first importance with many of the most respectable and intelligent farmers."

Horses.—See *Working Animals*, aforegoing.

Cattle.—*Breeds.*—P. 50. "There are very few of this species of stock reared in this county, a few in the open field lordships

lordships excepted; and these are so crossed and mixed with the breeds of other counties, which are often improperly chosen, and are so stinted in their food, as to render them comparatively of little value.

"In the few instances where attention is paid to the breed of cattle on the inclosed farms, the long horned are the kind most preferred, and are far superior to the original breed of the county, both in size and shape, as well as in the other advantages which ought to be attended to by every farmer who occupies a breeding-farm, namely, their extraordinary disposition to fatten, and to lay the greatest quantity of flesh and fat on the rump, loins, and other parts of the body, which always sell highest at market.

"The dairy farmers in the south-west part of the county, however, prefer the short horned Yorkshire cows, from which county they are principally supplied. And, as they never rear any calves, they sell them when a few days old, to a set of men who make a trade of carrying them to the markets of Buckingham, and other places, where they are purchased by dairy farmers, from Essex, to be fatted for veal for the London market."

Grazing Cattle.—("on a grazing farm of 170 acres of old pasture, and 70 acres of meadow, rent 300*l.*")—P. 25. "Soon after Ladyday, the farmer begins to purchase bullocks, and the breeds of Shropshire and Herefordshire are preferred. In the course of the summer a few Scotch and Welsh cattle are bought in. The stock never exceeds 70 bullocks and heifers. He begins selling off in September, and by the beginning of February the whole is disposed of.

"From the end of October hay is given twice a day in the field. The cattle are consigned to a salesman in London.

"The expence of sending them there, including the salesman's commission, amounts in summer to 6*s.* 6*d.* and in winter to 7*s.* each."

Dairy Cattle.—("on a farm of 200 acres pasture and 50 acres of meadow")—P. 25. "Milk from 45 to 55 cows; prefers the short horned Yorkshire. Plows none of the land, but makes as much meadow-hay as serves for provender in winter, and on which the cows are wholly maintained during that season. Purchases straw for litter, which generally costs about 30*s.* the waggon load. A few breeding mares are kept, and 5 or 6 young horses, but no young cattle."—P. 26. "There are several farms, where a small portion of the lands are in tillage."

Butter.—P. 26. "Butter, and milk for the hogs, are the only produce of the dairy. The butter is sent twice a week to London by the stage-waggon."

Calves

Calves.—N. p. 50. "Considering the distance which these calves are carried, from this county to Essex, being from 70 to 80 miles, it may be proper to give some account of the extraordinary manner in which they are transported. Sometimes 10, 15, or 20, are put into a cart, being laid on their backs on straw, and their feet tied. They are maintained frequently for 8 or 10 days together on nothing but wheat-flour and gin, mixed together, which are here called gin-balls. In this manner, most of the calves bred on the other farms in the county are disposed of; such a number only being reared as are necessary for keeping up the ordinary stock of milk-cows."

SHEEP.—*Breed.*—The well compressed particulars, here subjoined, relative to the different breeds of Northamptonshire, in 1794, do Mr. Donaldson much credit, as a Reporter of provincial affairs, in agriculture; and his information bears the semblance of good authenticity.

P. 53. "There are here three different breeds of sheep, which may be classed as follows, *viz.* The original breed of the county, the old improved, and the late improved, or new Leicester breed. About 50 or 60 years ago, when this district was in general in the open field state, no attention was paid to the improvement of the breed of sheep. The points which marked a good sheep, in the opinion of the people of those days, were, the wool thick set on the back, an open rump, loins wide, legs open, and bones clean from wool, opposed to what is now called *gum or coarseness.* They were generally sent to market from 2½ to 4 years old, and weighed on an average about 18 lb. the quarter. This breed, however, are now very rare, being confined to those quarters of the county where commons abound.

"About 25 years ago an improvement was attempted, by crossing the ancient breed with tups from Warwickshire and Lincolnshire, the breed of Warwickshire being noted for great bone or size, and that of Lincolnshire for the quantity of wool. With the success of this experiment the farmers seemed perfectly satisfied, as a general opinion prevailed that the animal would feed in exact proportion to the size of bone, and that an additional quantity of wool might be produced, without any detriment to the carcass. This practice, therefore, went on for many years. The new breed improved greatly in size, and the farmers gave themselves no trouble to ascertain whether the increase in size and weight could be accounted really beneficial or not. And so fixed and rivetted were they in the opinion of the good choice they had made, that it was not without much difficulty they could be persuaded of the possibility of introducing any additional improvement. This, however, has of late years

years been effected, and the new Leicester or Dishley breed (which form a complete contrast to the former) are pretty generally introduced, owing principally to the following circumstance: Mr. Bakewell, whose name stands unrivalled in this line, about the year 1788, instituted a society, consisting of himself and 15 or 16 other respectable farmers in Leicestershire and the neighbouring counties."

P. 54. "Of this number, the following members reside in this county:

"Messrs. J. and S. Robinsons, Wellinborough; Mr. John Tomlins, Rockingham Park; Mr. John Bennet, Watford; and Mr. John Manning, Arslingworth."

Mr. D. then touches on the merits of those breeds; enumerating a few of the pro and con assertions of their different admirers;—a topic that has, long ago, been worn threadbare; and which had been fully before the public, at the time Mr. D. wrote.—The following candid acknowledgement is a sufficient apology for his not entering the list of disputants; and forcing upon the public,—as many a Reporter has,—his own sentiments on the subject.

P. 56. "The writer of this Report pretends to no particular knowledge in regard to the different breeds of sheep, and is one of those who would be ready to suppose that the size alone is what stamps additional value on either a sheep or a bullock; and, therefore, what is here stated, is the substance of what he learned in the course of his survey, rather than his own private sentiments."

There is, indeed, an ingenuousness, and a vein of good sense, run through every part of this Report; making one regret that its Author has not gone over the ground a second time, and given a fuller account of the RURAL ECONOMY of NORTHAMPTONSHIRE.—The proof of my sincerity, in saying this, lies in the amplitude of the extracts that I have selected from his existing Report; which greatly exceeds, in proportion to the size of the Work itself, every other (I have yet examined) that has been sent in to the Board; Mr. CRUTCHLEY's RUTLANDSHIRE excepted.

"GENERAL

"GENERAL VIEW OF THE AGRICULTURE OF THE COUNTY OF NORTHAMPTON,

DRAWN UP FOR

THE BOARD OF AGRICULTURE,

AND INTERNAL IMPROVEMENT.

By WILLIAM PITT.

1809."

THE QUALIFICATIONS of this Reporter have been repeatedly noticed.—See his STAFFORDSHIRE and LEICESTERSHIRE, aforegoing.—I find nothing in the volume, now before me, which tends to alter, *much*, my opinion respecting them.

This is what may be termed one of the *mule* productions of the board; as it partakes of the *original* and of the *reprinted* characters; Mr. Pitt having collected some original materials, and incorporated with them a considerable part of Mr. DONALDSON's matter.—See the preceding article.

Regarding Mr. P's MODE of SURVEY, in this instance, he is commendably explicit. He has gone twice over the ground; his first Survey having, it would seem, been found wanting; and his Report, in consequence, not sufficiently full for publication.

The subjoined extracts contain the Reporter's own account of his undertaking.—P. ix. (" Preliminary Observations")—" the Board of Agriculture having resolved to have the different County Reports revised, and the matter therein contained thrown into one uniform system, agreeable to a specified plan, and it being found that several of the subjects contained

contained in this plan had been omitted in the original report, I was requested in the spring of the present year, 1797, by the President of the Board, to make a tour through Northamptonshire, to collect information on those particular subjects, or any other that seemed worthy of public attention: This I have accordingly endeavoured to do, and, for that purpose, have made several *tours* through the county; and, in addition to my own observations, have procured intelligence from many respectable practical farmers and graziers, and hope, in its present form, the survey of this county may, in some degree, meet the intentions and expectations of the Board, though I fear that, for want of a more complete local knowledge of the county, many particulars deserving attention may have escaped notice.

"The particular facts stated, and observations made by Mr. Donaldson, I find generally accurate. Where he appears to have been misinformed, corrections are attempted; but, upon the whole, his report has much assisted the writer of this survey, and tended to shorten his labour.

"One great feature of the county of Northampton is its common fields, which are generally upon good soil, and oftentimes very productive of grain and pulse. This circumstance naturally leads to the discussion of the often-agitated question respecting the utility of dividing such land in severalty; upon which subject the writer of this, without regarding private interest or opinion, has endeavoured to lean to the side of public good.

"Some pretty free remarks are made upon the forest-lands, and their present management and productions, which the writer has done wholly from his own ideas" (?) "of their present misapplication; and from his thorough conviction of their greater national utility, if in part disafforested, and thrown into a three-fold system, or division, of woodland, cultivation, and pasturage.

"The writer had intended to have availed himself of the patronage of several of the great land proprietors of the county, to whom he had recommendations from the Board; but finding, on his first applications, the principals not in the county, and the agents little disposed to forward his inquiries, without directions from their employers, he afterwards applied to practical farmers, and agricultural societies, from whose candour and liberality he has received such information as he desired."—"1797. WILLIAM PITT."

P. xi. "P. S. Having received some written papers of remarks by the Secretary, and Members of the Board, stating deficiencies and omissions still remaining unsupplied in the account of the agriculture of so interesting a county, I was induced, at their request, to make another tour, in the

the month of August, 1806, for the purpose of making farther inquiries and observations; and, on this occasion, gained information from many respectable characters, gentlemens' agents, and eminent graziers, whom I had not an opportunity of consulting before, and have no doubt but the additional matter thus obtained will render the work much more interesting, and more worthy of the approba- of the public."

P. xii. "I am obliged to the following persons for assistance and information in this Survey, and insert their names, in the order in which I received their communications;

"Mr. Smith, Tichmarsh, written remarks.

"Mr. Knight, formerly of Walgrave, but now steward to Lady Carberry, of Laxton-Hall.

"Mr. Pickering, formerly of Walgrave, but now of Kettering.

"Mr. Martin, Tansor-Lodge, near Oundle.

"The Lamport Society, collectively.

"Mr. Daniel Bosworth, Holmby-Lodge.

"Mr. Thos. Bosworth, Highgate-House, since dec.

"Mr. Ekins, Brixworth.

"Edward Bull, Esq. Pitsford.

"Messrs. Wright, Kettering.

"Mr. Roper, steward to his Grace the Duke of Grafton.

"Mr. Bull, Daventry.

"Mr. Whitmore, of Rothwell, and Mr. West, of Desborough, tenants to Thomas Motterson, Esq. of Staffordshire.

"The bailiff of Mr. Bosworth, of Brampton.

"The Rev. Mr. Brotherhood, of Desborough.

"*Oct.* 1806. WILLIAM PITT."

P. 280. "In the preceding pages, considerable pains have been taken in order to give a just account of the present state of husbandry in this county, for which purpose, not only the observations of Mr. Donaldson have been consulted and compared, but the writer has, personally, examined most parts of the county, and procured necessary information from many practical farmers; and he entirely agrees with Mr. Donaldson, that a spirit of improvement is certainly introduced, and has made great progress. In a farther examination of the county, in 1806, the writer has endeavoured to supply such deficiencies as the Board had pointed out; has expunged, cancelled, and new modelled, some articles; and made large additions to others; and is not aware, that, in its present form, he is capable of much improving it: and he hopes the statement here given may, in some degree, prove satisfactory to the board and the public. "*Oct.* 1806. WILLIAM PITT."

Beside

Beside the materials collected, in the manner above set forth, and beside the ample extracts from Mr. DONALDSON's Report, Mr. P. has quoted, pretty largely,—the *Annals* of *Agriculture*, and a *Tour in Northamptonshire, with a Visit at Wakefield Lodge* (the Duke of *Grafton's) in* 1791, by the SECRETARY of the BOARD; together with a few passages from the writings of DOCTOR DARWIN; whom Mr. Pitt styles "a *very profound* modern writer."

Added to those several sources of matter, the Reporter has inserted, in an Appendix, his TOURS in 1797 and 1806; with ROAD NOTES similar to those taken in Leicestershire. *These* however are few, and not of importance; appearing to be only the remnants of his memorandum books, after their contents had been mostly incorporated with the other matters, in the body of the work.

Mr. Pitt's MANNER has been mentioned. But, in his NORTHAMPTONSHIRE, we perceive a falling off. The *quotations* are slovenly; and in one point of view, unfairly made. A few of them are properly *marked* (with turned commas); but, in general, they are not:—so that, on a cursory view of the volume, the whole (except those few) appear to be *original.*—Even in going deliberately over it, it is difficult to determine where a quotation begins *or* where it terminates. For altho one end of it may be marked, the other is seldom to be found. Had I not kept Mr. Donaldson's book by me, for the purpose of collation, I could not have ascertained the several parts which he has taken from it.

Again, the *original matter* is immethodically thrown together; appearing as memorandum-book entries of the two surveys,—*posted* as into a ledger; without due examination and connection. Frequent repetitions, and some contradictions, are the necessary consequences.

Even the *dissertations* are mostly tissues of trite, thread bare ideas, loosely tacked together; and rarely impress conviction on the mind of the reader.

Those remarks are not illnaturedly intended to give offence to Mr. Pitt. But are meant to serve as cautionary hints to those who may, hereafter, write on similar subjects.

Number of pages, in the body of the work 281.—In the appendix, 30 pages.

A Map of the County. No other engraving.

NATURAL

NATURAL ECONOMY.

EXTENT.—P. 2. "It contains, according to Mr. Donaldson, 910 square miles, or 582,400 acres; and, according to Mr. Carey, 1000 square miles, or 640,000 acres: and I am disposed to believe the extent of the county not over-rated by this latter estimate."

ELEVATION.—P. 3. "The highest point of land in the county, probably, not exceeding about 800 feet perpendicularly above the sea; for the highest level of the main line of the Grand Junction Canal, at Braunston Tunnel, in this county, is 375 feet above the tide of the Thames at Brentford, and it is very probable no hill in the county exceeds this level more than about 400 feet perpendicularly, which falls below the mountainous region of this island."

P. 4. "I have made observations on many mountains both of England and Wales, and have found, almost invariably, that the mountainous region commences at between 800 and 900 feet perpendicularly above the level of the sea. By mountainous region, I mean rocky impracticable land, incapable of cultivation, huge masses of rock breaking through the surface with an insufficiency of vegetable mould. Very little grain is produced above this elevation."—For similar remarks, see NORTHERN DEPARTMENT, p. 426.

P. 5. "The following table exhibits the elevation of sundry points of land in this county, perpendicularly, above the level of the tide of the Thames at Brentford: they are all from accurate actual survey, taken from the Grand Junction Canal, except the summits of the hills, which are by estimate.

Particular Spots.	*Elevation.* Feet.
"The river Ouse, near Stony Stratford	200
The river Nen, above Northampton	195
The Grand Junction Canal, at Bilsworth, and Weedon	315
The Grand Junction Canal, at Braumston Tunnel	375
Buckby Road, about half a mile east of Daventry	430
The summits of the hills around Daventry, which I suppose the highest land in the county, about	800"

SOILS.—Mr. Pitt sets out with censuring Mr. DONALDSON, for speaking of the "great variety of the soils" in Northamptonshire,

amptonshire, p. 6. And, in p. 7, we are told—"the soil of the county, in general, is equally adapted for corn or pasturage, and fertile in both." Yet, in p. 9, Mr. P. says—"Rothwell common-field and neighbourhood is a light turnip soil, and turnips are grown on it on an extensive scale. Upon all these *light tracts of land* a considerable quantity of *rye* is also produced.

"Notwithstanding these instances, much the greatest proportion of the land of this county is of a strong heavy staple, applied to the culture of beans and wheat before enclosure; and, when enclosed, generally laid down to permanent pasture. The lighter enclosed lands are kept more in tillage, and therefore produce a larger proportion of grain. The soil of the country has, therefore, a *considerable variety*, but seldom changes abruptly, or attains the extremes of sand or clay; and, upon the whole, may be pronounced fertile and productive."

In his further tour, in 1806, this Reporter found still further occasion to alter his sentiments, concerning the matter; and, after wandering, in a desultory way, through some pages, he at length makes up his mind on the subject.

P. 13. "The soil of Northamptonshire may, I think, in general, be classed as follows:

"1. The black or dark-coloured soils, being generally a deep strong loam, on a stony, or a gravel, or a clay-loam, bottom. Of this soil the county has the largest proportion, including almost the whole of its rich upland feeding-pastures, and a part of its cultivated common fields and enclosures.

"2. The red land, including the brown and snuff-coloured loams. This soil is pretty extensive, including a portion of the common fields as well as enclosures; in which latter state it is generally kept in tillage in the up and down system. In point of general produce and utility, this soil stands very high, and is of considerable fertility.

"3. The white or grey loams on limestone, inferior, I think, to the above. This, also, is contained in both common fields and enclosures, forms a good turf, and grazes well, and produces good crops in kindly seasons: but, in sudden transitions from moisture to drought, is apt to cake suddenly, to the great injury of the crop, especially on thin soils.

"4. Miscellaneous upland, including the light thin soils near Stamford, and those dispersed in other parts of the county, and not coming under or within the above descriptions; as the sands of Harlestone and light soils in other districts of the county.

"5. The soil of the natural meadows and pastures, and of

of the fen land, north of Peterborough. The natural valleys contain an excellent meadow-soil, particularly the banks of the Nen, near Northampton, and of the several rivulets which supply that river, the banks of the Welland, and, indeed, of all the rivers and brooks in the county. This soil consists of the decomposed matter of decayed grasses and aquatic vegetables, combined with the sediment of the streams of water issuing down such valleys; which, being drained and consolidated, form the basis of meadow soil.

"The second variety, or red and brown loam, extends through many parts of the county in various shades of colour and consistence."*

Prefixed to this Report is a "Map of the Soil of Northamptonshire." But by whom,—or whether the ostensible Reporter had any share in making it,—is by no means evident. For, on comparing it with his Road Notes, scarcely any coincidence can be found; unless in regard to the river-bank meadows.—But in this, as in most other instances, the *viewliness*, rather than the accuracy, of the thing appears to have been consulted, by the embellisher of the maps of the Board.

For the proportional quantities of the different varieties of soils, see *Rent*, ensuing.

FOSSILS.—P. 15. "The county of Northampton is not very famous for minerals; it produces no coal, and I believe not any of the metals. Its mineral" (Fossil) "productions may be classed as follow:

"1. Common clay, brick clay, (argilla communis,) is found and used for making brick and tile in various parts of the county.

"2. Limestone (calx lapis) in great plenty almost all over the county, and plentifully raised for the various purposes of burning into lime, either for mortar or manure; for building fence-walls for courts, yards, and, in some instances, for enclosures; and for repairing roads. This stone is sometimes tolerably pure calcareous earth; in other places, intermixed with argillaceous and other extraneous matter; and often contains a variety of marine substances. The principal lime-works in the county are at Duston and Kingsthorpe, from which 30,000 quarters are annually sold for manure; besides which, there are public kilns at Moulton, Hardwick, Blisworth, and many other places; as, also, many private kilns kept on by farmers for their own use. I also observed lime-kilns on the Union Canal, near the borders of the county.

"3. Marl,

* For Mr. DONALDSON's concise, yet clear statement, see p. 333, aforegoing.

" 3. Marl, (marga friabilis). Plenty of excellent friable marl has been found in executing the tunnels of the Grand Junction Canal at Braunston and Bilsworth."

P. 16. " Freestone for building is raised at Brackley; also at Kingsthorpe, near Northampton; and in many other places. This stone is often of a calcareous nature.

" Slate (shistus). Dug in considerable quantities at Collyweston in this county and used for covering buildings. The quarries of slate here are and have been very extensive: it is generally of a good size, but rather thick and heavy. Most of the buildings in that and the neighbouring townships are covered with it."

P. 17. " Good free-stone has also been discovered, and is now getting upon the Laxton estate (Lady Carberry's), and in the fissures of the stone have been found a good permanent paint, which was shown me, and described as being useful and valuable in painting and preserving gates, posts, pales, or any timber-work exposed to the weather. I suspect it to be of a ferruginous or ochery quality."

POLITICAL ECONOMY.

APPROPRIATION.—P. 22. " From the year 1794, when the above number of common fields was ascertained, to the present year, 1806, there have been about nineteen or twenty enclosures of common fields, so that there remain, at the present time, about seventy common fields unenclosed within this county."

For some account of the *Forests Lands*, see *Woodlands*, ensuing.

FUEL.—P. 228. " The fuel consists of wood and coal. The county produces plenty of the former; but the latter being, or having been, scarce and dear, wood has generally carried a pretty high price. Faggots are from 18*s.* to 20*s.* per hundred, of six score. Stackwood, for fuel, 16*s.* to 18*s.* the stack of 108 cubic feet, being a waggon-load, or from a ton and a half to two tons weight. Pit-coal, from the Staffordshire collieries, is now brought plentifully to Blisworth, by the Grand Junction canal; the price, 1797, at Blisworth, near the centre of the county, 10½*d.* to 12½*d.* per hundred weight: at Weedon, four miles from Daventry, 10*d.* to 12*d.* ditto. The above in 1797.

" In 1806, furze faggots, at Kettering, 14*s.* to 21*s.* per hundred, forming a waggon-load.

" Wood, for fuel, 1*s.* per hundred weight.

" Coal, per ton, 35*s.*"

MANUFACTURES

MANUFACTURES.—P. 243. "There is a considerable whip-manufactory at Daventry, in which I am informed some good properties have been acquired. Two master-manufacturers each employ an out-rider and a number of workmen. There is also, at Daventry, a considerable manufactory of silk stockings."

For the other manufactures of Northamptonshire, see Mr. DONALDSON'S account, p. 337, aforegoing.

For the effect of manufactures on the *Poor Rate*, see that article, ensuing.

INLAND COMMERCE.—P. 239. "The landed produce exported from the county chiefly consists of wheat, wheat-flour, oats, beans, timber, oak-bark, fat cattle, fat sheep, wool, butter, and cheese. The manufactured exports are shoes, lace, and wooden stuffs; these are sent to London, Ireland, America, and the West-Indian islands; also to various parts of Great Britain. Part of the heavy articles are sent by the navigation of the Nen, or the canals, the rest by land-carriage. The articles imported into the county are lean cattle, store sheep, coals, iron, deals, leather; and, Mr. Donaldson observes, thread for lace-making from Flanders. The coals are brought from the north, and up the Nen; or from the inland collieries, by means of the Oxford, Grand Junction, and Union, canals. It is very probable, that the return of the blessings of peace, and the finishing of these canals, would very much increase the commerce of the county."

POOR RATES.—After quoting Mr. Donaldson, Mr. P. says, p. 44. "By farther inquiries, in 1806, I find that the poor's rates in this county are extremely various. In some of the grazing parishes, where the population is small, they are little or nothing, except what is collected for county rates, church reparations, &c. while, in populous villages and some towns, owing to the failure of manufactures, they are 10*s*. or 11*s*. in the pound; and, during the scarcity of 1801, they were, at Kettering and some other places, actually 20*s*. in the pound and upwards.

"Desborough poor's rates...... 1801, 25*s*. in the pound.
Ditto .... 1805, 10*s*. ditto.
Owing to some church repairs, 1806, 12*s*. ditto.

"This parish has been many years enclosed, and has a declining manufacture of tammies, &c."

TITHES.—P. 41. "The Lamport Society inform me that most of the antient enclosed lordships, and almost all the open fields, are subject to tithes; some of which are taken in kind, though it is much to be wished that custom were discontinued, as being an almost insurmountable obstacle to improvements. They are, also, of opinion, that, where the

the tithes are collected in kind, the loss to the occupier is much more than the sum stated above,* and that it may be reckoned at 5*s.* or 6*s.* per acre.

"As a proof that no injury is likely to be sustained by the clergy by commuting tithes and allotting land in lieu thereof, I shall quote the instance of the living of Kettering, lately enclosed, which, in the open state, was worth from tithes from 200*l.* to 300*l.* per annum, but is now improved by enclosure, abolishing tithes and giving land instead, to between 700*l.* and 800*l.* per annum. This information from Messrs. Wright, Kettering.—1806."

CANALS—On this subject, which is intimately connected with agriculture, Mr. Pitt may be said to be "quite at home." It is evidently familiar to him. He is of course intelligent thereon; and his information is consequently valuable. I therefore transcribe the whole of his section, "Canals and Navigation."

P. 232. "This county was but, till lately, very indifferently accommodated with water-carriage. The only natural river that has been used for this purpose is the Nen, which has been rendered imperfectly navigable to Northampton; this has been in part effected by art, upon the antient system, which is so very incomplete, that, in general, a cargo, as I am informed, does not exceed four tons, notwithstanding the supply of water is sufficient for the conveyance of any burthen. The defective navigation of this river is sufficiently indicated by the trade and port of the town, which bears no proportion to its situation, opulence, or population: at the wharfs not a single vessel loading or unloading; a crane stands solitary, and not the least stir of business: a small deposit of coals and a few deals comprize all the visible articles of commerce. The system of the waters of this river, divided for the different purposes of turning mills, watering meadows, and for the navigation of the river, is so badly designed, and so ill applied, that no one purpose is well answered. A lock, given doubtless for the purest patriotic motives, in 1760, by John Spencer, Esq. of Althorp, is so ill placed, that it turns the navigation into a lower channel, where continuing the higher level would have been much preferable. The waters of this river run three-fourths to waste, when, by a proper system, a large proportion of it might be employed to the important purposes above-named.

"The navigation of the Nen, (such as it is,) continues from Northampton, through the county, by Thrapstone, Oundle,

* By Mr. Donaldson; at "from 3s. to 3s. 6d. an acre."

Oundle, and Peterborough, and, continuing north easterly, joins the Wisbech river, several miles below Wisbech.

"The projecting spirit of modern times has, however, endeavoured to supply these defects by different bold and daring undertakings, which have for their object the forming of navigable canals, in different directions, through the county, for the conveyance of vessels of heavy burthen; in the execution of which, hills and valleys are equally disregarded; the one can be perforated and the other filled up: the execution of these projects has been hindered, and in some measure suspended, by the stagnation occasioned by the war, and by the great sums of money that have been diverted from these and other purposes, and swallowed up in the immense vortex thereby occasioned.

"There are two undertakings of this kind now in hand, the one called the Grand Junction, the other the Union, Canal. These undertakings form a prominent feature in the modern political economy of the county. The Grand Junction Canal, so called from its object being to join the tide-navigation of the river Thames with the principal inland canals of the kingdom by the most direct line possible, and upon a scale sufficiently large to navigate vessels of 60 tons burthen, commences at the Oxford canal, at Braunston, in this county, from whence it is carried on, eastward, about a mile, and in that length elevated 37 feet by lockage; it is then continued upon that level about four miles and a half, one mile of which is an excavation, or tunnel, through or under a hill; this is called the Braunston Tunnel: it is afterwards lowered by lockage 172 feet to the level of the Ouse; in its course passing by Weedon; after crossing the great London road, it is carried over a valley, by an embankment of earth, near half a mile in length, and about 30 feet high. This embankment passing close to Weedon church-yard, the top water level is above the height of the body of the church, and nearly upon a level with the bells. Two public highways for carriages and one small river pass under the canal bottom, through the base of this embankment; the course of the canal is then continued north-easterly, recrossing the London road, and, afterwards, taking an eastern direction, passes Lower Heyford, Bugbrook, and Gayton, to Blisworth; this is eighteen miles from Brunston, and so far is the canal now navigable at this end. At Brisworth are erected extensive wharfage and warehouses for goods, two new inns on the canal banks, and there are five or six thousand tons of coal in stacks on the wharfs; a large number of coal-boats and trading boats in the port, and two new ones on the stocks, building.

building. A considerable hurry and bustle of business is created here by this canal.

" A collateral cut is intended from Gayton, near Blisworth, to the river Nen, at Northampton, with a fall of 120 feet.

" The trade of this canal makes a stop at Blisworth at present; very considerable difficulties having arisen in the execution of a tunnel, or excavation, of about two miles in length, under the high ground at Blisworth: the difficulties arise from the under stratum, on the line of the tunnel, which consists of a calcareous blue marl, extremely friable on exposure to air or moisture; and, the springs being powerful, the water, on coming in contact, converts this marl into a liquid mud, which has occasioned the blowing of the shafts and sheeting of the tunnel; and some time must yet elapse before it can be finished and rendered navigable.

" The locks on this canal are about 14 feet wide within, and are adapted either for the passage of a barge of 60 tons, or of two inland canal-boats abreast, each carrying from 20 to 25 tons. The line of the canal, after passing Blisworth, is by Stoke Bruern, Grafton Regis, and Cosgrove, near which it crosses the Ouse, and leaves the county; and from hence a collateral branch is intended to Stony Stratford; the main line crossing the counties of Buckingham, Herts, and Middlesex, joins the Thames at Brentford.

" The other canal in hand, called the Union Canal, from its object being to unite the navigation of the Trent and Soar with that of the Grand Junction and Nen, commences from the navigable part of the Soar, above Leicester, and is continued across the county of Leicester to Market Harborough, near which place it is meant to enter Northamptonshire and to be continued to Northampton, there to communicate with the Nen and the Grand Junction Canal. This canal is also upon a scale for barges of I believe about 40 tons.

" The completion of these two grand designs will leave nothing wanting to complete the navigation of the county, but the improvement of the Nen below Northampton, so as to be upon the same scale of navigation with these canals, a project easy of execution, and attended with much less difficulties than those encountered in the canals above described. This would render Northampton a kind of central port, and would much tend to increase the commerce of the county. These remarks made in 1797.

" In 1806, I find the Blisworth tunnel completed, and a very

very masterly and surprising work of art: the whole main line of this canal is also completed, and some of its collateral branches; but the communication with Northampton is by a rail-way: on this great concern, (the Grand Junction Canal,) 1,500,000*l.* have been expended; shares at present under prime cost, and dividends small, owing to improvements still making, and paid for from the tonnage; but hopes are entertained of its coming to pay a good interest upon the expenditure. Reservoirs of water and other improvements are in hand or in contemplation. The Union Canal, and some of the collateral branches originally proposed from this, still remain unfinished."

ROADS.—P. 231. Having quoted Mr. Donaldson's remarks, p. 338, Mr. Pitt says—"that some of the public roads should be indifferent is no wonder, when we consider that the county is a strong clay loam generally: that good materials for repairing them are often scarce, and at a distance, and that the passing of cattle and carriages along these great thoroughfares is incessant, and their numbers prodigious. The numerous droves of cattle, in wet weather, are nearly as injurious to the roads as any kind of heavy carriage."

P. 232. "Mr. Knight observes, the statute-duty is very irregularly performed. In some parishes it is done to the whole extent, whilst in others, whose roads stand in equal need of repair, little or nothing is done. This is frequently the case in grazing-parishes, where, if a horse or an ox can get along, they rest satisfied, having little occasion for good carriage-roads; this, however, is a great nuisance to others, and they ought not to be permitted to throw so great an obstacle in the way of the public."

MARKETS.—*Surplus Produce.*—Mr. Pitt (as a Canalist probably) has repeatedly touched on this topic.

P. 226. "The quantity of wheat and flour annually exported from this county is very great; but it was not possible, by any means, to ascertain the amount, as the greatest proportion is transported by land-carriage. The wheat is sold by the farmers to the millers in their neighbourhood, who convert it into flour, and dispose of it in the neighbouring counties of Leicester, Nottingham, and Warwick; and great quantities are annually sent down the Nen to Wisbech. A great proportion of the barley-crop is made into malt, and consumed in the county. The oats, and a great part of the beans, are consumed by the horses; a small quantity of beans are, however, annually exported to Wisbech and other places."

Again

Again, p. 239; for which see *Commerce*, aforegoing.

P. 270. "The supply sent by this county to the metropolis is considerable. It appears, from inquiries made by the Lamport Society, that the fat cattle annually sent there amount to about 15,000, and the sheep and lambs to 100,000, besides which the county has a considerable surplus of wheat, wheat-flour, butter, and cheese, which occasionally finds its way to the London market; and particularly butter, of which large quantities are regularly sent. A considerable number of hogs are also fatted in the county and sent to London: and the greater part of the calves bred in the county find their way there also, but these latter are carried out of the county young, and fatted nearer the metropolis."

SOCIETIES.—P. 266. "There are several small friendly societies formed in this county for the promotion of agriculture; consisting, generally, of respectable neighbouring farmers, who meet at stated times, and communicate with each other on such subjects as occur occasionally in their respective occupations. There is one, whose meetings are held at Wellingborough; another at Lamport, near Northampton; and a third at Peterborough: I believe they are all nearly upon the same plan. I attended a meeting of the Lamport Society, and am obliged to them for their friendly communications. I also had a letter from the secretary of the Wellingborough Society, (Mr. Robert Alderman,) requesting my attendance at their meeting, but it happened on a day that I could not make it convenient to attend.

"The object of the Lamport Society is chiefly that of opening a free and friendly communication between its members, on such subjects of cultivation or stock as may occur amongst them individually; to which is added, a fund for purchasing such books on agriculture and domestic economy as may be approved; also an inquiry into the merits of new discoveries or projected improvements; and a discussion of such subjects on agriculture as may be occasionally proposed."

Such "small friendly societies" of "respectable neighbouring farmers," appear to me to be capable of producing much good to practical agriculture.

RURAL ECONOMY.

TENANTED ESTATES.

ESTATES.—Northamptonshire, as Warwickshire, abounds in large properties, and the residencies of men of fortune.

P. 21. "There are many very considerable estates in this county; and by far the greatest part of the landed property is in the possession of noblemen and gentlemen, who reside at least some part of the year in the county.

"Mr. Young has observed, (Annals, vol vi. p. 465.); that 'the county of Northampton is remarkably full of large properties: we presently reckoned up, at Mr. Ashby's, of Hazelbeach, thirty-seven estates in it, of three thousand pounds a year and upwards; sixteen of which are from five thousand to ten.' There are many other estates under that sum, down to 500*l.* per annum; and a part of the county is in possession of that respectable class of men, who have been long known in England under the denomination of Yeomanry; who either occupy their own estates, of the value of from 300*l.* per annum downwards, or who rent extensive farms from gentlemen of large property."

IRRIGATION.—The Reporter has filled many a page with theoretic ideas, and stale opinions, on "watering;" but without taking into consideration the specific nature of the *water* employed; on which and the nature of the *subsoil*, the benefits of irrigation principally depend. The quality of the *soil* is often of less consideration. The Reporter ought not to have taken up his own and his reader's time, unprofitably, by *dissertating* on a subject with which he appears to have been, at the time he wrote, altogether unacquainted.

EXECUTIVE MANAGEMENT of ESTATES.—The subjoined intimations are inserted, here, for the sake of reiterating what has been repeatedly urged.—P. 279. "Another means of improvement, as suggested by a very intelligent person in the county, is in the hands of gentlemen, and is that of making a due discrimination between their industrious and negligent tenants; and giving a preference of encouragement to the former, instead, as is too often the case, of raising their rent in proportion as they improve the land, and continuing the dilatory sloven upon his old easy terms, without regarding the intrinsic and natural value of the land. And, where confidential agents are employed, regard should

should be had to their knowledge and skill in the best practical agriculture and natural value of land, and not merely to their adroitness in collecting and returning the most rent."

Rent.—P. 37. "The ancient enclosed land generally at grass, and applied to feeding sheep and oxen, or part mown for hay. In some parishes, of this class, little or no grain is grown; the rent generally from 25*s*. to 30*s*. per acre. These farms are the largest occupations in the county: I viewed one of six or seven hundred acres, and heard of much larger; but a considerable proportion of this land, of uncouth appearance and over-run with ant-hills, is, probably, at a rent of not more than 20s. per acre."

P. 38. "The amount of rents, in 1797, is stated to have been of open field farms, subject to thithes, 7*s*. 6*d*. per acre; of enclosed farms, from 10*s*. to 30*s*. per acre, tithe free; and of land in the vicinity of towns, from 30*s*. per acre, upwards. These rents are greatly advanced to the present time, 1806, and cannot now be less than as follows: of the thin soiled open field districts, which may be one-third of that class of land, 10*s*. per acre average; of the rich open field land, 10*s*. to 20*s*. per acre, 15*s*. average; of the poorer thin soiled enclosed land, which may be one-sixth of the county, 10*s*. to 20*s*. per acre, average 15*s*. per acre; and, of the rest of the enclosed lands, 20*s*. to 30*s*. per acre, average 25*s*. per acre. From this data, and supposing the cultivated land to be 600,000 acres, the rental of the county may be calculated as follows.

Acres.		*L.*
50,000	of the poorer thin soiled common field districts, open, or with some enclosures attached, at 10s. per acre	25,000
100,000	of the rich common field districts, open, or with some enclosures attached, at 15*s*. per acre	75,000
100,000	of the poorer or colder thin soiled enclosed land, including Easton, Collyweston, &c. at 15*s*. per acre,	75,000
350,000	of rich enclosed land, including the rich feeding pastures as well as tillage land, at 25*s*. per acre	437,500
600,000	Total.	Amount *L*. 612,500"

Those calculations are not copied, so much, for the purpose of showing the aggregate rent of Northamptonshire,

shire, as to convey some general ideas of the proportionate quantities and qualities of the lands,—the cultivated or culturable soils,—of that County.

RECEIVING RENTS.—P. 37. "The credit now most commonly given is one quarter, the rent due at Lady-Day being paid at Midsummer, and that due at Michaelmas paid at Christmas; but some landlords expect the rent within a month after becoming due."

WOODLANDS.

MR. PITT has furnished a long article on forests and other woodlands, in Northamptonshire. It is mostly, however, made up with extracts from Mr. DONALDSON'S account, inserted aforegoing; and from Mr. YOUNG'S tour, in that County. Mr. P. it is to be remarked, has not however taken every thing on trust; but has written in part from his own examinations; and one passage at least of original matter may be extracted with profit. But the difficulty of finding out that which is *really his own*, renders the task of extraction, not a little embarrassing and disgusting. How unpardonably negligent, or unfair, in a compiler, not to mark with exactness; so that his readers may distinguish, *at sight*, every page, passage, and line, which is not his own.

The following extract gives a good GENERAL VIEW of the WOODLANDS of Northamptonshire. It is brief, yet satisfactory; and is very creditable to Mr. Pitt as a Reporter.

P. 142. "The most considerable is that of Rockingham, situated in the north-west part of the county, which extends from near Wandsford, on the great northern road, towards Weldon and Rockingham, and still farther south west: as Mr. Donaldson observes, forming an almost continued chain of woodland country for near 20 miles, though I believe the length to be hardly so much. This forest is certainly very extensive, I penetrated it on horseback from Rockingham to Weldon, and again made an excursion from near King's Cliff, with frequent interruptions from mounds and fences, insomuch, that it is not possible, without a guide, to know the boundaries, but it very probably contains 8 or 10 thousand acres. The next, in point of extent, is Whittlebury, or Whittlewood forest, extending on on the south border of the county, according to Mr. Young, above 11 miles in length, and containing, by his estimate, 7000 acres. I crossed this forest from Brackley to Towcester, and made several pretty long excursions from the road; and again, in a circuitous direction from Pottersbury to Wakefield-Lodge, and thence into the London road, near Towcester: If to these two we add the third, viz. Salcey-Forest, between Northampton and Newport Pagnell, to the south of the road, we shall have an extent of forest land of about 20 thousand acres.

"The chaces of Geddington and Yardly are of considerable extent; the purlieu woods are both numerous and extensive, and cover large breadths of land. If to these be added the extensive woods and plantations that abound on private freehold property, I believe we shall have at least 20 thousand acres more woodland, making, with the forests, an extent of woodland, to the amount of 40 thousand acres. I believe this estimate not overcharged, the breadth of woodland, on many private estates, being very great; witness those belonging to the families of Exeter and Pomfret, as well as on many other estates in the county, very advantageously and ornamentally situated."

I perceive no other passage, which the Reporter can call his own (I believe) that is entitled to a place in this volume. His plan for disafforesting those "worse than waste" lands, together with his estimates, and calculations of profit, may serve to amuse a certain class of readers. But how, or by whom, is any one of the numerous plans that have been offered for the same purpose, to be carried into effect, under existing circumstances? (December 1812.) It is merely a waste of words to talk about it.

To change so mortifying a subject for one which is more cheering to the well wisher for the prosperity of the Country,—IN TIMES TO COME,—I will here insert Mr. P's opinion, as to the prospect before us, in regard to a continued SUPPLY of SHIP TIMBER, in England. In this opinion, we find something new. His ideas, in this instance, may be strictly said to be his own. The alarmists, in that matter, may, or may not, find comfort in the perusal.

P. 143. "Mr. Donaldson has made and procured many pertinent and judicious remarks on the management and abuses of the forest and the purlieu woods: he has also made other remarks, tending to raise an alarm respecting a probable scarcity of oak, for navy uses, in which I can, by no means, agree with him, and therefore shall give my reasons why there is no danger of such scarcity of navy-timber ever

ever occurring; and, if there was, that it would not be prevented by forest management, the land of which should be for the greatest part applied to the more valuable purposes of corn and pasture."

Again, p. 154. "Respecting the subject of the possibility of a scarcity of navy-timber, what reason can be advanced for harbouring any such idea? Has any want of it been experienced during the present long and extensive naval war? No such thing has been heard of; our commerce and spirit of enterprize are such, that we import the greater part of what is used for building and domestic uses: and the communications between the sea-ports and the interior of the kingdom are now so easy, by the canal-system, that it may be drawn from any quarter. So long as we exist as a maritime nation, and timber exists in any part of the globe, we cannot want the means of procuring it; and, the fact is, there is nothing like a scarcity of it, or the symptoms of approach, or probability of scarcity in our island."

The only remark which I have to make, in this place, is, that Mr. Pitt is a man of the Midland Counties (which, with little latitude, may be said to contain all the ship timber now growing in the kingdom) and has not, perhaps, a sufficiently extensive knowledge of the island at large, to decide on this important point.—Land carriage may be said to have, long ago, cleared the sea-coast districts; and canals are now taking off the produce of the interior.

AGRICULTURE.

FARMS.—For a notice on the *Sizes* of Farms, see the head *Rent*, aforegoing.

HOMESTEADS.—On this subject, the Reporter first treats us with the echo of Mr. Donaldson's remarks, and then favors us with the remarks, themselves. See p. 349, aforegoing.

PLAN of ARABLE MANAGEMENT.—Northamptonshire is marked by its forests and other woodlands, its common fields and grazing grounds. Its *inclosed arable lands* are less an object of consideration.

P. 79. "The course of crops most universally approved upon the red land is, 1. a crop at one ploughing of the turf, wheat, rye, oats, barley, or pease; 2 turnips; 3. barley, with seeds, and then at grass for two or three years; but though this is the theory, the practice is often as before stated, and two crops are taken either before or after the turnips, which

which course is practised and defended by some good farmers, who use lime and other manure freely, and say the system is productive and profitable, but condemned by others, who say, taking two white crops, after turnips, will exhaust the land too much to make it graze profitably after; on which account, it may be preferable to take the two crops before turnips, and one after."

OCCUPIERS.—P. 35. "Respecting the general character and disposition of farmers in this county, I can pronounce, that, as far as my observation goes, they are not at all wanting in enterprize, energy, or the exertions necessary to effect improvements. Witness the great progress already made in the improvement of their sheep stock, and the activity and acuteness displayed in laying in their beasts for fatting. I have also found them, in general, liberal, communicative, and free from those narrow jealousies which are often excited by the inquiries of a stranger, and which are, in some places, received with apparent suspicion and distrust, but which here seem to be regarded as a means of collecting general knowledge, to be diffused for the public good, and as a means of improvement."

MANURES.—*Lime.*—P. 174. "Several farmers complained to me of the injustice of Mr. Donaldson's observation, when he says, very little lime is used in this county as a means of improving the soil. On the contrary, I am assured that lime is conveyed, in very considerable quantities, from the lime-works at Kinsthorpe and Duston, near Northampton, from which works only 30,000 quarters are annually sold for manure, and conveyed by land-carriage to the very edge of Leicestershire, although the coals for burning it are very dear, being brought by land carriage many miles, from Hillmorton, on the Oxford canal, or from the Union canal, in Leicestershire: there are also public lime-kilns at Moulton, Hardwick, Abingdon, and Blisworth, at which not less than an equal quantity with the above (viz. 30,000 quarters more) is burnt for manure, beside a great many private kilns kept on by farmers for their own use.

"The above quantities, as sold for manure, were ascertained from inquiries made by the Lamport Agricultural Society; who farther informed me, that the above quantity of 60 000 quarters annually is used upon a district of less than 200 square miles; that it is laid on at the rate of 10 quarters per acre, the supposed average; and, consequently, that, within the above compass, 6,000 acres are annually dressed with lime, or near one acre in 20 upon the whole district; that some have tried as much as 15 quarter per acre; but the quantity recommended by Mr. Donaldson, of 300 or 400 bushels per acre, is thought very erroneous, both with

with respect to probable effect, and even expense, which could not be generally borne.

"I observed, myself, several persons dressing the land with lime, October 1797, previous to sowing wheat, and was informed, that the improvement from it is much the greatest upon the red soils, of which a large portion of the district I have mentioned as using the above quantity is composed. It is possible this particular district might not have engaged Mr. Donaldson's attention, for lime is certainly here in great repute. On the grey soils it is less used, not having answered equally well; probably, they already contain a large portion of calcareous earth; lime is, however, used in a greater or less degree in most parts of the county."

P. 177. "Since the above was compiled, in 1797 to 1806, the Grand Junction Canal has been completed, by means of which, fuel for burning lime is brought into the county with more facility, and lime, as a manure, has lost none of its former reputation."

Sheepfold.—P. 176. "Folding sheep is still practised, though less now than when the land was more generally in an open-field state."

P. 177. "Folding of sheep is also, in general, practised upon the fallow fields of all the open parishes; and, in the enclosed land where fallows are made, at Kettering, 150 sheep fold two acres per month, or 10 acres in the season; but a little fold-yard manure is strewed along the hollows where the sheep never lay: this is practised in all the open-field parishes. At Rothwell, 80 sheep fold an acre in three weeks, or about seven acres in a season. At Desborough the same. At Pottersbury, an inclosed country, the flock, although Leicester sheep, are folded upon the fallows all summer; and Mr. Roper says that they could not be otherwise properly manured. The fold is on a fresh spot every night, made with hurdles, and its size proportioned to the number of she p. Mr. Wright's fold, (Kettering,) for 150 sheep, contained 340 square yards; and, at Desborough, a fold for 80 sheep contained 230 square yards; the average seems to be about two and a half square yards to each sheep."

TILLAGE.—After copying Mr. Donaldson's censure of the Northamptonshire plow (see p. 353, aforegoing) the Reporter proceeds, p. 51,—"as I have frequently observed these kind of general remarks made by persons whose good sense and experience should have taught them better, it may not be improper to enter into a slight discussion of this subject, and to shew the absurdity of laying it down as a maxim, that two horses will plough properly in all kinds of land.

"What I have to say on this subject is in part anticipated by Mr. Smith, of Tichmarsh, who says: 'I have heard and read

read much on this subject, and have tried a great variety of ploughs myself upon Northamptonshire soils; but, from its adhesive quality, (for the most part,) I have met with none which scour so well, or run so easy, as the ploughs in common use.

"'It is ridiculous to assert, that two horses can plough a-breast in almost any part of this county; I mean, if land is ploughed of a sufficient depth, there is an adhesive quality in the soil, and no plough that I have ever seen will at times scour, so as to keep clean, consequently the draught must be considerably retarded. Double ploughs are only used upon light or gravelly soils, or in stirring strong soils in fallowing, and in dry weather only; if strong land be any way moist, they will not work at all.'"

ARABLE CROPS.—I find nothing to be taken from the fresh matter of the Volume before me, relative to the culture of these crops; excepting the following particulars concerning

WHEAT.—P. 81. "Wheat, which is cultivated in large quantities both in open fields and in enclosures, upon the red and friable soils. In common fields, it is universally sown on fallow, about three statute bushels per acre, in October: the general produce about three quarters, but sometimes rising to four quarters, per acre.

"On the red and friable enclosed land, or on the more tenacious heavy loams, wheat is often sown on fallow, for the particular management of which see Fallowing. The quantity of seed sown here is more than I have heard of in any other country. I am assured, by Messrs. Wright, of Kettering, that it is common to sow from three to four statute bushels per acre, ploughed in in October; and that, on the best soils, there is no economy in sparing the seeds; and that, on a well managed and well manured fallow, five quarters per acre may be expected in return.

"The manure used on wheat fallows in this country are farm-yard dung and the folding of sheep. Of the former, about twelve cart-loads per acre; and, of the latter, a hundred and twenty sheep will fold about ten acres through the summer. And this is practised pretty generally, not only in common fields, but on the fallows in enclosed land."

P. 83. "Wheat is here very generally sown broad cast, and I am informed, that, in the few experiments that have been made in drilling wheat, the result has, pretty uniformly, been unfavourable to the practice."

The Reporter enters on a wide discussion of the "Disorders of Wheat;" which he divides into 1. "Stricken or Blighted Ears." 2. "The Mildew." 3. "The Smut;"—p. 84.—But, in his own strictures, I perceive nothing that is new, or sufficiently valuable to require transcription. The

subjoined

subjoined intimation of a friend, however, is worth preserving.

P. 87. "A friend of mine, who has erected a threshing machine, assures me, that smutty wheat so threshed is cleansed from the smut by that operation; as, being beaten out in suspension, instead of laying solid on a floor, it receives no taint or discolouring, and the bladders, or unsound corns, may be dressed or blown out, thus losing only the smutty part, without tainting or discolouring the quantity."

The Disease of Smut.

I recollect the circumstance of my father having seed wheat thrashed upon a large wooden grate, to prevent the diseased grains or bags of smut, from being burst by the flail, on the thrashing floor; and a modern thrashing machine, it is more than probable, performs the operation, with similar effect.—The bladders of smut, being much lighter than sound grains of wheat, are effectually separated from them, in winnowing.

The *infection* of this disease is undoubtedly, I believe, communicated by the dust of the bursten bags of smut adhering to the downy ends of sound grains.

For a simple, accurate, and decisive experiment, on this subject, see Northern Department, *North Riding of Yorkshire*, p. 478.—And the following would seem to prove the position.—P. 89. "The following experiments for the Lamport Society on this subject, were made, by their desire, by Mr. Thomas Bosworth, of Highgate-House, in the autumn of 1798, and the succeeding summer.

"Ten beds of land, of one perch each, separated by spaces of three feet wide, upon which wheat was never known to have been sown before, were each sown with one pint of wheat, selected and prepared as follows:

"No. 1, sown with a pint of wheat, as clean as could be procured, without any preparation.

"Result, the crop less smutty than crops in general are, though not without smut, nor quite so clean as the seed.

"No. 2, sown with a pint of wheat the same as No. 1, steeped in strong brine, made with salt and water only, and dried with lime, as was all the rest that was wetted.

"Result, the crop cleaner than No. 1, it being difficult to find a smutty ear.

"No. 3, sown with a pint of the same wheat as before, but steeped in brine, in which smutty wheat had been steeped.

"Result, the produce considerably infected, insomuch that handful could not be taken without several smutty ears.

"No. 4,

"No. 4, sown with a pint of wheat, the same as before, to which was put a small quantity of smut dust, and mixed together.

"Result, the crop one-sixth part smut.

"No. 5, sown with a pint of the same wheat, as before, but mixed with a greater quantity of smut dust.

"Result, the crop nine-tenths smut.

"No. 6, and all the following, sown with wheat, taken from a very smutty crop, this without any preparation.

"Result, the crop full nine-tenths smut.

"No. 7, sown with very smutty wheat, steeped in soap-boilers ley.

"Result, the crop one-fortieth smut.

"No. 8, sown with very smutty wheat, but carefully washed in clean water.

"Result, this crop was not so clean as No. 7.

"No. 9, sown with very smutty wheat, steeped in strong brine of salt and water.

"Result, a greater proportion of smut in this crop than in No. 8.

"No. 10, sown with seed taken from the cleanest ears, that could be selected from a very smutty crop.

"Result, the crop one-fifteenth smut."

Thus, by those apparently accurate, and of course valuable experiments, it pretty clearly appears that the disease of smut is not only in a high degree *infectious;* but, from the result of the experiment No. 10, that it is, in some degree, *hereditary*.

By the experiment above referred to, however, it appears that wheat which was "not entirely free from the disease," but which was "thoroughly washed," produced corn that was "perfectly free from smut;"—while the produce from that which "was sown in its original state had a few smutty ears."

Seeing the beautifully simplex method, by which smutty wheat may be *thoroughly washed,—perfectly cleansed* from its foulness,—and seeing, in the above-noticed experiments, the efficacy of such ablution, in preventing the disease, it would seem to set at naught every other *preparation for sowing*.

I remember to have seen, many years ago, smutty or what is called "black wheat," cleansed from its blackness, in a ready and effectual manner; by way of preparing it, I think, for the manufacture of starch.

A quantity of it, perhaps a quarter, was inclosed in a large wheel, whose periphery, or outer rim, was formed with wire-work, resembling that of a corn skreen, supported by iron bars. This wheel, which, from what I recollect of it, was some

some ten or twelve feet, or more, in diameter, and two or three, or more, feet wide,—was worked (by the mean of a water mill) in a large trough or cistern of water, which was fed by a small stream passing through it. By the movement of the wheel, the wheat, immerged in water, was kept in continual motion among it; the foul water passing away with the stream, and its place supplied with that which was clear; the operation being continued, until the water passed away, free from impurity.

And how easily might a hand wheel, of a similar construction, be formed of a size to hold a bushel or more of wheat; to be worked in a shallow trough, placed in or by the side of running water;—or, for the want of this, under a pump,—or near a draw well, or clear standing pool,—to be supplied with buckets, and changed as often as it should become foul, until perfectly cleaned.

A larger wheel of this kind might be attached to a common grist mill; and seed corn be washed, at a trifling cost, by the miller.

TURNEPS.—P. 97. "Turnips are cultivated, in considerable quantities, upon all the red and light soils; but a large proportion of the county is too strong and harsh for the growth of this plant to advantage."

P. 98. "They are generally eaten off by sheep and lambs, being hurdled off in small plots. The hurdles, which are made of coppice underwood, are two yards long, and cost about 1*s.* each.

"But few cattle are fatted on turnips here; when they are, the largest turnips are drawn from the field, and given to the cattle upon a turf, or in a stall."

WOAD.—P. 107. "This plant is cultivated in this county, and prepared for the dyers, not by farmers, but by professional men, who make it their business, on the following system, about 50 acres of which I viewed growing upon the Catesby estate, near Daventry, August, 1806. Two wad growers live in the county, and one of them grows about 70 acres; it requires rich old pasture land, for which the wad grower pays the landlord from 5*l.* to 7*l.* per acre, per annum, for two or three years, the farmer being compelled to give it up for that term, and to take to it again afterwards, at the old rent."

P. 108. "It is not thought otherwise injurious (as the land must necessarily be kept clean from weeds) than by destroying the nutritious qualities of the turf, which requires many years to restore; the land will generally produce two or three good crops after, without manure. An approved course is to take, 1. oats; 2. wheat; 3. coleseed or turnips; 4. barley, with seeds; and afterwards to manure on the seeds,

seeds, so as to produce a turf. Some spirited managers have paid the wad-rent themselves, and continued grazing the land, rather than have it ploughed up."—A striking fact.

For the culture of this plant, see EASTERN DEPARTMENT.

TOBACCO.—P. 109. "Tobacco, a considerable patch, cultivated in Rothwell, for the purpose of dressing sheep for the scab, 1806"

CULTIVATED HERBAGE.—The following incident of practice is well entitled to a place, here.

P. 125. "On the black soil of Kettering Field, lately enclosed, Mr. Wright shewed me a striking and successful instance of an excellent pasture, raised by one of his neighbours, upon a large field, without ploughing or growing any crop, and which he deemed capital management, at least so far as the turning of tillage-land into pasture is concerned. This field, allotted and fenced from the common field, was, principally, wheat-stubble: having been well fallowed in the common field, the occupier, desirous of bringing it to immediate pasture, sowed, the succeeding spring, a plentiful allowance of red and white clover, particularly the latter, upon the wheat-stubble, without ploughing, tillage, or any crop, and harrowed it well in; it is now, Aug. 1806, well stocked with sheep, and an excellent pasture: the seeds were sown in the spring of 1805."

It may be a point which remains to be settled, whether, in converting arable land to a state of permanent herbage, without foregoing a crop of corn, the grass seeds ought to be sown with, or over, the corn crop,—or over the stubble, in autumn, or the ensuing spring. In the latter case, the young herbage would escape the danger of being drawn up weak and overlaid by the corn; and would of course rise in the most natural way. It would, however, be liable, on some lands, to be annoyed by spring weeds. Experience alone can determine it, on a given soil.

Rape Herbage.—I do not insert the subjoined extract, as a believer in the bold assertions it contains; but as a friend to rape herbage; which may often be cultivated with profit, incidentally, as appropriate circumstances may arise.

P. 99. "Rape, or coleseed, is cultivated, but not generally, the land for which must have the same preparation and manure as for turnips, and the seed should be sown before Midsummer, at the rate of a gallon per acre; it makes excellent sheep food, and is vastly more nutritive than turnips, insomuch, that I am assured the ley of sheep, in coleseed, is worth double the price to what it is in turnips; and that the fact is so well known to butchers, that, if they give 4*d.* per week for the keep of sheep in turnips, they will give 3*d.* per week to have them kept in coleseed."

Cichory.

Cichory.—The following notice I insert, as a material of agricultural history.—P. 104. "A whole field, of two acres or more, was laid down with this plant, sown amongst barley, in the spring of 1795, by Mr. Martin, of Tansor Lodge, near Oundle; in 1796, it was grazed with sheep; the stock it would carry throughout the summer, Mr. Martin informed me, was about six sheep per acre, and they did well upon it. In the spring of 1797, it was ploughed up, and again sown with barley, the crop by no means equal to what might have been expected, had the intermediate crop been clover. The chicory, a hardy biennial, or perennial, was by no means destroyed by the tillage given for the barley, but shot up among it in great abundance; and when I saw it, July 8th, it was grown through the barley, and going to seed amongst it. I reckon that the damage done by the chicory could not be less than 20*s.* per acre, and that it could not have been drawn out for that sum. Mr. Martin admits the impropriety of sowing barley so soon upon it; and it is a sufficient proof that this is an improper plant in an arable system, as it can only be extirpated by fallow. In permanent pasture it may be more proper; but even here it should be kept eaten off, to prevent the seed stalk becoming hard and tough, for, in that state, cattle will not eat it, and it has a weed-like appearance."

Sainfoin.—P. 102. "Sainfoin is cultivated upon the stony under stratums, in different places, in the parishes of Wakerly and Duddington; it had been mown, and I saw several stacks of the hay, the aftermath, August 13, going into blossom."

GRASS LANDS.—After quoting Mr. Donaldson's statement, and adopting his extent of meadow lands,—namely 40,000 acres,—Mr. Pitt says, p. 113, "The upland pasture occupies a still much greater extent, the strong deep loams having been found naturally disposed to turf, and affording a staple of herbage, highly nutritive to cattle and sheep, and upon which they fatten with great rapidity."

P. 136. "These districts having been long enclosed, and, consisting of deep rich loam, have (by the grass having long lain, and had time to strike deep roots) acquired a rich productive herbage of a highly nutricious quality, capable of forcing fat the largest oxen and sheep; and the occupiers having, by degrees, increased their capital, have the means of procuring and improving the most valuable live stock."

Having mentioned different methods of removing *ant-hills* (none of which requires notice here) we find, in this Report, the following elevating description of the ant-hilly pastures of Northamptonshire, p. 139. "In some of which the ant-hills are so abundant, that it is possible to walk over many acres

acres, step by step, from one ant-hill to another, without ever coming upon the level ground: it must, however, be admitted, that the most industrious occupiers, and best managers, have generally cleared their premises of these nuisances.'

LIVESTOCK.

IN a County so abundant in grass lands, as Northamptonshire is, a proportionate number of graminivorous animals may be expected to be found. Yet Northamptonshire cannot be emphatically styled a *breeding* country; unless so far as relates to SHEEP.—Its characteristic, in regard to CATTLE, is *grazing* and the *dairy*.

The following statement may serve to give a general idea of the *application* of the grass lands; and the *proportionate numbers* of the *stock* they support. It must, however, be received, as the Reporter appropriately intimates, as being little more than hypothetical.

P. 137. "I give the following estimate of the beef and mutton produced in Northamptonshire. It is very clear, from the nature of the subject, that every estimate of this kind, founded as this is, only on conjecture and general observation, must be uncertain; it is, however, the best I can at present produce, and may stand for future correction.

	Acres.
"The grass-land and green crops of the county I estimate at, about	400,000
Which land, I supposed stocked and occupied as follows:	
By horses	100,000
By dairy and store-cattle	100,000
By sheep and feeding cattle	200,000

"The beef and mutton produced in this county is supposed to be nearly equal in weight. The feeding cattle are very generally bought from other counties, at about two-thirds of their value when fat. The sheep are bred and reared in the county."

	Acres.
"I suppose, applied to the rearing and fatting of sheep	150,000
And to the feeding of oxen and other cattle	50,000
as above account,	200,000"

The estimate of the beef and mutton, produced in the County, appears to me to be too conjectural for insertion, here.

HORSES.

HORSES.—P. 215. "Horses are bred, in this county, chiefly for draught at the cart or plough, and mostly of the strong black breed: but the number bred being an insufficient supply, some are bought in from the counties of Derby, Lincoln, and York, generally at two or three years old."

CATTLE.—*Breed.*—P. 194. "The cattle bred in the county, at least those bred with any attention, are of the long-horn breed. Mr. Bosworth, who farms near the centre of the county, observes, an improved variety of the long horn breed is clearly the breed of the county; and, though the attention of but few has been directed to this object, yet there are, notwithstanding, instances of those who have pursued it with success."

"Respecting the sorts bought in from distant parts, in addition to the long-horn, the Holderness are chiefly used for the dairy; but for fatting every sort is bought in at one time or other. Staffordshire, Shropshire, Herefords, Pembrokes, Devons, North Wales, Scots, and Irish, are occasionally met with at the different fairs; and the grazier, if he wants, refuses no sort that looks kindly, handles well, and can be had worth the money: And many instances occur of each of these kinds growing in a superior degree, though I believe the superiority is generally considered as being with the long-horned breed, or with the Herefords."

Fatting Cattle, on Grass.—P. 129. "Of the cattle fatted in this county, a small portion only are bred therein, which are generally of the improved long-horned kind, but some short horns are also bred here; great numbers of Scots and Welch are bought in, as also Herefords and long horns from Staffordshire and Shropshire, and short horns from Lincolnshire and Yorkshire, both oxen and heifers; these are principally fatted at grass, and great numbers sold from the pastures; but some are kept on through the winter, and furnished with oil-cake, and hay, or turnips, and sometimes with ground barley or other grain, but not very commonly. I am informed, the best hay of this county, with a few turnips, will bring on the largest oxen sufficiently, without any assistance from more expensive food.

"Mr. Donaldson observes, that about one half of the enclosed land is old enclosure, and principally occupied as grazing farms; on this very little grain is grown, the land being principally employed in the fatting of cattle, or the breeding and fatting of sheep, or occupied as dairy-farms.

"When cattle have had the summer's grass, on the approach of winter they are often continued in the pasture, and hay given twice a day, on which they will do well. The cattle

cattle for sale are generally consigned to a salesman in London. It is a maxim, with a Northamptonshire grazier, to winter only the best and most thriving beasts, which are sure to pay the most. The beast that does not thrive well they are always most anxious to part with first.

"A great many half fat cattle are bought from Staffordshire and elsewhere, soon in the spring, to finish in the early feeding pastures of this county."

P. 131. "In a farther tour through this county, in the summer of 1806, I had an opportunity of examining several grazing occupations, some of which I am at liberty to detail, without concealing any particulars, and others not. Mr. Bull, of Daventry, very kindly sent a very intelligent friend to show me his grazing occupation, at Fawsley, of about 300 acres, and would have gone himself, but for the effects of an accident. The parish of Fawsley belongs to the Knightley family, who reside in it: it contains about 3,000 acres, without a single blade of corn, being wholly at grass and applied to feeding, and mostly to the fatting of oxen and breeding and fatting of sheep. Mr. Bull has here a rich grazing close of 210 acres, stocked, besides sheep, with oxen of various breeds; the number in this pasture, Aug. 1806, was 90 head of different breeds, Hereford, Longhorn, Scotch, and Welch: with some of mongrel breeds: some of the prime Herefords cost in 28*l.* each; and he admits, may come to 14 or 15 score the quarter; but does not in general prefer heavy oxen: has a great many more in other pastures; some of the Welch not expected to make more than eight score the quarter: says that many oxen, bought in last year, are now selling, at Smithfield, so as not to make more than prime cost, at 6*d.* per lb. which is the present price of hard growers, or inferior beasts; but the prime oxen are worth to 7½*d.* per lb. In general, one third of the value of an ox, in Smithfield, is more than the grazier gets for a year's keeping, united with expense, trouble, risk, and interest of capital. Many bullocks, of the Pontypool breed, (Monmouthshire,) are grazed in this neighbourhood, some so small as not to come to more than six score per quarter when fat: spay heifers also grazed in this neighbourhood, as well as bullocks."

P. 199. "The oxen, fatted in the county, are principally bought in, and grazed only, to make them up, about 10 or 12 months. I observed on this occasion very few short-horn or Holderness oxen; those in the graziers hands being principally Hereford, long-horn, Devon, Scotch, and Welch, with a few of mongrel breeds, bred most probably in the county."

P. 200. "The smallest breed of oxen I saw in the county are

are denominated Pontypools, from a fair in Monmouthshire, where they are bought; some of these, when fat, do not exceed six score the quarter; they are bred in Radnorshire, and other mountainous parts of Wales."

Mr. Pitt having been favored, by the Langport Society, with the points of excellence in an ox or cow, in a lean state, which denote a disposition to *fatten*, he has taken the trouble to versify their description; "for the benefit of the young grazier."

P. 201. "Let each steady grazier, to buy the right sort,
Fix on cattle sharp-chopped, but with neck rather short;
Neck fine underneath,—close-pointed the shoulder,
The chine thin at top,—hind parts wider and bolder;
Long ribs near together, not much bowed when standing;
Full wide in the breast, and the bosom expanding;
The loin short and wide, rather sloping than flat,
Hips large, and not pointed, with short rumps, mind that,
Twist deep, or a prospect of being so when fat;
The feet rather large, but the bone rather small,
The hide soft and mellow, not too thin, and that's all."

I do not insert the above lines to show Mr. P's qualifications, as a poet; but rather to prove his disqualification as a Writer on *grazing*, otherwise *fatting cattle*.—*Flat sides* and *short rumps* are among the worst qualities of cattle that are intended for the production of *beef*. I have known dairy cows, bearing the above description, valuable for *milk*.

P. 195. "The *number* of cattle annually fed or fatted in this county is considerable; it is computed that, besides what are consumed in the county or sold into the neighbouring counties, about 15,000 head are annually sent to London: this estimate is by the Lamport society."

The Method of Grazing.—P. 130. "Mr. Young observes, Annals, No. xxxvi. 'The grazing-lands here are stocked in the proportion of one ox and one sheep to two acres, besides which, one sheep is kept in winter: there is much winter fattening, and all upon hay, which is given in the barbarous way of scattering it about the fields, the stacks being made where it grows: a very great improvement might be made, in this part of their economy, by stacking their hay near to small farm-yards, which might be made with furze, faggots, &c. at a small expense; these would collect dung, and that would enable them to have cabbages for winter food, which would yield a much greater profit than hay.'

"Notwithstanding this theory, I find a very strong idea, amongst the occupiers of grazing farms, that stock will do much better, ranging at liberty, on old pasture-land, (where they meet with occasional picking,) and hay occasionally given them, than they will do confined in a stall or yard; particularly unless, in the latter situation, they have better

and

and more expensive food; also, in the present system, they require but little care and attention; and I believe the graziers will not be readily prevailed on to change it for stall-feeding and cabbage-cultivation."

P. 133. "As some compensation for the manure lost by the bullocks grazing at large, I found, on Mr. Bull's occupation, the dung collected together, in heaps, by a labourer with a horse and cart, which, after due fermentation, is again carried away and spread on the land."

Stallfatting of Cattle.—P. 135. "Mr. Bull, of Daventry, observed to me, that few fat oxen are stall-fed in this county; they can generally be kept in pastures to the end of January on picking, with the assistance of hay, and by that time, himself, and most graziers of the county, finish their fat oxen; a few, however, are occasionally stalled on oil-cake and hay."

Markets for Cattle.—See *Markets*, aforegoing.

Dairy.—P. 197. "Mr. Young observes, in 1791, in the neighbourhood of Wakefield Lodge, and upon the Duke of Grafton's estates, 'The principal and staple live stock of the neighbourhood are cows, the milk entirely applied to making butter which goes fresh to London, where it is sold by the name of *Epping:* many of the dairies rise to 30, 40, and some even to 50, cows.'"

P. 199. "In the parishes of Grafton Regis, Yardley, Gobion, Potterbury, and a large district in that neighbourhood, considerable dairies are kept, chiefly of the short-horn or Holderness breed of cows, and butter for the London market the principal object, which meets with a ready sale and quick return."

"In a tract of country, about Charwelton, and between Daventry and Banbury, considerable dairies are kept, of 20 to 40, and even to 60, cows each; butter and pork, for the London market, the principal object, which have an easy conveyance, ready sale, and the returns from which quickly come round: in this latter district a great many long-horn cows are kept.

"Dairies are also kept in several other districts of the county; some calves are fatted, but many sold, at a few days old, to be suckled nearer London: upon the whole, I suppose that this county barely supplies itself with cheese, but has a considerable surplus of butter and of pork fed from dairy-produce."

SHEEP.—*Breed.*—P. 203. "The *Commonfield Sheep*" Mr. P. says, "are much inferior to the antient-pasture sheep, longer in the leg, and smaller and less compact in the carcass, and, in some instances, horned; these sheep were meant for the fold, and if they would endure that,

and

and the necessary length of walk daily, to and from pasture in the fallow, or elsewhere, little attention was paid to other circumstances."

In p. 205, Mr. Pitt speaks of the *ancient Pasture Sheep*, as a superior variety, before the late crosses; but acknowledges "that (as it is well observed by Mr. Knight) within the last 18 years, by attention, and particularly by crossing with the Dishley breed, they have received such general and great improvement, that perhaps no other district can boast of superior sheep-stock to what may be found in this; the additional number bred upon the land, the much earlier age at which sheep are now ripe, the improved quality of mutton exhibited, weekly, at Northampton and other markets, in the County, and the advance in price now given for the use of rams, are sufficient proofs of the great improvement that has been effected."

Management of *Store* Sheep.—P. 210. "Sheds of hurdles, supported by stakes and covered with straw, or of hurdles set in the ground, with others laid across, and covered in like manner, are raised for valuable sheep in hot weather, and make them a comfortable and cool retreat, keeping off the heat of the sun, and the wind drawing and fanning them through the gullet thus formed."

P. 214. "The Lamport Society observe, that, when sheep have been a considerable time from water, in a dry season, they should not be allowed to run to water; as, when that has been the case, it has often been known that considerable losses have been the consequence."

The *Number* of Sheep kept.—It were unkind not to indulge the Reporter, sometimes, by attending to his estimates, and calculations, even tho we may consider them as little more than day dreams. They may set those to work who have a more intimate knowledge of the County.

P. 214. Under the article "Feeding" (see Livestock, aforegoing)—"it is estimated that 250,000 sheep are annually fattened in this county and which are mostly, if not wholly, bred therein: to produce this number, the standing stock of the county must be about 210,000 ewes, 250,000 yearlings, and 250,000 from one to two year old; one half of which latter may be disposed of before the second shearing, and the other half twice shorn; this brings the wool of the county, annually shorn, to 585,000 fleeces, which, at four and a half to the tod, would be 130,000 tod; and, at the present price, 32*s.* 6*d.* per tod, amounts to 211,250*l.* It must be very clear that this is a subject of uncertainty, but is given, as deduced by the writer, from general observation."

Fatting Sheep.—P. 128. "A very great number of sheep

sheep and cattle are fattened in the pastures of this county; of the sheep, a great part are bred in the county, but some are bought in from elsewhere. Wiltshires are bought at Weyhill fair, and a great number of the Cotteswold breed are bought at the fairs at Banbury; they are fattened through the summer in clover or old turf pastures, and great numbers are sold at the autumnal fairs to the London and other markets.

"When the winter comes on, the green crops are resorted to, principally turnips and coleseed, which are divided by hurdles, and small portions only given to the sheep at a time; they are, in part, sold off during the winter months, and, in part, fatted up on the spring-grass and then sold."

Markets for Sheep.—See *Markets*, aforegoing.

Profits of Farming.—The following observations agree, in almost every particular, so well with my own ideas on the subject, that I transcribe them into this volume, with great satisfaction. The ideas themselves, and the manner of imparting them, are equally creditable to the writer.

P. 46. "The expense and profit of farming, or, indeed, of any other private concern, is rather a delicate subject, and people are not easily persuaded to go into real matters of this nature for the sake of laying them before the public. It may, in general, be observed, that few fortunes are made simply by farming, and none rapidly. The object of the generality of farmers is to procure a decent livelihood; to bring up their family; and to make a suitable provision for such family and for a comfortable old age; in which, if they succeed, it must be by persevering industry, and they may be deemed fortunate. I believe this is all, that, in common situations and circumstances, can be either expected or effected.

"In a business so very much multiplied and divided as that of farming, it must naturally be supposed that the competition between the numbers employed in it must, by enhancing rents and diminishing the price of produce, bring the result to the lowest living profit; and that this is the case no one can doubt who is acquainted with the subject. In dear seasons, the reduced quantity and extra expense generally turn the balance against the seller, notwithstanding he is then generally abused with the charges of combination and monopoly.

"In a business whose sole object is that of raising and producing the necessaries of life, no great profits ought to be obtained; the nature of the case will not admit it, and that this is really the case will be equally proved by facts as by arguments.

"In

"In taking a general review of the farmers of a country, how small a proportion will be found in any thing like affluent circumstances; and, of that proportion, the success of the greater part may be traced, not to the profits of their profession, but to local advantages, and circumstances distinct from farming.

"In the common routine of management the farmer must be content with small profit; but even this, by persevering industry and length of time, may accumulate. Extra exertions, successfully made, may, sometimes, produce larger profits; as, in any other business, he, who excels his neighbour in skill and industry, will, probably, exceed him in gains. The arable farmer has little to expect beyond a bare subsistence, unless he possesses such superior skill and industry, or makes additional efforts in some other way, not generally made by others.

"In the grazing line a new field is opened for enterprise and speculation. The grazier is a kind of merchant; and on his capital and judicious management depends his success. The immense supply of London takes off all his stock when ready; and his profit, in a great measure, depends upon his laying in a judicious selection of lean stock upon reasonable terms.

"The system of breeding superior stock is another subject for enterprize and the exercise of judgement and skill, and success in which has been and may be attended with more than common profits; and, in this system, many persons are now exerting their abilities, and those who succeed, may, probably, get money. Upon the whole, it is pretty clear, that, if any thing considerable is made by farming, it must be by striking out of the common way and excelling the common stile of management. Sometimes fortunate connections may benefit the person forming them, and many persons better their circumstances by dealing in articles connected with landed produce; as, live stock, grain, pulse, malt, flour, butter, cheese, clover and grass seeds, timber, &c. or by getting employment as surveyors; but, in all common cases, the profits of farming will be found little enough, and no one, who knows the truth of the matter, will have reason to envy those who are making them."

HUNTINGDONSHIRE.

HUNTINGDONSHIRE.

THE FENS and other WATERLANDS of HUNTINGDONSTIRE,—have been brought forward, in reviewing the Reports from the EASTERN DEPARTMENT;—to which, by situation and natural affinity, they inseparably belong.

The UPPER GROUNDS of the County are here the object of attention. They are *naturally* and *agriculturally*, an extension of those of NORTHAMPTONSHIRE.—How irrational, and inscientific, to prosecute an AGRICULTURAL SURVEY, by *Counties!*

"GENERAL VIEW

OF THE

AGRICULTURE

OF THE

COUNTY OF HUNTINGDON.

WITH

OBSERVATIONS ON THE MEANS OF ITS IMPROVEMENT.

BY THOMAS STONE,

LAND-SURVEYOR, GRAY'S-INN, LONDON.

1793."

FOR some remarks on Mr. STONE'S QUALIFICATIONS, as a Reporter of Rural Affairs, see his *Lincolnshire*, in the EASTERN DEPARTMENT.

The few pages, now before me, is one of the very first sketches that were hurried in to the Board; and is one of the least intelligent of those sketches. Like his Lincolnshire, it is rather a didactic paper, on the *improvement* of the County, than a Report of its *present state* of *Agriculture.*

ture. Nevertheless, several passages of it require to be noticed, here; beside the few already transcribed from it into the EASTERN DEPARTMENT, under the division *Waterlands* of HUNTINGDONSHIRE, &c.

The number of pages (title, &c. exclusive) twentyeight.

NATURAL ECONOMY.

EXTENT.—P. 8. "From the observations I have been enabled to make, without an actual survey, this county may contain about 130,000 acres of commonable meadows, commons, and common fields; 23,000 acres of inclosed arable and woodland; 43,000 acres of inclosed pasture; and 44,000 acres of fen-land:"—in the whole 240,000 acres.

SOILS.—P. 8. "*The Soils* are very various, from the strongest clay, with the most shallow staple of soil, to the lightest loam; and from the richest pasture and meadow, to barren heath.

"The highest parts of the county are of the strongest clay; and such parts as are cultivated are chiefly common fields. As we proceed towards the lower parts, the soil is found of a milder nature, and better adapted for profitable cultivation."

POLITICAL ECONOMY.

APPROPRIATION.—P. 17. "If we examine the common-fields which are the subject of this enquiry, we shall find that, for the most considerable part, proprietors who have a property in many hundreds of acres, in any parish, have not more, than two or three acres at most, connected together. The residue lies in acres and half acres quite disjointed; and tenants under the same landowner, cross each other continually, in performing their necessary daily labour."*

TITHES.—P. 18. "It may be here observed, that the bishop of Lincoln has, with very great prudence and judgement,

* For a disadvantage of open fields, see the article *Sheep*, ensuing.

ment, suggested a regulation for a commutation of tithes in his diocese, (of which this county is a part), when common-fields are inclosed, which is found to answer so well, that, it is to be hoped, it will be every where adopted. By this plan, the money payments for tithes, vary, according to the price of corn from time to time ; a procedure equitable towards the land-owners and occupiers, and highly secure for the clergy, because it prevents the abuses which too frequently have befallen the interest of the clergy, in consequence of the mismanagement, of the allotments which have been made to them of land, given in lieu of tithes ; for it cannot be supposed that gentlemen bred up in colleges, are always competent to let the land they receive, so as to preserve the permanency of its yearly value. It is with pleasure I add, that wherever this plan has been carried into effect, it has been attended with the desired success*.

WATER-MILLS.—P. 28. " A considerable number of water-mills are placed upon this stream," (the Ouze) " which serve to increase the risque of damage, and more especially as the construction of their wheels are not generally on the improved plan, and as there is no certain guage or level generally observed to which the water shall be held up, nor any positive laws for throwing open flood-gates, upon the approach of an increased quantity of water."

RURAL ECONOMY.

ESTATES.—*Managers.*—P. 21. " It every day occurs, that persons wholly incompetent to the task they undertake, are thus employed, whose knowledge in agriculture was acquired in an attorney's office, a butler's pantry, or in an upholsterer's shop. Precedents of leases, made an hundred years ago, are handed down as the governing rule of their conduct ; and the grumbling farmer must take them, although the covenants are as opposite to what they ought to be, as the laws of Turkey are inapplicable to the subjects of Great Britain.

" The

" * Those who may be desirous of obtaining further information upon this subject, may consult the regulations in the acts of parliament, passed last session, respecting the inclosing of Milton Bryant and Riseley, in Bedfordshire."

"The profession of surveyor, is frequently taken up by persons, whose knowledge of agriculture was acquired by dragging a chain over some inconsiderable district of, perhaps, one or two neglected uncultivated counties; and whose subsequent employment, is rather directed, to the riveting the barbarous practices and prejudices of the country, than to prevent or remove them.

"No man is competent to regulate the husbandry of an estate, who has not been bred up in practical husbandry, and who cannot with facility apply every known improvement in agriculture, to a soil similar to that, on which it has been already applied with success."

WOODLANDS.—P. 16. "*Oak timber* is not much raised in this county, and there is very little fit for the navy; it is usually cut down when it begins to be most valuable for that purpose, and consequently when it ought to be spared.

"*The underwood* is not carefully selected and planted; the production of it, both in quantity and quality, is for the most part left to chance."

AGRICULTURE.

PLAN OF MANAGEMENT.—*Commonfields*.—P. 9. "The *common-field land*, in each respective parish, is divided into three parts; one part is annually fallowed, a moiety of which is folded with sheep and sown with wheat; and the other moiety is dunged and sown with barley in the succeeding Spring. The part which produces wheat, is broken up and sown with oats; and the part which produces barley, is at the same time generally sown with beans or peas; and then it comes in rotine to be again fallowed in the third year. This is the best husbandry of the common-fields, by which means any given spot, produces the same kind of grain or pulse every sixth year.

"But this is not invariably pursued; inasmuch as many farmers, whose conduct is not particularly watched over, attend to their immediate interests, without a due regard to their future, and sow wheat upon part of the land which should produce barley; and oats upon another part of the land, which should produce peas or beans.

"This mode of proceeding is called *cross-cropping*; its tendency is evidently to exhaust the land, and to render it much less fertile in future. The quick succession of the same kinds of grain, particularly so impoverishing a crop as as oats, as a substitute for any kind of pulse, must necessarily have that effect.

"With every common-field, there is a certain quantity of commonable high land, and meadow commonable at Lammas, when the hay is taken off.

"The quantity of common, is generally apportioned to the necessary quantity of sheep kept for folding the land, the same being originally laid out for that purpose; and where the quantity has latterly been found insufficient, in consequence of any improvements in the breed of sheep, or from the incroachments made by self-interested farmers, by ploughing up the balks and headlands adjoining or mixed with the arable lands, more land has been laid down for common."

WORKPEOPLE—P. 15. "There not being any manufactures in this county deserving notice, agriculture is the only means of occupation. But from the uninclosed and uncultivated state of the country, and the little employment and encouragement given to the husbandmen, in respect to constant work throughout the year, the labourers continue with the farmers during the winter season to thrash out heir grain; and on the approach of summer, they set off for more cultivated counties where labour is more required. Whereas, were a proper system of husbandry introduced, these labourers would have constant employment in their town neighbourhood.

"There is a scarcity of comfortable cottages for the poor in this county; and the farmers are more studious to prevent this very necessary class of men from making settlements amongst them, than to provide them useful and profitable employment—the most distressing circumstance resulting from which is, that on the approach of harvest, inhabitants in the country cannot be found to reap, gather, and embarn the corn; and were it not for the accidental peregrinations of the Irish, of manufacturers from Leicestershire, and persons of other distant counties, the corn must be spoiled in the fields. No wonder then, as the execution of this necessary and important business depends upon chance, that, in some parts of the county, in times when labourers are scarce, a guinea and upwards *per* acre is frequently paid for reaping wheat and oats, which, according to an equal scale in the price of labour, might otherwise be performed for seven shillings; and it has often occurred, that at a critical time in harvest, when labourers have been wanted extremely, half a guinea *per* day, and even upwards, has been paid to them."—*Village manufacturers*, how useful to agriculture.

GRASSLAND.—*Pasture*.—P. 13. "The pasture land is under

der no proper system of management, being generally too wet, covered with ant-hills, which are highly prejudicial to the produce; and from the unevenness of the surface, it is impossible to roll it, which is the surest means of destroying worms, ants, and other vermin; so that the sweard is not half so productive as it otherwise would be"

Meadows.—P. 28. "Along the banks of the Ouze from St. Neot's to Earith, is a large quantity of rich meadow-land, which is subject to be overflowed, at all seasons of the year, when the water comes down from Bedfordshire and Buckinghamshire with any considerable rapidity: it very frequently happens, that the crops of hay are either considerably damaged, or totally carried away; the water, which might be made a source of great advantage, is, in the present state of things, on such account, an evil of no small magnitude."

HORSES.—P 15. "This county is not famous for any particular breed. The farmers' horses are of the heavy black kind, and they do not generally look forward to the advantage that might be derived, by selling them off for more valuable purposes when mature."

CATTLE.—P. 14. "*The neat cattle* will not bear any particular description; they are for the most part purchased when young at distant fairs, and are the *refuse* of the Lancashire, Leicestershire, and Derbyshire breeds, or are bred from these sorts, without any particular care in selecting them.

"From the open state of the country, dairy-farming is not much followed; and the cows are used for suckling calves in the Southern part of the county, to supply the London market.

"*Oxen* are purchased for grazing without any particular choice in the breed, and unfortunately are never used in husbandry."

SHEEP.—P. 15. "The *sheep of the common-fields and commons* are of a very inferior sort, except in some few instances, and very little, if any, care is taken, either in the breeding, feeding, or preserving them; and from the neglected state of the land on which they are depastured, and the scanty provision for their support in winter, and the consequent diseases to which they are liable, their wool is also of a very inferior quality, yielding at the rate only of from 3 to 4 pounds *per* fleece, and generally bearing an inferior price to the wool produced on the pastures."

P. 14. "The *sheep*, upon the *inclosed pasture land*, are a mixed breed. The Leicestershire and Lincolnshire kinds have been introduced, but they are very inferior to the most

most perfect of either sort. In some instances, attempts have been made by a few graziers, towards an improvement, but with a view rather to the ram or tup-trade, than that of making a complete and radical improvement in their respective stocks. *The wool*, in the inclosed pasture, weighs, at an average, about 7 pounds *per* fleece. It is of a pretty good quality, and sells at the same price with that of Leicestershire and Lincolnshire."

"GENERAL

"GENERAL VIEW

OF THE

AGRICULTURE

OF THE

COUNTY OF

HUNTINGDON.

AND

OBSERVATIONS ON THE MEANS OF ITS IMPROVEMENT,

WITH AN

APPENDIX, containing an account of the advantages to be derived from an improved outfal at the port of Lynn; and answers to the objections which it is supposed will be urged against that measure.

DRAWN UP FOR THE CONSIDERATION OF

The Board of Agriculture and Internal Improvement.

BY GEORGE MAXWELL,

OF FLETTON, NEAR STILTON.

1793."

THIS is another "original Report," on quarto paper, which has not been "reprinted;" it being one of the few that were ready to be delivered to the members of the Board, within the year 1793;—presently after Mr. Stone's, from the same County, was fit for delivery.

The sketch which is now before me, has also, been noticed (as Mr. Stone's) among the Reports from the EASTERN DEPARTMENT; and some valuable passages of it, relating to the *Waterlands* of *Huntingdonshire*, &c. are registered in that volume.—The BOARD, in a prefatory notice, speaks of it thus:—

P. 5. "The following valuable paper, respecting the present state of husbandry in the county of Huntingdon, and the means of its improvement, was drawn up at the desire

desire of his Grace the Duke of Buccleugh, a member of the Board of Agriculture, who requested Mr. Maxwell to lay before the Board his sentiments on the husbandry of the different counties in his neighbourhood.* It is now printed, in addition to Mr. Stone's Observations on the same subject, for the purpose of its being circulated there, that every person, interested in the welfare of that county, may have it in his power fully and deliberately to consider, the obliging communications of both these gentlemen."

Mr. MAXWELL'S QUALIFICATIONS, so far as they could be estimated, by the sketch under review, have been spoken of with approbation, in the volume above mentioned. Mr. M. at the time he wrote, appears to have been intimately acquainted with the rural concerns of Huntingdonshire, and well enabled to undertake the task of reporting them.—It is therefore (I repeat) to be regretted that the Board have not more largely profited by his superior abilities.

The Reporter thinks and writes like a professional man of the higher class. Were I inclined to cavil at any part of his MANNER, it would be at the warmth and wordiness of his arguments. On the drainage of the fens, he is evidently a partisan; and in proposing plans of improvement of the County at large, he is not less ardently desirous to impress his opinions on the minds of his readers. But this is the age of *eloquence*.

The number of pages, in the whole, are only fortyseven; and they mostly relate to the FENS;—and to PROPOSALS for IMPROVEMENTS;—not more than seven or eight of them being appropriated to the EXISTING STATE of the UPLAND PARTS of the County.

NATURAL ECONOMY.

EXTENT.—P. 16. "The general state of the county at present, is nearly as follows: it consists of 106 towns and hamlets, each of which (according to the best information I have been able to collect), after deducting the fens and skirty lands, may contain, on an average, about 1,500 acres, making in all nearly 160,000 acres; which, when added

* In p, 28, under the head "Improvement by Inclosure," the Reporter says "on this head of improvement it is the less necessary to trouble the reader"—"as the author will have another opportunity of stating his sentiments upon the subject, in the account which he intends to lay before the Board, of the agriculture of Northamptonshire:"—a work, I believe, which has not appeared.

added to the 49,000 acres before-mentioned of fen and skirty lands, the county may be supposed to contain in all about 210,000 acres, including woodlands. Other calculations, however, carry its extent considerably higher."

CLIMATURE.—P. 7. "The climate, on the whole, is pretty healthy, considering that all the East or North-east part of the county is skirted by the fens, and that but a small part of it it well supplied with water, either from springs or rivers."

WATERS.—P. 14. "The Ouze and the Nene, are the only two rivers, which communicate with the county of Huntingdon, the former falling into it near St. Neot's, and winding through several parishes to Huntingdon, and from thence through several other parishes into the Great Level of the fens, which it enters at or near Erith; and the latter dividing the Northern part of Huntingdonshire from the county of Northampton."

SOILS.—P. 7. "The county of Huntingdon possesses several distinct sorts of soil, viz. 1. Fens or Moor; 2. Skirty Land; 3. Meadow Land; 4. Strong deep stapled soil, either consisting of clay, or of gravel, with a mixture of loom; and, 5. Thin stapled light clay."

P. 14. "The borders of these rivers," (the Ouze and Nene) "are fine rich meadow land, which cannot easily be rendered more productive than they are, and perhaps contain about 1000 acres.

"Beyond the Skirty lands of the fens, and the meadow above-mentioned, we come into a strong fertile country composed either of a deep clay, with a mixture of loom or a deep gravelly soil with loom."

POLITICAL ECONOMY.

APPROPRIATION.—P. 16. "Of the 106 towns and hamlets above-mentioned, forty-one are wholly inclosed, and also a very considerable portion of the others; hence, after a deduction for woodlands, it may fairly be presumed that about one half of the high land parts of the county is uninclosed."

PROVISIONS.—P. 19. "Butcher's meat is generally 1*d.* or 1½*d. per* pound under the London market; and bread nearly as high as in London."

MANUFACTURES.—P. 19. "There are no manufactures carried on in the county, except the brewery (and that not for exportation), together with a little wool-stapling; but the women and children (at least such of them as are able to to work), may have constant employment in spinning yarn, which is put out by the generality of the country shopkeepers; though at present it is but a very indifferent means of employment, and they always prefer out of doors work when the season comes on."

RURAL ECONOMY.

ESTATES.—P. 7. "The old inclosed part is, generally speaking, in the hands of large proprietors; but property in the new inclosures, and the open fields, is pretty much diffused."

WOODLANDS.—*Timber.*—P. 20. "The county is rather thin of timber, which may be imputed to the very great demand for it in the fens."

"The *underwood* is sold at a higher price by the pole, considering the uses to which it is applied, than in most other counties; and this I take to be the natural consequence of a small stock of timber; for I believe it is a well founded maxim, that if woodlands are very full of timber, the underwood cannot be very profitable. Woods that I am well acquainted with, have produced near 20*s. per* acre *per annum*, as long as I can remember; whilst the adjoining fields, of as good, or a better quality, are let at an improved rent, of about 15*s.* or 16*s. per annum.*"*

AGRICULTURE.

FARMS.—*Sizes.*—P. 7. "There are many, of what may be called large farms, in the inclosed part of the county, viz. from £. 200 up to £. 500 *per annum.* In the open fields the farms are mostly under £. 150 and down to £. 50 *per annum.*"

STATE of HUSBANDRY.—P. 16. "To say that the best possible management is practised, would be going a great deal too far; but the county of Huntingdon, may fairly put in its claim, to be considered as one of those districts, which are approaching to somewhat like perfection; for, independent of the good quality of the different species of corn it produces, which, perhaps, is fully as much owing to some inherent principle in the soil itself, as to any other circumstance;

* We are not informed, however, how this produce, by the acre, was calculated. See EASTERN DEPARTMENT, *Secretary's Lincolnshire.*

stance; few parts of the island, if the facts relating to other counties were fairly stated, would be found to furnish a more abundant crop; and instances here are very rare, of farmers resorting to any other manure, than what is produced from their own farm-yards; a strong presumption, that either the natural soil, or the system pursued, cannot be a very bad one."

PLAN of MANGEMENT.—P. 14. "Great part of this land is still in an open field state, where each particular occupier, is necessarily tied down, to whatever course of tillage is pursued, by the parish at large. This on the best of the land, is a four years' course, viz. 1st, fallow; 2d, wheat or barley; 3d, beans; 4th, barley or wheat; and there are seven common fields in the county, which are managed in the same way."

Under the head "Improved System of Husbandry," the Reporter leads us to a novel plan of management, through the blind lane of analogy;—sometimes a specious, but, frequently, a dangerous road. His proposals, however, needed not elevated arguments to recommend them to notice.—I do not mean, by saying this, that I can follow the proposer, implicitly, through the whole of his plan.

P. 30. "To come to the point—the system I would recommend is this:—one half or two thirds of the land to be always in grass, or a still greater proportion where the soil is better adapted to grazing than to plowing; the remainder to be kept in tillage in the following divisions and successions of crop:

"1st. Clean deep winter and spring plowing for a *vegetable crop*," (?) "of whatever kind is best suited to the soil, as turnips, tares, or coleseed; this is to be hoed, but not to stand for seed.

"2d. A crop of white corn, of whatever kind is best suited to the soil, and with this, clover 20 *lb. per* acre.

"3d. Clover either grazed or mowed, but not to stand for seed.

"4th. Beans, sheep fed* and hoed, or some other *meliorating crop*" (!) "suited to the soil.

"5th. A crop of white corn suited to the soil.

"This system I should be glad to see adopted on *all soils whatever*, except fen land," (?) "which I think, from experience, is not well suited to it, for the reasons before given. It has been carried into practice on deep strong land in this county, and the following is a statement of what

"* Sheep feeding" (rather sheep-weeding) "of beans is found to be a very beneficial practice."

what relates to 30 acres, comprizing one division of the tillage land:

"1786—Clean plowing without dung—coleseed, an ordinary crop—sheep fed.

"1787—Barley—one bushel and a half *per* acre sowed—no dung—produce six quarters *per* acre.

"1788—Clover—no dung—mowed twice; an enormous crop both times.

"1789—Beans—three bushels *per* acre—sheep-fed—no dung—produce seven quarters *per* acre.

"1790—Barley—one bushel and a half *per* acre—no dung produce a little above six quarters.

"1791—Clean-deep plowing—dunged and coleseed—sheep fed—wonderfully strong.

"1792—Barley—one bushel and a half *per* acre—in many parts rotten on the ground—produce five quarters *per* acre—clover in a great measure destroyed.

"1793—Clover, an ordinary crop, partly for the reason above stated, and partly from extreme drought, but the land clean and very lusty.

"The land is worth more, by at least 5*s*. an acre, than at the beginning; and it is worthy of remark, that the other portions of the same farm, which, during the same years, have been managed exactly in the same manner, with the advantage of dung from the beginning, have borne no better crops, nor indeed quite so productive; and I am really of opinion, that if no dung had been used in 1791, the subsequent barley and clover crops would have been much better.

"After all the volumes that have been written upon farming, RATIONAL SYSTEM is the only true ground-work of general improvement;* and I should be glad to see any objection that can be offered to the above plan; for it seems to me, to admit of every crop that is useful to man or beast, without deviating from the general rule of management. Instead of coleseed, any other vegetable—instead of barley, any other white corn—instead of clover, any other grass seed—instead of beans, any other pulse grain—and instead of barley again, any other white corn may be used—whilst a small portion of either division may be set apart for supplying such seeds as from their exhausting nature are not admissible for general cultivation. In short, from experience, I will be *bold* to affirm, that (except in such cases as no human foresight can prevent) it will neither

* Who ever recommended a plan which the proposer did not think "rational"?

neither fail to afford a luxuriant produce, nor to assist our own operations of improvement."

On the enviable site, on which this plan appears to have been adopted (perhaps as an improvement of the common-field practice, abovenoticed) it may be found eligible. Indeed, I scarcely know any system of management, among the thousands that I have been obliged to *study*, which might not be found "profitable" on *such* lands!

I will go a step further, and say that, in Huntingdonshire, or any district where farms are to be be found, or where they could be profitably *created*, with "one half or two thirds" of their lands kept continually in PERMANENT HERBAGE, to raise or assist in raising manure,—Mr. Maxwell's plan might be profitable. But, in the kingdom at large, not one *arable* farm, in one hundred, bears, at present that description; nor one in ten, I apprehend, that could be profitably brought to that state.

WORKPEOPLE.—P. 18. "The price of labour is 12*d.* and 14*d.* a day to common labourers, from the end of havest until hay-time begins; then 18*d.* a day until harvest; and 2*s.* 6*d.* a day in harvest, with beer in times of carrying; and if hired by the month, or for the whole harvest, about two guineas, board and beer;—women, 6*d.* *per* day weeding; 10*d* hay-making; 1*s.* harvest-work. They work from light to dark in winter; and from six to six in the spring and summer months (except harvest, when they work from light to dark.) The poor in general have dwellings suited to their station; and as almost every one of them may grow his own potatoes, and have constant employment, if he pleases, they are naturally as little disposed to emigrate from Huntingdonshire, as from other counties."—This does not accord with Mr. Stone's account; p. 402, aforegoing.

WORKING ANIMALS.—See *Horses*, ensuing.

SEMINATION.—P. 17. "The usual allowance of seed, is, four bushels *per* acre of barley, five of beans, and three of wheat."

PRODUCE of ARABLE CROPS.—P. 17. "Were I to hazard an opinion of the produce from the best of the inclosed lands, I would say, that the average is five quarters *per* acre of barley, four of beans (which are a precarious crop, but very productive in a good season), and three and a half of wheat, meaning in all cases to include the thithes."

HORSES.—P. 18. "Mares are generally used all over the county for the same purposes as before-mentioned, with respect to the fens; but the high-land farmer does not breed near so many colts as the fen man, though in general

general they have an eye to the keeping up of their teams without going to fairs; which every farmer, attentive to his own interest, must necessarily have in view."

CATTLE.—P. 18. " This is not a breeding county for *neat* cattle; nevertheless, many of the graziers rear a few, and those are generally very good ones; but a great many cattle are fed, the choice and management of which is an article of country business pretty well understood in Huntingdonshire."

SHEEP. P. 17. " Great improvements have been made in the breeding of sheep since inclosures were adopted; and few parts of the kingdom can boast of more useful and profitable sheep, than what are kept in the inclosed parts of Huntingdonshire; though these will not bear a a comparison with some others in point of nicety in shape, and undoubtedly admit of a still farther improvement, but to what degree I will not undertake to say. They are of the polled sort, and not easily distinguished from the generality of the Lincolnshire and Leicestershire sheep, with each of which, the breed has been a good deal mixed. Their wool is good of its sort, generally fetching as high a price as any long wool whatever; and I believe weighs, upon an average, about eight pounds a fleece."

The old Huntingdonshire breed were distinguishable, from the old Leicestershire, and the old Lincolnshire breeds, by the comparative shortness of the legs and necks; the frame being altogether more compact.

"GENERAL VIEW

OF THE

AGRICULTURE

OF THE

COUNTY OF

HUNTINGDON,

DRAWN UP FOR THE

CONSIDERATION OF THE BOARD OF AGRICULTURE,

AND INTERNAL IMPROVEMENT.

BY R. PARKINSON.

1811."

MR. PARKINSON's ABILITIES as a Reporter of Rural Affairs have been noticed; in reviewing his account of RUTLANDSHIRE, aforegoing. What is there said, p. 256, might here be repeated.

The same MODE of SURVEY, which is there described, was observed in surveying HUNTINGDONSHIRE; notwithstanding the number of parishes amount to more than one hundred.

The *original* MATTER COLLECTED, respecting the UPPER GROUNDS, or natural lands, of the County, consists principally of lists of parochial memoranda, digested under separate heads, as in Rutlandshire.—In *general remarks* and *recommendations*, the Reporter has not been sparing.

The *extracts* and *papers*, inserted in this volume, are of some length. But they mostly relate to the *Fens*, and have been noticed in the EASTERN DEPARTMENT. Mr. MAXWELL'S REPORT, however, relating to the UPLANDS, is repeatedly noticed; but Mr. STONE'S is not once mentioned!

Mr.

Mr. Parkinson's INFORMANTS would seem, by a list given, to have been as numerous, as the parishes in which his enquiries were made. There appears, however, to have been only one, who afforded him much GENERAL INFORMATION; namely, Mr. SCOTT, of Chatteris;—a man of superior intelligence.—See the EASTERN DEPARTMENT, p. 212.

Regarding the work before me, as a LITERARY PERFORMANCE, it resembles, in most particulars, the Report of Rutlandshire.—It abounds more, however, in *expatiations*, on particular points;—not relating, so much, to "the agriculture of the County of Huntingdon," as to general topics of conversation, among the eloquent in agricultural disputations; in which theory and practice, good sense and no sense, accuracy and error, are interwoven; and frequently in a manner that renders them difficult to be unraveled.—In one instance, however (concerning manures) I have endeavored to unweave the webb; which, in that case, is moderately short. Some of the longer and still less coherent *dissertations* would require a volume, fully to discuss them, and bring out their enveloped errors, into open daylight. The looser *arguments*, the vague opinions, and favorite dictations,—the offspring of strongly rooted prejudice,—remind one (as I have before intimated) of the loud talkings which are heard at fair and market meetings.

The number of pages, in the body of the work, 298; in the appendix (consisting of Mr. Scott's paper on draining the fens, &c.; and Mr. Vancouver's, on the Eaubrink Cut, which is taken from his Report of *Cambridgeshire!*) fifty three.

A map of the County; and a sketch of Whittlesea Mere.

NATURAL ECONOMY.

EXTENT.—P. 1. "It contains about one hundred and ninety-four thousand nine hundred and fifty acres; the land, according to the best information I could obtain in each parish, is nearly in the state which the following table exhibits."

The totals of the several descriptions of lands exhibited are these:—

	A.	R.	P.
Arable	120,465	1	30
Meadow	20,227	0	0
Pasture	37,482	0	37
	178,174	2	27

Common

	A.	R.	P.
Brought forward	178,174	2	27
Common	4,858	0	0
Heath	160	0	0
Fen Lands	4,950	0	0*
Waste	2,165	0	0
Plantations	69	2	0
Woods	4,573	0	0
Total	194,950	0	27

CLIMATURE.—P. 8. "The climature on the whole is tolerably healthy, considering that all the east or north-east part of the county is skirted by fens, and that but a small part of it is well supplied with water from springs: indeed to all my inquiries with respect to the healthiness of the climate, except in one instance, the parishes were represented as being healthy, and this one was said to be unhealthy on account of the badness of the water, especially in the summer season."

N. P. 9. "On this subject, Mr. Scott observes, that the air of this county, varies perhaps as much as any district in the nation of the same size, the highland parts being very salubrious; but the fenny parts, through the broad shallow stagnating meres, and bad state of draining, impregnating the air at times, with immense quantities of putrifying effluvia, used to be as unhealthful as perhaps any part of Great Britain. And from this cause the inhabitants were frequently afflicted with agues, and fevers; particularly strangers who were not natives of the fens, to whom these complaints frequently proved mortal; especially if they were in low circumstances. But the county is now, through the great improvements in draining the fenny parts, tolerably healthful in general, and improves almost annually."

SOILS.—The Reporter, here, as in Rutlandshire, notices the soil or soils of each parish; but does not attempt to arrange them in districts, or to speak, in any way, of the prevailing soils of the County, at large.

Prefixed to the volume is a "map of the soil of Huntingdonshire,"—besprinkled with blotchlets, like a variolus face. But in this instance, as in others, the painting and the letterpress are strangely at variance. In the *book*, the prevailing

* This quantity, however, comprizes the "unimproved fens," only. The fen lands, which were "under the plow," are classed among the uplands!

prevailing soil of *Huntingdon*, *Buckden* and *Buckworth*, the three first parishes particularly examined, is "clay"; but, in the *map*, they are marked by "red" pustules; which denotes them to be "sandy and light highland soils."—Are the boards maps "town-made"?

For a general account of the soils of Huntingdonshire, see Mr. Maxwell's remarks p. 407, aforegoing.

FOSSILS, &c.—N. P. 16. (Q. by Mr. Scott?) "There are scarcely any minerals, except gravel and turf moor, at present discovered and noticed in the county of Huntingdon. Which greatly surprizes me, because the surface in this county in several places is very much like, and has several symptoms exactly similar to the surface of Staffordshire, where mines are found; and are now wrought to the infinite advantage of the public. Indeed I think that there are other mines to be found in the county of Huntingdon, and several other adjacent counties, where they have never yet been properly sought for. I have often thought when riding over Somersham heath, and examining the surface, &c. that there is a coal mine under it, in that part of it towards St. Ive's."

POLITICAL ECONOMY.

APPROPRIATION.—See the head, *Extent*, p. 414, aforegoing.

Commons. P. 87. "Most of the best commons in the county are now enclosed, except in the parish of Bluntisham and Earith, where some fine soil commons still lie in a barbarous state."

Common Fields?—P. 93. "More than two-thirds of this county are enclosed, and from several parishes being enclosing this year, it will be observed, that this very meritorious spirit of improvement is by no means on the decline, which is highly gratifying to any one possessing or at all valuing the welfare of his county."

Advantages.—P. 41. "The great advantage of enclosing is strikingly conspicuous in several instances, the rent being more than doubled."—See *Poor Rates*, ensuing.

PROVISIONS.—P. 269. "It may be observed generally speaking, that butchers meat is generally 1*d.* or 1½*d.* per lb. under the London markets; and that bread is nearly as high as it is in London."

FUEL.—P. 270. "In the county of Huntingdon coal is principally burnt in the better kind of houses, but common faggots,

faggots, black oak, turf, &c. and turf and wood, in most farmer's kitchens and offices, and in cottages among the lower classes, stubble, bean straw, reed, dried dung, &c."

MANUFACTURES.—P. 281. "There is a manufactory at Kimbolton for lace; poor rates increased. At St. Neot's, a very large paper mill worked by patent machinery. At Standground, two very large manufactories for sacking."

POOR RATE.—P. 44. "The poor-rates are rather more than 3*s.* 6¾*d.* on an average of the whole county; they are highest at Abbotesly and Yelling, which it will be observed are both *unenclosed parishes*, and are the lowest at Chesterton, which is an *enclosed parish;* and about half of it under the plough."

TITHE.—P. 44 "Very little more than half the parishes are exonerated from tithe, but where enclosures have taken place, this desirable event has also taken place as far as was practicable, the greatest possible advantages always being the result in every respect."

CANALS.—P. 279. "The beneficial effects of one are very sensibly felt at Ramsey, by which they convey their corn and other commodities to market, and receive timber, &c. in return, which is certainly highly advantageous, and promotes the purposes of agriculture very much, by keeping their horses at liberty for such purposes."

ROADS.—P. 274. "From the above account the state of the roads may be seen in every parish in this county, which it may be observed is frequently given as *very good or very bad*, which is indeed very much the case. There being many turnpikes in this county, they are generally speaking very good and well formed; materials are very scarce in many parts, which has occasioned a power to be given (as I am informed) to the commissioners, to pick off, all the stones that can be found on any of the farmers lands;* these stones from their being of so hard a nature, and having *no dirt* among them make very good roads, which are certainly very desirable; but the farmers complain very heavily of the great injury done them by such a proceeding."

P. 275. "The private roads are very much neglected in many parts of this county; as to roads being convex or concave, I should think none were ever intended to be made in the latter method, but many of these private roads may be so called, never perhaps having had any attempt made at their improvement since the time they were originally

* Is this information authentic? If it is, was it *right* to give the commissioners *such* a power? The *public*, no doubt, may be benefited by it.

nally laid out, though that might be a century ago; they are really many of them in such a state as no person could scarcely credit, remaining ridge and furrow as they were at first, when laid out, worn into great holes in the middle or at one side, so that all wet must remain upon them especially as the drains by the sides of the roads have been so neglected, that there is scarcely a vestige or mark of them remaining."

SOCIETIES of AGRICULTURE.—P. 286. "There is one established at Kimbolton."

RURAL ECONOMY.

TENANTED ESTATES.

ESTATES.—P. 24. "The old enclosed part is said to be, generally speaking, in the hands of large proprietors; but property in the new enclosures and open-fields is much diffused." Mr. P. gives a list of "the names of noblemen, gentlemen, &c. who own estates in this county."

TENURES.—P. 31. "Rather more than half the county is of a freehold tenure, the remainder, (with the exception of about one thirtieth part of the whole, which is leasehold) is copyhold."

FENCES.—It appears, by Mr. Parkinson's parochial memoranda, that the prevailing farm fences of Huntingdonshire are "quick thorn hedges."

N. P. 94. "Mr Scott mentions, that Mr. John Ashton of St. Ives was shewing him a close where he had planted a white-thorn hedge eight or ten years before; but it grew very slowly, although he kept it very clean, and it was well guarded with posts and rails, and he mucked it very frequently; but it was a hot burning soil. Whereupon Mr. Scott advised him to put clay to the young thorn plants instead of muck, and cut them down, which he did, and they have continued in a healthful thriving state ever since."

Sodburning.—Mr. P. is an advocate for this mode of "Improvement."—I insert the subjoined passage; as it may serve to corroborate my own ideas, on the effect of sodburning cool, clayey lands.—See my YORKSHIRE.

P. 207. "I have known the practice of paring and burning from a very early age; my first knowledge of it was on land which was probably as improper for it as any land could be, the soil being clay which burnt to a red ash, something

something like brick, but notwithstanding all this, the grass was always finer and of a better quality ever after, and this, although the land was far from being treated as it ought to have been, as I do not recollect its ever having the manure produced from the crops grown on it, and carried to it again. I am clearly of opinion, that there are many hundreds of acres in this county of poor stiff coarse clay, covered now with *whin* or *thorn-weed*, thistles, large overgrown ant-hills, and a sort of coarse bad *hassocky* grass, and not keeping more than a ewe and half an acre, which if pared and burnt and the crops taken from it, which I have directed in the 7th section of Chap. IV* it would not only produce the advantages there laid down, but when it came to be laid down again would keep infinitely better double the number of sheep and cattle, a convincing proof of the *land being improved*."

TENANCY.—P. 45. "There are no leases granted in the greater part of the parishes, and in some of them they are only made for three years, which is much too short a space of time to be of any material benefit to either landlord or tenant. It may be observed that the leases run from three to four, to six, seven, nine, twelve, fourteen, and twenty-one years."

COVENANTS.—P. 37. "In three-fifths of the parishes, the repairs are done by the landlord, in one-fifth of them by the landlords and tenants conjointly, and the remaining fifth by the landlords or tenants solely."

RENT.—P. 41. "The rents run from 5*s*. per acre, to 30*s*. per acre; in a very few instances to as high as 40*s*. in one instance to as high as 120*s*.; but that it will be seen is in the neighbourhood of Huntingdon, where such rents are given for small pieces of land, for the conveniency of gentlemen, tradesmen, &c. keeping a horse cow, &c."

WOODLANDS.

ON the subject of Woodlands, proper, I find nothing *original* in this Report. The observations of "a former Reporter" (Mr. Maxwell) are inserted. And a short notice of Mr. Welstead, steward of the duke of Manchester, on *grubbing up* woods, is likewise inserted. But Mr. Parkinson's end and aim, in his chapter "Woods and Plantations,"

* A section which does not appear in the book.

Plantations," is to reiterate and extend, in a desultory way, his arguments in favor of

TIMBER TREES in HEDGES:—See his *Rutlandshire*, p. 265, aforegoing.—By his parochial memoranda, under the head " Enclosing," the hedgerows of Huntingdonshire are tolerably well stocked with *oak*, *ash* and *elm*.

Mr. P. not only recommends planting trees, in hedgerows, for *shade;* but " in the angles of fields, and such like places," for *rookeries;* especially in the fens, where " those birds are much courted, from their destroying vast quantities of the grubs, so destructive to crops" ; p. 170.

For Mr. Parkinson's opinion, respecting *Rooks*, see that article, ensuing.

AGRICULTURE.

FARMS.—*Sizes.*—At the close of his table, " Size of Farms, Rent." (p. 41.)—Mr. P. says, " It will be observed by the foregoing list that there are many large farms in Huntingdonshire, though small ones very much preponderate."

Plans of Farms P. 37. " The farm-houses are in many cases inconveniently situated for the occupation of the land, and of course whatever is produced must be had at an expense considerably beyond what would be necessary, in case the contiguity and convenience which generally attach themselves to enclosed farms, were established."—This topic has already been discussed. See Mr. Donaldson's Report, p. 349, aforegoing.

Draining Farms.—P. 204. "Under-draining has been done in some of the parishes in this county, by the *mole plough*, which is much approved of, on those strong clay soils, taking the precaution to make a great number of head grips or ditches which latter are the best, and should be made deeper than the mole plough has gone. Great care must be taken to keep the ends of the mole plough drains open as they are to silt up."

I am glad to be able to register an instance of this implement being received, in some degree, into practice.

PLAN of MANAGEMENT.—The Reporter has assigned no inconsiderable part of his Volume to this subject; which, as I have repeatedly intimated, allows of immeasurable space for its discussion.

His section " Expences and Profit of four Rotations of Cropping," fills nearly forty pages; and that entitled " Course

"Course of Crops," furnishes an addition of twelve pages; beside incidental remarks, interspersed in other sections; and this, it may be said, without bringing out any thing, which a practical man, or even a student, can profit by.—In those long stories, the begining is lost in the middle, and this forgotten before the reader has reached the close; where rarely any useful result is drawn, to reward him for his labor in going through them.

The only part of the three sheets of letter press, now under view, which calls for particular notice, here, relates to Mr. Maxwell's remarks on this subject. See p. 409, aforegoing.

After copying the whole of Mr. Maxwell's system, and his remarks upon it, Mr. P. says, p. 111.—"I must enter my decided protest against the system of farming without dung, here laid down by the reporter from whom the above is extracted, as being pregnant with the most mischievous tendency, and striking at the main spring of all agricultural improvements, for I consider manure properly disposed of to be so;"—and proceeds to fill, page after page, with relevant and irrelevant strictures, concerning the point to be settled; drawing, in this case, his conclusion.

P. 114. "Upon the whole I differ with him in respect to *dung and quantity of seed,* and on account of his seeming wish to bring such a system into *universal* use; I agree with him in many of his remarks, and especially in that respecting 'common broad-cast husbandry;' only I wish for the adoption of a practical as well as rational and profitable system of management, adapted not to a *few acres* but to the *kingdom in general.*"

It really did not strike me, while sitting in judgement on Mr. Maxwell's system, that he meant to discard, altogether, from English husbandry, the use of dung! I did not conceive that a writer of Mr. Maxwell's mind could *sport* so ill grounded and impractical an idea. I rather thought that Mr. M's practice had been principally confined to the Mudlands of Huntingdonshire; and I was willing to put the most favorable construction on his words. He does not *hold out* any such idea; which is only *indirectly* conveyed.—I therefore deemed it right to smile at an error which I was not aware that any practical man could suffer from; rather than to enter into a serious refutation of it.

If Mr. Maxwell would allow me to make an apology, for what Mr. Parkinson seems to consider as dangerous doctrine, it would be by saying, that, about the time Mr. M. wrote, an elevated notion had gone forth, that plants of of the leguminous or "broad leaved" kind, so far from *exhausting* soils of their vegetable nutriment, not only draw their own nourishment from the atmosphere, but actually *inhaust* them,—fill them with food for succeeding crops!—And Mr. M. it is pretty plain, had imbibed some portion, at least, of that sublime theory. His expression, "meliorating crop," is a sufficient evidence.

WORKPEOPLE.—At the foot of the list of parish notices, under the head "Price of Labor," we find the following statement.—P. 268. "The above accounts give an average of the weekly wages being at about 11*s.* 3*d.* in winter and 13*s.* 8*d.* in summer, exclusive of meat and drink, which are given in some places, and of the harvest months, in respect to which there is a great deal of difference in some parishes."

P. 285. "*Servants* live very well in this county, pork and dumplings, or puddings and potatoes being the food of threefourths of the parishes; with milk pottage, or milk and bread for breakfast, and in the harvest in many of these they are allowed mutton, beef, &c. in the remainder of the parishes they are kept on beef, mutton, pork, bacon, dumplings and puddings, have milk, &c. as in the others for breakfast."

WORKING ANIMALS.—P. 227. "I observed but one farmer who used oxen in this county."

P. 230. "Although ox teams might be very profitably made use of in many parts of this county, it seems to be only impracticable on account of the perverseness of servants, for in conversing with farmers on the subject, their general remark was that they should never be able to get their men to execute it. I observed one farmer particularly to say that he had used oxen, but his men used very unpleasant and refractory expressions in his presence, and his scheme ended in the death of one ox from being overdriven, and in another being very much injured, and this in the neighbourhood of a much respected nobleman's estate where many oxen are drawn; but prejudice, and especially that of labourers, is a wonderful thing."

ARABLE MANAGEMENT.

TILLAGE.—*Plowing.*—P. 99. "It may be seen by recurring to the foregoing pages on this subject, that in some places it is done by pairs of horses abreast, and by three abreast in the fens, where the men are very expert at ploughing, never having a driver, but guiding their horses by a line; it is said that a fen ploughman has been known to win a considerable wager by ploughing an acre of high land

land without a single balk, keeping his mares always in a trot, even at the land's end, those being the two conditions of the bet; a proof not only of his own expertness, but that his plough was constructed upon true principles of mechanics. On strong land for the first ploughing four horses at length, and a driver are generally used, and in some instances *six* or *eight* horses and a driver, this is for *summer fallowing*."

Summer Fallow.—P. 102. "Summer fallows are practised, and said to be essentially necessary, over all this county, with the exception of the following parishes.

"At Broughton—Fallowing said to be unnecessary, being better to sow tares instead of it. At Buckden and Conington—Summer fallows not necessary. Haile Weston—The system of summer fallows might be abolished, were the open-fields enclosed. Hemingford Grey and Abbots—Summer fallows unnecessary and very improper. Huntingdon and Kimbolton—Summer fallows unnecessary. Morborn and Overton Longville—Summer fallows unnecesary. Paxton Magna—Summer fallows not necessary, seeds might be substituted for that purpose. Ramsey and St. Neot's—Summer fallows not necessary. St. Ives'—Rapes or tares instead of summer fallowing. Somersham, Stebington, and Stewkley Magna—Summer fallows not necessary. Stewkley Parva—Summer fallows not necessary on dry land, but very necessary on the strong land, more barley by two quarters per acre being grown where it is practised. By the above account it will appear that very little more than one-sixth part of the county disapproves of the practice of summer fallows, and from the strong-rooted bias which farmers have in this county, especially for this which I must call an abominable practice, (!) it will be long ere the system is banished, notwithstanding the very obvious benefits of so doing."

MELIORATION.—The species of melioration of soils, which require to be spoken of, in this place, are.

Yard Dung.	Lime.
Compost.	Gypsum.
Sheepfold.	Shade.

Under the head "Manures," the Reporter arranges his parochial notices on that subject.—By them it appears that YARD DUNG and SHEEPFOLD are the prevailing means of bettering the condition of arable lands, in Huntingdonshire:—the *dung* being principally used for the *barley* crop, *sheepfold*, for *wheat:* not in the common fields, only; but in the arable inclosures:—a practice, which, it is probable, originated in the former; and has been implicitly continued in the latter, through habit.

In

In reviewing this Reporter's Rutlandshire, I was urged to speak, with freedom, on the extraordinary doctrines there propagated, concerning the subject now under cons deration. See p. 268, aforegoing, and I am here, again, arrested and irresistibly constrained, to examine, further, his novel theories of melioration.

1. *Farmyard Manure* and " Compost Dung."—Concerning these articles, we are already in possession of some of this Writer's sentiments. See as above—In the subjoined extract, however, we shall find a few practical remarks, on the advantages of *composting* yard manure, with mold, or earthy materials.

P. 212. " There are other advantages accruing to the making of compost, especially in the mixture of horse, cow and pig dung, the manure being much more efficient when thus put together than though used separately, horse dung being of a hot light nature, cow dung of a very coherent kind, and pig dung being of a very saponaceous nature and very rich, (the latter is much preferred in Huntingdonshire as a manure); thus when all well combined together the very best of manures is produced; the next advantage is that what by leading the manure, making the compost-hill, turning it over, and spreading it on the land, there can scarcely be any one part of the land on which it is thus spread but what must reap the benefit of their combined qualities. Another very material advantage of compost is, the opportunity of adding whatever kind of earth may be thought proper for the land, on which it is about to be laid, or even for particular parts of a field, such, for instance, as clay to sand or loose gravel, and sand or gravel to clay soils, but for the clays of this county gravel would be found most beneficial. From the very great care which is taken of *stubbles* in this county, *immense quantities of the most beneficial manures would be made;* and although the expense of compost-making may seem great to those who have never been used to making it, yet as it certainly is to be made for about 1*s.* 6*d.* per load, I hope that will not be made an objection to so great an improvement, but that it will be universally adopted to the total subversion of the ruinous practice of *sheep-folding.* I know of no manure at once so cheap and so good; when properly made it is reduced to fine *garden earth,* which certainly is the most proper food for all plants, besides *it is prepared* and got into this state *previous* to its application; while it stands to reason that *long strawy dung* being applied, it must have *time* to get *reduced and incorporated with the soil before it can become food for plants,* thus here is a self-evident advantage. When dung is laid on land

land in a long state, though it may have had much *salt* in it at the time, yet there is certainly great opportunity for the sun and wind to dry and exhale from it its most fertilizing particles.

"In the ploughing and harrowing process long dung is liable to be drawn in lumps, so that some parts of a field get no manure, and others too much, while compost dung is not liable to this very great objection; as it is readily dispersed, every plant receives from it an equal benefit; there is therefore a much greater probability of an even crop of corn yielding much more grain, and probably not so much straw. In the turnip crop long dung is in every respect objectionable; in the first place it is a certain encourager of the fly, in harrowing in the seed it sticks in the harrows, and thereby the turnip seed is drawn into patches, consequently the crop must be so; if the crop be harrowed after it is up, the long straws are the occasion of many plants being pulled up; and lastly, in hoeing, it prevents, by hanging and clogging up the hoe, that operation from being done as it ought."

It is, in a great measure, to obviate this inconveniency that dung is turned up in the yard, or piled in the field;—the very practice that is so evilly spoken of, by this Reporter. —How ill considered, and of course inconsistent, are this Writer's *discourses.*

Compost.

I have long been a friend to the forming of composts; as may be seen in my Minutes of Agriculture. I am "free to confess," however, that I have never practised it, on the *grand scale* which is recommended by Mr. Parkinson;—nor with earth and *stubble* alone! I have, nevertheless, had sufficient experience to know that, in ordinary situations, the quantity of *offal mold* to be found in the corners of farmsteads, and by the sides of roads, of a quality that is fit for the purpose, *is soon worked up.* And, were the practice to be made general, and to be carried on, in the manner, and to the extent, recommended by Mr. P. no inconsiderable part of the soil of a country would be required for the purpose. Yet we have no intimation where the "immense quantities," and the different qualities, spoken of, are to be *procured.*

Where marl, or other fertilizing fossil, or where the mud of an estuary, or large river, or the soil of a deep salt marsh (see the Western Department, article *Sea Sludge)* can be had at a moderate expence;—compost of a superior quality may be formed. But, in common cases, I know of one method, only, of providing mold of a proper quality, and in great quantity, suitable to this purpose.

This

This method I have practised; and I take the present apt opportunity of mentioning it to my readers.—To those who may be in the habit of making clean fallows; and of forming compost; or of flooring their strawyard, or bottoming and covering their dung piles,—with mold; the hint may be of use.

It is merely that of going over a clean fallow with a cart, and filling it with soil, taken up in single spadefuls; especially where the surface is seen to lie the highest. The next plowing or harrowing will level the surface; which will be rather improved, than disfigured, by the operation.

I cannot quit this topic without conveying to my readers some further strictures of this Reporter, concerning the "SALTS" and "BLACK-WATER" of dung hills.

P. 211. "YARD DUNG.—By the general account of right manures, it may be seen that this is the usual application in this county, except sheep-folding, and it is made use of in a long state, being either immediately carted on the land or laid out into hills, or turned over in the fold-yards; this last is the most general practice, and is the worst of all, as from being thrown, a fermentation is caused, and also a very long exhalation, both by the moisture it naturally retains, and continual rains falling upon it; from which not only greatest part of the nutritious qualities of the dung, but all the salts are evaporated from it, the latter running off in copious quantities of black water; and the fermentation is not strong enough to kill the seeds of the weeds, which may be seen from weeds growing on the tops of dunghills which lay long enough to give the seeds time to vegetate. I know from experience, that was the dung applied in its raw state about one month after it is made, and mixed up with earth, it would produce three loads of good and efficient manure, where one load is now produced; and the manure so made when applied to the land would cause infinitely better crops, than the manure made in the present method. It is worthy the farmer's strictest attention to preserve by every means in his power, the salts of dung, for on them depends his well doing in all agriculture, and I have no doubt but in the present slovenly method of making manure, or rather I should have said management of it, that one load of straw dung has (if it were weighed) more salts in it than three loads, after it has undergone all the evaporations which he so unnecessarily exposes it to; it therefore behoves every one concerned in agricultural pursuits to give this subject the most serious consideration."*

The

* I have purposely refrained, in this instance, from *marking* the wildnesses observable in the Reporter's wanderings over the field of melioration:

The Reporter and a friend having tried some experiments with this said "black water" (as others have done) *without success*, he thus *accounts for it*.

P. 215. "Before I leave this subject I must say a word or two respecting the effects of the black water which is seen to run from manure hills, and caution every one to prevent its escape as much as possible, which is alone to be effected by making the dung into compost, where it is absorbed, and thus becomes the very essence of manure; whereas if once it escapes it can never be applied to *equal advantage*, either by watering land with it or in any other way. When I lived at Doncaster, I applied this black water, of a seemingly much richer quality than it even commonly is, to one land of meadow as an experiment, thinking that I must have a very superabundant crop of hay, and at the same time very much improve my land for future crops, but I was far from finding this to be the case. Having some lucern growing in *drills*, I then turned my thoughts to that, and watered one drill of it very sufficiently, and another not so much; I could not perceive that I had benefited it by these applications, indeed, on the contrary, part of my crop was even injured by it. Being much puzzled by these experiments, and being intimate with the late Mr Drummond of Bawtry, a very intelligent and able agriculturist; I informed him of the failure of my experiments, and found that he had been doing the same thing with the like result. I therefore consider it as *blood*, which while *in the body* is the *spring of life*, but when once taken thence, it can never be *returned into the body*, to be of the *least service*, but on the very contrary it must *injure* what it before was the *sole cause of sustaining*." So much for analogical reasoning, from premises that have no natural analogy.

The experimentalist ought, surely, when he published his experiment, to have explained, in more explicit terms, whether the black water which he used, was merely such; or whether some of the sediment or mud, which is usually deposited beneath such water, was mixed with it.—If the former, he might with nearly equal propriety, and similar expectation, have made use of some well browned beverage, such as is not unusually drank at table, under the inappropriate name of toast-and-water.—Limpid water may be *colored*, in a variety of ways; without adding much (if at all) to its virtues, as a manure.—A few chips of recently felled oak would give a *height* of *coloring* to as much water

melioration:—not merely to avoid the endlessness of the task; but lest I might thereby interrupt the *entertainment* of my readers.

water as is generally seen in a dung yard;—would, indeed, make it much *blacker*, than the BLOOD of a DUNGHILL!—which, when spread over ground, in quantity, as a mean of irrigation, may communicate to it a favorable effect; especially when applied during heavy rains, when some part of the *substance* of the dung is necessarily borne away with it, to the ground. But *clarified* dung water, carried to a garden, in pails, or to the field in a water cart, has never, I believe, been found to answer the expectation of the experimenter.

2. *Sheepfolding.*—This practice, the Reporter styles "pernicious"—"miserable"—"abominable"—"ruinous!"—Like other practices, it is good or bad, right or wrong, according to the application of it. It is proper or improper, agreeably to circumstances.—On the southern chalk hills, where there are extensive sheep walks, which are too thinly soiled, too ungenially situated in regard to climature, and at too great a distance from the homestead to which they severally belong, to be profitable as arable land;—on which walks, a breed of sheep, adapted to folding, are depastured; having open arable lands adjoining, upon which they are driven to the fold, without stepping off their owner's occupation;—*there*, sheepfolding has long been "the main spring of husbandry." And any light lands that have not been commonly folded upon, yet where given circumstances will allow that a proper variety of sheep can be employed in thus *manuring* them,—the advantage will generally be found striking. But on lands that have been folded upon, every third or sixth year, during centuries of time, and especially if such lands are in a state of inclosure,—and the sheep are to be driven through dirty lanes, perhaps, some distance, from the pasture to the fallow, miring their coats and dropping their dung as they go,—and the breed of sheep altogether unfit for such employment, even on high open downs, (circumstances, these, which belong to many or most of the folded lands and flocks of Huntingdonshire)—it is no wonder that the evils of *such* a practice should be seen and felt. But how "pernicious"—how "abominable" it is to condemn, without exception, the entire practice of sheepfolding, because it may *there* be *improperly conducted.*

3. *Lime* and *Gypsum.*—Here we shall find the Reporter entering the depths of *agricultural Chemistry!* and furnishing his readers with a fair specimen of his manner of writing on rural subjects.

P. 209. "It may be observed by the reader that where lime has been applied in this county, the produce does not seem to be increased, but I am of opinion that it does not arise from lime not being proper for land, but from the misapplication

application of it, and from not well knowing the nature of it: lime has been understood by many to be a vegetable matter, when it is on the contrary calcareous; a corrector but no promoter of vegetable substances, consequently it has, from this ignorance of its qualities, and its being misapplied, been very frequently condemned by men, otherwise of real judgment and of long experience; it has by them been frequently applied *instead of dung;* it ought never to be applied but where there is a sufficiency of vegetable matter to produce vegetable plants. When I wrote the first edition of my Experienced Farmer, I was not very well acquainted with the true nature of lime; what gave me the correctest idea of the great difference between vegetable matter and calcareous substances, was the application of gypsum and Nova Scotia plaster in America.

"The opinion of farmers in that country of lime, &c. is in all cases as utterly wrong as it has been, and still is in many instances in England, for they chiefly apply it there as a *manure*, expecting it like dung to promote the growth of plants. The soil of America being so very poor, where I sowed turnips in drills with a small quantity of *compost dung* and *gypsum*, &c. it made the difference of a *moderate crop* and *none at all*, or about three to one; but where no *compost* was applied, the *gypsum* by *itself* was of no avail. From this and many other similar instances which have fallen under my observation, I am thoroughly convinced that *lime ought never to be applied* but on land that has *much vegetable matter in it*, either from *very high dunging*, before lime is applied, or from some other cause having naturally a *superabundance of vegetable matter*. On old land newly ploughed up, and *not pared and burnt*, acting as a corrector, it gives more grain and less straw. I do not think that lime can be advantageously applied to any green crop, as most green crops want much vegetable matter, except after turnips are sown in hot sandy land; if it was spread on the surface it would be serviceable, especially if it were done after rain; I found gypsum to be of very great service when thus applied on the hot soils of America. I have also found it to be beneficial on the clover crop in that country, where the soil had any vegetable matter in it to support the plant, but of no effect at all where the land was not in what is called good heart. I have seen some hand-bills and advertisements out in London, offering gypsum for sale as a manure, I wonder that farmers can be induced to buy it as a *manure*, because if they would take a quantity of it without *earth*, it would not suffer any plant to grow, and if mixed with half the quantity of earth, or in equal portions of it and earth, plants would be only then produced

produced *(if at all)* of a very weak kind. Thus we may compare what it *would* do on a *large scale,* from what it *will* do on a *small one.* I do not think that lime is so great a corrector as gypsum; I also know that the *sole* use of the latter arises from its quickly cementing, and thus preventing (where moisture has been previously given as well as manure) the heat of the sun from exhaling the moisture or nutritious quality of the manure; the plant is consequently kept moist at the root, it therefore grows well, and quickly gets a shade from its own leaves." *

How does this agree with the idea of calcareous substances being correctors? For we are here told that gypsum is a greater corrector than lime. Yet its "*sole*" use "arises from its quickly cementing, &c.": † thus forming, merely, a sort of parasol, or sun shade. This aptly leads us to division

4. *Shade.*—What is said on this species of melioration is found in the section "Hemp;" which is not a prevailing article of farm produce, in Huntingdonshire, where "there is very little of this article grown,"—and would therefore seem to have been brought forward to give an opportunity of explaining the benefit of SHADE, in the *production* of *vegetables.*

P. 145. "There is but very little of this article grown in this county, though there is a great deal of land adjoining to the fens where it might be grown to very great advantage, while, at the same time that it would yield a great profit, it would be a much better preparation for a wheat crop than a summer fallow. It has been supposed that even *grassing* hemp on land left a kind of manure on it, but from the experiments which I have seen tried, or tried myself, I believe that any *other substance* would have the like effect; but as it is required in the natural process attending hemp, that it should be laid on land, *two birds are killed with one stone.* As it has always been observed that where hemp has been laid to wither, that such spaces of land have borne better crops than other lands adjoining, it follows that if the land where the hemp was grown, was to have its own crop laid on it to wither, it would be benefited thereby; thus so far from hemp injuring land, as is often supposed, it would prove a real benefit. As a convincing proof of this I mention that, being in Norfolk, I was shown by Sir John Sebright's steward a crop of wheat which was growing on a piece of land, which had been under preparation for that crop

* The above is the whole of Mr. P's section, "Lime."

† The word *sole*, in the Report, is printed in italics.

crop in the summer before, and on the middle of the field there had been laid some hemp for the purpose of withering it; the square space where the hemp had laid was clearly discoverable, and the wheat growing there, was not only stronger in the straw, but finer and much heavier in the ear. This happened before I went to America, and from it, as may be seen in my first edition of the Experienced Farmer, I had formed some idea of the very great utility of excluding sun and wind from the soil as much as possible; of this I became thoroughly convinced from my experience in America, where the heat is so very extreme. I am now therefore decidedly of opinion, that the benefit resulting to land from grassing hemp on it, proceeds merely from the exclusion of sun and wind, and that could land be covered with *tiles* or *boards*, that the effects would be more beneficial from so doing, than from covering it with hemp, flax, &c. But this latter method can only be done for tillage purposes, as the covering up grass land, would destroy the roots of the grass, and turn them into real vegetable substance, which fairly proves the great advantages of doing so much on tillage lands, as thereby the roots of corn, weeds, grasses, &c. would be reduced to vegetable matter, so needed in the production of all crops. I observe in Mr. Young's Annals of Agriculture, an instance of the beneficial effects of grassing hemp on a piece of clover, which having had one year's crop taken from it, was by such means enabled to produce another crop in the next year, equal to the first year's; now, as in the countries where hemp is grown it cannot cover *much land*, and there being many places where it cannot be grown, I wish to impress it upon my reader's attention, that these benefits do not result from any natural or peculiar quality in the hemp itself, but purely from the *shade* it affords to the land. Under the head, course of crops, there is an account of one for several years without any dung; the land where that was done was in all probability of such a nature, that it would produce smothering crops for any length of time; but by what must this be occasioned? certainly by shade and the exclusion of sun and wind, which supply it with vegetable matter; but however I must here again observe, that there are but few spots of land where this is to be effected *without dung*, and that all lands may furnish an adequate supply of dung for their own purposes. There are nevertheless many places where hemp, wheat, and beans might be taken to eternity, as where land is of that very superior quality at the beginning, two of those crops so overshadow the land, that neither sun nor wind can penetrate to it during the hot months, both hemp and beans being in full leaf during these months

months, and then it is but exposed during the cold winter months, greater part of which time exhalation is prevented by snow or frosts. This is a great reason in favour of the hemp culture, but there are still further reasons for its being a good crop for land, where it is of a quality proper for its production; it is to be observed that four bushels of hemp-seed is very thick sowing, six of such seeds not being larger than one bean, and that the leaves of hemp are much more smothering than those of beans, and also that in its early stage it grows so remarkably thick, that it shades land much more than any other crop; the leaves of hemp are also so numerous and very broad, that a great part of the rains and dews which fall is taken in by the leaves for the support of the plant, and the land is kept dry under them, (as an illustration of this particular point, it may be proper to observe that this is the case under large trees from their taking in the dews and rain by their leaves,) so that if the land has been well prepared and weeded, it will be a total impossibility for weeds to grow under a hemp crop. I have known an instance nigh Wisbech, of hemp being sown on land where many of the couch roots were left in it at that time, and when it came to be pulled, the roots of couch were nearly all destroyed. Upon conversing with the farmer to whom this land belonged, he informed me that he had had that land for many years under hemp, wheat and beans, that during the time it was under the two latter crops, it got to have couch in it again, but that the hemp crop always destroyed the couch: this he thought was effected by the natural *quality* of the hemp; this was, however, by no means the case, and arose only from its being very thickly planted, for had it been planted at *the distance* which it is necessary to plant *beans*, that they may prove productive, he would have found that hemp would no more kill couch, than beans would." *

General Observations on Manure, and the Food of Plants.—Throughout the chaotic mass of matter, here brought together, we catch some practical ideas; such, I mean, as have risen out of the Writer's own practice, or from observation on the practice of others.

Regarding the first and second species of fertilization, above spoken of, namely, *yard manure* and *sheep fold*, I have nothing farther to say, here. Nor is there any thing, respecting the third,—*lime* and *gypsum*,—on which I have more

* Does not this unsay what had just been said about beans "over-shadowing the land?"—And what a knockdown blow is it to *drilling!*

more to offer; excepting what relates to the *incrustation* of the surface of the soil, by gypsum, in America; and the suggestion that lime may answer a similar purpose, in England. And, on this subject, I have only to say that I do not, cannot, comprehend how a *crust* is to be formed over an acre of ground, by a few bushels of gypsum, of such a texture, as to permit seedling plants to rise and flourish; and, at the same time, to prevent the moisture in the soil from evaporating.

It is Mr. Parkinson's new opinion on the effect of SHADE IN GENERAL, *in promoting vegetation*, that is most entitled to consideration, in this place.

It must be known to every well experienced cultivator that what is called a "smothering crop," as a full crop of pease or vetches, a crop of potatoes heavily topped, or a rank crop of Buckweet, not only "smothers weeds," but leaves the soil in a mellow well colored state; and, generally, enables it to throw out *one* productive crop, in immediate succession. But, unless on the mudbanks, on which Mr. Parkinson's observations are founded, or other rich soils, it fails not to cause an excess of exhaustion, which requires the soil to be replenished by manure; or to be suffered to remain in a state of herbage, until it has recovered itself. Even the potatoe crop, tho generally highly manured for, is *now* pretty well understood to produce that effect.

Full crops, of the above description, evidently act as STIMULANTS; and exhaust the soil, not only by their own produce; but, under ordinary circumstances, enable it to throw out and mature another crop, in succession.

How, it may be asked, is this beneficial effect produced? To my mind, the cause appears obvious; the effect being a necessary result, I conceive, of an ordinary process of nature.

MARCH 1814.—This article was written, in December and January, 1812-13; when I was, instinctively as it were, impelled to pursue the subject now under consideration; until I saw, with sufficient clearness, to satisfy myself, the rationale of this important natural process; and intended to have inserted it, in this place. But having, since, read Sir H. DAVY'S ELEMENTS of AGRICULTURAL CHEMISTRY, with attention; and finding in them some positions which appear to me to be insecurely founded, I have determined, on revising this article for the press, to reserve my remarks until I shall have a favorable opportunity of drawing together my ideas, concerning the VEGETABLE ECONOMY and the FOOD of PLANTS:—Subjects that have long engaged some share of my attention.

ARABLE

Arable Crops.—Under the section " Seed and Produce," is a tabular statement of the quantity of seed sown, and of produce reaped, in the cultivation of the five following species of arable crops, in the several parishes of the County. The average quantities are these (p. 126).

Wheat	$2\frac{3}{4}$	bushels sown	$20\frac{1}{4}$	produced.
Barley	$4\frac{1}{2}$	——— ——	$30\frac{3}{4}$	———
Oats	$5\frac{1}{4}$	——— ——	25?	———
Pease	$4\frac{7}{10}$	——— ——	$20\frac{9}{10}$	———
Beans	$4\frac{9}{10}$	——— ——	21.	———

Wheat.—The only particular, in the culture of this crop, which calls for attention, here, relates to the

Stubble.—P. 128. " Stubbles; these are more correctly managed in this county than in any which has fallen under my observation; in many parts of it they are mown and harvested as carefully as any other part of the produce, being brought home, stacked up and taken proper care of, for thatching the following years, stacks, buildings, &c. &c. Farmers here have learned the great necessity of doing this, which is far from being the case elsewhere, many farmers insisting that stubble *being ploughed in* acts as manure, and is therefore beneficial; but farmers in this county observe, (which is perfectly right), that so doing is a real injury to the succeeding crops when ploughed in, the stubble leys between one furrow and another, letting in the wet, so that every fall of snow or rain, gets intermixed with the soil, and thus the land gets much more wet than it would otherwise do; thus the land is in winter quite starved, and in summer for the same reason, the sun and wind so penetrate into it that it is then much too dry, consequently ploughing in stubbles is a real injury; and every one must allow that the grand desideratum is to keep land *dry* in *winter*, and as *moist* as possible in *summer*."

When the wheat crop is intended to be followed by another crop to be sown the ensuing autumn or spring, on one plowing, the practice, here recommended, is eligible; and not peculiar to Huntingdonshire.

Rape Seed.—Tho the following account may be thought to border on the miraculous, I think it right to insert it, here, on Mr. Parkinson's authority.

P. 138. " There have been many prejudices against letting this crop stand for seed, on account of its doing injury to land; this is certainly an unfounded prejudice; I have myself known an instance of land bearing this crop for fourteen years and sustaining no injury, and I was informed by a very intelligent agriculturalist at St. Neot's, that a piece of land in a field had been in rape-seed for eight years,

years, while the other parts of it had been managed with other crops, and that land which has grown the rapes is by far the best in the field. Such instances prove the crop to be an advantageous one to land, as well as a profitable one to the farmer; and were the straw to be burnt on the land, as has already been mentioned, it would be still more advantageous in every respect. The same gentleman at St. Neot's is decidedly of opinion, that landlords preventing their tenants from paring and burning, and growing rapes for seed, cause a real injury to both parties, and that the process would improve instead of injuring land."

On the fens, marshlands, and mudbanks of Huntingdonshire,—something resembling the above results may have taken place. But let not the owners of its upper-grounds listen, too attentively, to the doctrine held out.

TURNIPS.—P. 133. " Soil. Chiefly gravel and skirty lands, but some sown on almost all soils."

HEMP.—See the article, *Melioration*, p. 430, aforegoing.

CULTIVATED HERBAGE.—In the section, " Artificial Grasses," the Reporter has given a list of parochial memoranda, terminating with this remark:—P. 158. " By the above account it will be seen that nearly five-sixths of the parishes are in the habits of growing artificial grasses, a great proof of their acknowledged utility."

Half a century ago, this indirect praise of the Huntingdonshire practice, might have conveyed meaning and utility. But where is now the County or district of England, in which the utility of " artificial grasses!" is not understood.

GRASS LANDS.—P. 161. " One very great reason, for the land of this description" (poor clayey soils) " laying in pasture in its present very neglected state, is to be attributed in a great degree to its laying so *very remote from the farm buildings*."

Mr. P. very properly recommends, where a sufficient extent of those lands lie together, (belonging of course to one proprietor) to build homesteads within them, and to divide and drain them. At present, they certainly impress the mind of a traveller with ideas not very favorable to the rural management of the County.

Watering Stock.—In the section, " Waters," Mr. P. has inserted parish notices, as in his Rutlandshire; and, at the close, says p. 19, " by the above account it may be seen that the greater part of the county is watered by ponds."

LIVESTOCK.

In a chapter bearing this title, is set down, tablewise, the number of horses, and of each description of cattle, in every parish

parish (I believe) in the County. The totals stand thus (p. 223.)

Cows 4,809.—*Stores* 709.—*Fatting Cattle* 1,198.—*Calves reared* 2,399.—*Calves* suckled 130.—*Horses* and *Mares* 4,686.—*Foals* 647.

HORSES —The breed appears, in Mr. P's table of live-stock, to be wholely of the "cart kind."

CATTLE.—*Breed.*—P. 224. "The cattle in this county, considering the number, are remarkable for being of a very inferior sort, such as it is impossible to describe under any regular method, but they may truly be said to be of all kinds but good ones. There were but three instances which came under my inspection of any attempt being made at improving the breed. At his Grace the Duke of Manchester's there was an assortment of short-horned Yorkshire cows, and a bull of rather an useful kind; his Grace had some calves rearing, which looked very promising.

"Mr. Nichols, of Stewkley Parva, is making an improvement from Yorkshire cows, or short-horned, and a bull of the Hereford kind."

"Mr. Ladds, at Steeple Gidding, has got some of the long-horned Leicester cows, the best that I saw in the county of any kind."

DAIRY.—Another history of *Stilton Cheese!*—After copying the account of "Mr. Nichols, in his History and Antiquities of the County of Leicester,"—the Reporter proceeds, p. 232,—"but Mr. John Pitts, landlord of the Bell Inn, Stilton, as well as Mr. Maxwell, contend with the the greatest probability of truth, that the famous Stilton cheese was first made at Stilton in Huntingdonshire.

"Mr. Pitts' reasons for maintaining that opinion, are given in the following account, drawn up from Mr. Pitts' own relation of the case. 'Mr. John Pitts, landlord of the Bell Inn at Stilton says, that he has every reason to believe, that the cheese known under the name of Stilton, was originally made at that place; that one Croxton Bray, a very old man, who died about the year 1777, aged about eighty years, remembers very well when a boy, that he, his brothers and sisters, and the people of Stilton in general, sent their children about to collect all the cream in the neighbouring villages, for the purpose of making what is called Stilton cheese. The receipt for making it is, the cream of the evening and morning, and the new milk all mixed together. This must have been long before Mr. Cooper Thornhill's time. Mr. Thornhill selling great quantities, and wanting more than could be had at Stilton, and knowing that Leicestershire produced excellent milk, and having relations in that county, he sent a person to them to instruct them in the mode of making it.'"

SWINE.

SWINE.—P. 257. " They are generally of a mixed breed in Huntingdonshire, except in two or three instances."

This being a species of livestock, respecting which Mr. Parkinson speaks as a well experienced practical man, I insert the subjoined passage. The close, however, is the only part of it which I particularly recommend to my readers attention. —P. 259. " Notwithstanding all that has been advanced by Mr. Bakewell on this subject, I am convinced from experience that to breed in and in, is not only an improper, but an idle way of breeding useful animals. With respect to the sows getting too fat during the time that they are in the breeding state, were they not to have food of some sort to satisfy their appetite, it would cause them to have the mange, to get lousy, and unhealthy; and I have frequently in summer had great numbers of those pigs at grass, where sheep, cattle, and horses were grazing; and here they have got much fatter than they ought to be; the only means therefore of preventing the misfortunes attendant upon their bringing forth their young, is to take them into a sty a few days before they are to yean, keeping them rather scanty of food, which should be of a scouring nature such as bran or pollard, and water; and if soap suds were put amongst it, so much the better, as it would operate more like physic, and their bowels being emptied they would be cooler within, than being kept scanty of food during that time, and for a day or two after yeaning; the sow will be restless and not so much inclined to sleep, will pay more attention to her young ones, and from the expectancy of food, will lay listening, and should she tread or lie down upon one of her brood, she will then quickly get up, or as quickly move her feet."

The following minutiæ of management are also entitled to attention.—P. 259. " In the time of suckling keep the sow very well, and have the sty so formed, that the young pigs may have a place to run in, into which the sow cannot enter, and in that part, place some very good food; that they may learn to drink milk and eat corn, give them milk mixed with meal of any kind, or corn unground would be better, or even the milk by itself at first; then mix it by degrees with some unground corn; for by mixing the milk and meal together a kind of paste is formed, and as it is nearly impossible to prevent the youngsters from getting their feet into it, and then jumping upon one another, they thus get so smeared with the mixture that they are much injured by it."—The number found in Huntingdonshire was 11,481. (p. 242.)

SHEEP.—Having spoken, at some length, of Mr. Parkinson's opinion respecting the sheep of the Midland Counties, in in reviewing his Rutlandshire, (p. 278, aforegoing)—the reader will do well to refer back to that account, before he peruse the following extracts, concerning those of Huntingdonshire.

P. 243. "The sheep of this county, generally speaking, have now much more the appearance of the new Leicester than any other breed, although from the general account it will be seen that they are chiefly said to be a mixture of the Lincoln and Leicester; a great part of them are very inferior to what they ought to be, and as I before said, are, generally speaking, of the new Leicester, many of them being of the very worst of that species; which are the most unprofitable that are kept of the polled or improved kind. They are many of them very little better than dunks, which kind of sheep are very light in carcass, and worse in wool; and if they are to be made fat at all, are worth but little, and there are indeed many of them which it is as utterly impossible to make fat, as it would be to fatten any one who was in the last stage of a consumption. I saw sheep of the new Leicester kind in this county, not worth having, as a gift, to keep a year; for sheep of a good sort bought at a market price would yield *more profit* for a year's keep than they would *be worth*. I observe in the former report, that the wool was then about 8 lb. per fleece on an average of the whole county (that was thirteen years ago); and it now will not yield 6 lb. per fleece on the average, which is in proportion to the declension in the weight of fleeces in the county of Rutland."

The Reporter, however, would seem to have thought it prudent, in writing *this* Report, to blunt the asperities, and to rub off some of the rust of prejudice, observable in his Rutlandshire, against "the new Leicesters;"—thus continuing.—"I should be sorry for the reader, from my observations on the new Leicester, to think that on that account I infer that the whole of the sheep of that species are bad, as this is far from being the case; but there are many reasons why there are so many bad new Leicester sheep, for almost every man who rode a new Leicester ram, turned tup breeder; and perhaps his stock proceeded from a very bad ram, and an ewe of the same kind; by such means they have spread very rapidly, and on some account there are great numbers of very bad sheep of that kind; they are allowed by the cutting butchers in London to be of two descriptions, viz. *very good and very bad*, the best of the new Leicester sheep being probably the best carcases of any, and worth more money at an *early age* than any other sheep; it is allowed on all hands, that an old Lincolnshire sheep, having about what the cutting butcher terms one-fifth

fifth of the new Leicester, is the most profitable sheep that comes to the London markets.

"I am clearly of opinion that a very good new Leicester ram, put to any ewe of another breed, will improve the carcass more than any other breed of sheep whatever, but not so the *fleece*. The different crosses which have been taken to old Lincolnshire ewes, old Leicesters, Oxfords, Rutlands, and many other counties where long wool is produced, have reduced the *weight of wool* one-fourth, nor do I think that the *quality* is any thing improved, for though *finer*, much of it is *curled* and *mossy*."

Here we have the Reporter's opinion corrected to 1811, concerning the *best* of the new Leicester breed. Let us now listen to his account of the *worst:* a race of beings, by the way, which I never met with, but in the works of this writer.

P. 245. "The term dunks, which I have used, seeming to be strange to many breeders in this county, it may not be improper to say something respecting them; they are small formed, a short head, broad in the forehead, and large in comparison with the neck, which latter is very thin, and what many have plumed themselves much for procuring, and what is termed a fine or thin crag, the small end of a neck of mutton being by such termed offal; their eyes being like those of a frog, their ears standing wide and rather hanging down; their necks, as before observed, small, with no neck vein, but falling off immediately from the shoulder, the blade bone of which stands up much higher than the chine, seeming to act in a loose manner, their ribs being round, and like the hoops of a cask so as to be very hollow within, and having from their inaptitude to fatten but very little flesh or fat there; and although when alive they handle to advantage, and appear to have some fat upon them, yet when killed and their entrails taken out, they are so very light of flesh, that the light will shine through the loins within two or three inches of the back bone, their hind quarters being generally very short (what is termed wiped away) being light in the thigh, so that when *fairly* cut, the leg is very small and light, and their tails are very small; thus, from the extreme smallness of their necks and tails, they are small also all along the back, which is the prime part of every animal; in cutting up they are proved to have very little of that prime flesh on each side the back bone which they ought to have, therefore what was thought to be a perfection, has fairly proved to be the greatest imperfection; from this want of flesh they have very little fat either *within* or *without*.

"I have seen some of such sheep when killed, being as fat

fat as it was possible to make them, weigh 56 lb. a carcass, or 14 lb. per quarter, when I am clearly of opinion that the sheep which ought to have been grazed where they came from, would at the same age, with the same food, have weighed 80 lb. a carcass, or 20 lb. per quarter. Now from this calculation, there will be a difference of 24 lb. a sheep; at 8*d.* per lb. it will be 16*s.* a piece difference, then the wool will be 9 lb. as before, and 9*s.* in all 1*l.* 5*s.* which at one sheep and a half per acre will be 1*l.* 17*s.* 6*d.* which being divided by four, for the four years, will be 9*s.* 4½*d.* per acre, which is certainly a sum very much worth every breeder's strictest and most serious consideration.

"Now the sheep termed dunks being so imperfect from nature, it seems to me to arise from their *deformity*, (!) and is similar to a deformed shape in the human race, it being very seldom that a man who is deformed, is inclined to be of large size or fat. It appears that their head, although not very large, yet is heavier than it ought to be, in proportion to the chine; as when they move, their heads seem to shake, similar to a paralytic affection; and if they meet with the least obstruction, such as ant-hills, &c. they will tumble down on their knees, and from the shaking of the head, when they come to be killed, at that part of the neck which is called the crag, there is found a bloody substance, which is obliged to be cut off and thrown away, being totally unfit for use, and instead of those sort of sheep having less offal than sheep of a greater weight, they have *much more*, for as many of them weigh but 56 lb. a carcass, were the head, the bones, the skin, (although very thin), the pluck, blood, entrails, &c. weighed and proportioned to their useful flesh, (which in fact should not be termed *useful* but *usable*) there would be found much more offal in one of them, according to their weight, than in a sheep which weighs 160 lb. when the latter would probably have 40 lb. of fat in them, and the former not more than from 7 lb. to 9 lb. Instead, therefore, of their having *no offal*, as has been boasted, it fairly appears they are nearly *all offal*, or at least *unprofitable;* and instead of those *nice* breeders having bred sheep which were to pay the greatest profit for the food which they consume, they have so far missed their aim as to breed animals of so delicate a frame, as to have neither much flesh nor wool, and consequently paying the least for food.

"From all my experience, I am of opinion that these small sheep consume as much food as those do which are as large again; from their extreme tender constitution, without much care they will starve and waste away; now there are small animals which are of a hardy nature, such

as

as Scotch sheep, Mountain sheep, on the commons in Westmoreland and Cumberland, which would live where a good Lincolnshire sheep or a new Leicester would be starved; but those sheep I have alluded to, require as much or more care to keep them *even alive*, than any sort whatever, for when they are seen in pastures with other sheep of the *good kind* of New Leicesters, the latter will be very fat, and the former as poor as "*church mice*;" I saw an instance of this in this county, on a farm which was in every instance managed to the greatest nicety; so much so that it is very probable there is not one farmer in England who could excel the occupier of it, every thing being managed in the correctest manner, and he has also attended equally to his breed of sheep as to the other parts of the farming process."

I ought perhaps to make some apology for encumbering this abstract of what is valuable, with so copious an extract of what is only *curious*. But should any of my readers be cloyed with the sweets of useful knowledge (as many a reader is liable to be) this may serve to renovate his appetite, for more valuable information.

Management of Sheep.—P. 162. "I observed one very good method in the pastures of several parts of this county, to prevent sheep from getting overcast. Two posts are placed ten feet apart, and a strong rail fastened to them, against which the sheep can rub their backs, by which means it is very seldom they have any sheep overcast; a very great advantage." *

The number of sheep set down, in this Report, is 141,558.

POULTRY.

* Rubbing Rails. This simplex, but valuable, modern invention, or discovery, owes its origin, I believe, to my late brother;—who observing that his sheep resorted to a low branch of a hedge tree, which happened to stretch out, horizontally, from the stem, at the height most convenient for them to rub their backs,—on the under side of it,—fixed a rail at the same height (by the means of two short posts) in the middle of the pasture;—to which, in like manner, they repaired, to rub themselves.

This must have taken place nearly thirty years ago; during which time I have been recommending, and erecting, rubbing rails, in various parts of the island.

The height, at which the rail is required to be placed, depends, of course, on that of the given sheep. But to accomodate it to sheep of different heights, one end of it is requisite to be placed higher than the other.—In a wide walk, or grazing ground, several of these rails should be put up; for, otherwise, the sheep will travel from every part of it, to gratify themselves, if one, only, be set up; making beaten tracks to it, like rays from a center,—as the buffaloes, in America, are said to make, in travelling to the salt licks.

By

Poultry.—I copy the subjoined notice, respecting *turkies*, tho it belongs not to the practice of Huntingdonshire. It may be useful in that or any other English County.—P. 263. " *Turkies*, geese, fowls and ducks, are not much raised in this county with a view to profit, but are chiefly raised for individual conveniency. Turkies might be raised to a profit, by the *lower classes of society* in the way they do in Ireland, where they feed the young turkies on sharp nettles, shred with a small quantity of oatmeal and milk mixed among them, which is not only a cheap food, but much better than any other food, as young turkies require something hot; pepper has been generally used in England, but nettles are a more natural food, keeping them more healthy than *foreign* aid, and being a weed of a very noxious nature, I strongly recommend this pratice of thus raising turkies, as I know no animal which brings so quick and so great a profit, their first cost considered."

Pigeons.—P. 264. " There are 271 dove cotes in this county, there being dove-houses in three-fourths of the parishes, many having from six to ten, and one having twelve cotes; but generally running from two to four in each parish; they are found to be extremely serviceable in picking up seeds of weeds, &c. in the winter, and are a very encourageable species of fowls, as it has been proved in Nottinghamshire, where the farmers fearing that they were injurious agreed to destroy them, but they soon found their error, and now give every encouragement to them."

These are rather singular ideas.—There can be little doubt of pigeons being useful, at certain seasons, in picking up the seeds of weeds, especially in a *weedful* district. Were there a law to oblige the proprietors of dove cotes to kept them shut up, during seed time and harvest,—as, we are told,

By constant use, the ground will be worn away, beneath the rail; when it will of course become too-*high*, and useless.—In this case the hollow requires to be filled up, with gravel or other hard materials; or the rail to be shifted; which is the work of a few minutes, only.

The rail ought not to be too large, or too flat, on the under side; so as to render it ineffective; nor too weak, so as to bend with the powerful exertion which large sheep apply to it. A square rail, with one of its angles placed downward; but sufficiently rounded off (and of course made smooth) to prevent its injuring the fleece,—is the most eligible.

The utility of Rubbing Rails is not merely that of preventing the restlessness of the animals, and thereby inducing them to lie the more quietly in their pasture; but to prevent long wooled sheep from getting " laid;"—from turning upon their backs to rub them on the ground; and not being able to recover their legs again, are, in that helpless state, liable to be lost; or to have their eyes pecked out, while still alive, by birds of prey.—For a valuable remark, on this disaster of sheep, see Eastern Department, *Secretary's Lincolnshire.*

told, there now is in France,—they would assuredly be "an encouragable species of fowls;" if not to the husbandman; to the epicure, at least.

ROOKS.—In the Reporters chapter, "Woods and Plantations," he recommends the planting of tall-growing trees, particularly willows, in the fens; to entice rooks to nest in them; "which birds are much courted in the fens;"—and, doubtlessly with much propriety. For altho, in seed time and harvest, rooks are injurious to the arable farmer, more especially, perhaps, in dry seasons; yet, in the spring months, during the breeding season, they are assuredly beneficial, in the neighbourhoods of rookeries; by collecting grubs and other reptiles, for their young; most especially in rich grassland districts, where brown beetles are wont to deposit their eggs.

The subjoined account of the *habits* of rooks are creditable to Mr. Parkinson, as an observer of nature.—P. 170. "It may not be improper here to say a few words respecting rooks; on my farm, at Slane in Ireland, there was the largest rookery I ever saw, and I was far from finding them do me any damage, for in fine weather they used regularly to fly, seemingly to very great distances for their food; in foul or stormy, or wet weather this was not the case: now as the author of an ingenious publication on the grub, has discovered that those reptiles leave their cells in this kind of weather, it is certain that rooks are of most essential service in devouring them at such times, which partly accounts for rooks staying near home at such times, their instinct teaching them that food will be provided for them there; I could always have a very near guess what kind of weather it would be from the rooks at Slane, for if they sat on the trees after sun rise, although it might then have every appearance of being fine, yet it was certain to be rain all or greatest part of the day, when that was the case."

PROFIT.—In reviewing this Reporter's Rutlandshire, p. 280, aforegoing,—I spoke my sentiments, unreservedly, on the amusing calculations there exhibited, concerning this topic.—In his Huntingdonshire, similar calculations, but still more bulky, are found.—See the head *Plan of Management*, p. 420, aforegoing.

To deem those lucubrations inoffensive might be wrong; as they may tend to lead the unwary astray, without a reasonable expectation, or even hope, of their putting any one into the right road of practice.

OXFORDSHIRE.

THIS COUNTY, unnatural, in regard to its lands,—and inconvenient, with respect to its outlines, may be said to be,—as a subject of rural report,—perversely situated.—Its aukward limbs extend themselves into THREE NATURAL DEPARTMENTS.—Inverting the map,—the head of the County is of chalk; which forms the north western point of the range of chalk hills that are the northern boundary of the *Southern* Department.—Its neck and shoulders, and lower extremities, are formed of vale lands; that accord, in soil and situation, with the *Midland* Department:—while a broad belt of limestone lands (an extention of the Cotswold Hills) parcel of the *Western* Department, begirts its more corporate parts.

To save my readers, as well as myself, some trouble and embarrassment, I will *here*, extract all the novelties and excellencies which the two Reports sent to the Board, from OXFORDSHIRE, may be found to contain; and refer, from the review of the *Southern Department*, to whatever may, in right, belong to it.

"GENERAL

"GENERAL VIEW OF THE AGRICULTURE OF THE COUNTY OF OXFORD,

WITH

OBSERVATIONS ON THE MEANS OF ITS IMPROVEMENT.

BY RICHARD DAVIS,

OF LEWKNOR IN THE SAID COUNTY,

TOPOGRAPHER TO HIS MAJESTY.

DRAWN UP FOR THE CONSIDERATION OF

The Board of Agriculture and Internal Improvement.

1794."

THIS is one of the "original" sketches which were sent *hastily* in to the Board, almost immediately on its institution;—namely, in January 1794:—an apology, this, for its brevity, and its want of intelligence, on a variety of topics belonging to rural affairs.

Mr. DAVIS'S QUALFICATIONS would seem to be those of an estate agent, or land surveyor. He apprizes his readers, however, in p. 33, of his "being a practical farmer on a small scale." The following is Mr. D's own account of his performance.

P. 26. "Thus far* contains the report of the most material occurrences, that presented themselves to my view or attention, both in the course of my tour round the county, and in divers observations made at former times; in which I have avoided entering too far into particulars, lest the report should become tedious aud uninteresting. For though

* Mr. DAVIS divides his Report into three parts; namely,—the "Introduction."—"Part I, present State of the County."—And "Part II, Means of Improvement."—The above extract closes Part I.

though I should be deficient in gratitude, were I not to acknowledge the assistance that I received, in every part of the county, from some of the most intelligent gentlemen and farmers, as well as from my brethren in profession; yet *I found the answers they supplied to the general questions issued by the Board of Agriculture vary so much*, that to have given the whole of them, would have come within no moderate compass. I therefore judged it best, to select the most important practices only, and such as were in the most universal use. I have further omitted mentioning the names of many skilful improvers, both gentlemen and farmers, in order to avoid being personal, by reporting some particular improvements which attracted my notice, whilst there might be others equally meritorious which escaped me, for want of having been informed of them. It therefore remains to treat of such improvements as have not been previously mentioned, under the distinct heads already enumerated; and for many of which I am indebted to the respectable authorities before recited."

How much good sense is to be perceived in these remarks. Had others of the Board's Reporters possessed the like penetration and candor, fortunate would it have been for the purchasers and reviewers of their works.

Number of pages thirtynine.

A sketch of the County divided into districts.

NATURAL ECONOMY.

EXTENT.—P. 7. "It contains 14 Hundreds, one City, 12 Market-towns, 207 Townships or Parishes, and about 450,000 acres; of which the part North of Oxford contains 309,000 acres, and the part South of Oxford 141,000 acres; as appears by the Topographical Survey which I have lately taken, and is now engraving by Mr. Carey."

SURFACE.—P. 9. "There are no hills of any steepness or elevation, except the range of Chiltern hills; the rest are only gentle declivities, which tend to vary the landscape, without preventing the labours of the plough."

CLIMATURE.—P. 9. "The Climate of Oxfordshire may be accounted in general cold, particularly the Westward part of the north division, where the fences consist chiefly of stone walls, and consequently afford little or no shelter. It is cold also upon and near the Chiltern hills, especially on on the poor white lands at the foot of the hill; where it is always to be observed, that the frost will take effect sooner, and continue longer on that soil, than it does on the deeper lands farther situated from the hills. The climate of the Chiltern country is moist, on account of the fogs, which are more frequent on the hills and woods, than in the vale."

WATERS.—P. 7. "In so far as the counties of Oxford and Berks are *contiguous* they are *separated* from each other by the rivers Isis and Thames. The river Thame, which runs through the County, falls into the Isis at Dorchester, and, from that place, the river takes the name of Thames. Other rivers in Oxfordshire are, the Charwell, which divides this County from Northampton on a part of of the boundary only; the Windrush, the Evenlode, the Glym, and the Ray; besides numerous streams of inferior note: so that this County may be considered as inferior to none, in point of being well watered."

SOILS.—P. 7. "The soil of a very considerable part of this County is shallow; of the stone brush kind; notwithstanding there are interspersed in divers places, rich loams, sands, and clays; the description of which will be more particular, by dividing the County into two parts, viz. the North and the South Division, and afterwards, subdividing each of those parts, into several districts.

"The *North Division*, may be divided into four districts, to wit,

"1. The Northern corner of the County, containing in a great measure the Banbury and Bloxham Hundreds, is chiefly strong, deep land, partly arable, and partly in a pasture state, appropriated principally to the dairy.

"2. South of the last is a very large extent, where the higher land or flat part is shallow, and, in general, more or less stony, in an arable or convertible state; the sides of the hills a good loam or mixed with clay, in a pasture state; and the bottoms, more of the clay allotted for meadow land, by the sides of the several rivers, which add to the fertility and beauty of the County.

"3. The South West corner contains the forest of Whichwood, great part of which is woodland; and near to that, in the Bampton Hundred, the soil is more gravelly, with parts of black loam and clay, much of which is adapted to pasture and meadow. The situation is low and wet, notwithstanding which there are divers tracts of arable land in this district.

"4. The district on the North side of Oxford, in which is comprised the common of Otmoor, is a deep rich soil, part arable, part in pasture, and part meadow land.

"The

"The *Sauth Division*, may also be divided into four several districts, namely,

"1. The part contiguous to and South of Oxford, which consists of various soils, part light and sandy, and part deep and rich; some being arable, and some in a pasture and meadow state. In this district is comprised a considerable tract of woodland, near to Stanton St. John.

"2. From thence southward, by the sides of the Thame river, is a pretty large tract of deep land, the greater part of which is in pasture.

"3. Between the preceding district and the bottoms of the Chiltern hills, the land is mostly in an arable state, chiefly deep and good, but diminishing in goodness as you approach the hills; when it consists of a poor white maum, being a mixture of white earth and chalk.

"The Ickneild way, which crosses this County, may in a great measure be considered, as dividing the last described district from the range of Downs, which are in most places above the Ickneild way, and used as a sheep pasture, being poor land. South of which,

"4. There is a large tract of land called the Chiltern hills, the soil whereof is a mixture of chalk, with some loam and clay, but all full of flints. Much of this is appropriated to the growth of beech; but there is also a considerable tract of inclosures, mostly in an arable or convertible state, with some large wastes or commons; and some vallies of meadow land bordering on the Thames."

POLITICAL ECONOMY.

APPROPRIATION.—P. 22. "There are in most of the uninclosed parishes, either small or larger tracts of wastes or down-land, which are appropriated chiefly to the feed of sheep. The range of Chiltern hills, which cross the southward end of the county, are of this description, being in many places too steep to plough. In the more northern part of the county there are considerable tracts of down-land belonging to most villages, which are often overrun with ant-hills and coarse herbage, being of little value, and chiefly appropriated to the pasturage of young cattle; or sometimes, where they are good enough for that purpose, and sufficiently extensive, of oxen for the use of the plough.

"The most considerable, and at the same time most *valuable* tract of *waste*, in this County, is the common of Otmoor

Otmoor, situated near Islip; which contains, as near as can be ascertained, about four thousand acres, and is commonable to eight adjoining townships. This whole tract of land lies so extremely flat, that the water, in wet seasons, stands on it a long time together, and of course renders it very unwholesome to the cattle, as well as the neighbourhood. The sheep are thereby subject to the rot, and the larger cattle to a disorder called the *moor evil.* The abuses here (as is the case of most commons where many parishes are concerned) are very great, there being no regular stint, but each neighbouring householder turns out upon the moor what number he pleases. There are flocks of geese likewise kept on this common, by which several people gain a livelihood."

"It is not easy to ascertain the quantity of the other waste or down-land in this County; but it must be great, as there remain at this time *upwards of an hundred uninclosed parishes* or hamlets, to which there are wastes belonging in greater or lesser quantities, although on most of them the commonable rights are stinted."

In page 28, Mr. Davis enters on the general subject, as to the *objections* and *advantages* of "Inclosure."—But I perceive nothing in his remarks, concerning the former, that is sufficiently new or excellent to claim particular notice, here: even under the present irrational (absurd and senseless may we say) mode of *obtaining permission to improve the land we live in,* and *allay the hunger of its underfed inhabitants,*—the measure, in a general point of view, wants not the aid of ingenious argument, to show its utility*.—I will here copy Mr. D's enumeration of *advantages.* They are well brought together.

P. 30. "The first of these is *getting rid of the restrictions* of the former course of husbandry, and appropriating each of the various sorts of land *to that use to which it is best adapted.*

"2. The *prevention of the loss of time,* both as to labourers and cattle, in travelling to many dispersed pieces of land from one end of a parish to another; and also in fetching the horses from distant commons before they go to work.

"3. There is a much better chance of *escaping the distempers* to which cattle of all kinds are liable from being mixed with those infected, particularly the scab in sheep. This circumstance, in common fields, must operate as a discouragement

* The above *indignant* remark was dictated by the existing circumstances of the moment;—by the scarcity and dearness of corn, and the consequent riots and executions that had just taken place, when this article was written; namely, in February, 1813.

couragement to the *improvement of stock;* and it is a further disadvantage, that the occupier is *limited both in regard to number and kind of stock*, instead of adopting such a number and kind as are most suitable and proper.

" 4. The farmer has a *better superintendance of his labourers*, when within the bounds of an inclosed farm, than in an open field."(?)

" 5. The great benefit which arises from *draining lands*, which cannot so well, if at all, be done on single acres and half acres, and would effectually prevent the rot amongst sheep, so very common in open field land.

" 6. Lastly, the *preventing of* constant *quarrels*, which happen as well from the trespasses of cattle, as by ploughing away from each others land."

An instance of *appropriation without inclosure*, which is mentioned by Mr. D, is admissible into this register.

P. 23. " The objection of the damage arising from hedges, may be entirely done away, by altering the clause in acts of parliament respecting the fencing, and leaving it optional to each proprietor either to fence his allotment, or leave it open after it is allotted to him *in several;* which was done in the last sessions of parliament, in a Berkshire inclosure act, where there was a large tract of distant down land, on which it would have been difficult and expensive to raise a quick, and there were no stones at hand of a proper kind for walls."

For an instance of the individual plots of *common meadows* being *changeable every year* (as the pieces of " runrig" arable lands were, formerly, in the Highlands of Scotland—no one tenant cropping the same land two following years)—see *Grass Land*, ensuing.

For the *business* of appropriation respecting *Tithes*, see that article, ensuing.

Manufactures.—P. 26. " The chief *commerce* carried on in Oxfordshire may be confined to the blanket manufactory at Witney, the shag manufactory at Banbury, and the glove and polished steel manufactory at Woodstock; and I have been informed by the farmers, in each of those neighbourhoods, that labourers are quite as plenty for the purpose of agriculture there, as elswhere.

" The employment of the female poor, on the southward side of this county, is lace-making; but in the middle and northward side, the more general employment is spinning."

Tithes.—P. 31. " It has long been disputed, what is the best system to follow when tithes are to be commuted. In this county, many inclosures have taken place within a few years, wherein all the several methods have been pursued. In divers of these inclosures the land has been left titheable

as

as before, because the tithe-owner and proprietors did not agree on terms. In others, *an annual rent* has been fixed, to be paid out of each estate, *varying according to the price of corn*, taken at stated times; and this method has been satisfactory in many cases. But the most usual mode is to set out an *allotment of land in lieu of tithes*."

RURAL ECONOMY.

TENANTED ESTATES.

ESTATES.—P. 11. "In regard to property, there are a few noblemen and gentlemen who have large estates, which, with the addition of the possessions belonging to the church, and the different corporate bodies of the university, form a considerable portion of this County. There are also many proprietors of a middling size, and many small proprietors, particularly in the open fields."

WOODLANDS.

GROVES.—P. 20. "The woodlands in this county may be divided in three sorts; viz. *groves*, or *spring woods*, consisting of trees only; *woods*, consisting of timber trees and underwood; and *coppices*, consisting of underwood only. Of the first of these descriptions may be considered,

"The *beech woods* of Oxfordshire, which are confined to the Chiltern country, and consists of trees growing on their own stems, produced by the falling of the beech-mast; as very little is permitted to grow on the old stools, which are generally grubbed up. They are drawn occasionally, being never felled all at once, except for the purpose of converting the land into tillage, which has been much in practice of late years. The beech wood thus *drawn*, is either sold in long lengths, called poles, or cut short in billet-lengths, and sold for fuel. It requires some judgment to thin these woods, so that the present stock may not hang too much over the young seedlings; at the same time, that in a south aspect an injury may take place, by exposing the soil too much to the sun; for it is to be observed, that the north side of a hill will produce a better growth of beech than the south side."

WOODS.—P. 21. "Of the second kind are the *woods* before-mentioned, in the vicinity of Stanton St. John, called the *Quarters*. The soil here being a strong clay, is well adapted to the growth of oak. There are many spots

spots of woodland of this description dispersed about various parts of the country.

"COPPICES do not abound in this county. Indeed there are very few of any extent, except those called coppices in the forest of Whichwood; though these having trees in them, are more properly woods."

P. 9. "Upon a GENERAL VIEW, besides the woods before mentioned," (see *Soils*) "and some few other particular spots, the face of the County is marked with little woodland; except in those places which are near to the towns or capital mansions."

AGRICULTURE.

FARMS.—P. 11. "The size of the farms varies so much, that it is difficult to speak on that head; but they may be considered, generally speaking, as less than in most parts of England."

PLAN of MANAGEMENT.—*Open Fields.* P. 11. "The present course of husbandry is so various, particularly in the *open fields* of both Divisions, that to treat of all the different ways of management, would render this report too voluminous. It may suffice, generally to remark, that some fields are in the course of *one* crop and fallow, others of *two*, and a few of *three* crops and a fallow."

"In those fields that are cultivated in the course of *one crop* and a fallow, wheat, barley, and oats are the chief grain that is produced; and sometimes, by agreement of the occupiers, a few tares are sown in the fallow field, to cut green for the horses.

"In those fields that are in the course of *two crops* and a fallow, the wheat crop succeeds the fallow; and the other field is sown either with barley, oats, pease, or beans, or with all of them.

"In the open fields that are in the course of *three crops* and a fallow, the most usual rotation is the following, viz.

Fallow, Beans, pease, oats, or tares,
Wheat, Barley, or oats:

so that when a hitching takes place, it is either in the bean-field or fallow field."

Inclosures.—P. 12. "The present course of husbandry in the inclosures is likewise variable, but less so than in the open fields. On the strong deep lands, or clay soils, the course of three crops and a fallow is very general, and some clover is raised; but when the soil becomes more dry, and is not too much injured by the treading of cattle, turnips are introduced and fed off; and this is found to answer, notwithstanding

withstanding there may be considerable depth in the soil, insomuch that some damage will happen in a wet season."

WORKING ANIMALS.—P. 25. "*Horses* are almost universally used for draught. In many parishes having open fields, there may not be sufficient pastures for oxen, but in all inclosed parishes, where there are pastures, oxen might be introduced with great advantage; particularly in the vale, where there are no flints nor stones. There are many teams of *oxen* in the county, chiefly belonging to gentlemen, which draw by collars and traces; but the difficulty of procuring proper persons, that have been used to go with them, may be the reason of their not being in more general use. It is a custom with many farmers, who do not breed their own colts, to purchase them for their teams when rising two years old; some of which are sold for carriages, road waggons, or London drays, according to their strength and size, at four or five years old, and often yield good profit. But those horses, which are kept after that time to be worn out, may be considered as an annual loss; which is not the case with oxen; particularly as a profit will always attend an ox in case he meets with an accident, which is not so with a horse."

IMPLEMENTS.—P. 37. "It has often occurred to me, that painting all the implements of husbandry (a circumstance seldom attended to by farmers), is not a waste of money, because it adds to the durability of the wood; at the same time that it has a neat appearance, and prevents the same machine from being of different weights when wet or dry." This is, at least, an *ingenious* idea.

TILLAGE.—*Plow Team*.—P. 14. "It is seldom seen that less than four horses are used, even on light lands; though in many places two horses with a proper plough, would be quite equal to the work. The using more horses than are necessary, seems to be little attended to by the farmers of this County."

TURNIPS.—P. 14. "I have heard it recommended, though I cannot speak as to the effect, to mix old and new turnip seed together, which will come up at different times: and further, to steep one half of the seed so mixed, and not to steep the other; by which methods the plants coming at four different times, may stand the better chance of escaping injury by the fly or grub."

GRASS LANDS.—*Common Meadows*.—P. 15. "The open field meadows, are often situated a considerable distance from the villages, and besides, generally lying in very narrow slips and parcels, are frequently even in *lots changeable every year*. These common meadows seldom receive any assistance of manure, because the arable lands, consume

consume the whole of the manure in the preparation for the wheat crop. There is also another reason why the common meadows are neglected in this respect, because the after-feed is the property of all the occupiers in the parish at large."

"The greater part of these meadows are near rivers, and are situated so low, as to be overflowed occasionally after hasty rains, and now and then even in hay time, insomuch, that the crops are either entirely swept away, or so greatly damaged as to be of little value, except for littering the farm yards."

Inclosed Grass Lands—P. 16. "The inclosed pasture, or meadow land, is chiefly confined to the middle part of the County near to Oxford, where there is a pretty large tract of deep rich soil; from the pasturage of which, besides the quantity of butter made, which is considerable, a great number of calves are suckled, and the veal sent to the London market. On various parts of this district there are some oxen, cows, and sheep fatted."

"Many of the pasture grounds are full of ant-hills, and the herbage growing thereon is coarse, and refused by the cattle, who will be much reduced for feed, before they will touch it, even when the young grass shoots up amongst the old, which is dry and withered."

LIVESTOCK.—P. 23. "The stock of *cattle, both cows and sheep*, of the late Mr. Fowler, of Rollright, which were sold by auction in the year 1791, reflects high honour on this county, and on the person who reared them; and although much of this stock was dispersed to different and distant places, yet there still remain in the county (in regard to the sheep stock in particular) divers of the lots purchased at the auction, and other stock bred from them since, that do credit to the judgment of the breeders, and to those persons in whose possession they now are."

"MR FOWLER'S SALE.	£.	s.	d.
'13 Bulls (of which 9 were only one year old) sold for	1648	10	0
28 Cows and Heifers - - - - -	2331	0	0
2 Bull calves - - - -	70	7	0
7 Cow calves - - - -	211	1	0
3 Welch cows, used as nurses - -	28	6	6
Total of the neat stock	4289	4	6
85 Rams, sold for - - -	1239	18	0
92 Ewes - - - - -	622	19	6
53 Theaves (or two year old ewes) - -	270	15	0
40 Ewes tegs (or yearling ewes) - -	132	12	0
18 Wether tegs - - - - -	25	10	0
5 Shear-hogs - - - - -	8	10	0
Total of the sheep stock -	2300	4	6
Total of the neat stock -	4289	4	6
Total amount	6589	9	0"

HORSES.—See *Working Animals*, aforegoing.

CATTLE.—*Breed.*—P. 24. "In the northern part of the County at Rollright, Chastleton, Bruern, and other places, are some of the remains and produce of the late Mr. Fowler's stock of the long horned kind, which (as well as his sheep) originally descended from Mr. Bakewell's breed of Dishley, to whom every farmer attentive to the breed of cattle is greatly indebted. Various other kinds of cows are found in different parts of the County, particularly the Lincolnshire and Warwick; but they do not appear to be in so much esteem as the Leicester and Yorkshire, though probably more hardy, and therefore better adapted to the poorer soils."

SHEEP.—*Breed.*—P. 24. "The breed of sheep is much attended to in the Northern District of the County. The Gloucester and Leicester breeds have each of them their advocates; and great care has been taken to bring the respective sorts as near as possible to perfection. Both kinds are fatted to great weights; and the rams of each are let out or sold at high prices. While the public opinion is divided as to the comparative merits of these two celebrated breeds, the judicious farmer will of course consider well his flock of ewes, and the situation and circumstances of his farm; and then take his cross from that *strain* which will furnish the points in which his present stock is most deficient, and the sort which are best adapted to the soil on which they are to be maintained.

"In the *Southern Division* of the County, the Leicester and Gloucester breeds of sheep are rarely met with. The Berkshire Nott sheep with mottled faces, and the horned sheep, are here most prevalent; these horned sheep are bred originally from the Wiltshire, and sometimes a strain from the Hampshire is preferred by the farmers; or in those places where lambs are reared early, the Dorsetshire breed is in good esteem on that account. An opinion has been received in some places, that those sheep which are bred on the land they are intended to be kept upon, are more healthy and profitable than others, that come from a different, or better soil; on this account, near the Chiltern country where the pastures are chiefly poor downs, and consequently require the hardiest sort, many flocks consist of a small kind of horned sheep, of which little can be said in favour, either of their excellence or shape; but the Berkshire Nott sheep appear to be gaining ground of these native flocks in estimation; it having been observed, that when the Berkshire and the horned sheep have been mixed in the same flock, the former have proved themselves the most hardy, by keeping in tolerable condition at such times

times as the feed was short, and the latter went on badly. It has also been remarked, that the horned sheep require to be oftener changed in their pasture, and will not eat the grass when stained by many of them lying in a small compass, so freely as the Nott sheep will; and it is another general observation, that the Berkshire sheep, when killed, prove heavier and fatter, than they appeared to be when alive; the reverse of which is the case of the horned sheep. The South Down breed of sheep have been partially introduced, but by gentlemen chiefly, and are also in great estimation."

SWINE.—P. 26. "The *Pigs* in most esteem with farmers are those which will prove of a large size when fat; but I am convinced no sort is so profitable to a small family, or a poor man, as the Chinese, or a cross between that kind, and the breed of the country; because they are maintained and fatted on less food than others, and by a cross they will come to great size.

"It is worthy observation, that many boars are fed for the purpose of making brawn, which forms a considerable article of trade at Oxford, and other parts of the county."

"GENERAL VIEW OF THE AGRICULTURE OF OXFORDSHIRE.

DRAWN UP FOR

THE BOARD OF AGRICULTURE

AND INTERNAL IMPROVEMENT.

BY THE SECRETARY OF THE BOARD.

1809."

THE SECRETARY of the BOARD of AGRICULTURE being publicly known, as a Writer on rural Subjects, renders any prefatory remarks of mine, on his QULIFICATIONS as such, in a manner unnecessary; even if I had not already had occasion to speak repeatedly concerning them.—See the Review of his Reports to the Board, from the EASTERN DEPARTMENT.

The MODE of COLLECTING INFORMATION, adhered to, in this case, as in *Lincolnshire*, *Norfolk*, and *Essex*, is principally,

cipally, but not altogether, that of an ENQUIRING VISITANT,—putting down, it pretty evidently appears on the face of the work, *every* prompt assertion and opinion, which happened to pass in CONVERSATION.—Pages after pages are filled with contradictory assertions, and opposing opinions, associated in such a manner, I fear, as to set the informants, whose names are exhibited in whole length, "by the ears;" and, what may be worse, thus seeing their opinions and assertions held up to public view, may tend to root their prejudices and errors, absurd as some of them *must* be, the more firmly in their minds *

So far from profiting by Mr. DAVIS's sensible remark, and mode of proceeding, (see p. 445, aforegoing)—the author thus attempts to defend his own "principles."—Preface p. vi. "I have too often addressed the readers of the Reports, to render an explanation of the principles by which I am governed in these works necessary; and have therefore only to request, that they will bear in mind the very material object of that GENERAL REPORT, in which is designed to be conveyed a *concentrated* view of the *National Agriculture;* the practices that deserve commendation; the deficiencies that demand improvement; the means of spreading whatever is good; and of remedying whatever is defective. That work can only be built on the minute details of the various Surveyors; whose facts, though too numerous for entertainment, will not be useless in the hands of those, whose business it will be to reduce the whole to order and consistency. †

"Upon the circumstance of repetitions, which at first sight may appear too numerous, one observation should be made: suppose that in the quantity of seed, time of sowing, or any similar point of management, there is a very near resemblance, I have heard it remarked, that one line would contain the matter as well as a page: thus,

"*Seed wheat two bushels.*

"But it may be asked, is such a general average, that of all farmers indiscriminately? or only of good ones? or of those

* It is here to be remarked, however, in justice to the Reporter, that the produce of his visits was not, as I have said above, *altogether conversational.* Some instances of *transitory observation* appear in his work.

† Now, this is what I have been employed upon, during thirty four years; and I hope that in a very few years more, with the assistance of the Board's Reporters, I shall effect a complete CONCENTRATION of NATIONAL AGRICULTURE.—Thanks to this Reporter for affording me so fair an opportunity of saying so.

those the Reporter *conversed* with, whether good or indifferent managers? If variations, do they tend to lessen or increase it? How far does the practice of the best correspond with that of the rest? And then, who are what the Reporter calls *good?* Who knows that they really are so, if not named? Hence the satisfaction of finding the authority every where named. Without minutiæ of this sort, the reader, from the first page to the last of a book, has always the writer between him and the farmer, and not as a transcriber, but as a calculator of effects or averages. I know not how other readers may feel, but to myself, in examining the description of a district, I wish to see authority named for all that is possible; as it is not only a proof that the writer has had such *conversations* on the spot, but that there exist *sufficient judges resident in the country*, (!) who know whether the farmers named were, or were not, proper men to apply to."

In appreciating this Writers qualifications, as a Reporter of rural practices, in the EASTERN DEPARTMENT; article *Secretary's Lincolnshire*;—I spoke pretty fully concerning the "principle" of making books of *names;* about which, or their wearers, the PUBLIC can have no acquaintance.—They may belong to men of mature experience and sound judgement; or to novitial amateurs, who cannot possibly possess either of those essentials.—They may belong to men of *disinterested* character, who have no other view, in their communications, than that of *promoting the good of society;* or to "spirited" breeders,—to the letters of male stock,—who may have an *interest* in *deceiving;* or to men of lively imagination, who may have a pleasure in it.

If, as I have said, on the occasion above referred to, the qualifications of the several contributors had been scrupulously declared in a prefix to the work, the author might, with some degree of propriety, have shifted the responsibility, from his own, to their shoulders.

In a topographical work, a multitude of names, warring against each other, might afford to the natives of a County, or a *neighbourhood*, amusement, and perhaps merriment. But, to the AGRICULTURAL PUBLIC, what is the worth of a crowd of names, without being duly informed, as to what manner of men they belong?

It is here proper to observe, however, that, in the instance now under view, the want of attention, spoken of, is less blame-worthy, than in that above noticed. For, in *some* cases, the general characters of the informants are *incidentally* given. In others, the names of their residences may appear.

But of what avail are those particulars, to a stranger in

in the County, or, in many instances, to nine tenths of its own inhabitants? For it is not so much the popular character of the man, or the name of his farm, as the SPECIFIC QUALITY of its LANDS, the particulars that are attached to its SITUATION, and the GENERAL PLAN of MANAGEMENT on which it is conducted,—that is to say, the ATTENDANT CIRCUMSTANCES on which his ASSERTIONS and OPINIONS are GROUNDED,—that require to be explicitly given, before any PRACTICAL KNOWLEDGE can be immediately drawn from them.

It concerns one to find a veteran Writer appearing to be conscious that his own authority will not pass current with the public. In his Lincolnshire he says, p. 67, "My authority, personally, cannot be what the reader wishes." And, in the above extract, he intimates that "the reader ought not to have the writer between him and the farmer."

There are doubtlessly cases,—especially those in which any doubt may be involved, wherein it may be requisite to call in authorities. But to call them in, on every occasion, no matter how frivolous, or absurd, can have no better effect than that of swelling out a volume.—Any writer whose own authority, on ordinary occasions, is *insufficient*, must be wholly disqualified, as a public writer, on any subject of science, or the useful arts*.

From what aptly rises out of those considerations, it would seem to be ascertained, that the public and the Board have, *as yet*, NO AUTHORITY for the principal part of the contents of their Reports,—from this Writer at least. For *mere names are none:* and if *Reporters are none*, where shall it be looked for, but among the "sufficient judges resident in the Country:"—consequently, in the momentous event, so long *talked of*, all the sufficient judges, of every and all the Counties of the Island, will require to be convened, to *assist* in framing a GENERAL REPORT!

Unfortunately, however, for that stupendous work, the "judges," as well as the informants, of the earlier Reports—are many of them "now no more;" and before the grand work be finished (perhaps, ere it be begun) the remainder may be "in the silent grave."—Hence, as a "doomsday book," for the information of future generations, the whole

(on

*And it is to be remarked, here, that, in going over the ensuing abstract (which was formed many months before this remark suggested itself) it will be perceived to consist, in no inconsiderable part, of information for which there is no other authority, than the Reporter's own;—in direct contradiction to the principles laid down!—Nevertheless, it will be found to contain much valuable matter—conveyed in a satisfactory manner.

(on this Writer's principle) may be without authority, and of course without worth.

The following is the author's apology for undertaking this work.—Preface p. v. "The anxiety of the PRESIDENT of the Board to have the Reports of the English Counties finished, induced him to propose my examining a county in the summer of 1807; but having already executed that task in five counties, and being sensible that such works are more advantageously performed by various persons than by a few, united with the resolution that Essex should be my last labour in this way, I begged him to excuse me: difficulties, however, having occurred in procuring a Surveyor for Oxfordshire, that county alone remained unassigned, and the PRESIDENT again applied to me to undertake it; and finding him much set on completing the kingdom, I complied with his request, however contrary it was to my own judgment and inclination.

"A hope had long been entertained, that it would have been executed by Dr. WILLIAMS, Professor of Botany in the University of Oxford: had the undertaking been so fortunate as to have been placed in such able hands, it would have been executed in a manner more to the satisfaction of the Board."

Number of pages three hundred and fortysix.

Map of soil of Oxfordshire.

The plates of implements &c. *unnumbered;* for reasons assigned in the *Secretary's Essex*—EASTERN DEPARTMENT.

NATURAL ECONOMY.

EXTENT.—P. 1. "In the Table of Poor's Rates drawn up under the inspection of the Right Hon. George Rose, the contents are stated at 474,880 acres."

SOILS and SUBSOILS.—In extent and climature, the Secretary closely follows Mr. DAVIS. But, in treating of soils, he makes his own division of the County, into DISTRICTS, in manner following;—the map of the County being colored, accordingly.

P. 3. "This county contains three distinctions of soil, that are so marked by Nature, as to allow of little doubt respecting them.

"I. The red-land of the northern district; which, in fertility, much exceeds that of any other portion of equal extent.

"II. The district of stonebrash.

"III. The Chiltern hills. These are defined by their outlines, so as to render the annexed Map, I trust, satisfactory. The remainder of the county is so various, and the different

different soils so intermixed, and the contiguous tracts of each so small, that they may be classed together under the title of,

" IV. Miscellaneous loams. The proportionate extent of these soils, taking the total of the county at 450,000 acres, may thus be stated in the estimation of Mr. Neele, Map Engraver to the Board:

	Acres.
Red-land	79,635
Stonebrash	164,023
Chiltern	64,778
Miscellaneous	166,400
Total	474,836

" *I. The Red-land District.*—Very nearly the whole range of country 13 miles, from Banbury to Chipping Norton, is enclosed by Act of Parliament, and improved in product very greatly. Much in grass, but much, also, arable. It is all redland on gritstone till within three miles of Chipping Norton, where the yellow lime stonebrash begins.

" The soil in the more northern part of the county is the rich red loam and sandy on a red gritstone rock, which they break for the turnpike-roads, of which it makes execrably bad ones, but the stonebrash good."

P. 5. " This red district, in respect of soil, may be considered as the glory of the county. It is deep, sound, friable, yet capable of tenacity; and adapted to every plant that can be trusted to it by the industry of the cultivators. It extends into Northamptonshire, Warwickshire, and will become an object to be traced by the Surveyors of the Board, I believe, from Devonshire to Nottinghamshire."

" *II. The Stonebrash District**.—The predominant feature of this extensive tract is, a surface of greater or less depth, of a loose, dry, friable sand or loam, apparently formed of abraded stone, and abounding with many fragments of it. This is generally limestone; in every place that I viewed, it is so, and the uniform intelligence was to the same purport. If forms an excellent turnip soil, and is productive in wheat. Modern rents rise to *20s.* per acre, tithe-free; and much rises to *25s.*

" Bignal is stonebrash; and on Mr. Forster's farm I found, that in these limebrash lands there are many springs, which spew up upon the slopes, and greatly injure large tracts of them; and in digging Mr. Forster's capital drains four

* A continuation of the eastern limb of the COTSWOLD HILLS; which stretch across Oxfordshire, to the confines of Buckinghamshire.

four feet deep, there is found under the surface, brash of 12, 18, and 24 inches deep, a bed of blue clay apparently, which digs up very firm, and hardens in the air; but *by trial with vinegar*, I found it a marl. Under this is a vein of white marl, very rich in calcareous earth, as I judge, from its effervescence with acids; under this is a rock of rough white limestone. These blue and white substances, Mr. Forster has spread on the surface-stonebrash, and found them very beneficial.

"In the vales, various loams are found, and some tracts of good meadow. Of course, in so large a tract of country, many variations are met with; from poor, loose, sandy, slopes, to deep and more heavy soils, which have been called (but I conceive erroneously) clays."

P. 7. "*III. The Chiltern District**.—The basis of this tract of country is chalk; in some places very white, and to the eye, pure; in others imperfect, but in all consisting, in much the greater part, of calcareons earth. The chalk is covered to various depths with loam, generally sound and dry, and well adapted to beech-woods and sainfoin, which may be considered as the more peculiar products of the whole district. The clay which forms this loam abounds more or less, and but rarely takes any character that permits an arrangement with argillaceous soils. The most distinguishing mark of the surface-loam is, a very considerable quantity of flints; mostly brown, rough, rusty, and honey-combed; many to perforation, and many, also, with a sparry incrustation. Some of these I found, that effervesced with spirit of salt, as I expected that all would have done; but was disappointed in various trials. Some of the best soils are the most covered with these flints; so that strangers, unacquainted with soils, are apt to think that land must be miserably poor which is worth 20*s*. per acre.

"On the banks of the Thames, and in some other places where the hills recede, the soil is an excellent sandy loam, free from these peculiarities, and yielding many turnips; a crop which also do well on the flinty hills."

P. 8 "*IV. The District of Miscellaneous Loams.*—Having marked off, as in the Map, the three preceding districts, there remains a large portion of the county to which no particular characteristic can be assigned: it includes all sorts of soils, from loose sand to heavy clay.

"Descending the Chiltern hills, from Stockenchurch to Tetsworth, the vale is open field, and the soil exceedingly good; a brown strong loam on a moist bottom, yields great crops of wheat."

The

* The southwestern extreme of the range of CHALK HILLS, which are an inseparable portion of the *Southern Department*.

The Reporter touches on the soils of different parishes; as they were noted, no doubt, in crossing the Country;—but in so devious and indistinct away, as not to convey much useful information.—To ascertain, *in detail*, the soils of a vale or mixed-soil district, no other than Mr. VANCOUVER's method can be profitably pursued. See Mr. V's *Cambridgeshire*, and his *Essex*; in the EASTERN DEPARTMENT. Also his *Cambridgeshire*, ensuing.

POLITICAL ECONOMY.

APPROPRIATION.—*Commons*.—(Chapter "Wastes") —P. 227. "Except the two large tracts of Whichwood-forest and Ottmoor, the waste land in Oxfordshire is not very considerable.

"*Ottmoor*.—Mr. Weyland, of Wood Eaton, had the goodness to shew me this large tract of waste, in a manner which I could not have done but through his attention, who requested a farmer (Mr. Jones) who turns much stock on it, to conduct us in a little tour over the whole of it. Mr. Jones conceives it to equal the amount of four square miles, or 2560 acres: it is a very singular tract, nearly upon a dead level, surrounded on every side by high lands. I searched and inquired for bog and peat, but have reason to believe that there is no such thing upon it, or if there be, in a small proportion The soil is generally a good loam, which would form most valuable farms, and be applicable either to tillage or pasturage, were it drained; but more adapted to the latter than the former. To the eye it is level; but there is equality of surface enough to make the waters draw down to one part of it more than to the rest: so that part of it is very wet in October, after a long series of fine weather, and the rest quite a dry sound turf. The river Ray runs across it; and apparently, there would not be any difficulty in draining it."

P. 236.—"WHICHWOOD-FOREST.—	Statute Measure. A.	R.	P.
"King's coppices	1649	2	10
Baron's ditto (Duke of Marlborough)	1041	3	17
——————(Mr. Fettyplace, &c.)	346	0	33
Keeper's lodges and lawns	134	0	23
The open forest	2421	1	15
	5593	0	18
The chase woods	487	3	4
Blandford-park	639	2	17
	6720	1	39

"The

"The rights of common upon the forest are for horses and sheep only—no cattle or hogs; but the number of both, by trespass, are very great.

"*Soil.*—The soil of the forest, over which I rode above 16 miles, in order to examine every part of it, I found to be either a reddish good loam, or the common stonebrash of the extensive district in which it is situated. At one spot, where some ponds were choked up with weeds and mud, there is found peat earth, which Mrs. Stratton has used very successfully for her exotic plants demanding that earth, and is a hint of the origin of bogs. The whole forest, were it enclosed, would lett at least as well as the surrounding country, which (except certain properties) runs at 20*s.* per acre.

"*Copses.*—There are 34 copses in the forest; 18 of which belong to the King, 12 to the Duke of Marlborough, and four to certain individuals; these may average about 100 acres each. The king's are cut at 18 years growth, and the Duke's at 21. There is a right, and consequently the practice, of fencing these off when cut, by a hedge and ditch, for keeping out all commonable cattle and sheep for seven years; after which, all must enter: the deer are never excluded. These copses return, on an average, about 6*l.* per acre, clear: the cutting costs 40*s.* and the faggoting 2*s.* 6*d.* per 100; but these expenses are paid by the purchasers. Eighteen years producing 6*l.* is in the ratio of 6*s.* 8*d.* per acre per annum. The open forest produces nothing, but a certain quantity of brush-fuel, and browse for the deer.

"*Timber.*—I did not see one very fine tree of navy oak in a ride of 16 or 17 miles; but a considerable number of thriving ones, which appear to be of 60 or 70 years growth, and which promise in 100 years more to be valuable; but when these trees are compared with the space of land in which they are found, they cease to be an object of any consideration. Next to oak, ash seems to abound, and then beech, with some elms. There is not the smallest reason to judge from the appearance, that, in its present state, this forest will ever be productive of navy timber in the least degree answerable to its extent.

"*Enclosing.*—In riding over the forest, I found many very beautiful scenes, particularly where the *nut* fair is held, a glen by Mr. Dacre's lodge, and others approaching Blandford-park, &c.: there are vales," (valleys) "also, of the finest turf. Several of these scenes want nothing but water, to form most pleasing and finished landscapes. The present ranger, Lord Francis Spencer, has made several roads, by way of ridings, through the forest; and no person can doubt, but that to the residents who live on or near it, this

this fine wild tract of country affords many agreeable circumstances which may operate, in a measure, to prevent an enclosure which ought, for a thousand reasons, to take place as soon as possible. No reasonable person can propose or desire, that a measure should be effected to deprive any one of any sort of property; the object is merely to make a large tract of good land productive to the public: to whom it shall be apportioned is not of the smallest consequence; the cultivation is greatly to be wished, and this would take place on its being made private property, in whatever hands it might be placed. The person whose feelings would be most apprehended (the ranger), is fortunately of much too liberal a mind to oppose any measure really and substantially for the general benefit; and there are no circumstances (the mere pleasure of wandering alone excepted) which may not be fully compensated, by the solid and valuable consideration of allotments.

"Nor is it in the view of productiveness alone, that such an enclosure is to be wished: the morals of the whole surrounding country demand it imperiously. The vicinity is filled with poachers, deer-stealers, thieves, and pilferers of every kind: offences of almost every description abound so much, that the offenders are a terror to all quiet and well-disposed persons; and Oxford gaol would be uninhabited, were it not for this fertile source of crimes. This is a consideration that will surely have its weight with every man who sees the evil, and must consequently wish for the only remedy the case admits.

"A fact, which bears also on this point, and flows from it, is a circumstance mentioned by Mr. Pratt, of Fowler'; that poor-rates in the parishes which surround the forest, and have or usurp a right of commonage there, are higher than in others under similar circumstances, except in that of being cut off from the forest."

P. 87. (Chapter "Inclosing") "This has been the capital improvement of the county; for proportionably to the extent of it, more land has been enclosed since I first travelled in it, which is about 40 years ago, I conceive, than in any county in England; but such has been the general inattention in preserving accounts of the various particulars which render such inquiries interesting, that most of the industry I exerted was in vain.

"*Waste Land Enclosed.*

	Acres.
Fringford	230
Steeple Aston	188
Skipton	150
Black Bourton	1636

"Westwick

	Acres.
"Westwick	750
Burford	90
Cropedy	800
Broadwell	800
Claydon	540
Tudmarton	500
Stratton	300
Ensham	500
Coggs	298
Adington	237
Brightwell	225
Melcomb	300
Stoke Lyne	1186
Burford	80
Westcot	200
Wigginton	1190
Hampton	204
Alvescot	600
Mollington	180
Ensham	1000
	12,559

"There remain near 100 parishes unenclosed."

Common Fields.—(Chapter *Wastes*) P. 239. "In the open fields in the district around Baldon, there are no division baulks, which in so many counties are sources of weeds and depredation: if encroachments are made, the matter is settled by a jury. It is an acknowledged and well-known fact, that men have ploughed their land in the night, for the express purpose of stealing a furrow from their neighbour; and at all times it is a constant practice in some, to plough from each other. Such a practice is some apology for tacking this article to the Chapter of *Wastes*."

Another *Disadvantage* of Common Fields.—P. 102. (by J. Chamberlin) "I have known years wherein not a single sheep totally kept in the open field has escaped the rot. Some years within my memory, I am of opinion the rot has killed more sheep than the butchers have. As one instance of prevention, I occupy about 300 acres enclosed from the most rotten part of an open field, where the rot often nearly cleared the whole field. The first year was dry, and my sheep took no harm; I got the land drained and cleaned in a short time, and have not lost one sheep of the rot since I had the farm, which is now nineteen years."

Advantages of Inclosing.—P. 269. "Mr. Pratt, of Fowler, who has known the country many years, and has had much experience

experience as a valuer of land and tithes, and has acted as a commissioner in several enclosures, is convinced from a variety of observations, that the improvements which have taken place in 30 years are prodigious, especially from enclosing turnips and sheep: and that the food for mankind wherever enclosures have taken place is fully doubled"

"Mr. Davis has known the county well for more than 20 years, and the husbandry is incredibly improved in almost every particular: if you go into Banbury-market next Thursday, you may distinguish the farmers from enclosures from those from open fields; quite a different sort of men; the farmers as much changed as their husbandry—quite new men, in point of knowledge and ideas."

PROVISIONS.—P. 327. "Provisions in 1768; mutton, 4*d.* to 4½*d.* per lb.; beef, 4*d.* to 5*d.* per lb.; veal, 3½*d.* per lb.; bacon, 8*d.* per lb.; butter, 6*d.* to 7*d.*—At present (1807), mutton, 7*d.* per lb.; beef, 6½d. to 7*d.* per lb; veal, 7½*d.* per lb.; bacon, 10*d.* per lb.; butter, 10*d.* to 1*s.* 1*d.* per lb.

"This rise deserves attention, and should silence much of the vague assertions heard in common conversation, of the enormous rise of provisions: the contrary has been the the case here: the rise of some is great; but when we look back through this long period of accumulating national wealth and prosperity, and compare this rise with a multitude of other circumstances, it will cease to surprise, and appear, as in truth it is, moderate.

"The rise is,		
	Mutton, ...	64 per cent.
	Beef, ...	50
	Veal, ...	114
	Bacon, ...	25
		4)253
	Average meat, ...	63

"Bacon, the lowest of these, is the article that most concerns the poor.

Butter, ... 76."

MANUFACTURES.—*Shags.*—P. 44. "At Bloxham 70 people on the round: many shag weavers out of employment. Many such weavers in Banbury, &c.; a rough coarse velvet made there: perhaps 1000 have been employed; but not at present: bad for farmers, ready for the parish, and a heavy burthen to the country; nor so well disposed as the country labourers. This fabric, like that of Witney, has travelled to the North. The unemployed, sent round from farmer to farmer for employment,

ment, were beginning to riot had not the yeomanry come in."

Blankets?—P. 325. "Witney—Formerly noted for the weaving manufactory, now very much declined. Instead of upwards of 400 hands employed about five year ago, there are now (1807) about 150."

"The manufacture at Witney declined for so many years, that there was very little expectation of its ever reviving. When I was there 39 years ago, there were above 500 weavers in the place, but it sunk gradually to half that number, and even lower; and very great distress was found in the place; and it was threatened with the utter loss of every means of giving bread to its numerous poor: but very fortunately for its inhabitants, the spinning jennies were introduced, with other machinery, especially the spring looms, by which one man does the work of two. As much wool (skin, not fleece wool) is wrought here as there was 40 years ago, which was then estimated at 7000 packs, and trade is increasing; machinery at present earns 4000*l.* a year, and the place, I was assured, is flourishing. But in respect to the state of the working hands, the medal must be reversed; for the former state of the manufacture having nursed up a great population, the effect of the introduction of machinery gave with such a population the power of keeping down wages in such a manner as to deprive the poor of any share in, or at least leaving them a very small one in, that prosperity which has pervaded the kingdom, and so greatly raised the general wages of labour."

Such I have long foreseen must necessarily be the effect of complicate machines of manufacture,—blowing up the bubbles of trade, and blasting the fair *prospects* of a country.

P. 326. "The fact of the present poor-rates, which are 11*s* in the pound, rack rent, is a strong confirmation of the preceding particulars; and by the way, shews how very pernicious manufactures *may* become to the landed interest."—This is a doctrine which I have been preaching, during a length of years; and I am glad to find it strengthened by a *Political Economist* of consideration.

Polished Steel.—P. 328. "Woodstock—About the beginning of the last century, the manufacture of polished steel was introduced here by a Mr. Medcalfe, which at one period was very flourishing, and employed a considerable number of hands; but from the cheapness with which articles of the same description, namely scissors, watch-chains, and a variety of trinkets, can be produced at Birmingham and Sheffield by means of machinery, a manufacture, however elegant, that is wholly completed by hand, was not likely to to stand a competition, and consequently it does not now employ above ten or twelve persons, who probably may earn from a guinea to a guinea and a half each per week.

"The Woodstock polished steel is wholly made of the old nails of horses' shoes, formed into small bars, and applied according to the various purposes required. Its lustre is extreme, and it possesses the property of being repolished at a trifling expence to its original brilliancy, though covered with rust, an advantage it maintains over the articles which are generally substituted in its room. A chain made here, and weighing only two ounces, sold for 170*l.* A box in which the freedom of the borough was presented to Lord Viscount Cliefden, cost 30 guineas; and a garter star for His Grace the Duke of Marlborough, cost 50 guineas. It is the number and the fineness of the studs, each of which is screwed in, that enhances the value and the expence of the Woodstock polished steel articles. A pair of scissors will sell, according to the workmanship, from 5*s.* to three guineas: other articles in proportion; yet it is by no means a profitable business to the manufacturer."

Gloves &c.—(In continuation) "About fifty years ago, the manufacture of leather into breeches and gloves began to be established here; and has gradually risen to a degree of reputation unrivalled, and to an extent which furnishes employment to the poor for many miles round. The making of breeches, indeed, from the disuse of leather in that article of dress, except among military men, has dwindled away to little; but in the same proportion the manufacture of gloves has been rising. Between 60 to 70 men are now employed as grounders of leather and cutters of gloves, who can earn from a guinea to 30*s.* weekly; and no fewer than 1400 or 1500 women and girls are engaged in making of gloves, whose wages, according to their diligence, will run from 8*s.* to 12*s.* per week.

"The leather grounders have a peculiar art, in dressing the skin in such a manner as to give it at once fineness of grain and tenacity of substance. The sewers too produce very durable work, and the neatness of the fabric is universally admired. Woodstock gloves likewise possess this advantage: they may be washed several times, and look well and feel comfortable to the hands till they are quite worn out. A pair of doe-skin gloves, which will cost about 5*s.* will last a gentleman who rides daily, nearly twelve months; hence they are not only more elegant, but cheaper than the gloves generally made in other places."

COUNTY

County Rates.—P. 45. "The county-rates in Oxfordshire, by the extraordinary good management of the magistrates, and the highly to be commended exertions of the gentleman who has so ably filled the Chair of the Sessions for above twenty years, have been kept down in a manner that should be an example to other counties. It does not amount, on an average, even to *3d.* in the pound; and yet a new gaol has been built at Oxford: of the management of which, details have been spread through the kingdom, and I believe have been productive of much good in various districts."

Tithes.—On this subject, all I find that calls for insertion, here, are the following *cramp*, and not readily comprehensible, paragraphs; without names!

P. 39. "In general, of arable land fairly lett, one-fourth of the rent. The University of Oxford is supposed to possess the property in whole or in part, of one-sixth of the county. By the expression *in part*, I conceive tithes to be meant."

P. 40. "In most of the enclosures that have taken place about Bicester, one-ninth and one-fifth have been given for tithe. At Lower Heyford one-fifth and one-ninth. At Hampton Poyle the same, but the land not assigned; a corn-rent. The Commissioners fixed the bushels payable by each person, according to the quality of the land, and the price is regulated every year on that of Oxford market at Lady-day and Michaelmas."

"Tithe is various in Oxfordshire; a few rectors have one in fifteen, and others one in twenty. This arose from varied endowments; half the tithe was settled on the rector, and the other half perhaps given to some religious house, and on the suppression came into lay hands. That the tithes came from the land-owner, appears from the manor farm, and that only, being in so many cases tithe-free."

Canals.—P. 14. "There is a canal at Banbury, within thirteen miles of Chipping Norton; yet barley is carried in quantities by land, 44 miles, to Birmingham, and coals brought back, and sold as cheap as those from Banbury."!

P. 325. "The Birmingham canal is of immense importance to Oxfordshire, immediately connecting London, through Oxford, with Birmingham, Manchester, and Liverpool, and with the Wednesbury collieries."

For a serious evils of canals, see *Grass Lands*, ensuing.

Roads.—P. 324. "I remember the roads of Oxfordshire forty years ago, when they were in a condition formidable to the bones of all who travelled on wheels. The two great turnpikes which crossed the county by Witney

Witney and Chipping Norton, by Henley and Wycombe, were repaired in some places with stones as large as they could be brought from the quarry; and when broken, left so rough as to be calculated for dislocation rather than exercise. At that period the cross roads were impassable but with real danger. A noble change has taken place, but generally by turnpikes, which cross the county in every direction, so that when you are at one town, you have a turnpike road to every other town This holds good with Oxford, Woodstock, Witney, Burford, Chipping Norton, Banbury, Bicester, Thame, Abingdon, Wallingford, Henley, Reading, &c. &c. and in every direction, and these lines necessarily intersect the county in almost every direction. The parish roads are greatly improved, but are still capable of much more. The turnpikes are very good, and where gravel is to be had, excellent."

PUBLIC INSTITUTION.—In a short appendix, the Reporter suggests the endowment,—with two hundred pounds a year,—of a professorship of Agriculture and Rural Economy, in Oxford;—and to furnish the vestibule of the Ratcliffe Library with BOOKS and Agricultural IMPLEMENTS.—And, in making his proposal, he says "I am supported by the respectable opinion of a most able professor." But his plan, alas! is no sooner formed, than it decomposes;—and passes off, in literary gass.

P. 345. "I could discover but one objection to such a plan: Sir Roger Newdigate by his will left 2000*l.* for the purpose of removing the Pomfret statues, &c. to the Ratcliff Library: all that are worth exhibiting might be placed in the apertures of the circumference, and be no impediment to the plan proposed: this is not the fear: but it is to be apprehended that if the execution of the plan of decoration was begun, similar objects would, by a natural extension in the hands of artists, gradually fill all the space, and absorb all the money. Utility would fly before the schemes of elegance; and the plans of Agriculture fade away amidst the visions of *Virtu.*"

RURAL ECONOMY.

TENANTED ESTATES.

ESTATES.—*Sizes.*—P. 16. "I was *informed*," (?) "that there is in the county one estate, that produces above 20,000*l.* a year *on the table;* one of 12,000*l.*, one of 7000*l.*, one

one of 6000 *l.*, one of 5500 *l.*, two of 4000 *l.*, and several of above 3000 *l.*"

PURCHASE of ESTATES.—P. 17. "Price of land,—may be estimated in Oxfordshire, in the opinion of Mr. Turner, of Burford, at 26 years' purchase, at a fair rent, yielding $3\frac{1}{2}$ per cent. on the capital invested."

TENURES.—P. 16. "The tenures by which land is held in Oxfordshire, are similar to those general through the South of England. Freehold and copyhold leases for lives remain here: and church and college leases, both for lives and years, abound greatly. The fine usual, one year and an half's rent; but the rent itself raised in many cases considerably."

DRAINING Estates.—The idea, conveyed in the subjoined extract, may, in particular cases, be found valuable; altho it might incur much expence to execute it.—In going over Mr. Foster's farm at Bignal, says the Reporter,—P. 244. "One circumstance I could not but take particular notice of, as I had never seen it before: the ditches seeming to be very shallow, I found, on examining them, that a hollow-drain was made at the bottom of them, and then filled to the depth I saw. The reason is, that if they are left open to a sufficient depth to take the water away, the sides shatter down, so as soon to stop the drains."

In forming common shore, or discharging drains, along the sides of fences, where the substratum is of a loose, slipping quality, an expedient of that sort might be found greatly beneficial.

SODBURNING.—This operation appears to be much practised in Oxfordshire:—not only in breaking up sainfoin leys, but rough grounds in general; especially on the limestone lands, or *Cotswold Hills of Oxfordshire.*

IRRIGATION.—P. 268. "No watered meadow in the county, but there might in various parts of it be a great deal. At Brightwell there might be much, but the millers will not permit any; and it is decided in this county, that a proprietor has no right to effect any operation on his own property that may tend to lessen the quantity of water, if there be any mills below him. This may be good in law, but it is horrible in politics: wind and steam will grind corn, and therefore a water-mill has little pretention to utility; and if it impedes irrigation, is a nuisance."

In every County and District in which calcareous rising grounds are found, whether the substructure is of chalk or limestone, the waters which rise on their margins seldom, perhaps scarcely ever, fail of being greatly beneficial to the effect of irrigation; and, speaking from a general and practical knowledge of the subject, there are, I doubt not, many hundreds, probably some thousands of acres of land, in in Oxfordshire, to which the practice might be profitably applied.

TENANCY.—On *Leases*, I find not a line which requires preservation. Nor on *Covenants* do I perceive any thing new or excellent; excepting a recommendation, for a stone-brash farm, of the sixshift, or true Norforlk husbandry; together with a seventh of sainfoin.

RENT.—After putting down a number of local prices, the Reporter closes his section with the subjoined statement. —Page 39.

" Red land, ...	79,635	... at 30*s*.	£. 119,452	10
Stonebrash	164,023	... at 20*s*. ...	164,023	0
Chiltern, ...	64,778	... at 16*s*. ...	51,822	8
Miscellaneous, ...	166,400	... at 25*s*. ...	208,000	0
Total ...	474,836	Ave. 22*s*. 10*d*.	£. 543,297	18"

CHOICE of TENANTS.—A few entries are made of opinions, on the subject of *capital*. The majority of them approximate to ten pounds an acre; which is a large capital. The following passage, however, shows the *required increase* of capital.

P. 71 " Thirty-nine years ago (in 1769), all Mr. Seckers's king's taxes came to 1*l*. 8*s*. 6*d*.; at present they amount to from 30*l*. to 40*l*."

Even in thirteen years the rise in the required capital of an occupier is shown, by the subjoined statement*, to be considerable.—P. 74.

	Rise per Cent.
" Labour	37
Artizans	35
Rent	20
Tithe	33
Rates	169
Average	58"

AGRICULTURE.

FARMS.—*Sizes*.—P. 30. (after copying what Mr. Davis says on this topic) " Upon the whole, they are too small to be consistent with good husbandry, and I found this to be the fact in many parts of Oxfordshire.

" About

* Taken from " a comparison of the expenses of farming in Oxfordshire, in 1790 and 1°03; returned to the Board of Agriculture." p. 72. By whom, or on what occasion, that statement was made, is not mentioned.

" About Stoken-Ash, none larger than for 200 or 300 sheep.

" The largest farms in the rich Thame district, do not usually exceed 300 acres.

" For some miles around Blenheim, farms are in general from 100 to 500 acres: here and there a larger, and some smaller. The great farmers are generally the best cultivators."

HOMESTEADS.—Respecting those, we find little more than severe censure; excepting what is said of the *neatness* of the *stacks* and *stack yards* of Oxfordshire, comparatively with those of Norfolk and Suffolk.

Building Materials.—P. 21. " Oxfordshire is under favourable circumstances in regard to a great plenty of building materials: stone and limestone abound in every part of the county; slate for ordinary buildings is found in several districts; timber remains in parts of it to a tolerable amount; but the new enclosures, as well as the open fields, are very naked: nor is the pay of artizans so high as in various parts of the kingdom."

" The Bishop of Durham, at Mungwell, has barn-floors made of beech, which, being cut down in winter, and when sawn out, laid in water for six weeks, have proved extremely durable."

COTTAGES and COTTAGE GROUNDS.—P. 23. " A large party of intelligent farmers whom I met at Mr. Fane's, all agreed, that it was highly beneficial for cottagers to have each half an acre of land. Were it only for employment to keep them from the ale-house, the object is considerable, and would alone answer the expense; but it is advantageous in many other respects "

I am well pleased to find the Secretary of the Board descending to half an acre of cottage ground. The following puzzling circumstance, perhaps, may account for it.

" Formerly, many cottagers about Baldon had two, three, or four acres, and they kept cows; now, still having the land, they keep no cows: their rent, from 30*s*. to 42*s*. per acre, and all applied as arable. A query founded upon this —How far the system could do here? Probably the scarcities banished the cows: Did they not sell their cows, and plough the ground, tempted by the high price of wheat? But how came they permitted to plough? Did they not give up cows when butter was 20 per cent. cheaper than at present?"

P. 24. " The exertions of my Lord Bishop of Durham, in building cottages, are of uncommon merit, and almost equally deserving commendation, whether the design or the execution be considered. His Lordship has raised six pairs

pairs of them; they have each a very good garden, and conveniences for pigs. They cost building something above 100*l.* each, and two guineas is the rent paid for them. They are very substantially and conveniently built."

"Rent in money is not the object; but to place the inhabitants in such a state of ease and comfort as shall tend to habits of industry, sobriety, and honesty."

This is an amiable principle, which might well be adopted, by every man of large landed property.

P. 25. "The wives and daughters of the cottagers receive all the flax they please, which is given them to spin into thread; and when they return such thread, they are paid the full price for spinning it. The Bishop has it woven into cloth, according to the fineness of the spinning; and this is sold to the cottagers' families at 2*d.* a yard lower than the ordinary price."

P. 330. "In the parish of Kempsford thirteen acres were assigned for the use of the poor, under the management of the parish officers. It was assigned in portions according to families, to do what they would with it—not lett to them, to avoid the difficulty of turning out in case of necessity: they have uniformly applied it to potatoes. The parish hired the land, and paid for it, and took the rent (the same) of the poor. The poor have found it of great benefit, and would not relinquish it on any account. But it is not made a means of lowering rates but in a very trifling degree."

I have peculiar satisfaction, in transcribing the following remarks of the MARQUIS of BLANFORD.—They are evidently the result of experience and consideration, the dictates of an unprejudiced mind.—They speak to the heart, as well as to the understanding.

P. 338 "It certainly is an object to every landlord, and it ought to be to every tenant, to make the situation of the poor industrious man as comfortable as possible; for we must know, that without his labour our farms would be of little value. But though every cottage ought to have land enough adjoining to it to raise vegetables, and in general has, I doubt whether it would be practicable to allow sufficient to keep a cow. Property is much divided in this part of the county, and many cottages belong to persons who have not more land than what the house stands upon, with the garden; and I fear that it would not answer to any cottager to rent an acre or two of land of a farmer. I likewise fear, that if the quantity of land here recommended were added to each cottage, the labourer would have great difficulty to find the money to buy a cow; and

if

if he should have the good fortune to do it for once, we know that if any accident should happen to this cow, that he must become a petitioner to raise money for a second. I mean not, however, to urge any thing against the interest of the poor man, but wish merely to submit to your consideration the propriety, or indeed the policy, particularly at the present time, of publishing an idea that may tend to make the industrious poor man discontented, and in consequence unhappy in his situation, which, in many instances cannot be relieved, and I believe we all find that the greatest happiness we enjoy is contentment."

OCCUPIERS.—The following lively remarks are entitled to preservation.—P. 35. "In regard to the character of the Oxfordshire farmers a remark may be made at present, which will not probably be just twenty years hence; and I well know, was not the case twenty, thirty, and forty years ago; when I found them to be a very different race from what they are at present They are now in the period of a great change in their ideas, knowledge, practice, and other circumstances. Enclosing to a greater proportional amount than in almost any other county in the kingdom, has changed the men as much as it has improved the country: they are now in the ebullition of this change: a vast amelioration has been wrought, and is working; and a great deal of ignorance and barbarity remains. The Goths and Vandals of open fields touch the civilization of enclosures. Men have been taught to think, and till that moment arrives, nothing can be done effectively.* When I passed from the conversation of the farmers I was recommended to call on, to that of men whom chance threw in my way, I seemed to have lost a century in time, or to have moved 1000 miles in a day. Liberal communication, the result of enlarged ideas, was contrasted with a dark ignorance under the covert of wise suspicions; a sullen reserve lest landlords should be rendered too knowing; and false information given under the hope that it might deceive: were in such opposition, that it was easy to see *the change*, however it might work, had not done its business. The old open-field school must die off before new ideas can become generally rooted."

The juncture of time at which the materials of this report were collected, was *critical*,—and somewhat inappropriate;—a dangerous time to *listen* in —It is clear, not only

* This is written in the true spirit and style of *reform!* for which this writer would seem to have a strong natural taste. He may be said to live but in the *bustle of revolution!* See EASTERN DEPARTMENT.

only from what is said, above, but from the volume at large, that *wild* rather than *practical* ideas were, then, afloat.

PLAN of MANAGEMENT.—P. 110. "Of all the circumstances in the management of arable land, in which the greatest revolution has taken place in the husbandry of this kingdom, none equals that which is to be found in the arrangement of the crops. Forty years ago, the knowledge of a true system was to be found only in the practice of Norfolk and Suffolk,* and that solely on turnip soils; and the public having had little or no information of the fact, there prevailed throughout the kingdom such ignorance of what was right, and such a practice of what was wrong, that little could be expected till such a very material point was examined and explained. New ideas in this respect have been spread, and agriculture has been improved in our counties pretty much, in proportion to the courses having been well or ill regulated. At present, we shall find in Oxfordshire something to commend, and something wherein improvements may be suggested.

"Let us, in the first place, examine the courses which are actually found."

In consequence of that determination, the reader has to pore over twenty pages, filled perhaps, with a hundred courses; as different and changeable, as the winds in March, or the weather in April;—without any general inference, useful or otherwise, being drawn from them.

P. 120 "Mr. Freeman, of Fawley-court, has engaged a steward and bailiff from Northumberland (Mr. Foster), in order to introduce the system of agriculture practised in that county. He has also lett a farm contiguous to his own, to Mr. Hairbottle, from Northumberland. This gentleman brought a colony from his own county with him, both men and women.

"The course Mr. Foster practises, and enforces among the tenantry by means of leases, is the following:

1. Turnips,
2. Barley,
3. Broad clover for one year,
4. Wheat, which is the favourite course of Northumberland."

This is a palpable error.—Mr. Bailey, twenty years ago, declared it to be impracticable. See his Report of *Northumberland*, p. 69; or my Review of the NORTHERN DEPARTMENT, p. 50.

Messrs.

* Saving and excepting the practices of DEVONSHIRE and the MIDLAND COUNTIES; which are of much older date.

Messrs. F. and H. appear to be farmers of fashion, or shall we say, *young* farmers,—rather than farmers of Northumberland.

P. 121. (In continuation) "This rotation is the well-known Norfolk system; and it is of such merit, *where it can be regularly practised,*" (!) "that not a word can be said against it. But neither Mr. Foster nor Mr. Hairbottle seem at all aware, that by clover being repeated every fourth year, the land grows what the farmers call in the East of England—*sick* of it. This has been experienced in so many different districts, and under the most excellent management, that it is idle to form a doubt concerning it."

FOUR YEARS ROTATION.

Why, then, has that course been cried up, for the last "forty years;"—during the major part of which it must have been *known* to be *impracticable?*—Even were clover and turnips as permanent on land, as beans and wheat are, it would be altogether impractical,—as a *general* plan of management.—In the neighbourhood of a LARGE TOWN (as I have before observed;) or where there is a large proportion of PERMANENT and NATURALLY FERTILE GRASS LANDS, belonging to a farm,—*the two situations being very similar in effect,*—it might be practised. But on a farm that is wholely arable,—that is to say, distitute, or nearly destitute, of PERENNIAL GRASS LAND,—and in a situation where the whole of the manure requires to be produced upon it,—by a regular number and arrangement of livestock, kept within it,—as is frequently the case,—where could the stock be pastured, during the summer months?—The clover crop is never-failingly recommended to be mown, once or twice, as the best preparation for the wheat.—Hence, not even a sheep could be *summered* on such a farm:—and a large majority of arable farms, throughout the kingdom, are nearly so circumstanced.—It might better be termed a course in the clouds, than in Norforlk, or Northumberland.

The Reporter goes on to account for what he terms "the favorite course of Northumberland."—"The agriculture of Northumberland" (he says, same page) "may be *new;* for I remember that county many years ago, in a state but emerging from the desolation of the *Borders.* Clover is certainly a new article in it, and it may not yet have experienced the defect to which I allude."

Now Mr. Bailey told us, in his masterly Report, p. 69, nearly twenty years ago, that the Northumberland occupiers had to "complain that their soil was tired of

turnips

turnips and clover."—What shall we say of the Report which is now under review?

But let us proceed:—" Nor is it well ascertained, that the climate will subject it in the same degree to this misfortune as has been experienced in the South and East of England. It is possible, that a greater degree of humility may prevent the evil; but this remains to be discovered. In the vicinity of Henley, the case is abundantly different: the farmers there have the same complaint which has occurred in so many other counties, and they have accordingly been forced to vary their crops with a view to this circumstance. These Northumberland gentlemen will not be many years before they feel the effect of it; and in that case, this regulated *system* must give way, or the effects will be extremely injurious." *Hear! Hear!*

WORKPEOPLE.—P. 322.

" Day labour in winter, ... *L.*	0	9	6
——————— spring and hay, ...	0	11	6
——————— harvest, ...	0	19	0
Women per diem in hay, ...	0	0	0
——————— harvest, ...	0	1	2
Reaping wheat, ...	0	10	0
Mowing barley, ...	0	2	4
Thrashing wheat per quarter, ...	0	3	7
——— barley, ...	0	1	10
——— oats, ...	0	1	6
——— beans, ...	0	1	5
Mowing grass, ...	0	2	8
Hoeing turnips, ...	0	6	6."

P. 318. " All the women about Baldon reap in harvest."

WORKING ANIMALS.—*Horses.*—P. 283. " Mr. Cozins, of Golder, in common with so many good farmers in Oxfordshire, never permits his horses to rest in the stable at night; they are always turned into a yard he made for that purpose, along one side of which is a range of sheds for them to retire under, provided with racks and mangers; and a bin against the opposite fence, in case any younger horses should be mastered by the older ones. This system he holds to be of much consequence in keeping the teams healthy."

P. 286. " *They!* do not (in the Dorchester district) soil upon clover, considering it as very unwholesome for them. Mr. Latham knows a farmer who has his team all distempered by this practice: some blind, others swelled legs; and others broken winded: it was from second cropped clover soiled in September.* In order that the soiling upon

* A hint, this, to *mere soilists*.

upon tares may last the longer, they are sown at several times, and spring tares also to succeed the others. *They* have an idea that much water is unwholesome for horses, and therefore are very careful in letting them have it.*

"Mr. Bonner, of Bensington, soils his teams on vetches, and never turns them out: some do it on clover, but vetches considered as much better, and healthier for the horses, as the former is apt to fill them with humours, and even to affect their sight: he thinks that horses must have a sound constitution to stand long soiling on clover.

"Mr. Costar, of Oxford, who keeps above 100 coach horses, soils them on vetches; they are in summer racked up with them, and always do well: none can be in better condition."

Oxen.—On this interesting topic, we find a succession of pages, which comprize a few valuable passages.—In the following observations of Mr. Tuckwell of Cygnet, there is much good sense, and evidence of experience.—I transcribe them with much satisfaction.

P. 291. "In regard to the benefit of working them, he could not readily conceive how any one could doubt it (note, it is the common husbandry around Burford, almost every man having them); that they are much more profitable than horses, he has not the shadow of a doubt: to keep one team of horses is useful, but all the rest should be oxen. Whenever they are not found useful, he thinks, from all he has observed, that the reason is their being improperly fed and driven. To make it so cheap a scheme as to work on straw, or any oxen that are not in good flesh, is the sure way to fail; they should be so well fed at all times, worked or not worked, as to be kept in good flesh; if they were always full half fat, it would be so much the better; they then are in heart, will work without losing flesh, and are always ready to fatten in proper time: an ox should be fattened not so much by change of food, as by merely resting from labour. Thus managed, they are as strong as any horses, and will work just as well; or at the most, the difference is not more than as four horses to five oxen: but with him, four oxen have all this summer done more work than four horses. To turn them to straw because they do not work for a month or two, he holds to be very unprofitable, and while at work, they should never lose flesh, and always thrive though worked. To let them go back in winter, and feed just when they work, is utterly unprofitable

* Horses, on green herbage, in a stable, as at grass, may require but little beverage.

unprofitable. The worst food he gives when they do not work, is cut straw, with a mixture of ordinary hay.

"If they are hard worked in barley sowing, he gives them a little barley meal night and morning, the quantity small; but at all events does not let them lose flesh, as that is much more unprofitable than improving their food. Driving is another object of much consequence; they want more attention than horses to keep them equally in work. All plough at length, both horses and oxen, and in harness.

"In health, and general freedom from disease, they are superior to horses; he does not even recollect having a lame ox."

P. 293. "Mr. Pinnal, of Westall, near Burford, one of the greatest farmers in the county, keeps more oxen than horses, and has one farm of 300 acres without a horse upon it; and he has not the least doubt, but that oxen are, upon the whole, as cheap again as horses. Upon a farm at Westall, of 600 acres, he keeps ten horses and twelve oxen: the country is all stonebrash, and upon above 2000 acres, he and Mr. Bagnall have not more than twelve acres of meadow; so that the common idea, that oxen can only be kept profitably where there is much good grass land, is completely refuted by the practice of this great and well managed farm. They keep between fifty and sixty Hereford oxen, which is the breed they prefer."

Again—"Mr. Pinnal thinks that they cannot be in too high order for work, and that the reason why the use of oxen has in many cases failed, has been nothing more than bad feeding. They lie out in the yard in winter. All the farmers in this vicinity have more oxen than horses; and far more than they had, ten, fifteen, or twenty years ago. He is very certain, that five oxen will do as much work as five horses; yet two oxen do not cost more than one horse. (?)

"Mr. Pinnall agrees with Mr. Tuckwell, that driving attentively is a great point in rendering oxen successful."

P. 296. (The Reporter.) "The result of those inquiries forms an object particularly interesting at this period. The annual import at present, of a million sterling in corn, no inconsiderable portion of which is for oats, and the well founded apprehensions that a deficiency may happen beyond the power of import to supply, united with the increasing population of the kingdom, prove that either the consumption of corn must be lessened, or the culture of it increased. That sufficient encouragement does not exist for cultivating those wastes, which, if cultivated, would

be

be under corn, their present state is a lamentable proof: and as every proposition for a general enclosure has been successfully opposed, it does not appear probable that the quantity of corn produced will be materially increased."

TILLAGE.—*Ridges.*—*Depth* of *Plowing.*—*Stale Furrow.* —Much is said concerning these particulars of management; but nothing of consideration is made out.

Fallowing.—P. 109. "Mr. Davis, of Bloxham," (not the original Reporter,) "never saw any land upon which a naked fallow is necessary; none even on the stiffest soils. He has been a practical farmer many years on a large scale, and has seen many counties minutely in his business, but was never yet convinced that any such necessity existed. Every one who knows this gentleman, knows that he has long been a Commissioner of many enclosures, having been employed upon 26 at the same time, and is an excellent practical farmer."—But on what sort of soil is not mentioned.—Mr. Davis may be a good commissioner; yet a bad farmer of summer-fallow land. Therefore, pass we on.

"Mr. Cozins, of Golder, is a decided advocate for frequent fallows: upon the strong soils of his farm, he is of opinion that they must recur every third year, insomuch, that he fallows after beans, and clover, and vetches. To expose the land to the sun is of such importance with him, that it cannot be done away. In fallowing for wheat, he ploughs the land five times; not for freeing it from couch, but for the sake of letting the sun into it.

"I have published cases, in which an extraordinary degree of fallowing has produced bad crops: Mr. Fane found a very different result; for having fallowed one year for wheat on his Chiltern-hill farm, and being disappointed in sowing it, he continued the fallow another year, and then sowed wheat, and the produce was six quarters per acre."

It would have been interesting, though perhaps somewhat painful, to have been present at the first meeting of those three informants, after their several prompt opinions were thus held up to public view. The two latter are *Agriculturists*, the first a *Land Valuer*;—and gentlemen of that profession may sometimes find an advantage in shapeing their arguments and opinions, agreeably to their auditors;—or, in other words, are too well *mannered* to offend the ear of fashion.

MANURE.—*Yard Dung.*—In 1807, the subject of "long dung and short dung" was in a high state of fermentation, in Oxfordshire; as it was in Norfolk, in 1804.

The

The Reporter himself, however, would seem, in the present instance at least, to have furnished the barm. And finding it, in one case, to work kindly, he thus throws a taunt at those whose cold comprehensions prevent them from being susceptible of its influence.

P. 255. "I beseech you, gentlemen, to go on carting, turning, mixing, *mining*, and rotting; give your manure to the sun and to the winds; continue to expend no trifling sums in the reduction of four to one, in order, by studied operations, to render your one less valuable than the fourth of the original four: it is a wise conduct, therefore stick close to it, and argue strenuously for it over the next bottle you drink. *Mine* away; see that the heap lies light; keep the carts off; take care that the air pervades it, and let the sun shine and the winds blow—Who's afraid?"—Bravo!

The instance of practice in which was seen the wonderful workings of long dung, occurred in that of "Mr. Shrubb of the White Hart Inn," Bensington;—who perhaps had fifty or a hundred corn-fed horses in his stables, with but little space in which to stow away their dung; and whether the manure raised by them was spread on the land, in a long or a short state, its advantages could not fail of being great, and obvious at sight.

In the following instance, we see a disadvantage of that practice.—P. 256. "The Bishop of Durham, at Mungwell, keeps his dung till it is quite rotten, and all fermentation over, whether it is his own made at home, or that bought at the town of Wallingford.

"The farmer who occupied the farm before his Lordship had it, used long dung; and by that means filled the land so full of weeds, that the practice has been carefully avoided ever since."

It is perfectly childish to talk about the application of dung, in a long or a short state, without, at the same time, specifying the nature and existing state of the land, and the crop for which it is about to be applied.

Pigeons' Dung.—P. 262. "Sir C. Willoughby spreads this manure as a top-dressing for barley, and finds the use so great as to prove the benefit of a dove-house, were there no other object. In order to increase the quantity, he carries into the pigeon-house the poultry dung, and seeds of weeds from the barns (the heat killing all). The effect of the dressing is seen to an inch."

Lime.—This is not a prevalent manure of Oxfordshire.—The ideas collected, concerning it, are crude and contradictory.

Ashes.—These are the principal extraneous manure of the

the County:—mostly peat ashes, from Newbury in Berkshire;—also some coal ashes.—The quantities of the former, that were said to be used, is scarcely credible,—chiefly on clover and sainfoin leys.

P. 264. "Mr. Sarney, of Soundes, has sown 5000 bushels of peat-ashes in one year, and 3000 or 4000 per annum many times. The price, 8*d*. per bushel.*

"Sir C. Willoughby, 25 to 40 bushels of coal-ashes. This manure is largely used by Sir C. Willoughby; and a trial he made, comparatively shewed that those of the Newcastle and Wednesbury coals are of equal benefit—there was no difference. Wood-ashes far better, but cannot be obtained in large quantities."

Rags.—"Rags are likewise in use."

Gypsum.—P. 267. "Mr Sarney, of Soundes, sowed six bushels of gypsum per acre, on clover, in March, and the effect immense.

"Mr. Davenport, at Shirborn, in 1807, sowed it on sainfoin and clover, and it did no good whatever."

SEMINATION of Wheat.—*Drilling.*—P. 135. "Scarcely any drilling in the northern and eastern part of the southern division, but a little in the southern part of that district."

P. 138. "The drill husbandry in this county must be considered as in its infancy; all that can be said of it in praise is, that there are some features which promise improvement."

WHEAT.—A digested (not well digested) detail of memoranda, nearly a sheet of paper in length, is found under this head. Little, however, of practical instruction can be gathered from it. Nevertheless, some useful ideas require to be transcribed.

Soil.—P. 139. "It is a mark of the general fertility of the county, that wheat succeeds well on all the soils to be found in it."

P. 140. "Mr. Newton, a very able manager at Swincombe, dungs his layers intended for wheat in August; ploughs and sows, and then runs the fold lightly over it. This is found to do well."—Of what specific quality is his soil?

Tillage for Wheat.—P. 140. "Mr. Bonner, of Bensington, ploughs his layers for wheat as shallow as possible; but a full depth for turnips. If the land for wheat has been dressed with rags, or penned with sheep, he is fearful of burying the manure; but another reason for shallow ploughing

* Exclusive of carriage?

ploughing is, that the wheat loves a firm bottom to root in."

P. 141. "Sir C. Willoughby ploughs his clover lays as shallow as possible for wheat, and especially if manured, whether by dung or fold, on sandy land, as the soil cannot be too tight."

"A party of excellent farmers," (without *names*) "invited by Mr. Fane to meet the Writer of this Report, all agreed, that in ploughing a clover-lay for wheat, it should be as shallow as possible; and I found, in riding over the country, that this maxim seemed every where to be adhered to. If any reasoning be applied to it, it must be that of leaving a part of former furrows solid for the roots of the plants to fix in; as all know that this grain loves a firm bottom, and that too loose a one causes a root-fallen crop."—On light, loose soils, this practice may be judicious. But let not the occupiers of closely textured, cold clayey lands, take it up too hastily.

The *Time* of *Sowing* Wheat.—The practice of the Cotswold Hills of Glocestershire appears, by this Report, to extend into Oxfordshire;—the time being given by the first rain which falls in August or September.—This, however, is probably confined to the limestone lands, only.

Mode of *Sowing*.—P. 143. "Generally ploughed in on fallows, and harrowed in on clover: very little drilled."

Varieties of Wheat.—P. 148. "Spring wheat has been cultivated by various persons in Oxfordshire for about eight years past."

The *Quantity* of Seed.—This is set down as being very small; as 1½ to 2½ bushels. But this likewise, it is probable, belongs to the Oxfordshire Cotswolds only; and early sowing may account for it.

Covering the Seed.—It seem to be an almost general practice on the lighter lands of Oxfordshire, to fold sheep on them, immediately after sowing; or to drive them over it, at that time. This admirable practice is not peculiar to Oxfordshire.—The roller gives only a partial pressure. The dints and hollows of the surface receive little benefit from it: whereas the picked hoofs of sheep, if they be driven thickly and repeatedly over it, press upon, and close up the fissures and pores of every part; and not only tend to shield the soil from the effect of drought; but to prevent or check the ravages of sodworms, and other destructive reptiles, which inhabit soils of that nature;

The following is an extraordinary instance of compression.—P. 302. "As soon as the wheat is sown, he" (Mr. Cripps) "drives his sheep two or three times up and down every land, and does not find that it hurts the sheep much. And

And this system of treading is of such importance, that he would not be precluded from it for 20*s.* an acre. The practice is considered as so harmless, relative to the sheep, that it is not uncommon for a flock-master to lend his flock for this purpose to a neighbour who has none. The object would not be answered by any system of common rolling. Last year he had a piece of clover land wheat, much eaten by slugs; and in November got broad-wheel carts loaded with stones, and drew them three horses a-breast, across, till the surface was well whelled upon. This operation killed the slugs, and the wheat proved as fine a crop as could be seen."

Produce of Wheat.—P. 153. "From all I saw and heard in the county, and combining the intelligence with the quality of the soil, I estimate the average produce of the whole county at three quarters; exceeding rather than falling short."

Stubbles of Wheat.—P. 153. "These are cut and gathered in the vales; but on the hills they cut closer, and therefore do not follow the practice."

BARLEY.—*Produce.*—P. 156. "The nearest estimate to be given of the average produce of the county, is four quarters."

BEANS.—*Semination.*—P. 161. "In the south district of Oxfordshire, nearly all the beans I saw were dibbled: 15 inches the common distance of the rows."

POTATOES.—P. 185 "This root, upon the whole, is but little cultivated in Oxfordshire, compared with what it is in most of the counties with which I am best acquainted."

TURNIPS.

AGAIN, we find the Secretary of the Board harping on his favorite string,—still lingering on the new-fangled notion of expelling the plow (as a body might say) from the field of agriculture. See the EASTERN DEPARTMENT.

P. 166. "Mr. Davy, of Dorchester, sows trefoil for spring-food, and breaks it up very late in the spring for turnips; and he finds, that there are no finer turnips than those which he gains in this manner. All the circumstances which tend to shew that good crops may be gained without the usual number of ploughings, should be noted, that hereafter, like scattered rays of light, they may be brought to one focus." (!) "The land thus managed, cannot have been ploughed since the spring-sowing of the preceding year, and turnips are *supposed*" (?) "to demand more ploughing than any crop; but here we find that the want of of more tillage is made up by the roots of the trefoil, and the dung and urine of the sheep that eat it. The next time the land comes round for turnips, a regular fallow" (?) "is given; not because the turnips want it, but that weeds may be the better destroyed by the *variation of the tillage*." *(a laugh.)*

We have no information regarding the nature or the state of the land, in this case; nor any account of the loss sustained, in the intervening crops (whether of corn or herbage) by the want of sufficient tillage—by the foulness and the consequent *inertness*, which necessarily took place; nor of the extra labor which the next fallow took, to bring it to the state of culture which a crop of turnips, in a *continuable* course of practice, essentially requires.

In the section "Turnips," which occupies a succession of pages, I find nothing, *else*, which requires particular notice, here;—excepting Mr. Lowndes's method of preparing the ground, early in June (provided, let us hope, it can be properly prepared, thoroughly cleansed and maturely cultured, by that time) and permitting it to remain until the season of sowing, and until rain fall; then, partially breaking, and slightly furrowing, the surface, with the "Wiltshire eleven-share plow." p. 171.

This method is not entirely new, nor peculiarly eligible;—I have seen a similar practice, in Devonshire; in which was used the "tormentor" of that country; and which is a much more efficient implement, for the purpose; as it more effectually destroys the weeds which have taken root: whereas the Wilshire "drag" or "drag plow,"—not acting entirely as a *sub-plow*,—will necessarily leave, uncut, many strong, deep-rooting weeds, of several weeks growth, perhaps, to encumber the surface and obstruct the hoe.

I have noticed this particular of practice, the rather, as I formerly met with an instance of a corresponding nature, in Norfolk; in which the turnip fallow was suffered to lie, some time, between the two last plowings; the seed weeds that rose in the interim being turned in with the common plow, at seed time; and this with good success.—See my NORFOLK; Minute 71.

There are soils and seasons in which this principle of management may be found highly eligible; more particularly on light land, in a dry season. The only objection to it, perhaps, is the abridgement of culture which it of course occasions, at a critical season. It is not the turnip crop, alone, that is to be looked forward to. The crops of herbage and corn that are to follow it, and the state of the soil, at the end of the course, are important objects of consideration.

BULBOUS

BULBOUS RAPE.—The culture of this very valuable crop appears to be fully established, and its management to be well understood, in Oxfordshire.—The following are the Reporters own remarks upon it.

P. 182. "The intelligence in this respect is almost uniform, and I examined such a multitude of crops in this year so unfavourable to all turnips, and found the culture so well understood and so successfully practised, that it is impossible, with any degree of candour, to be sparing in commendation. It appears, from a variety of experiments, that May is the right time here for sowing them: the season, however, extends through the whole month of June. They are all sown broad-cast, and hoed out from nine to twelve and fourteen inches asunder. Good farmers give, all two, and some three, hoeings: nor is the attention of hand-weeding wanted, except in a few instances, in which I have seen too much charlock scattered over some crops in autumn. The use of them in feeding sheep is well understood, and they are much relied on for the late and difficult season in the spring. The improvement of slicing, and giving them in troughs to penned sheep, much deserves attention; and the great importance of their application in the fattening of oxen, from stores preserved for that purpose, well deserves the imitation of many other counties."

The roots, or rather bulbs, have there been applied to a purpose which may not be thought of, in other districts;—namely that of *fatting swine.*

Might not *working horses* be profitably fed with them; and perhaps a small quantity of corn, *in spring seed time?*—This would probably be found to be more wholesome food, than dry meat, alone, at that parching season.

P. 181. Mr. James Paine "has found the application of them in fattening porkers to be the most profitable of all: they should run about as in common, only with as many Swedes as they can eat." (?) "Nine porkers paid him each 6*d.* per diem, for six weeks together, eating this root, which is a very remarkable fact, and highly valuable for the cultivators of this root to be acquainted with. His two brothers confirmed the fact, and had had great success in the same way themselves."

For a commodious contrivance, used in slicing them;—see *Sheep*, ensuing.

SAINFOIN.

ON the limestone lands of Oxfordshire, as on those of Glocestershire (the Cotswold hills) sainfoin is a prevailing crop, and the culture of it well understood.—It is also grown

grown on the chalk lands, of the southern extreme of the County.

I perceive nothing in this Report, however, that is sufficiently new or excellent to require notice, in this place; excepting the practice of sowing *ashes* over it; as has been already mentioned, under the head, *Manures*, aforegoing. The subjoined extract shows, in a striking manner, their very extraordinary effect.

P. 191. "Mr. Fane manures all his sainfoin with peat or coal ashes every year: 12 bushels of the latter, or 16 to 20 of the former. The benefit of the culture he finds to be immense: he has had 50 good waggon-loads of hay from 14 acres, and on an average, two loads an acre. But this produce depends very much on manuring; for the fields which, with ashes, will give two loads, may not yield half a load without. This vast superiority has been long well understood. Mr. Fane's father thought his bailiff very extravagant in such constant buying of ashes, and objected to it. The bailiff ashed a field in the common manner, except about one acre, and there spread none. At crop time he took his master over the field; and when Mr. Fane came to the spot not manured, he stopt his horse, and asked the man what could be the matter with that bit? When the reason was explained, the conviction was complete; and the bailiff had orders to proceed in buying all the ashes he wanted."

But the most extraordinary circumstance which occurs, in going over the ten or twelve pages that are appropriated to this crop, is, that the Writer of them appears to be unacquainted with the specific nature,—the essential quality,—of sainfoin land; as the two following paragraphs pretty clearly show.

P. 194. "There are considerable tracts of dry hard gravel, with a good red sand surface, in the Dorchester district, upon which it might be conceived that sainfoin would do well; but it has been tried by Mr. Davy, and by Mr. Latham, and it was not found to answer."

P. 198. "It has been found, in many trials around Chipping Norton, that sainfoin will not succeed upon old heath land, on which furze was the spontaneous growth: it presently goes off, and is lost."

It were just as rational to expect that aquatic plants would florish on an arid mountain, or alpine plants within the margin of a lake, as to *try* to make sainfoin *anwer*, on non-calcareous lands.—It may be known, with a great degree of certainty, where sainfoin may be profitably cultivated, before its seeds be sown. If a stratum of calcareous rubble mixed with white efflorescent matter lies beneath the

the soil, there sainfoin may be sown, with a certainty of success; and with a duration proportioned to the depth and degree of calcariosity of such substratum,—and to the management it may receive.—Soft calcareous rock, also, especially if rent, and divided by fissures, will promote its growth with certainty.

Its *duration*, however, does not wholely depend on the nature of the substratum. Much is due to *management*. Suffering it to be eaten down with stock, in the spring, or during the summer months, shortens its duration.—On the contrary, letting it stand, until it reach its full growth, particularly if occasionally permitted to mature its seed, prolongs it;—most especially, no doubt, where its field of pasturage is in the clefts of rocks;—down which it will descend to almost any depth; if not cheked by improper treatment.

In the Report under view, we find *general*, and of course jarring, opinions, about the proper time of *repeating* this crop!—If the field of pasturage be *confined*, and the former management has been *judicious*, it will be some length of years before this crop will be found to florish, again, on the same land.—On the contrary, if the feeding stratum be *deep*, and *rich in calcareous*, matter; and the treatment has been *injudicious*, so as to prevent the roots from striking downward, and otherwise extending themselves,—much unexhausted pasturage will of course remain; and the same land may be cropped again, in a few years, or immediately; with the required success;—under, it is to be understood, more appropriate management.

GRASS LANDS.—On these, we find but little information; scarcely any of the Reporter's own collecting. Indeed, Oxfordshire is not, emphatically, a grass-land County. The subjoined passages are the only one that is entitled to transcription.

P. 207. "At Water Eaton is the best grass land in the county; it is under dairies. I examined these fine meadows, and found their appearance and stock to justify the character I had heard of them; but they are subject to summer floods, which sometimes do much mischief, insomuch, that Mr. Rowland has had five hundred pounds' worth of hay lost, or greatly damaged, in a single season."

P. 206. ("signed MS. Annot.") "A very large tract of valuable meadow land in Oxfordshire and Northamptonshire, on the banks of the river Cherwell, has been much injured, and in many places spoilt, by a navigable canal made immediately above its level, and, from Banbury to Oxford, very ill executed: the extent from the first-mentioned place to where the canal leaves the meadows,

is

is about 20 miles. It is rendered extremely boggy by the continual oozing of the water through its banks; and, in lieu of meadow-grasses of the best quality, with which it before abounded, is now over-run by *caltha palustris*, (marsh marigold), and other aquatic plants. This evil, if not remedied, will increase daily."—This serious evil of canals is not confined to Oxfordshire; and comes fairly against them, as an offset, in calculating their neat public value.

LIVESTOCK.

CATTLE.—*Breed.*—Oxfordshire possesses no breed of its own. In the first four notices, we find four distinct varieties; namely, the *Alderney*, the *Devonshire*, the *short-horned* and the *longhorned.*—Indeed, the Reporter tells us, after having filled nearly a sheet of paper, with conversational memoranda about them, that (p. 283.) "The intelligence relative to cattle in Oxfordshire, is not locally interesting. The county has no breed of its own; nor is any particular race so predominant as to afford much information that is particularly valuable; much the greater part of the county is arable; and in the very narrow districts where grass prevails, there is not much to excite the attention of the traveller."—A few short notices, however, relating to *fatting cattle* and the *dairy*, may have their use.

Fatting Cattle.—P. 273. "Some farmers fatten their cows on oil-cake, and for very large beasts it answers; but hay is more general."

P. 281. "The winter made cake is by far better than that made in summer; the latter is dry and hard."

"Mr. Coburn, of Witney, has built a very complete ox-house for stall-feeding: he fattens Herefords chiefly on hay only, and has sold as high as 36*l.* and 37*l.* per ox. The hay is cut into chaff, and about a sack of barley to finish each ox, ground into meal."

P. 282. "Mr. Singleton, of Bampton, who grazes largely, buys Hereford oxen in the spring, and some in the autumn: the former are turned to grass, and in November to hay and bean-meal, or that of barley, but beans better: gives half a peck twice a day, hay at the same time."

P. 283. "In hay feeding, they find that such as heated in the stack loses much of its *proof*."—This seems to be contradictory of the practice of the VALE of GLOCESTER; where the stall fatters, with hay, give it, frequently, what they call a "double heat."

Dairy.—P. 271. "Mr. Cozins, of Golder, keeps about 100

100 cows, of which 12 are for the dairy, 54 for suckling, 10 drying off, and 40 fatting."

P. 272. "The rich district of Thame is applied to the dairy, or to suckling: the breed, the short horns. None bred but all bought in calf at three years old. They are kept a year and a half or two years, or proportionably to their time of keeping in milk. The dairy is reckoned more profitable than suckling; but also more troublesome."

"These cows are fed upon hay only, in winter; and eat the produce of two acres, which yield two ton per acre."—So that, according to this statement, each cow eats four loads of hay: that is to say, the produce of three or four acres of land of a middle quality, *in winter only*.—Yet we have heard, from the Board's Reports, of two or three acres of land (without perhaps saying a word about its quality!) being sufficient for a cow, *the year round*.

P. 274. "Sheep are kept among all the dairy cows."

P. 275. "No dairy-maid in this country milks, nor in Bucks or Northampton; all done by men or lads; and over in an hour, or at most an hour and a half, whatever the number of cows."

P. 278. "Waggons go from Bicester to London with butter, taking ten tons per week: chiefly loaded between Bicester and Wheatley."

P. 279. "Mr. Salmon, of Hardwick, keeps 80 cows, and has his three churns so attached to one standard of a water wheel, that they are all turned at once; and in case of frost, or a want of water, a horse-wheel works them."

SHEEP.—*Breed.*—Of sheep, as well as of cattle, Oxfordshire may be said to be destitute of a *native* breed: Formerly, the *Wiltshire*, the *Berkshire*, and the *Cotswold* breeds, would seem to have been the prevailing sorts. Of later years, the *Leicester*, and still later, the *Southdown* breeds, have, shall we say, been "*twisted in*." At the time the materials of the Report before me were collected, *crossing* appears to have been *in*, among fashionable flock masters; so that the aggregate flock of the County, *must* have been the compleatest medley!

I am under the necessity of using this indeterminate manner of speech; as I can find nothing resembling a definite account of the breed or breeds of the *County at large*, in the work before me. In the section "Sheep," though more than a sheet of letterpress in length, nothing is seen, saving memorandum-book entries, the products of CONVERSATIONS, with a *comparatively few* individual occupiers. I have, however, patiently endeavored to catch, and gather together, all the useful ideas I could, respecting

respecting the existing breeds of the County, at the time of conversing; and the above is the result of my endeavors.

Management of *Store* Sheep.—P. 300. "Mr. Davy feeds his sheep with the straw of pease and beans; preferring the latter, but given plentifully, that they may only pick off the pods: they have turnips also.

"In the Dorchester district, natural grass being extremely scarce, straw is given in large quantities to sheep. As soon as frosty mornings come, barley straw is given in the yards or standing pens; and afterwards bean and pea straw, which they are very fond of: they pick off the pods and tops, and do well upon this food. Bean and pea straw are sometimes carted to the field for their supply, and what they do not eat brought home to the yards."

P. 301. "Mrs. Latham, of Clifton, has one of the completest sheep yards, if not the most so, in this county: a shed surrounds three sides of it, in which are racks and mangers; it is 31 yards long and 16 broad: the sheds five broad, and it does very well for 200 ewes. They are brought into it from four to six weeks before lambing, and continued till it is over, going out in the day time. It is considered as a very excellent method, but attention should be paid that the dung does not accumulate, which by fermentation injures the sheep; it is therefore carted out at several times."

Fatting Sheep.—P. 312. "Mr. Payne, and Mr. Wyat, of Hanwell, have a house on four wheels, to cover a man and boy in using a machine for *slicing Swedes*;" (!) "a man and boy will cut enough for 100 sheep, and give them in troughs: no scooping or waste, and answers better than any thing; and also gives under sheds, and they thrive much better, most advantageously, never go backward, but thrive well in all weather."

Folding Sheep.—P. 302 (Q. Mr. Cripps of Burcot's practice?) "Folding goes on in summer for turnips, then for wheat, previous to sowing, and for a month or six weeks after Michaelmas, if the weather permits, and will be folding after the wheat is quite green."

P. 307. "Mr. Sotham does not pen in summer: he wants water, and therefore the sheep are left out for the dews. He is clear that more sheep may be kept without penning than with it; and more is lost in the sheep than the land gains. In summer they lie under hedges, and if penned, must go to the pens empty: they do far better without it.

"Mr. Pratt, of Fowley, has a very high opinion of folding sheep, though all in the country are long woolled; and he is confident that more sheep may be kept on a farm by folding than without it: his reason is, that they stain their food

food so much less, by taking them from their feeding ground, where they are sure to rest too much in the same place, if not driven from it. *Mr. Pratt, do you ever fold fatting sheep?* Never. *Why not?* They will not do so well if they are folded. *Mr. Pratt, can that be beneficial to an ewe which keeps a wether from fattening?*"

Might not those smart questions, to puzzle a simple swain, (perhaps) be parodied in this way, with equal propriety?—"Pray, Mr. Pratt do you *work* your *fatting oxen?* &c. &c. &c.—Oxen are worked to *till* the ground, and sheep are folded to *manure* it. The detriment to the team or the flock is so much. But if the value to the land be greater, the practice is good."

MERE AMATEURS in AGRICULTURE,—having no comprehensive knowledge of the art,—are liable to dwell upon, and enforce, a few individual points,—generally the last they have listened to,—without being at all aware of the manner in which they operate on the GENERAL SYSTEM,—in PRACTISING the ART AT LARGE.

BUCKINGHAMSHIRE.

BUCKINGHAMSHIRE.

THIS COUNTY, in like manner, as Oxfordshire, is aukwardly thrown across the line of demarkation, which naturally separates the *Midland* from the *Southern* Department:—not only occupying a portion of the chalk hills; but bending over them, into the vale lands that lie at their feet; —the northern margin of the vale of London.—

The main body of the County, however, being situated within the limits of the MIDLAND DEPARTMENT, it is proper to bring forward the Reports what have been given of it to the Board of Agriculture,—in this place.

"GENERAL VIEW

OF THE

AGRICULTURE

OF THE

COUNTY OF

BUCKINGHAM,

WITH

OBSERVATIONS ON THE MEANS OF ITS IMPROVEMENT.

BY MESSRS. WILLIAM JAMES,

AND

JACOB MALCOLM,

OF STOCKWELL, NEAR CLAPHAM.

1794."

REGARDING the QUALIFICATIONS of Messrs. JAMES and MALCOLM, as *agricultural* Reporters, we find no intimation, either from the Board or themselves; saving what their Report affords. From their prompt recommendation of *planting* and their *modest* suggestion that "it might be adviseable, perhaps, to appropriate the whole (as near as may be) of these wastes" (6000 acres) "to the growth of timber only;" because—" we can import corn, when we cannot import English

English oak," p 35;—we are led to the idea that they are conversant with that *very useful art,—when judiciously employed.*

But we perceive not a page, nor even a passage, which convinces us that they were, at the time of writing, sufficiently versed in PRACTICAL ENGLISH AGRICULTURE, to enter on the task of surveying and reporting the practice of a County; especially of one which is situated at a distance, from the place of their residence;—" Stockwell near Clapham" being in the County of *Surrey.*—Their only knowledge of the rural affairs of BUCKINGHAMSHIRE appears to have arisen in a TOUR of ENQUIRY.—Yet no inconsiderable part of their brief sketch is occupied by didactic recommendations of *improvements!* while (judging from what appears in their Report) they might be said to be unacquainted with the groundwork and bearings of it *established practice;*—strangers to the fundamental principles, and general state, of its existing management.

This required censure is not peculiarly applicable to the performance under review; but might be used, with nearly equal force and propriety, concerning a majority of the Board's Reports.

This is one of the " original Reports" to the Board, in 1794.

The number of pages—sixtythree.

NATURAL ECONOMY.

SOILS.—P. 8. " It appears that the county is principally composed of rich loam, strong clay and chalk, and loam upon gravel. As to the first, its ability to produce good crops without the assistance of much manure, is evident from the uniform verdure of the herbage (as it is chiefly applied to the dairy, farming, and only occasionally mowed) and the very great supply of butter which is produced from that land."

POLITICAL ECONOMY.

APPROPRIATION.—The Reporters appear to have been commendably assiduous to obtain information, on this important subject; they having minuted, in making their tour the state of " Inclosure," in which they found the county.

county.—Their details, however, are seldom of general import; though they may, in time to come, be of local interest; as data in the topography of the County.

Common Pastures.—P. 35. "From the extent of the county, it might have been expected, that a much greater portion of waste land would have been met with. It does not, however, appear to be above 6000 acres."

For an account of Wadden Chace, see *Woodlands*, ensuing.

Common Fields.—P. 27. "As it is a subject of no small importance to the grand object which the Board of Agriculture has in view, we have been the more particular in ascertaining, with as much exactness as possible, short of actual measurement, the quantity of common field lands throughout the district."

After inserting their parochial minutes, the Reporters say, p. 32. "Putting these several parcels together, then, we find that the county of Buckingham contains about 91,906 acres of common-fields, exclusive of the wastes."

Under the head, "Obstacles to Improvement" the Reporters speak of the disadvantages of common fields.—The following remarks are entitled to transcription.

P. 58. "But these are not the only obstacles to the common-field husbandry; the slovenly operations of one man are very often of serious consequence to his neighbours, with whose property his lands may lie, and generally do lie very much intermixed. Every one is aware of the noxious quality of weeds, whose downy and winged seeds are wafted by every wind, and are deposited upon those lands which are contiguous to them; and which before were perhaps as clean as the nature of them would admit, to the manifest injury of the careful and attentive farmer. Inclosures would, in a certain degree, lessen so great an evil: they would also prevent the inroads of other people's cattle, as particularized in the parish of Wendover, and in which one man held eighteen acres in thirty-one different allotments."

Manufactures.—P. 46. "The principal manufactures in this district are those of paper and lace. Lace is made in many parts of the county by women and children; the best hands can earn from one shilling to eighteen-pence per day. But all these manufactures together do not employ so great a number of hands as to produce any particular effect upon the agriculture of the district."

Tithes.—The Reporters speak, at some length, on the subject of tithes, as an obstacle of improvement.—Their observations, however, are *general*; and do not arise out of their survey of *Buckinghamshire*. Nevertheless, the concluding paragraph is noticeable; as comprizing a distinction

tinction between *clerical* and *lay* tithe-owners; which is *just*, where the former are *resident*.—But the *nonresident Clergy* may well be classed, as tithe owners, with lay impropriators.

P. 62. "In whatever point of view tithes are considered, whether it be in the hands of the clergy, which is placing them in the best situation, and where they were originally designed to be; or whether they are in the hands of the lay impropriator, who, generally speaking, has no other interest in the parish, and therefore less mindful of being upon good terms with the inhabitants; they are in either case strong obstacles to every improvement upon agriculture."

RURAL ECONOMY.

TENANTED ESTATES.

ESTATES.—P. 10. "In looking over the division of the manors of this county, it evidently appears, that originally they were in few hands; consequently that the property possessed by individuals was large, which is indeed to this day in some measure the case; but the great influx of wealth has of late years been the means of making that property more general."

"On the hills are the seats of the Earl of Inchiquin, Countess of Orkney, Lord Boston, and the very improving seat of Lord Grenville, together with other families of lesser note. In the same division, but in the lower parts, are to be found the seats of the Dukes of Marlborough and Portland, Marquis of Lansdowne, Earl Beaulieu, Sir John Dashwood, William Drake, Esq."

P. 11. "In the northern part, the magnificent seats of the Marquis of Buckingham, the Earl of Chesterfield, Sir William Lee, Bart."

DRAINING Estates.—P. 40. "Another mode of draining, or, as it is provincially called, reclaiming of bogs, is now carrying on upon a very extensive scale, upon the Marquis of Buckingham's estates in this county. This noble personage is giving all possible support and encouragement to every branch of agriculture, and his wishes and intentions are very ably seconded by the great attention and industry of Mr. Parrott. The buildings and other erections are conducted upon a neat and improved plan, and will, doubtless, in a short time prove useful models for that part of

of the county. The mode of draining alluded to is this: A well is dug out from six to ten feet deep,* and about three feet wide, through different stratums of soil, until they cut through the gravel to the quicksands; then with a machine they bore, until a spring is found, which may sometimes lie as low as from twelve to eighteen feet.† The water then boils up and continues running, by which means the hole is kept open. A hollow drain is then made with rough stones, from the lower side of the well (if there is any inequality, and if not, on that side which is nearest to the ditch or receptacle) into which the water is to be conveyed, and this about nine inches square, or larger, as the case may require; after this the well is filled up with rough stones, nearly to its top, and higher than the top of the drain, and upon these stones is placed as much of the soil which came out of the well as will fill it to the surface, and then it may be sown with white clover, or with grain, and occupied in the same manner as the rest of the field. It is scarcely credible what large tracts of land a few of these drains will completely make dry; and therefore we are happy that we have it in our power to answer in so particular a manner this important question."‡

SODBURNING.—P. 41. "*Paring and Burning*—is no where practised in this district that we could discover."

IRRIGATION.—P. 18. "In the district now under consideration, we find large tracts possessing in so high a degree

* From three to six feet are frequently sufficient.

† This must be false Report. If "they cut through the gravel to the quicksand," the borer is not wanted. But boring was, then, the fashion.

‡ DRAINING WELLS.—A fact which is sufficiently remarkable to be mentioned, here, is that, for some years past, I have been practising a method of draining which almost perfectly resembles that above reported; without being in the least aware of its prior existence; until I sat down to review the Report which is now before me; my plan having risen, by long continued and slow degrees, out of my own practice.—See my NORFOLK, *Minute* 65; first published in 1787; and from a hint there thrown out, the above reported practice *may* have originated.

In many cases, it is a most valuable method; especially in those of boggy tumors, on the slopes of rising grounds; where draining wells, sunk at a trifling cost, will often give more radical effect, than superficial drains, cut at ten times the expence, could produce.

There are, doubtlessly, some few cases, especially in hilly districts, in which the *borer* may be beneficially applied, at the botton of the *well*. But if *this* be sunk to the lodgement of the offending waters, which, in ordinary cases, it ought and can, it is not required. I have never used the borer with any other view, than to *find* the water; and thereby to avoid unnecessary labor, in sinking wells.—See my TREATISE ON LANDED PROPERTY, 4to edition, p. 95. Or the 8vo. edition, p. 110.

degree the advantage of watering, that the farmer can flow his grounds when, and where he pleases, brooks and rivulets running through the greater part of these fine meadows, with few or no mills to interrupt or to controul him in the free application of their fructifying streams. Would it be believed, then, that excepting in the neighbourhood of one or two of the paper-mills, there is scarce one acre of land watered throughout the county? Concerning so singular a circumstance the Board may rest satisfied that we have omitted no opportunity of getting information; having made every possible inquiry among the most intelligent and best informed men.

"One very respectable gentleman farmer, in the Vale of Aylesbury, assures us, (and this was confirmed by others) that their meadows were by nature so rich, that watering, as it is practised in other countries, made their crops of grass so rank and coarse, that two acres of their natural meadow-grass, not watered, though less in quantity, was superior in quality; and worth more than two acres and a half of similar quality of meadow, in a watered state."

TENANCY.—P. 45. "The leases generally run for twenty-one years, confining the tenants to two crops and a fallow, sometimes to three crops and a fallow, interdicting clover and green food; these are principally confined to the common-fields. In the southern part of the county, a more liberal extension prevails; the leases run from fourteen to twenty-one years: in a few places leases are granted for three lives."

WOODLANDS.

BEECH WOODS.—P. 41. "From Marlow to Fingest, and through that space which is bounded by the road leading from London to Oxford, on the south side, and by the River Thames on the north, one sixth part of the land is supposed to be covered with beech wood, and which may yield a profit of from fourteen to twenty shillings per acre per annum. These woods require but little attention, as the old trees shed a sufficient quantity of seed to keep the wood constantly full of young plants. This valuable wood is converted to a variety of purposes, one of which is the affording an abundance of fuel to that part of the county where coals are scarce.

"In the parish of Wycombe there are 700 acres of common (beech) woodland. In the neighbourhood of Chesham are large thriving beech woods, under good management. In

In the parish of Amersham are woods of fine beech, growing upon chalk; and in the beautiful park of William Drake, Esq there is a variety of thriving timber."

WADDON CHACE.— P. 42. "Waddon Chase is divided into several coppices, containing together 2200 acres, part of which is shut up for a certain number of years, and then laid open to the deer, as well as to the commoners, for so many years more. The coppices produce large oak, ash, and other timber, as well as underwood; but from the custom of the deer and the commoners cattle being suffered to depasture thereon unlimitedly, the young timber is at this time totally destroyed. If the deer were confined to one spot, and the chase and commons divided among the parties interested therein, it would be a very important advantage gained to the proprietors, and a great national benefit, inasmuch as the growth of oak and other timber would be encouraged. Nine years is the customary time for shutting up the coppices, and then they are laid open for twelve years; and it is lamentable to see the havock that is made among the young timber the first year these coppices are opened."

AGRICULTURE.

FARMS.—*Sizes.*—P. 11. "As so great a portion of this county is in dairy and grazing farms, it might have been expected, that many of them would have been very large:" (?) "on the contrary, however, it appears, that there are not many of 500l. a year, two or three of 1000l. and the generality from 60l. to 250l. a year, throughout the county."

BUILDINGS of Farms.—P. 45. "The old farm houses, and their correspondent offices, are by no means worthy of imitation; but those erected of late years are upon a better plan, and are generally adapted to the size of the farm: some are built with brick, and covered with thatch, with proper leantoos; others are built with mud and timber for quarterings, and covered with thatch also. The dairy farms are obliged to have many out-buildings for the convenience of the cattle, as well as for milking; these are methodically arranged over the farm, in order to prevent the fields from being poached by often driving the cattle over them, and also to preserve the milk from that injury which driving them much would certainly occassion."

STATE of HUSBANDRY.—P. 18. "On the southern part, the

the land is generally high and the soil light, either on gravel or chalk, and appears to be under as good managemen. as that soil is capable of. The farmers are at great pains and expence in purchasing manure, and in collecting every sort of materials that constitutes or assists in the increase of manure; and that is not only applied with judgment, but is aided by the most modern agricultural improvements, as well by repeated cross ploughings, and drill husbandry, as by the cultivation of every sort of green meat, as turnips, &c.

"The grains chiefly grown are wheat, barley, oats, beans, and here and there saintfoin.

"In the northern part of the district, and even as far as Northamptonshire, a very different system of agriculture prevails from what we have noticed in the southern part. Perhaps no two districts can differ more in that respect, than do the two divisions of this county. As we have observed in the former a sedulous attention to the best modes of improvement; so we mut remark in the latter, a general appearance of bad management. In the former, the lands are ploughed in a husband like manner, in such straight and moderate sized lands as are most suitable and convenient for the nature of the soil; the latter, though in possession of as fine a loamy soil as is in the kindom, plough their lands in a compleat serpentine form, to the middle of the ridge, which they make so aukwardly high, that they become dangerous to waggons or carts, either carrying manure to the land, or carrying the crop from it.

"Such is the custom about Aylesbury and Buckingham. So rich and fertile is the soil there, that we were assured it was considered a disgrace to a farmer, to suffer a heap of manure to be seen at the end of his field, to plough in straight lines, to disturb an ant-hill on his pasture, or to permit more water than falls from the heavens to pass over the meadow."

The Reporters continue the work of censure, to the no small disparagement of North Buckinghamshire; but not with that sort of discrimination and judgement, which conveys to the mind of the experienced reader, that they were qualified for the difficult undertaking. In the central and northern parts of the County, permanent grass lands prevail. There, grazing and the dairy are the prominent objects of practice.—Aration is of course a secondary pursuit.

P. 11. "In the vale of the northern district, the land is composed of pasture, meadow, and arable. In the

Chiltren

Chiltern it is principally arable, with a great portion of beech wood."

PLAN of ARABLE MANAGEMENT.—P. 20. "*Rotation of Crops considered.* Throughout the district" (?) "the practice is nearly the same, turnips fed off, barley and seeds; the latter mowed the first summer once, and grazed, ploughed up, and laid fallow for wheat. This is the practice about the hamlets of Chesham. In the neighbourhood of Wendover, the rotation is wheat or pease, barley, sometimes oats, and fallow upon the chalk, wheat, beans, and fallow upon the clays.

"In the neighbourhood of Hardwick, the custom of the leases confines the farmer to three crops and a fallow; and one farmer in that quarter had received notice to quit his farm, because he had deviated from the specific terms of his lease *in sowing clover*. In the parish of Weedon, which is all common-field, the rotation is two crops and a fallow; wheat or barley, beans, then fallow."

WORKPEOPLE.—P. 39. "The rate of wages in the interior parts of the county, is as follows; yearly servants: head men eight guineas; boys three guineas; day labourers one shilling per day.

"In the southern parts ten guineas are given to the head men; four guineas to the boys; and nine shillings a week to the day labourers.

"The ploughmen go out at seven o'clock in the morning, in the summer, and return at three in the afternoon. In the winter, from eight to three.

"The labourers, in the summer six months, work from six to six, taking half an hour to breakfast, and one hour at dinner; and from light to dark in the winter six months, taking the same time at meals as in the summer."

WORKING ANIMALS.—P. 24. "It does not appear that oxen are now used in any part of this district."

"The horses are of the heavy black kind, and are bought in at two or three years old."

IMPLEMENTS.—*Plows.*—P. 24. "Loose handle swing ploughs, drawn by five and sometimes six horses, and low wheel ploughs, both of them heavy and clumsy."—"In the southern parts they use the Rotheram, the Kentish turnwrist, the swing, and the high wheel ploughs."

TILLAGE.—P. 22. "From what has been before said, it will appear that fallowing makes a very particular practice in this county. In a variety of the inclosures the tenant is confined by lease to three crops and a fallow; in the common fields to two and a fallow."

MANURES.—P. 23. "In the neighbourhood of Brickhill, marl is found of a rich quality, and perfectly blue: this is used

used as a manure upon the lands, loams or gravels, and is applied at the rate of thirty to forty cart loads to an acre, when the land is in the tilth, or in fallow, after the first ploughing, which generally happens in the months of April or May: it is at a certain time ploughed again, harrowed, and then sown. Peat-ash has been found an uncommonly good meliorator of the strong clays, and has been used also in the parish of Brickhill. In the environs of Chesham and Amersham, &c. yard-dung and rabbit's dung are used, as are hair and hoofs brought from Smithfield (at a very great expence) which are found to be great fertilizers of these cold and strong soils. The sowing of ashes and soot, brought from London, upon the young clover and wheat, at an expence of two pounds per acre, is found to answer very well."

On the CULTIVATION of INDIVIDUAL ARABLE CROPS in Buckinghamshire, not a syllable is observable, in this Report of its agricultural practices.

GRASS LANDS.—These are the inestimable treasures which give character to the husbandry of Buckinghamshire.—*Grazing* and the *butter dairy* are its prominent objects.—For some idea of the quality of those lands, see those articles, ensuing.

On the *general management* of grass lands, however, we find very little information, in the performance under view. In suggesting improvements, the Reporter says, p. 47, "the ant-hills, which abound in many places in great numbers, require the attentive consideration of the farmer, and should be destroyed without loss of time. Many farmers, wedded to old customs, without being able very often to assign a plausible reason for their adherance to them, have with much seeming confidence assured us, that a greater quantity of grass was produced by their being there, than there would be if there were none; and that they are of opinion the grass springs earlier on the south side of those hills than it does upon the plain surface; and lastly, that they afford shelter to the young lambs."

There is doubtlessly some truth in each of the two latter popular notions; but certainly not enough to warrant the occupiers of such neglected lands, in suffering them to lie in a depreciated state, the rest of the year.

LIVESTOCK.—Notwithstanding the prevailing character of the County of Buckingham, the accounts given, in this Report of its practices, concerning the different species of pasturing stock (dairy cows excepted) are inconsiderable.

Under the head, "Improvements suggested," we find the following general remarks.—P. 51. "With regard to the stock of the district, the opinion universally prevails, (as we we have before observed) that until the open fields, as well as the wastes, shall be inclosed, and the humidity of the soil reduced to a state of aridity, by draining, and that a greater liberality of cropping is allowed, it will be in vain to think of changing the breed of the sheep.

"The cows, oxen, and hogs, have each their peculiar merits, and appear, upon particular inquiry, to be as well adapted as may be to the ends proposed by keeping them."

CATTLE.—From what appears in this Report, Buckinghamshire would seem to have no distinct breed of its own. The dairy cows and the grazing stock are chiefly bought in.

The DAIRY.—The butter dairy being a branch of country business which is familiar to every one, in the environs of the metropolis,—it aptly excited a peculiar degree of attention, in the original surveyors of Buckinghamshire.

Cow Grounds.—The soils of the grazing lands of this County are repeatedly spoken of, as being of a peculiarly fertile quality. And in p. 15, it is said—"An acre and an half, or two acres of land, are conceived to be sufficient for a cow, both summer and winter."—Yet, in page 39, we are told, "the soil of the dairy farms is, for the most part, a surface of loam upon a bed of clay, and is in many places so wet, as to produce a rank, sour, and unwholesome herbage:"—a species of land, this, of which a full sized dairy cow, would require from three to four acres, to support her throughout the year.—And see Mr. PRIEST'S account, ensuing.

Cows—P. 14. "*The Cows*—consist of the short horned Lincolnshire and Yorkshire breed; but very different from those which are kept for the milk, in the environs of the metropolis. These are bought in after the first or second calf is dropt."

Dairy Room—P. 16. "The dairies are kept with that exact neatness which must be pleasing to every inspector, and to which we are happy to pay our tribute of commendation."

Milking.—P. 15. "The cows are generally milked by men."

Churning.—P. 15. "A mill has lately been introduced into some of the dairies, which is worked by one horse, and turns one or more churns at the same time."

P. 16. "In one instance, we observed a bull made use of for turning the machine, which animal appeared very tractable."—A dry cow, or one stale in milk, might be eligibly employed in this service.

Markets for Butter.—P. 15. "The butter is sent to London to the different dealers, who contract for it at ninepence per pound (of sixteen ounces) in the summer half year, and ten-pence halfpenny in the winter half-year. The

carrier

carrier finds baskets, cloths, &c. fetches the butter from the dairyman, and delivers it at one penny per pound."

SUCKLING;—namely the practice of fatting calves for the butcher; as in Surrey, &c.—P. 16. "In the neighbourhood of Medmenham, Hambledon, little and great Hampden, &c. &c. a great number of calves are suckled; these are for the most part bought of the dairy farmers, who do not think it worth their while to suckle or to raise any as a supply against any deficiency which may be occasioned by death, &c."

GRAZING CATTLE.—P. 17. "*Oxen and Cows.*—These constitute the principal stock of the grazing farms; the former are composed of Yorkshire and Herefordshire beasts, which are bought in lean, from twelve to fifteen pounds per head; the latter are barren cows, purchased from the dairymen.

"Perhaps (the Pevensey Level and Romney Marsh excepted) no land in the kingdom is better calculated for this purpose than the Vale of Aylesbury. Its amazing fertility soon makes a visible alteration in the appearance of the animal, and the extraordinary size they afterwards attain, is a proof of the quality and ability of the land. They are grazed about ten months."

"If grass becomes scarce, they are finished off with hay, and sometimes a mixture of oil-cake and barley-meal."

SHEEP.—P. 14. "North Wiltshire withers for store, and Berkshire ewes for breeding, are the prevailing sheep of the county. Some of Mr. Bakewell's breed have been lately introduced, and promise success: but the wetness of the soil, occasioned by its tenacity, produces very serious losses by the rot. One gentleman farmer has assured us, that he had lost upwards of 600 sheep during the last eight years; and urges as a reasou for not changing the breed, or improving it, the inaptitude of the soil to the support of sheep."

"GENERAL

"GENERAL VIEW

OF THE

AGRICULTURE

OF

BUCKINGHAMSHIRE.

DRAWN UP FOR

THE BOARD OF AGRICULTURE

AND INTERNAL IMPROVEMENT.

By the REV. ST. JOHN PRIEST,

SECRETARY TO THE NORFOLK AGRICULTURAL SOCIETY.

WITH AN APPENDIX,

CONTAINING

EXTRACTS FROM A SURVEY OF THE SAME COUNTY,

DELIVERED TO THE BOARD BY MR. PARKINSON.

1810."

THIS is the *third* Report from the County of Buckingham.

The first (the true original) is that of JAMES and MALCOLM; the subject of the preceding article; but of which not a syllable is uttered, in the volume now before me; nor of the notes which were probably made on its broad margins:—Nothing, at least, is avowedly taken from it.

The second is that of Mr. PARKINSON; of which no other mention is made than what appears in the APPENDIX.—The extracts there placed, consist of parochial tables, similar to those which Mr. P. inserted in his *Rutlandshire*, and

and *Huntingdonshire* Reports, and which are spoken of aforegoing*.

Hence, the BODY of the WORK, now under Review, is to be considered as the production of Mr. PRIEST.

Mr. PRIEST'S QUALIFICATIONS, as a Rural Reporter, are not difficult to estimate. He has, obviously, thought much on rural subjects; but as evidently wanted, at the time he wrote, sufficient experience, to enable him to judge, correctly, on the various branches of country concerns. As an AMATEUR,—an admirer of the art,—he certainly (judging I mean from the work before me) ranks high among that class of Rural Economists.

Mr. P's MODE of SURVEY,—or rather, shall we say, his method of collecting information,—was, doubtlessly, by the mean of ENQUIRY,—rather than by that of personal examination.—What length of time was appropriated to his tour through the County, no intimation is made; nor at what season of the year it was performed;—excepting what is incidently noticed in the section Climate, p. 7, where Mr. P. says—"During my residence in Bucks, from the twelfth of September (1808) to the first of October, scarce a day passed *with* rain."—Are we, from this, to conclude that the entire work of "SURVEYING" a County, and recording the various circumstances, relating to its Natural, Political, and Rural Economy, was completed in the space of twenty days?—

What

* May it not, without impropriety, be asked—where is the rest, the main part, of Mr. P's REPORT of BUCKINGHAMSHIRE; which he mentions in that of *Rutlandshire*? p. 144.

The subjoined is the TABLE of CONTENTS of the APPENDIX.—P. 366. "The following Appendix comprises tables delivered to the Board of Agriculture by Mr. R. Parkinson, author of the Experienced Farmer:

"No I.—An Account of the Extent of the County, as delivered to Mr. Parkinson, upon enquiry and upon conjecture.

"No. II.—The Names of Proprietors of Estates.

"No. III.—The number of Farm-houses and Cottages.

"No. IV.—The Size of Farms.

"No. V.—An Account of Parishes tithable, and not.

"No. VI—Poor-rates in 1806.

"No. VII.—An Account of the Profit of an Acre of Land for six years, upon the Rotation of fallow, wheat, beans.

"No VIII.—An Account of the Profit of an Acre of Land of the same quality for the same time, upon an improved system.

"No. IX.—A Statement of Crops, Dr. and Cr. upon 50 Acres of the same quality as the last, upon a new system, convenient, as it is presumed, for Bucks.

"No. X—Effects of Enclosing.

"No. XI.—An Account of the Seed sown per Acre, and the Produce of the Crops cultivated.'

What a want of *explicitness* in the Board's Reporters, and neglect of their duty to the public, not to have accompanied their several performances with open, plain, circumstantial accounts of the way in which the matters, they contain, were procured;—the better to enable their readers to appreciate their works.—It is proper to remark, however, that Mr. Priest's communications, with the gentlemen and superior tenantry of the County, appear to have been respectable.

The items of information obtained are thrown together, under the respective heads of enquiry given out by the Board (though not always with scrupulous fidelity) after the manner of the SECRETARY of the BOARD.

Viewing the MANNER, or authorship, of this Report, we find little to praise; unless it be, that Mr. Priest writes like a clergyman, priding himself on his learning. The prominent blemish observable in his work is that of dwelling on trifles,—of expatiating on minutiæ;—on which, for want of mature judgement, he is of course incapable of deciding.

The *errors* und *incorrectness* of *language* are innumerable. But they are, it is probable, (many of them at least) those of the press.—How disgraceful to the Board's Editor (if they employ one) to suffer such improprieties to pass:—not in the Report under notice, only; but in many or most of their publications.

The number of pages, in the body of the work, three hundred and sixtysix; in the Appendix fortysix.

A map of the County;—with some engravings, and many cuts. But no one that merits particular notice.

SUBJECT THE FIRST.

NATURAL ECONOMY.

EXTENT.—By the two tests of measure and weight (agreeably to *Dr. Watson's* method, see NORTHERN DEPARTMENT) Mr. Priest estimates the contents of the County at nearly 400,000 acres.

P. 4. "Thus then we have the number of acres taken from Cary's Map,

"By weight 396,013
By measure, ... 391,040

From which, if we take an average, we shall probably state it as accurately as it can be found to be, 393,526 statute acres,

acres, which, for the sake of round numbers, we will call 393,600 statute acres."

P. 5. "If we suppose the woods to be computed at 20,000 acres, the waste lands at 8000 acres, and the water 500 acres, we shall have the number of acres remaining, 365,100: but from these we must deduct for roads and towns, one-tenth; whence we find in the whole county only 328,590 acres of arable and pasture land."

Mr. PARKINSON, in his parochial table, inserted in the Appendix, sets down "total number of acres," thus (page 372.)

Meadow	54,819
Pasture	114,601
Arable	184,482
Commons	1,061
Glebe	,100 (!)
Waste	1,821
Woods	18,594
Water	36 (?)
The sum of which is	375,514:—

instead of that sum, however, stands, at the foot of the column headed "total number of acres," these figures 75,504.

CLIMATURE.—Having made a few remarks of comparison, between the climatures of Buckinghamshire and Norfolk, Mr. P. proceeds to define the term hyetometer.—P. 8. "The etymology of the word will be evident to a Greek scholar, but for the sake of others, must be explained to be from (ὑέτος, *pluvia*, which signifies) *rain* and (μέτρον, *metrum*) *measure*."

On examining the diagrams, and reading the description, of this hyetometer, we perceive it to be a very uncouth, immechanical, clumsy sort of RAIN GUAGE:—a beautiful little *native compound*, this, which fits the mouth of an English agriculturist, much better than the far fetched, five-syllable word that is here *unnecessarily* introduced.—But *Greek compounds* have, of late years been "all the rage"—the reigning fashion.—And it may be pardonable, in mountebanks and showmen, to follow it; and to employ school ushers to make them up; as toils wherewith to catch "apes of fashion."—Even in science and the arts, where a term is *required*, and the English language is *incapable* of furnishing one, with the desired aptitude in sense and sound, it may be right to call in foreign aid. But, in the case under notice, such assistance was not *wanted*.—Let this be an apology for these observations.

In page 10, is inserted a table of the *quantities* of *rain* which

which fell in twelve different parts of the kingdom, in 1806. But, unfortunately, or rather shall we say, unpardonably, no *authority* is given! we have nc mean of judging of the accuracy of any one of the columns,—other than that of its being found in a Report to the Board of Agriculture!

This, on first viewing it, had induced me to pass it over, as a thing unworthy of a place in a register of more authentic truths. But finding it, on examination, to contain nothing repugnant to *probability*, I determined to insert it, here, on the *assertion* of Mr. Priest; who could not, personally, attend to the whole.

P. 10.—" QUANTITY OF RAIN

WHICH FELL AT THE FOLLOWING PLACES IN THE YEAR 1806.

In Inches and Decimals.

	Chichester.	Sandgates, near Chertsey, Surrey.	London.	Dis, Norfolk.	Chatsworth, Derbyshire.	Lincoln.	Horncastle, Lincolnsh.	Nottingham.	Ferriby, Kingston-upon-Hull.	Lancaster.	Dalton, Lancashire.	Kendal.	Vicinity of Edinburgh.
In January	—	2,85	2,66	2,37	3,96	—	3,49	2,80	3,74	5,75	5,40	7,90	2,66
February	—	1,12	0,86	1,28	2,57	—	1,35	1,10	2,33	3,94	4,02	5,14	1,08
March	—	2,09	2,22	1,94	2,05	—	2,25	1,74	3,51	0,87	1,43	1,32	0,48
April	—	0,82	0,72	1,75	0,73	0,90	1,80	0,88	0,89	1,06	0,74	0,56	0,74
May	—	0,82	1,44	0,35	1,52	1,40	0,60	1,50	1,38	0,00	2,58	2,12	2,23
June	—	0,82	0,64	0,76	2,05	1,71	1,40	1,95	1,50	0,69	1,45	1,43	0,20
July	3,57	3,92	5,56	2,57	2,53	1,82	3,37	3,24	3,52	3,06	4,38	4,63	2,74
August	2,47	1,55	2,60	3,40	2,42	1,63	2,10	2,55	2,78	5,37	7,15	7,18	2,65
September	2,67	2,24	2,72	4,62	1,78	2,58	1,86	1,70	2,49	3,63	3,94	4,85	0,98
October	3,07	1,28	1,02	1,48	1,52	1,34	2,40	1,10	1,22	1,51	3,08	1,99	1,92
November	4,80	4,44	3,64	2,49	4,05	3,59	3,50	2,75	4,31	8,94	8,37	9,32	4,47
December	6,20	4,01	3,76	2,50	4,90	3,18	2,73	4,25	3,20	5,89	7,27	7,15	1,71
	22,78	25,96	27,84	25,51	30,08	18,15	26,85	25,56	30,87	40,71	49,81	53,89	21,86

" N. B. No account received of the fall of rain at Chichester for the first six, nor at Lincoln for the three first months."

SOILS.

SOILS.—After a page or two of *leading remarks;* in which the soils of Buckinghamshire (or any other County) are *elegantly* compared to the rainbow (having previously called in SWIFT to his aid,)—the author enters on the business of *Report.*

P. 13. "Premising thus much, let us begin at the *northern part of the county*, and in as regular a manner as we can, trace to the south of it all the soils generally; for as to particulars, there is scarce a single parish where the soil can be characterized by one species of earth, or any one of the terms we have explained: even the Brick-hills, from a point between Wavendon up to Leighton, including Stockgrove, Linslade, and a part of Soulbury, of which the species of soil is more clearly defined than it can be in any other instance in the county; yet here it is not so uniform as not to require great caution in the description."

P. 15. "The *Middle of Bucks*, from the Ouse, on the north, and Watling-street, on the north-east, till we come to the Chiltern-hills, are various clays, with chalk under them, upon most of the hills."

The *Chiltern Hills* —P. 17. "These run across the country from east to west, after having passed from Cambridgeshire, on the border of Hertfordshire, and by Dunstable in Bedfordshire, enter Bucks near Eddlesborough, and thus pass by Halton, Wendover, Ellesborough, and Risborough, and leave Bucks near Bledlow, on the west. Upon the side of these hills in some parts, and at their foot in others, lies the Ikenild Way, which runs through the county; and which would not be noticed in this place, did not a remarkable circumstance attend it in its progress, perhaps accidentally, which is, that on the right hand side of it, towards the valley, the soil is so good a mixture of clay and chalk, as to be worth for a furlong in breadth, according to the estimation of farmers situated near it, at least 10*s*. an acre to hire, more than that on the left hand, between it and the hills. This circumstance was observed by Sir John Dashwood King, Bart. and his tenants at Halton, as well as by Mr. Grace, at Risborough. It is not wonderful that the lowest lands should be much richer than lands lying by the side of hills; but it is remarkable that this Roman road should thus separate for a considerable way, lands so distinct from each other in quality." * The

* This is certainly a little "remarkable;" but it is by no means, I conceive, *inexplicable*. At the feet of most, or all, of the chalk hills of England, lie narrow lines of rich, deep, and of course tender, clayey soil; which, in the SOUTHERN COUNTIES, is termed "maam," or maam soil; and, immediatly above this, the chalk commences; covered, in most cases, with a line of flints that have, in process of time, rolled down the face of the steep.—A more apt and obvious line for a road is scarcely possible to be imagined.

The *Vale of London.*— P. 18. We have but one district remaining, which as to soil differs from all other parts of Bucks; this is the south part, comprehended between Uxbridge, Colnbrook, Staines, Windsor, and Maidenhead. This is generally a gravelly loam upon gravel. Near the Thames peat is found."

"Map of the Soil of Buckinghamshire."—In a prefixed map of the County, Mr. P. has marked the qualities of its soils, in numerous parts of it, by *engraved initials*, "from observation taken in 1808, by the Rev. St. John Priest, in his Survey of that County." These initials are placed within oval lines of different dimensions;—G. denoting *Gravel*,—C. *Clay*,—S. *Sand*,—L. *Loam* &c. &c.;—and, in a few places, *verbal descriptions* appear.—This is a new and valuable method;—greatly preferable to the *fancy daubings* which accompany most of the Board's works.

Mr. Priest computes the extent of each species of soil, to be as follows. P. 19. "From Cary's Map, and the foregoing account of the soil of Bucks, we may compute the number of acres of each soil to be,

	Acres.
Of clay and loam, ...	238,720
Sand, ...	6400
The Chilterns, ...	122,880
Gravelly loam, ...	25,600
	393,600"

FOSSILS.—P. 19. "At Brill there is some ochre, which is used for painting; and which, after a tedious and expensive process, is worth from 8*s.* to 10*s.* per cwt.; umber is also found in small quantities; and near Newport there is a quarry of good marble, from whence Mr. Ward of that town has chimney-pieces, one in his kitchen, and another in an entrance room. This quarry, however, lies too deep for working, or for any advantage to be derived from it. Near Olney also is a quarry of freestone, which is bought for building at 2*s.* a cart load."

For an account of the *Tottenhoe Stone*, see *Homesteads*, ensuing.

SUBJECT THE SECOND.

POLITICAL ECONOMY.

APPROPRIATION.—*Common Pastures.*—P. 262. "There is but little to be said upon this Chapter. Exclusive of that waste apparent in unenclosed fields, subject to the open-field culture, the wastes which require particular notice,

notice, are those enumerated in the Appendix, No. XII."—It has so happened, however, that no Appendix No. XII. appears.

Again (same page) "In the Appendix, the number of acres of wastes in Bucks, is said to be 6382; but in that account there may be some conjecture, and some omissions. I have taken the number to be 8000, which probably will be found rather less than the truth."

Now, in Mr. Parkinson's table of Extents, those of "commons" and "wastes," *united*, make only 2,882 acres.

Common Fields.—P. 121. "Enclosing has within a few years made rapid strides, and the effect has in all cases in Bucks been so great, that it is rather a circumstance of surprize that there should be so many acres of land still in the open-field state."

Mr. Priest, however, conveys no idea of the quantity of commonfield lands which remained open, in 1808.—Nor does Mr. Parkinson supply the deficiency.—In the Appendix No. 10, Mr. P. gives a list of parishes inclosed in Buckinghamshire*; mentioning their names, alphabetically;—the dates of inclosure,—the number of acres inclosed,—and the effects of inclosing:

The subjoined is a specimen of Mr. Parkinson's table, entitled "Enclosing." P. 401.

"*Parishes Enclosed in Buckinghamshire.*

Parishes.	*Date of Enclosure.*	*No. of Acres Enclosed*	*Effects of Enclosing.*
Akeley *cum* Stockholt,	1794	485	Both corn and grass decreased: (!) but with favourable seasons some improvement may be expected.
Aston Abbots, ...	1795	640	Corn increased about one-fifth.
Aylesbury, ...	1771	1740	Wheat decreased about half; sheep decreased about half; milk cows about as many more; horses decreased.
Brickhill, Bow, ...	1790	1741	Barley decreased about three-fourths; beans decreased seven-tenths; oats increased three-fourths.
Brickhill, Great, ...	1771	1200	Butter increased twelve to one; pork six to one; sheep six to one; cattle considerably increased."

* But in what year Mr. Parkinson made his Survey does not appear!

Effects of *Inclosing*.—On this topic, Mr. Priest's observations, as well as those of Mr. Parkinson, are too general; and too inexplicit to be greatly useful. Standing, as they do, unaccompanied by the *nature* of the *soil*,—the *preexistant objects* and *plan* of *management*,—or any other *attendant circumstance* of the parish spoken of,—either *previously*, or *subsequently*, to the inclosure,—they are merely associations of words, which do not convey any valuable instruction.

MANUFACTURES.—P. 81. "It is strange, that employment for the poor should not have the effect of diminishing the poor-rates; but so it is. Every manufacture independent of the agriculture of the country, brings expenses upon the land; and those of this county militate very much indeed against its agriculture. The making of lace, and the platting of straw, employ all the women, boys, girls, and children, throughout the county: it is impossibie to pass a poor-house, without seeing some persons so employed. In towns, are schools of lace-makers and straw-platters; and so advantageous are these employments, that young women can earn from 9*d*. to 16*d*. per day readily; and in the straw manufactory, Mr. Grace, of Risborough, and Mr. Howard, of Buckland, informed me, that last winter some women earned 30*s*. per week. The consequence is, that the farmer suffers: no women nor young persons will work in the field; and the fact is, that but in very few places in Bucks were women to be seen in the field, making hay, or weeding. From these considerations it might be presumed, that the poor-rates of the county were not so high as in other counties, where the poor have no such resource. Not so.

"The rates at Stony Stratford have been 21*s*. in the pound, and are now from 12*s*. to 14*s*.

"At Newport Pagnell, they are 6*s*. in the pound.

"At Olney, from 8*s*. to 11*s*. in the pound.

"At Stoke-Goldington, from 8*s*. to 10*s*. in the pound."

While *agriculture* is doomed, by the law of the Country, to support idle, infirm and aged *manufacturers*, drawn together by high wages, and rendered unhealthy, by confinement and debauchery,—it is more *true* than strange, that the land should be burdened by heavy poor rates; and the operations of husbandry cramped, through a want of experienced farm workpeople.—For another notice of the evil, see *Workpeople*, ensuing.

POOR RATES.—P. 82. "The average of the poor-rates is 5*s*. $2\frac{1}{2}d$. in the pound."

Mr. Parkinson, at the foot of his table, in the Appendix, page 400, says,—"The average of the poor-rates through the

the county, is 4*s*. 11¾*d*. in the pound;" but, *when* we are not acquainted.

P. 347. "At Moulsoe, is a farm let for the express purposes of finding the poor with milk at a moderate price.* Observations upon such a practice extended to other necessaries of life for the service of the poor, might produce materials for a system of management highly beneficial to the public.

"At Halton, Sir John Dashwood King allows gardens to all his cottages, and used to offer premiums for the best cultivated, and to hold out other inducements to industry. Of late Sir John has turned his attention more towards the children of the poor, and held out inducements to them to find services as soon as possible, and to behave well in such services. Sir John has given clothing to every boy or girl when they first go out to service, or as apprentices, and if at the end of the first year's service they bring good characters. he allows every one two guineas."

Provident Societies.—P. 347. "*Box-Clubs*—Are established every where."

TITHES.—P. 72. "There is no part of the enquiry into the state of the Agriculture of this county, more pleasant to a Surveyor, and particularly to me whose principal income is derived from the Church, than that of tithes. Of the 204 parishes in Bucks, 82 are tithe free, that is, in general the farms are exonerated from tithes, by land given to the church as glebe in lieu of them; thirty are partly and chiefly tithe free, three pay a corn rent (as it is called); one has a modus, and the remaining 114 are tithable, of which it does not appear that more than one is tithed in kind, and that is Great Marlow. The method of paying by composition is general, and that composition fair and moderate."

Having mentioned various instances of appropriation, in which *lands* were set apart as SUBSTITUTES for TITHES,—the Reporter observes, page 75, "Many more instances of the same kind of *allotments in lieu of tithes*, might have been procured, but the rest are under the same circumstances as the foregoing: and these are sufficient to shew to those who wish to examine the subject, how desirable such allotments are in lieu of tithes, and to give that statement which is required. It will not be forgot, that these allotments took place at the time of enclosing open fields and

* I am happy to find that a plan of management, which, I believe, is *mine* (see my REPORT of the CENTRAL HIGHLANDS of SCOTLAND) has been carried into effect in Buckinghamshire.

and commons, and therefore are not perfectly applicable to enclosed farms. There are, however, some instances, where they might be applied to enclosed lands, and those not a few, if the Legislature would enable the parties interested to do it."

P. 75. "The instances of commuting tithe by a *corn rent*, fortunately are very few."—From this remark, we may infer that Mr. P. is an enemy to *corn rents*, as a substitute. But, in the instance he brings forward, the principle was injudiciously applied.

P 79. "The *composition for tithes* is generally such throughout the county, as to make them by no means grievous to the farmers: it is, as was said before, fair and moderate. This may require explanation, because it seems to presume that a composition, that is, an agreement made between a farmer and a parson, to pay in money the value of the tenth of the produce of his farm, may be *unfair* and *immoderate;* and this, it may be contended, is impossible, because, they say, if it were, the farmer would not agree to it: but that is only *begging the question:* as well may a farmer agree to pay an unfair composition, as a parson demand it. If those who take up the question will consider it impartially, they will find, that the value of the tithe of a farm is to the farmer himself much greater (perhaps by one-third), than to the parson: the farmer has but very little additional trouble or expense, on his part, to collect the tithes of his farm; whilst to the parson, the capital required, and the outgoing expenses of rates of collecting, of thrashing, and of carrying to market, are a most serious evil; so great a drawback, as to render the real profit of the tithes to him not more than two-thirds of the whole value, under the most favourable circumstances—I mean local circumstances, such as proper barns and offices, an equal and well-disposed variety of property in the parish, the form of that parish, together with the roads, and the situation of the parsonage-house, and glebes belonging to it—for these will all have effect upon the outgoing expenses of the parson. If then such a composition be made, as will take from the farmer a part of that profit which arises to him if he collects, over and above that which the parson would derive after paying his outgoing expenses, had he taken his tithes in kind; surely it is not unreasonable to say, that such part of the composition is more than the parson can be thought to be *fairly* and *moderately* entitled to."

These are considerately made, and just remarks; and, as coming from a son of the church, may well be deemed superiorly liberal.

P. 81.

P. 81. "In general the average" (of the ccmposition for tithes) "is 4*s.* 6*d.* per acre:"—but whether for arable lands, only, or for arable, meadow, pasture, and woodlands, jointly, is not, in any instance, expressed.

For an extraordinary *tithe case*,—see the head *Grass Land*, ensuing.

PUBLIC DRAINAGE.—P. 23. "In a survey of the streams and rivers in Bucks, with reference to its agriculture, it is impossible not to observe, that these streams, which would add so much to the service of agriculture by draining the land, are suffered to be filled with silth, rubbish, and all sorts of aquatic plants, and are by no means in such a state as to allow a sufficient passage for the water, which frequently runs down from the hills very rapidly; the consequence is, that along the Ouse and the Thame inundations take place at times, when much injury is done to the herbage and crops of hay. This is an evil which calls for a remedy, and that of a public nature. Some gentlemen, to whom this circumstance has been mentioned, have suggested, that there are no means of correcting this evil but by the appointment of Commissioners of Sewers."

INLAND NAVIGATION.—P. 22. (Section "Waters") "As to water to answer the purposes of markets, no county at the same distance from London is so well supplied. On the south from Henley by Marlow, Maidenhead, Windsor, and Staines, runs the Thame, navigable to London, the freightage upon which for barley does not exceed 2*s.* per quarter. On the east runs the Grand Junction Canal, into which are branches from Wendover, five miles from Aylesbury (the middle town in the county) and also from Buckingham, so that all parts are within a few miles of a navigation to the metropolis, and many not far from one, which in its northern direction communicates with the seas on the east and west of England, by the Humber on the one part, and the Mersey on the other; for the Grand Junction Canal, in its southern direction, runs into the Thame at Brentford and Paddington, and in its northern communicates first in a direct line with Nottingham, then north-east by Newark and Gainsborough, with the Humber, and so runs into the North Sea or German Ocean; and in its next branch by Coventry, Birmingham, Shrewsbury, and Chester, with the river Mersey, and thus with the Irish Sea."

P. 343. (Section "Canals") "This county has the advantage of the navigation of the Grand Junction Canal, which coming from the Oxford Canal at Braunston, enters Bucks near Cosgrave, from whence a branch goes to Buckingham, ten miles and a half: from Cosgrave the cannal passes by Woolverton, Linford, Fenny Stratford, to Leighton, and leaves the county at Long Marston: from Bulborne another branch goes to Wendover, six miles and a half.

"The freightage of barley to London is 2*s.* per quarter, and of other grain in proportion. The principal articles carried are iron, pottery, coals, timber, wine, all sorts of grocery, lime, and manures."

ROADS.—Mr. Priest speaks, loudly and long, on the intolerably bad state of the roads, in Buckinghamshire, at the time of his "Survey" in 1808.

The *parochial roads* were then, not only unpleasant, but unsafe; as he more than once experienced, in prosecuting his tour through the County. No cause, however, is assigned (excepting a want of resident gentlemen and the number of dairy farms)—nor any cure pointed out. The soils of vale districts are frequently deep, and materials often scarce.

"Even the *turnpike-roads*," we are told, page 340, "are not to be commended as such, except in certain parts; for by being traversed as they are by heavy waggons with wheels having conical rims, without much traffic by chaises or other carriages to cross and counteract the effect of such rims, and by being formed without gravel to fill up the interstices of the chalk, and unite with it, the same ruts are continually tracked, and so formed with inclinations to the middle of the road, that every shower of rain increases the bad effect of every preceding waggon."

SOCIETIES.—P. 362. "There is no Agricultural Society in Bucks."

SUBJECT THE THIRD.

RURAL ECONOMY.

TENANTED ESTATES.

ESTATES.—Mr. PARKINSON has furnished the Appendix with an alphabetical list of the *names* of *proprietors* of the parish or parishes in which they severally held lands, in ; which may serve to amuse many of the present day; and might have gratified antiquaries, in times to come, had the *date* been given.

TENURES.—I insert the whole of Mr. Priest's account of the ancient tenures and customs (many of them now appearing

pearing absurd, and are, in reality grievous to modern husbandry) that are still prevalent in Buckinghamshire; in which those irrational remnants,—disgraceful to civilized Society,—would seem, from the account of them which follows, to be singularly prevalent.

P. 24. The tenures of this county are various, and too much land is under the *worst kind* for improving its agriculture. The freehold estates are the same as in all other counties, and would undoubtedly wear a different appearance, were tenants properly encouraged by leases. The copyhold are, some of inheritance, others for lives. Of the former, many are subject to an arbitrary fine, not exceeding however, in any case, two years' rent: this is commonly upon alienation a fine of one year and a half rent, and sometimes less. Others are only subject to a fine certain, or that fixed by custom, and generally about two years' quit-rent, and in some cases a certain sum per acre, perhaps sixpence, with one shilling for a house. In general, in all such cases of copyhold, the lord of the manor is compellable to renew, and cannot take more than two years' improved rent. In the Chapter on the Obstacles to Improvement, these observations will be necessary. There are two other kinds of tenure, by no means uncommon in this county—they are leasehold estates, held upon lives, renewable at the end of any of them; or upon leases for twenty-one years, renewable at the end of seven. I say renewable, but this must be taken with reference to the parties themselves. There is no law or custom to oblige either the lessor or lessee to renew, and therefore but little can be expected to take place as to improvements upon such estates. With respect to leases granted by ecclesiastical bodies, it is required by law, that a certain portion of the reserved rent should be in corn, commuted for, however, by money, according to the best price of corn, when the payments become due. These tenures are not uncommon in Bucks, and have a tendency to prevent enclosures.

"The Rev. Mr. Causton, of Turweston, holds lands under leases of this kind for twenty-one years, renewable every seven. The lands are unenclosed, and chiefly arable open fields, subject to customs injurious to agriculture. There are here common pastures, upon which the occupiers of the arable open fields have a right to turn on stock, according to their occupation of (what is called) *yard lands*, or, as they were explained, *yards of land*. By a yard of land, however, no determinate number of acres is to be understood, as it varies in different places from 28 to 40 acres. Such lands are found in almost all the open fields, and are said to amount to 91,906 acres. These yard lands are described in old law books by the terms *virgata terræ*, which should be translated, 'portions of land measured by the *virga*, the whip or *rod*.' They are all nearly of the same breadth, viz. between five and six yards. Now, five yards and a half make a *rod*, or *pole*, or (*pertica* corrupted into) perch. A yard land will not be the same in one place as in another, because, although the breadths of these portions are the same, the lengths will vary according to the extent of the field so to be divided.

"Yard lands are attended with peculiar rights. At Water Eaton, a yard land consists of 30 acres, and for every yard, the proprietor has a right to turn 24 sheep upon the commons, during the time either agreed upon or limited by custom, or otherwise.

"At Whaddon there is much yard land, copyhold with fines certain, with two large common pastures. The right of turning cattle upon these, is, for sheep, from All-hallow-day, called here *Holymas*, to Lady-day; and for neat stock, from the 23d day of May to the 1st of November. Here is also a *chace* (or forest in the possession of a subject), which is divided into 21 copses, of which 21 belong to —— Selby, Esq. of Winslow, and seven to New College, Oxford. These copses consist of timbers and underwood Of Mr. Selby's, occupied by his son, W. Lowndes, Esq. one is cut every year, and from that time it is shut up for nine years from all cattle, after which, for the remaining term of years until the next cutting, it is open and common, from May to November, for the great cattle of those who have a right to turn in; and these are any persons residing in the parishes (which are six) in which the chace lies. Busky-leys (a word compounded of *busky*, woody, and *leys*, fields) are somewhat of the same nature, except that they have not been the property of the Crown, as chaces have. These chaces have as many deer as the proprietor of them thinks proper.

"There is one open pasture field, called the *Stroud*, consisting of 40 acres, which is divided into portions of land, belonging to different proprietors. This has peculiar rights. It is shut up from the public at Lady-day, and in the middle of June, or when the majority of proprietors think proper, is pastured with 40 cows; and when the corn is carried from the arable lands, then these 40 acres are thrown open to the public, and remain common until the next Lady-day. The rent of these 40 acres is estimated at 16*s*. qer acre.

"At Bletchley, including the hamlet of Water Eaton, there are many yard lands, of 30 acres to a yard.

"At Stewkley there are 104 yard lands, of 30 acres each; and here, as in Water Eaton, and in most of the open fields, the tenure is the same, viz. copyhold and leasehold."

SODBURNING.—P. 267. "This practice is gaining ground every where, and is allowed to be the best way of bringing sward land to tillage." It would seem to be of modern introduction, in Buckinghamshire; see the original Report, page 499, aforegoing.

TENANCY.—This Reporter's section, "Leases," is nearly a sheet in length. It might be termed a dissertation, or essay, recommendatory of long leases.—He has called in Algebra to his assistance. But Fluxions, even, could not have served him. His arguments, if such they may be named, are ill founded,—rest on one side, only; and of course are, in effect, without foundation. Like other sticklers for long leases, Mr. Priest forgets, or witholds the fact, that the *rental values* of *lands* have been nearly *doubled*, with in the last twentyone years; consequently that the proprietors of farms, which were let on twentyone years leases, twenty years ago, are now receiving little more than *half* their rightful income.

I speak, here, of the main body of the lands of the kingdom; not of the comparatively few, which, now, require *marling*, or *drainage*;—operations, by the way, which PROPRIETORS ought to *perform*; or to *allow for*; if done by the tenant;—and to let their lands, accordingly.—Proprietors ought,—I presume to say,—to do so, for their own interest, if young men; or for their successors, if otherwise. It is, I conceive, *unfair* (as I have elsewhere said—EASTERN DEPARTMENT) for a proprietor, in the decline of life, to do it; and I will here say—it ought to be *illegal*, in any man possessed of an intailed, or other lifehold estate, to let the lands in their possession, *under existing circumstances*, for more than six years *certain*;—with a clause of *renewal*, every *third year*, so long as the proprietor and the occupier can agree.

After much learning, science, and time, unprofitably spent, this Writer brings out (but not in proof of the solidity of his arguments) the following interesting information.—P. 96. "It is strange, that after arguing for the sake of Bucks in favour of leases, as well on account of landlords as tenants, it should be necessary to record instances where leases have been refused: but so it is. At Drayton Parslow, after the enclosure, farmers were offered leases, but refused them; pleading, 'they durst not engage in leases, until they had tried what the land would do.' The same was the case at Weedon, and in other places, which I am allowed to state only in general terms."

I have

I have met with instances of a similar kind. Hence, may we be allowed to intimate, that tenants have more penetration, prudence, and foresight, than their landlords?

RENT.—Mr. Priest opens his section, "Rent," with the following appropriate observations.—P. 67. "The rents, as they are set upon the Chiltern Hills and the south of Bucks, appear to be moderate, and to do credit to the landholders, whose object must be, not to keep rents so high as to render farmers little better than day-labourers with the power of bailiffs, nor so low as to make them careless and slovens. They should be so regulated as to be spurs to industry, by enabling farmers to make such an appearance in the world as is consistent with their profession, and by actuating them to carefulness and diligence."

Among the pocket-book memoranda, on this head, we have the subjoined.—P. 69. "Mr. Westcar will forgive the mistake, if it is one, to state, that the rent of Kreslow is 30*s*. per acre."

P. 71. "*Recapitulation.*—The average rent of the arable farms, is £1 0 6

	£	s.	d.
The average rent of the arable farms, is	1	0	6
That of the dairy farms, ...	2	0	0
And that of the farms of a mixed nature,	1	5	10
	3)4	6	4
Whence, the average rent of the whole, is £.	1	8	$9\frac{1}{3}$

"This, however, is too much, because in the rent 2*l*. per acre for the dairy-farms, tithe included, and therefore deducting 3*s*. 6*d*. per acre for tithe, the average rent of the dairy-farms cannot be stated at more than 1*l*. 16*s*. 6*d*. per acre; by which alteration, the average rent of the whole county can be estimated only at 1*l*. 7*s*. $7\frac{1}{3}$*d*. thus,

	£	s.	d.
Average rent of arable farms, ... £.	1	0	6
——————— dairy, ...	1	16	6
——————— mixed, ...	1	5	10
	3)4	2	10
Average of the whole, ... £	1	7	$7\frac{1}{3}$"

WOODLANDS.

P. 255. "Beech is by far the most abundant wood in Bucks. The woods of beech are so numerous as to give the

the country a very rich appearance. The general use to which they are applied is in the manufacture of chairs in Bucks and in London: they serve also as fuel, and in some cases are used for repairs and for barn floors; in which instance the joists are of oak."

P. 256. "Mr. Ayton. at Missenden, prunes the trees in his woods. He has very fine beech trees."

AGRICULTURE.

FARMS.—Mr. PARKINSON has furnished a list of the *number* of *farm houses*, and of cottages, in each parish of the County. The total number of farm houses, he makes out to be 2,039.

Sizes of Farms.—Mr. Priest says, page 48, "without pretending to extreme accuracy, it may be stated, that there is one farm of 1000 acres, one of 900 acres, four or five between 600 and 700 acres, ten between 500 and 600, twenty-four between 400 and 500, and that the rest are from 400 acres down to ten (see Appendix, No. IV.): thus the average of the size of farms is 179 acres. If, however, we take it for granted that the number of farms, as stated in the Appendix, No. III., is 2039, and that our computation of the number of acres of arable and pasture lands, as given in p. 6, is 328,590 acres, then it will follow that the average of the size of the farms is only a little more than 161 acres.

"From these averages take the mean, and we have the average of the size of the farms in Bucks, 170 acres."

HOMESTEADS.—P. 44. "It is not possible to speak in high terms of the general state of farm houses and offices in Bucks: they are too often seen in a state, though not positively bad, yet such as by no means carry the appearance of such riches as the naturally apparent produce of the county ought to indicate."

Building Materials.—By the following notice, it appears that bricks and tiles, as well as lime, are burnt with faggots, in Buckinghamshire;—as in Surrey, and a few other Counties.

P. 45. "Many kilns in Bucks burn lime, bricks, and tiles, over the same fire at the same time. At Buckingham there is one, the walls are 24 inches thick, and the room is a square of 14 feet, and its height 22 feet. This kiln burns 50 quarters of lime, which are laid at the bottom, and form arches in which the fire is made, upon the lime

8000

8000 bricks are laid, and upon the bricks 6000 tiles. The tiles when burnt are ten inches long, six inches broad, and half an inch thick. These require 1500 of furze faggots, which are bought at 19*s.* per thousand."

Rural Architecture.—The Tottenhoe Stone.—P. 14. "According to the analysis of it made by Edward Hanmer, Esq. of Stock-grove, who found it to consist of,

	Weight.
Calcareous earth, ...	78.5 parts.
Silex, ...	17
Argillaceous, ...	4.5
	100 parts.

"This stone is so soft, that it may be scraped with a sharp knife, and the edge of the knife not be blunted. It is also so brittle, or rather, so easily broken into the laminæ, of which it is formed, that in building it is necessary to place those parts of the stone uppermost which lie so in the quarry, as was the case at Tyringham, in this county, in Mr. Praed's house, and at Halton, in the church built by Sir John Dashwood King, and is the case in a most splendid Gothic mansion now building by the Right Honourable the Earl of Bridgewater, at Ashridge."

This may be an accuracy of management which ought to be observed, in using other calcareous freestones.

COTTAGES.—Mr. PARKINSON sets down the number of cottages at 8,938.

Mr. Priest,—page 46,—"I could make no particular observations upon these buildings: they are, generally speaking, as good as are to be found in other counties. They have mostly gardens attached to them, or, if not, the cottagers are allowed to make themselves gardens by the side of the roads, and upon waste grounds: these are to be seen upon all the great roads through the county. Nothing more materially tends to teach the poor honesty, than this circumstance of allowing them to have property which they can call their own: it is by this means they can become practically acquainted with the value of property; and feeling how intensely they would deprecate all infringement upon their own, it may be presumed they would be less likely to make depredations upon that of other people. Habit will in this instance prevail as in other cases, and thus practice and habit will have the desired effect of producing more honesty amongst the poor than it is possible for the best delivered precepts to instil into them."

These sentiments are admirable; and they are the more to be admired and valued, as coming from a *preceptor*.

FENCES.

FENCES.—Speaking of the fences of new inclosures, Mr. P. informs us, p. 124, "they were, many of them, undertaken by one person at Aylesbury, who finds labourers, whitethorn, posts and rails, and who agrees within a certain time to raise such fences as shall no longer require posts and rails to protect them than for that certain time, at the end of which time he removes such of the posts and rails as remain."

This plan is new to me.—Where men of experience, and who are trustworthy, will undertake,—it appears, in theory, to be most eligible.—A man of that description, by undertaking a large concern, and having plants of his own (prepared during the passing of a bill, and other preliminary business of inclosure)—with workmen that are habituated to the several operations belonging to it, may do it cheaper than tenants, or bailiffs, of individual proprietors can; and, in most cases more effectually; the fencing, cleaning and keeping up the fences, being of course done by regular sets of labourers, who are acquainted with the different operations; and are superintended by an employer, who has a personal and important interest, in every part of the business: while the proprietor is relieved from much trouble and anxiety; and, perhaps, the mortification of seeing, after several years of vexation, his fences imperfect; and a disgrace to his estate.

OCCUPIERS.—*Capital.*—In the section, "Expence and Profit," Mr. Priest inserts a few memoranda, on the subject of capital employed, by occupiers in Buckinghamshire. And, on *arable* farms, the result would seem to be ten pounds, an acre. His information appears to have been got chiefly from tenants.

STATE of HUSBANDRY.—P. 5. "In an agricultural view, Bucks may be divided into three parts—1st, Into arable farms; 2dly, Into dairy farms; and 3dly, Into farms of a mixed nature, partly arable and partly grazing.

"The arable farms are disposed throughout all the flinty and turnip lands upon those chalky hills of Bucks which form a part of the Chiltern-hills, and from them to the river Thames on the south, together with the sandy lands in the Brick-hills, Soulbury, and Linslade, and some parts of the Vale of Aylesbury. These farms contain but a small portion of the pasturage. The dairy farms, or farms of pasturage, contain but little arable land, and comprise most of the interior parts of Bucks (except some parts of the Vale of Aylesbury), from the Chiltern-hills, which cross the county from east to west, until we come to Watling-street, from

from whence to the extremity of the county, are farms generally of a mixed nature.

"In this view of Bucks, we compute that one-half of the county consists of arable farms, of which the proportion of the ploughed land to the pasture is as five to one; one-third consists of dairy farms, of which the proportion is as one to sixteen; and one-sixth consists of farms of a mixed nature, having the proportion of arable to pasture as five to three."

		Acres.
P. 6. "By section first, Bucks contains	......	393,600
Deduct for { woods, 20,000 acres; waste, 8,000; water, 500 }		28,500
		365,100
Deduct one-tenth for roads, &c.	....	36,510
And there remain	....	328,590

"These, according to the principles already laid down, must be divided into farms, thus:

	Acres of Arable.		*Acres of Meadow and Pasture.*
One-half into arable farms, containing	136,913,	and	27,382
One-third into dairy farms, containing	6,443	—	103,087
And one-sixth into farms of a mixed nature, containing - - - - -	34,228	—	20,537
Whence the whole county will be divided into	177,584	—	151,006"

In the section "Size of Farms," we find a long chain of memoranda, relating, not to the sizes of farms, merely, but often noting in the true Secretarian manner, the number of cows, sheep, hogs, &c;—without mentioning the *quality* of the *lands* of which the farms severally consist, or any other circumstance belonging to them, than the number of acres, and, in some of them, the proportion of arable and grass lands!

I perceive not one of them which demands admission, here. I will, nevertheless, insert the following; as it regards a popular character; who, if one may be allowed to judge from a glance, is good as well as great.

P. 52. "Mr. Westcar, of Kreslow, whose name as a grazier is deservedly known all over the world, and to whose excellent judgment of stock, and its management, any testimony of mine can be but of little avail, occupies under Lord Clifford about 900 acres, of which between 60 and 70 are ploughed, under no system but that of being subservient to the pasturage. There is no instance where the

the effect of great industry, and a perfect acquaintance with the nature of buying, feeding, and selling of neat stock to the best advantage, is more fully displayed than in this gentleman. The only advantage which this estate seems to possess above some others in this county, is the power of wintering stock, having a sufficient quantity of straw from the arable land."

PLAN of MANAGEMENT.—In a section headed "Rotation of Crops,"—twenty pages in length,—I find not a line that is entitled to extraction; saving a *quotation* from "NAISMITH'S ELEMENTS of AGRICULTURE;"—which is as follows.—P. 170. "It should be remembered, that the fertility of a cultivated field is often acquired by its having lain in pasture. The quantity of food from cultivated crops is not always in proportion to the extent of the land cultivated. The county of Ayr, in the west of Scotland, contains a great deal of good soil. It is much more than forty years since I remember the inhabitants of that county passing in crowds with horses, pack-saddles, and empty bags, to the east, to bring pease and barley, of which they made a kind of bread to serve them in summer. At that time the farmers were under no restraint as to the proportion of their farms which they might have in tillage. Soon after, a gentleman who had the management of a great estate in that county, made a regulation in the leases, by which the farmers were bound to have never more than one-third of their farms in tillage. Other proprietors adopting the same regulation, it became general, and the farmers were afterwards restricted to plough no more than one-fourth. Of late this county, though not less populous than formerly, sends always a great deal of grain to the neighbouring districts; and instead of empty bags and pack-saddles, sends carriages loaded with cheese to Leith, to be shipped for London. Thus, by laying land which has been in tillage, frequently in pasture, the future fertility of the country is enhanced, and its present produce is not diminished."

Yet we find more modern books resounding with the praises of "Norfolk husbandry"!—of keeping arable lands only one year in a state of herbage, and mowing them, twice, in that year; consequently of "all tillage, no pasture;" as was the case, formerly, in the County of Ayr.

WORKPEOPLE.—In the section "Labour" is given a list of parochial notices, relating to the rates of wages. But they vary so materially, and no average being drawn, I perceive nothing in the chapter, entitled "Rural Economy"!—excepting the subjoined notice,—which is proper for insertion, here. Indeed, the rates of labor have altered so rapidly of late, and are now more rapidly altering (April 1813)

1813) that a register of them can be of little value; unless to antiquaries, in future.

P. 335. "The wages of dairy-maids have risen much within a few years, on account of the lace and straw manufactories, and it is with difficulty they are procured at all."

In the Midland Counties, where oceans of malt liquor may be said to be swallowed (rather them drank) by farm workpeople, *brewing* becomes an art of some consideration, to farm occupiers. In the section "Barley," Mr. Priest speaks of "beer" as follows.—P. 192. "No where is more care taken in brewing. Every farmer makes a point of keeping good beer; and next to the dairy, the cellar is the best room in his house. The general practice is to brew twice in a year, viz. in November and March, and not to broach a vessel in less time than a twelvemonth. As the beer in general, in the county, is very good, the particular mode of brewing it shall be given.

"Without mentioning particular names, it may be sufficient for the purpose to state, that the different proportions of ingredients used were these:

			Gallons of Beer.
Some of	1 bushel of malt and	1 lb. of hops, make	6
Others,	1 ———	1 ———	8
	1 ———	1 ———	9
	1 ———	1 ———	$12\frac{1}{2}$
And others,	1 ———	1 ———	$13\frac{1}{2}$

"Their method of brewing is not peculiar. *One only occurred singular*, and as that is a saving of utensils as well as labour, at every time of brewing, it deserves to be stated, particularly as the beer was as good as the generality of beer in the county. Mr. Smith, of Aylesbury, never draws out of a tub more than half the beer, except once in three years, when he empties a tub, and takes off the head to clean it. Into a tub which has had half the beer drawn out, he pours new beer; but this new beer comes immediately from the copper, without having been cooled and worked, into the tubs, where it is to remain, and where it is worked with yest, and then closed up as soon as the fermentation is finished. By this method two expensive utensils are saved, as well as the labour and time of putting the beer into them."

WORKING ANIMALS.—*Horses.*—P. 317. "The height of horses in general use in Bucks, is from $15\frac{1}{2}$ hands to $16\frac{1}{2}$ high; their colour black, and tails long. It is very common for farmers either to breed colts, or to buy them at two years old, from 20*l.* to 30*l.*, keep them till they are five years old, and then sell them for 50 or 60 guineas."

P. 316. "We find it an invariable practice in Bucks, to soil

soil horses in the stable or the yard, in summer, upon vetches, or clover."

P. 318. "Soiling is very general, and if as much care were taken to lessen the number of horses kept, as to preserve economy in the quantity of food upon which they are kept, Bucks might vie with any county in the management of horses."

Oxen.—P. 290. "But a few gentlemen keep oxen."

IMPLEMENTS.—On this topic, we have a chapter of twenty pages; comprizing as many diagrams, in copper or wood. The subjoined is the opening of the chapter.—P. 101. "There is but a small variety of implements in Bucks, and, except the horse-churns already described, but very few worthy of record. The ploughs generally used, deviate more than any I have seen, from the best principles laid down by writers upon them."

These principles the Reporter undertakes to explain. Unfortunately, however, for the progress of this essential department of rural knowledge, he would seem to be more conversant with the general principles of mathematics, and with some knowledge of mechanics, than with the operations of implements, and the animals of draft, in the PRACTICE of HUSBANDRY.

The following passage makes one smile; though there is some truth in it.—Speaking of the practice of Buckinghamshire, in using five or six horses in a plow (see the head *Tillage*, ensuing)—the Norfolk agriculturist thus describes the operation.—P. 110. "It is enough to make the heart of a spectator ache, who knows the effect and the absurdity of it, to see five horses at length drawing a plough, and that perhaps upon a rich loam, where the force required is not more than 3 cwt. He cannot but think that in such cases the first horse draws the second, the second the third, the third the fourth, the fourth the fifth, and the fifth the plough, and that in fact the principal part of the draught lies upon the first horse," (!) * "and that sometimes it is transferred from one to another, so that now one draws, then another, and then another, and so on through the team, whilst the boy walking by their side alarms a sluggish one or two with his whip, and then the plough runs along with the ploughman almost crazed at the tail to keep in the ground: all the while the horse next the plough, who seldom

* Which is of course the farthest from the implement. Yet the learned and scientific mechanist had previously laid it down as a fundamental principle (p. 105) that "the farther he (the horse) is from his work, the less effective will be his exertions:"—a position, this, by the way, which, *in practice,* has but a narrow foundation.

dom puts his shoulder to collar except at the end of a *bout'* staggers and reels under the enormous weight produced by the horses before him."

This is talking like a townman, or a mere light-land occupier.—By catching seasons, and taking the soil while in the humor, any land may certainly be plowed, with a good implement and two good horses. But there are, doubtlessly, soils among the vale lands and high ridges of Buckinghamshire which ought not to be plowed, at all times, with two horses, abreast. The practice of using five or six, here, as in the vale of Glocester, has no doubt originated in the strong soiled common fields; which, perhaps, wherever the feudal husbandry took place, on deep *running* clays, were broken up for fallowing, after the spring crops were sown (when not only a strong implement, but a powerful team was necessary) and this for a wise purpose (as I have elsewhere suggested); namely that of preserving them in a somewhat cloddy state; and thus preventing their surfaces from *fluxing;*—from being run together by heavy rains.

And a further motive to this practice was to reap the benefit of the feedage which the stubbles afforded sheep, during the early spring months; when, under feudal regulations, such pasturage was of course valuable.

If the occupiers of Buckinghamshire continue to follow the same practice, in their inclosed lands, no censure can be too severe for them.

MANURES.—P. 268. " *Manuring.*—In some way or other, is practised for every crop." (?) "The different sorts used are, marl, chalk, lime, gypsum, ashes, soot, malt-dust, yard-dung, rabbits'-dung, pigeons'-dung, woollen rags, composts, and sheep's-dung."

A few memorandum-book entries appear, under each of those heads. But little of import arises from them.

Marl, we are told (same page), " is found at Brickhill: it is used there 80 loads per acre; but Mr. Turney thinks 60 loads per acre, repeated every seven years, the best way of using it."—But of what description, or specific quality, no account is given.

In the section " Soils," however, we meet with an analysis of the marl of Wing;—page 16,—" there is also a marl, which Mr. Hanmer, of Stockgrove, has analyzed, and found to consist of,

	Weight.
Calcareous earth, ...	43.2
Argillaceous, ...	30 7
Siliceous, ...	26.1
	100"

Chalk

Chalk is of course peculiar (in Buckinghamshire) to the "Chiltern" district. It is procured by sinking a shaft, or shafts, in the piece of ground to be chalked; as in Hertfordshire, &c.

Lime would seem not to be a prevailing manure, in Buckinghamshire. Yet it is to be had at very cheap rates, in different parts of the County.—P. 45. "*Lime* is of various prices. At Brickhill, 2*s.* 4*d.* per quarter of eight bushels; at Hillesdon, it is 2*s.* 9*d.* per quarter; and at Wavendon, it is 3*s.* 6*d.* per quarter. At Buckingham, it is 6*d.* per bushel; and at Risborough, 9*d.* per bushel."

P. 271. "*Gypsum*—Is a manure about which every one is enquiring, many making experiments, and no one able to give much account."—A few experiments have been tried with it, in Buckinghamshire. But no one that requires particular notice here.

P. 272. "*Ashes*—Are universally used upon the clover leys, from twenty to fifty bushels per acre. They are brought from London by the Grand Junction Canal, or otherwise, and cost at the wharfs about 6*d.* per bushel.

"Mr. Forster, of Wendover, purchases yearly as much ashes as cost him 100*l.*"—We are not informed of the sort of ashes which are there in use. But, from the above notices, the only ones on the subject, they would seem to be the ashes of coals, mixed with the miscellaneous gatherings of the London "dust holes."

Under the head "Yard Dung," a few immature ideas, about long dung and short dung, appear; and an *ingenious* remark or two thereupon.

P. 276. "*Woollen Rags*—Are used upon the Chiltern Hills by most farmers."

Sheep Fold.—The following circumstantially reported information is well entitled to a place, here; as a remnant of FEUDAL HUSBANDRY.

P. 278. "*Sheep's Dung*—By folding, is the most universal manure in Bucks, insomuch that sheep are hired for this purpose. The practice, however, of hiring sheep, exists only upon farms in the south of Bucks, where there are common-fields, and beyond the Chiltern Hills north, upon lands under the open-field culture, and has distinct usages.

"The practice in the neighbourhood of Salt Hill, Slough, &c. is to hire them from Bagshot-heath, with or without a shepherd; if with a shepherd, some allowance is made for him, but if without a shepherd, the sheep are turned upon the common-fields to feed when they go from fold, and no other allowance is made for them. On the other hand, should they go from the fold to good enclosed pasture, which

which is very rare, those who lett the sheep, pay in some cases 2*s*. 6*d*. and 3*s*. per score. Such sheep are procured as soon as the corn is harrowed, and remain there till the latter end of November or beginning of December. It is probable, that last November, within two miles of Cippenham Court, there were not fewer than 3000 sheep hired upon different farms, in the manner and for the purpose now stated.

"Farmers who adopt this practice save at least 15*l*. per cent. in capital on the score of sheep, keep all their land under the plough, crop it according to convenience, not system, and have no care about the injury which sheep may sustain from folding: whether these are advantages equivalent to the loss of the profit to be derived from a systematical management of sheep and stock, is surely very doubtful, and to be estimated only by local circumstances, and principally by the vicinity to London, and the great road to Bath and Oxford, which gives the farmer an opportunity of selling hay and straw, and taking no care about winter food for cattle. It is not practised by Mr. Langton an excellent farmer at Cippenham Court.

"The second usage of sheep's-dung is, that upon heavy lands unenclosed under the open-field culture. These lands generally are in such a state as to discourage, and in fact prevent farmers from keeping sheep of their own. But poor men with a capital just sufficient to buy *a sheep*, either having a right upon the commons of the unenclosed lands, or gaining a right from those who have, go from one open-field to another with their little flocks of *four score* sheep each, to fold upon the fallows for the occupiers of such fallows, for which they receive usually 1*s*. per score per week, if they have the means of feeding their sheep by their own right; but if not, they fold for the right of keeping their sheep upon the commons. In a few instances 1*s*. 6*d*. per score per week was paid, but this depends upon the state of the sheep and their size, together with the state of the food upon the commons. No one would be surprised that farmers have recourse to hired sheep in such cases, who could see the state of the lands upon which the sheep are folded, or the food to which such sheep go from fold. Mr. Hardy, of Newport Pagnel, whose judgment upon subjects of this kind is highly valuable, writes thus: 'Many of the farmers keep no sheep, but hire flocks to fold their lands from April to October, for which they pay to foreign shepherds 1*s*. 6*d*. per week a score. For this practice there are perhaps several reasons: dread of rot, insufficient winter keep, and want of capital.'"

P. 312.

P. 312. "Mr. Turney observes, that folding upon sandy land has not so good an effect as upon heavy land." (?)

TILLAGE.—The Norfolk Secretary, as has been intimated above, writes like a light-land occupier, without any practical knowledge of strong lands, or of the commonfield husbandry. Yet he has been pleased (no doubt) to fill a sheet and a half of letter-press, with loud censures of the Buckinghamshire practices, relative to lands of that quality; and even to those, which, through the want of wisdom (some where) still remain subject to feudal Governments;—of which he speaks as a stranger, from the interior of Africa or America, might;—accompanying his schemes of *improvement* by diagrams!

ARABLE CROPS.

Ample room is allowed by the Reporter for the discussion of this highly important branch of agriculture; and for describing the culture of the several species that are prevalent in Buckinghamshire.—To wheat, alone, a whole sheet is appropriated.

Mr. PARKINSON, in the Appendix, page 405, gives an "Account of the Seed sown per Acre, and Produce of Crops cultivated;"—in two hundred parishes.

The averages come out, thus:

Seed.		*Produce.*	
Wheat	2½	Wheat	21¼
Barley	4	Barley	30¼
Beans	4	Beans	23¼
Pease	3½	Pease	24
Oats	4½	Oats	33.

WHEAT.—*In Common Fields.*—P. 171. "The general practice throughout the county is to give the land a complete summer-fallow, by four ploughings length ways of the ridges, without harrowing until the seed is sown: the twitch-grass is picked out by men with three-tined forks. The seed is sown broad-cast and then harrowed, and sometimes ploughed in."

Inclosed Lands.—Tillage.—P. 172. "Upon this point practices vary and opinions differ. Some farmers prefer a fresh, some a stale earth; some a complete fallow; others a bastard summer till, after mowing the clover crop once; some a single ploughing after mowing the clover twice in the first year; others a single ploughing after feeding the clover crop in the first year, and mowing it the second, and a few beans."

The

The practices and opinions of nearly twenty occupiers are noted. Scarcely any two of them are alike. Yet many of them may have been *right*, under their several ATTENDANT CIRCUMSTANCES—of *soil*, *situation* and *previous management*; few of which appear. What, let it be asked, can be the use of such notices?

Manure for Wheat.—P. 176. "At Westbury, Mr. Graves folds sheep upon his clover-leys, after they have been once mown, before they are ploughed."

Time of *Sowing* Wheat.—P. 177. The time of sowing wheat is *universally* as soon as possible in the month of October:"—without regard, shall it be said, to soil or situation?

The *Method* of *Sowing* Wheat.—P. 177. "This is generally done by sowing broad-cast and harrowing in the seed, except in a few instances upon the Chiltern Hills, where the land is laid into four-furrow work, or as they are there called, into *little lands*, in which cases the seed is ploughed in."

Quantity of *Seed*.—P. 178. "As to quantity, there is but little variation. This rises from two to three bushels, and in some cases more. See Appendix, No. XI. where the average is 2.5245 bushels, *i. e.* 2 bushels 2 pecks and 1½ pint nearly per acre."

Stubbles of Wheat.—P. 183. "*Stubbles*—Are gathered together, and either stacked or laid in the farm-yards in November."

The *Acre Produce* of Wheat.—On this topic, the Reporter's calculations are curiously *exact*. After noting that of sundry individuals, he says,

P. 185. "From these accounts, the average is 28.6 bushels per acre, that is, 28⅗ bushels. The account in the Appendix No. XI" (Mr. Parkinson's) "is 21.266 bushels. From these two, if we take the mean, the average produce of the county is 24.933 bushels; that is, 24 bushels 3 pecks and 11½ pints *nearly*." (!)

His more elaborate calculations, concerning the *County produce* of that crop, do not appear to be sufficiently well grounded, to merit admission into this Register.

BARLEY.—*Method* of *Sowing*.—P. 189. "This is done by drilling, in a few instances, upon one earth; by sowing broad-cast, and harrowing in; but in most instances, by ploughing in half the seed, and harrowing in the other half."

Quantity of *Seed*.—P. 191. The average quantity of seed sown by the above account is 3.5833 bushels per acre: by Appendix No. XI. it is 4 09788, of which two the mean is 3.84059 bushels per acre."

The

The *Acre Produce* of Barley.—P. 191. "The average produce of the above account is 44.73 bushels per acre; but by Appendix No. XI. we find it 30.62365 bushels, from which two we get 37.6768 bushels per acre as the average produce."

Those are nice calculations;—done, it might be said, to the decimal fraction of a barley corn.—The Norfolk Secretary appears to be, not a man of learning, merely, but what is infinitely more estimable, a man of science. In this instance, however, science only serves to hide, not to discover, truth.—The eye, dazzled by the fractions, is led away from the integral parts.—It is not *probable* that the average produce of barley in Buckinghamshire is even thirtyseven bushels. It is scarcely *possible* that it should be fortyfour and a fraction. It is nevertheless asserted, in page 190, that "At Tyringham barley crops yield from 7 to 10 qrs. per acre." But this must, assuredly, be a *hoax*.

Under *extraordinary* circumstances, crops of extraordinary magnitude are sometimes produced. But to speak of such, in a *general* way; and most especially to place them in a *Report*, as the *average produce* of a *County*, can serve no better purpose than that of encoraging *exorbitant renters* to injure, not only their tenants; but, eventually, themselves and their estates.

OATS.—P. 193. "There are but few instances of the cultivation of oats in this county."

PEASE.—P. 196. "Pease are but very rarely grown."

BEANS.—P. 197. "Beans are sown upon all soils broad-cast, by drilling and by dibbling: generally upon one earth, and very often mixed with pease: some farmers manure for them. In the open-field culture they follow wheat."

PEABEANS.—P. 199. "When pease and beans are mixed, the proportion of seed is one of pease to three or four of beans—in all, four bushels per acre."

POTATOES.—P. 220. "*Potatoes*—Form but a small part of the produce of Bucks: except in gardens, and by the poor on the side of roads, they are but little cultivated."

P. 221. "Mr. Sheppard, of Thornton, has this year made an experiment to ascertain the propriety of pulling off the blossom of the potatoe. The public will-be obliged by his communication* of the result."

CARROTS.

"*T. Sheppard, Esq. of Thornton, has very obligingly communicated the result in these words: 'My friend Mr. Smith's report of potatoes is as follows: half a bushel more and of better quality on *seventeen* poles of ground where the blossoms were cut off, than on *eighteen* poles of ground on which the blossoms remained on the potatoes."

CARROTS.—P. 218. "No carrots are grown in Bucks."

PARSNEPS.—P. 219. "The Rev. Dr. De Salis, of Wing, has cultivated parsnips so successfully, as to have been honoured with a medal by the Society of Arts on that account, in whose Transactions the particulars of his experiments have been published. At present no parsnips are grown."

This circumstance is an evidence (not a proof) that parsneps are an unsuitable object of field culture, in this island.—Yet considering their saccharine quality, and the facility with which they may be raised, on lands that are adapted to their growth, reason suggests much in their favor. The practice of Guernsey and Jersey, where cows are (I was informed by the late DOCTOR DE SALIS) principally fed upon those roots,—may be founded on a degree of necessity; owing to a scarcity, there, of natural herbage.

TURNEPS.—In the section, "Turneps," of the work under review, I find nothing of peculiar interest to notice, relating to the practice of Buckinghamshire; saving the subjoined mysterious,—to me, altogether incomprehensible,—passage.

P. 208. "To this preservative* may be added, Mr. Forster's method of giving quick vegetation to his turnips, by his process of turning the earth over them, and thus producing fresh evaporation. This is the best of preservatives for turnips in their infant state, for which purpose the tilth cannot be too fine."

The *consumption* of turneps, in Buckinghamshire, is thus noticed.—P. 210. "Very little of the turnip crop is consumed by *neat stock*" (cattle,) "and none of it by milch cows: its general use is for sheep, which are fed upon the land with it by certain portions."

BULBOUS RAPE.—P. 215. "Mr. Ayton's bailiff objects to this plant," ("Swedes"!) "except in a small proportion of the whole turnip crop. Being obliged to sow them early, viz. by the latter end of May, he says the land is not sufficiently cleaned and tempered for a fallow."

This is a just remark. The evil, however, may be avoided. The prevailing practice of the Swedes themselves (as I was some years ago informed, by the Chevalier Edelcrantz, is to *transplant* their "ruta baga."—a practice which I have pursued with success. The seed may be sown

* Namely that of sowing ashes over seedling turneps, "in a morning when they have a little dew upon them,"—to save them from the "Fly."

Query,—what species of *Fly*?—Tenthredo?—Aphis?—or Chysomela?—The last is a species of *Beetle*.

sown in autumn, or in the spring (sooner or later, according to the poverty or richness of the soil and the situation of the seed bed) and the plants be put in, about the time of sowing turneps (as toward the latter end of June or the beginning of July); sooner or latter according to the state of the season, and the state of the soil to be cropped. By planting on WATERED RIDGETS, a crop may thus be *insured.*—See my WEST of ENGLAND, Minute 64.—Also NORTHERN DEPARTMENT, page 83.

P. 214. "Mr. Westcar, of Kreslow, feeds his horses upon Swedish turnips, and thinks much advantage arises from it. He sows them in June.

"Mr. Swannell, of Filgrave, sows Swedes so as to finish about the 25th or 26th of June. He cuts a few for bullocks, if his hay does not last out the season. Pigs fatten quickly upon Swedes, and pay well."

The latter end of June is in ordinary situations, too late to sow the seeds of this plant, in the field, for a crop. The latter end of May, or the former part of June, under ordinary circumstances, and when roots of the full size are desired, is I believe, in a par of seasons, a more eligible time of sowing. But vegetation, in the county of Buckingham, would seem to be peculiarly rapid; for, in the section "Turnips" of this Report, is the subjoined entry.—P. 206. "Mr. Turney, of Brickhill, sows turnips so late as the 8th or 10th of August: if he sows them before, the turnips grow too large before Christmas, and mildew. If he wants them for fattening sheep, he sows them earlier."

In common cases, we may I think set down a month, at least, as the difference between the proper time of *sowing* bulbous rape (in the field) and that of *transplanting* it. And it would be difficult to calculate the advantages to be gained (under ordinary circumstances) by a month's tillage, in the month of June!—An advantage, not to the fallow crop, only, but to the four, five, or six crops of corn and herbage, which, in many or most cases, ought to succeed it.

CABBAGES.—P. 214. "Cabbages are grown by very few."

RAPE HERBAGE.—P. 213. "Coleseed, or rape, is not grown in this county."

TARE HERBAGE.—P. 200. "Tares are grown for horses and sheep; for soiling in the one case, and feeding in the other: sheep either feed them upon the ground, or they have portions mown for them, and given to them, so that the land may have equal portions of their dung.

"Tares are sown upon arable land in three ways: first, upon

upon heavy land, upon a fallow for wheat, when they have the power of fertilizing the soil by overshadowing it; and next upon a wheat-stubble, to be followed in the succeeding year by turnips, or a crop of corn; or thirdly, to be fed or mown, and carried off by the next June, so as to admit a crop of cabbages or turnips in the same year."

CLOVER.—P. 222. "*Manuring.*—This is universally practised. In February or March farmers lay about ten sacks, *i. e.* forty bushels, of ashes per acre, which cost at the wharfs 6*d.* or 7*d.* per bushel."

Here, as in Oxfordshire, sowing ashes over clover appears to be an established practice. After noticing several instances of it, the Reporter says, same page, "From these instances we see the quantity of manure is variable, but the practice is invariable, where ashes are to be procured from London, and where they are not, some other kind of manure is substituted."

SAINFOIN.—P. 227. "Sainfoin is grown upon the Chiltern Hills, but is not well spoken of. The general remark is, that it will not *stand* long: *it dies away*:"—perhaps, through improper *management*. But concerning this, we have no information.

GRASS LANDS.

Mr. Priest appropriates separate sections to "Meadows" and "Pastures". By the former would seem to be meant the low, flat *water-formed* grass lands, on the banks of rivers; and, by the latter, the permanent herbage or "old grass lands" of *upper-grounds*:—whether they happen to be kept in a state of continual pasturage, or whether they are occasionally mown for hay.

MEADOWS.—P. 233. "Those meadows in Bucks which lie along the Ouse and the Thame, both that part of it which runs through the middle of the county, and that which bounds it from Herts, are very liable to floods, which enrich them much: indeed, farmers think the overflowing of these rivers of service sufficient to supersede manure, even though the meadows are mown year after year."

PASTURES.—P. 234. "Pastures in Bucks form a prominent feature in its agriculture: they are numerous, extensive, and though not in general so rich as in some counties, yet very valuable. In the south part of Bucks, and upon the Chiltern Hills, the pasture land is very small in comparison with the arable, but in the rest of the county pastures form large dairy farms, and almost half the farms of a mixed nature, except in the instances of land under open-field culture, where about one-third is sward, as is the case at Stewkley, Bletchley, &c."

General Application of Grass Lands, in Buckinghamshire. —P. 234. " Of pasture and meadow land (for it is difficult to speak of them separately), some farmers make a point of mowing and feeding" (pasturing) " alternately, that is, of mowing those parts one year which were fed in the preceding, where meadows will allow it: others keep a certain part for feeding, and always mow the rest."

Mowing Grounds.—P. 244. " *Hay-making.*—Great care is taken in the making of hay in all parts of Bucks. As soon as mown it is spread over the field: it is then raked into small rows, and put into small cocks: this is the process of one day. The next day these cocks are spread again about the pastures, and before night put into larger cocks than before. The next day, if the hay was not dry enough, it is thrown out again, and either put into still larger cocks than on the second day, or immediately carried to the rick. I saw a great deal of *pasture* and meadow *hay*, which was stacked within three days after it was mown, and some without being cocked at all:"—the weather of course being remarkably fine.

Grazing Grounds.—P. 245. " *Stock.*—This consists either of bullocks and sheep, or of cows and sheep. The farms upon which neat stock is grazed, are but few in comparison with those which consist of dairies, and none which carry on both grazing and dairying.

" Of *grazing stock* no farmer would acknowledge he had pasture rich enough to fat a beast upon an acre. There are, however, a few spots which will do this, particularly at Quarrendon.

" At Berryfield, Mr. Rose says it is hard stocking to put even one beast, an ewe and lamb, upon an acre and a half. By a beast is meant here, and throughout this Report, the Hereford and Devon.

" At Tyringham, the pastures carry two bullocks to three acres."

" At Filgrave, they allow a beast and two sheep to two acre.

" At Olney, the average is one bullock and one sheep and a half to two acres.

" At Cold Brayfield, a bullock to three acres, and not a sheep to an acre.

" At Eythorpe, pastures carry a bullock upon one acre and a quarter, with a sheep upon an acre.

" The average value then of the grazing pastures is very little more than a bullock of 125 stone, of 8 lb. to the stone, and two sheep to two acres."

Dairy Pastures,—will be spoken of under the general head, *Dairy*, ensuing.

The

The *Sizes* of Pasture Grounds.—P. 241. "This varies from 20 to 300 acres, but the most common size is from 50 to 100 acres."

IMPROVEMENTS of GRASS LANDS,—By *Banking:* (an aukward provincial term, for removing ant-hills).—On this subject Mr. P. has given a lengthened article. A portion of it is, at least interesting.—

P. 236. "Mr. Morris, banked last year twenty acres, as has been mentioned in Chap. VII. Sect. 10, the turf of which banks he burnt, and spread the ashes in the winter upon the crowns of the ridges from which they had been cut. In the spring, without ploughing, he dibbled vetches, and sowed oats, purple and Dutch clover, trefoil and ray-grass, and the produce of hay was about a tun per acre:"—a moderate crop.

"Mr. Barge, another tenant of Mr. Coke, banked a few acres two or three years ago in the same manner, and upon the crowns of the ridges sowed oats, and reaped a good crop. The next year he sowed upon the same land, without ploughing or scarifying, spring wheat and Dutch clover: the produce was very good, and the sward is now restored. This last instance of banking had nearly been attended with very serious consequences, for the land upon which these crops of oats and wheat grew, was tithe free; but as the crops were crops of corn severed from the soil, the parson contended the modus was broken, and he had a right to tithe in kind. Upon this question the opinions of persons of high authority were taken, and it seemed to be a very doubtful case; the occupier contending, that as the soil had not been *broken* by the plough, or otherwise, the modus still remained good; and the parson, that as the crops had been *severed*, he had a right to his tenth. The best opinions seemed to be, that although the parson *might* have a right to his tenth of that single crop, yet as the modus was not broken, it would scarce answer his purpose to be at the expense of bringing the matter to issue, and therefore it was dropped."

By *Draining*, &c.—P. 241. "In order to destroy rushes after proper drainage by open and hollow drains, the most effectual method is to mow them in the spring. Dr. De Salis, of Wing, had a pasture allotted to him upon the enclosure there, which in its then state, was extremely boggy, and full of thistles and rushes, and not worth more than 5*s.* per acre. By under-draining, spudding thistles, and mowing rushes, he has made the meadow nearly as good as the best he occupies, and worth at leass 35*s.* per acre."

By *Dibbling in Tares.*—This method of *improvement* is equally novel aud curious, as the first abovementioned.—

P. 201.

P. 201. ("Section Tares") "Having stated the different ways in which tares are grown upon arable land, it now becomes necessary to shew how they may be grown with success upon pasture and meadow. Instances of this practice occurred this year, and have been pursued before, upon farms at Hillesden and Cowley, belonging to T. W. Coke, Esq. of Holkham, in Norfolk, in imitation of the system first adopted by Mr. Salter, just now mentioned.

"Mr. Salter's method, which he pursues systematically upon meadows and pastures that want improvement, is, to feed them as bare as possible; then in the spring, about April, or later, to dibble two bushels of tares per acre, either alone, or mixed with pease, in holes about four inches apart from each other."

P. 203. "When this process of dibbling is finished throughout the pasture or meadow, or as soon as the dibbling is advanced far enough, so that the teams may not be stopped, Mr. Salter sets on mould, or any scrapings he can get together, from 12 to 20 cart-loads, or more, which he spreads, and makes as fine by the harrows and roll as he can. Upon such parts of the pasture as will grow oats, Mr. Salter sows them broad-cast upon the mould already spread, where it is thick enough: then he harrows again. He then sows of ray-grass, two bushels at least, and eight or nine pounds of Dutch clover per acre, and brushes them in with a pair of harrows, or a gate bushed. In imitation of this method of growing tares, Mr. Morris last year dibbled tares upon 20 acres of pasture, which had been banked in the preceding autumn."

In reviewing a Report of NORFOLK, by the SECRETARY of the BOARD, I noticed this great discovery of Mr. Salter; which happened some time previously to 1804, when the Secretary's Report was published; namely six years before the publication of that of Mr. Priest. Yet all that we now hear of this discovery, from Mr. P.—a man of Norfolk, and a warm advocate for this "practice" (if such it can be properly called) is what we read above; namely,—that Mr. Salter "pursues his method systematically upon meadows and pastures that want improvement." But we are not informed what sort of defects his meadows and pastures lie under; nor of the quantity or quality of the "improvement," which is thereby produced.

So endeth the Reports, about this childishly puffed off discovery. See EASTERN DEPARTMENT, page 394.

LIVESTOCK.

Little can be expected on this subject, in a Report from Buckinghamshire;

Buckinghamshire; which is not a *breeding* County. It may be said to have no breeds of its own. There, as in other rich grassland districts, the rearing of livestock (sheep generally excepted) is left to less fertile situations. The *vale* lands of *this* County are here more particularly meant.

HORSES.—On this species, not a syllable is said; excepting what relates to the horse as a *working animal;*—see page 529, aforegoing

CATTLE.—*Objects.*—P. 286. "Cattle are kept in this county for two purposes, for beef and for butter; very few for work."

Fatting Cattle.—Breed.—P. 286. "For beef, most graziers prefer those of the Hereford breed, being esteemed the quickest feeders. A few are of opinion, that the Devons are most profitable, being light of offal. But to determine this question with certainty, no one at present is able. Indeed the general observation upon them is, that there are good and bad of all sorts, and that it is absurd to ask which is the quickest feeder. Animals, like men, they say, vary as to their improvement by food, and therefore no one can say in general terms, how much weight of beef a given quantity of food shall produce in a given time, much less can he determine this point as to a particular animal, or a given number of animals of a specific breed."

The Reporter remarks on those sentiments; but not with success.—P. 287. "Mr. Westcar prefers, generally, the Hereford ox for grazing, but buys and sells at any time any grazing stock which answers his purpose."

Food of fatting Cattle.—Summer fatting.—P. 294. "No other food in summer from May to November 1st, is used, either for grazing or milking stock, but grass. The general practice in grazing is to buy beasts in the spring, and to send them to market before Christmas, except some prime or choice beasts."

Winter Fatting.—P. 291. "Whatever beasts are kept after Christmas, are either stores and fed upon straw and hay, or prime beasts, and kept at a great expense upon oil-cakes and hay: there are but few exceptions to this practice."

Management of fatting Cattle.—P. 296. "With respect to fatting of beasts, no other exists but that which is to be derived from good pastures. A good Buckinghamshire grazier, however, daily watches well the improvement made in a beast, and sells accordingly. If an animal is thrifty, he improves it as long as he can: if not, he sells it as soon as he can, remembering the old maxim, '*the first loss is the best.*'"—rather say, the *least.*

The

The *market* is of course Smithfield.

DAIRY.—On this leading branch of the husbandry of, Buckinghamshire, Mr. Priest has industriously collected,—or rather shall we say dispersed in his pages,—numerous items of information. Some of them are found in the section "Farm Houses and Offices"; others, in that of "Size of Farms"; others, in the section "Pastures"; and the rest scattered in that of Cattle:—the notices being there intermixed with those relating to *Grazing*.—They are here drawn together, and digested, I believe, agreeably to the most natural arrangement of the subject.

Cows.—Breed.—P. 288. "For the dairy, the favourite cow is the Yorkshire short-horned cow, called the Holderness. This breed of cows, upon rich pastures, is esteemed the most productive. There are however some dairy-men, who prefer the long-horned Leicester. The Suffolk cow is introduced in a few instances, and approved, where the food is less luxuriant. The Alderney is also found in the yards of a few gentlemen, who are more curious in their choice of breed. A principal reason for the preference given to the Holderness is, that after having kept them in a dairy from three years old to six or seven, they are then ready of sale to Londom milkmen, or for grazing. There are also some Welsh cows kept.

"The Rev. Mr. Rush, of Stone, gives an excellent character of the Alderney cow. He had two such, the one a calf of the other, and for a considerable part of a year they gave 11 lb. of butter each per week.

"S. Freeman, Esq. of Fawley Court, keeps 20 cows of the short-horned Yorkshire breed, from the stock of Sir George Strickland, late of Boynton, near Bridlington, in Yorkshire. He has also two or three Alderneys, for the sake of *thickening* the cream."

How procured.—P. 290 "Cows are either bred by those who keep them, or bought at four years old."

Food for Dairy Cows.—P. 295. "*Food in summer* for cows is almost universally two acres to a cow. It is to be observed, that in this allowance for a cow as well as for oxen, stated above, sheep are also fed; but that account is reserved for the section appropriated to them.

"Mr. Hayward, of Stoke-Goldington, keeps a cow to two acres of pasture.

"Upon extremely rich pastures, as at Whaddesdon, it is not esteemed so beneficial to the farmer to keep a dairy as to graze oxen."

P. 293. "*Food for Cows in Winter.*—Hay is invariably the food for cows in winter upon the dairy farms, and of this the general allowance is from two to three tons per head.

head. If then a cow requires for her summer keep two acres, scarce less than two will be necessary for her winter's keep."—See the preceding article of review, p. 505, aforegoing, &c. &c. &c. *

General Management of Dairy Cows.—P. 296. "*Management* with respect to the dairy is neat and simple. Cows are kept from four years old so long as they are valuable (that is, good milkers), or sold at eight years old to London milkmen, or graziers, unless disposed of before that time for want of winter food."

Disposal of Cows.—See the last extract.

Diseases of Cows.—P. 304. "The most prevalent distemper is that of making red water. The method of discovering whether a cow has this distemper, is to drive her into water, and she will instantly give proof of it. This distemper seems to abound most upon wet pastures, and to be most fatal to cows not bred upon them. Dr. De Salis, at Wing, by under-draining and treading abundantly a very wet and boggy pasture, has prevented this distemper, which used to attack cows fed upon it."

Dairy Room.—A minutia, in forming the feet of the walls is entitled to notice.—Instead of letting them rise perpendicularly from the floor,—as they are usually built,—a triangular footing is formed, (more particularly under the milk trays and dairy shelves) some fifteen or twenty inches wide at the base, and sloping back, to the height of twenty or thirty inches, according to circumstances; thus filling the angles, formed by the floor and the walls; in which angles, wetness and dirt are most liable to lodge; and where it is most difficult to be removed. By this simplex contrivance the labor of cleaning is lessened, and the work more effectually done: thus contributing, at a small expence (where freestone flags can be had at a moderate rate) to the neatness, and what is of greater consequence, to the SWEETNESS of a DAIRY.

Milking.—P. 297. "The Cows are milked in the summer in one corner of a field, or in a milking-house, by men, and carried home in pails hanging upon a wooden shoulder sling

* Cow GROUNDS.—In page 246,—section "Pastures,"—Mr. Priest says—"Of *stock for the dairy*, a minute examination of the account stated in Chap. IV. Sect. 1, under the article Size of Farms, will give as an average of cows 32 to 151 acres, for summer and winter food;"—which is nearly five acres to one cow!—How perfectly useless it is to talk about the proportion of cows to acres; without explicitly describing the quality of the lands, and the size of the animals to be supported by it.—Here, I drop the unprofitable pursuit—IN PRACTICE, the due proportion readily presents itself.

sling (as it is called). At Fawley Court only, the dairy-maid milks as well as the men; and at Aylesbury some milk is carried home in a large tub swinging upon a frame supported upon an axle and two wheels."

P. 289. "Mrs. Freeman is extremely neat and regular in the management of the dairy. This is the only instance I met with in Bucks, where the dairy-maid *milks cows*, and where cows are constantly milked *three* times a day, by which means Mrs. Freeman is quite sure the quantity of milk is increased."

Raising and collecting the *Cream*.—P. 297. "In general, the receptacles of the milk are made of lead, but few wooden trays are used. At Fawley Court, Mrs. Freeman uses trays made of tin."

"Mrs. Freeman had also stone trays, but those of tin were preferred. The observation made was, that lead is not esteemed wholesome, and that the cream rises as soon and as thick in tin as in leaden trays, and that the tin trays are much less expensive.

"In most dairies the milk is skimmed every twelve hours, twice in summer, and oftener in winter. The cream from the first two skimmings is put into the cream cistern to make the first butter, and that which is afterwards skimmed, makes what is called an *after butter*. The milk is in many instances skimmed five and six times:" (?) "in this practice I found but one deviation, which was at Fawley Court: there Mrs. Freeman skims the milk only once, and that after twenty-four hours. When the milk has been thus skimmed, the invariable practice is to convey it into the hog-tub."

The tedious practice, above noticed, would seem to be peculiar to Buckinghamshire (and perhaps the other "lump butter" districts). I have not met with it, nor heard of it, in any other. By *sorting* the cream, a quantity of rich *market* butter may doubtlessly be procured:—and so far the information is valuable.

P. 298. "It is by no means a common practice, but at Stoke-Goldington, Mr. Hayward, after once skimming the milk *doubles* it, that is, puts two leads of milk together, making the milk now double the depth it was before, and thus skims it twice or thrice, or as often as it will admit of being skimmed. The skimming dish is made of tin, circular, being about a foot in diameter, with holes in it, and a handle upon the top of it."—This is something new.

Preserving Cream.—Not noticed.

Churning.—P. 298. "Butter is made twice in a week, in churns usually turned by a horse. The time usually given for the butter *to come*, is an hour and half. I watched one

one churn which held eight dozen*, and found it went round forty-five times in a minute. I had no where an opportunity of trying or learning the degree of heat in the churn.

"The butter made in Bucks is esteemed very good. Its colour, firmness, and flavour, are excellent."

Making up or *manufacturing* Butter.—Not noticed, unless as follows:—

Market for Butter.—P. 299. "The manner of sending butter to London, gives the dairymen but very little trouble. The butter is made in lumps of 2lb. each, and is packed into a basket made of oziers, which is called a flat. Flats are parallelipipedons of different sizes, but all of the same depth, viz. 11 inches. They hold from three to ten dozen of butter; that is, from 36lb. to 120lb.; they have each on three of their sides, three marks, one on each side, viz. a figure to denote the number of dozen pounds which the flat holds, a letter to denote the farmer's name whose butter it carries, and the name and residence of the carrier. These flats, together with the cloths in them, are the property of the carrier who receives the butter, the carriage of which is paid by the butter factor in London. The only trouble which the dairy-man has, is to carry his butter upon a horse to the nearest point where the carrier passes, to make his agreement with his butter factor, and monthly or otherwise to receive his money."

Produce of Butter.—P. 302. "From the best information gained, the average quantity of butter from a cow for forty weeks, is 5lb. per week."

The average produce of a *cow*, throughout the butter-dairy districts of the kingdom, is, I believe, three firkins,—of fiftysix pounds, each;—that is 168lb. The produce of Buckinghamshire is, therefore, according to this report of it, above par; being more than three and a half firkins. But this may be accounted for, in the richness of the pastures, the practice of creaming repeatedly; and in the circumstance of the cows being chiefly bought in; and are of course *chosen* for *milking*, only.

The Reporter, however, seems to think that even 200lb. are a low produce; and, in justification of that opinion, gives, in page 301,—an "account of the butter produced upon a small farm in the county of Norfolk, that was sent to me as Secretary of the Agricultural Society of that county, and with proper certificates."—The first line of which account (for ten years) stands thus:—P. 302. "In 1797, the produce

" * This is the way of speaking of the quantity of butter, and means dozen of pounds in weight, reckoning 17 oz to the pound, one ounce being allowed for waste."

duce of butter only from 12 cows, was 63 firkins sold:" add to this, the "butter used in the house," two and a half firkins (the Reporter's estimate.) The gross produce, that year, of twelve cows, was sixtyfive and a half firkins; or very nearly five and a half firkins, a cow!—from the lean arid lands of Norfolk!!—Surely, the breed of the cows, the quality of their food, and the management, throughout, ought to have been *explicitly certified*, to render the account in any degree credible.

Mr. P. "computes" the *produce* of the *County;* but his calculations are too conjectural for insertion, here.

CHEESE.—P. 298. "No cheeses are made, except in the summer a very few cream cheeses by particular persons, for Buckingham, Aylesbury, and Wycombe markets, and a few at Fawley Court by Mrs. Freeman."

Thus, in Buckinghamshire, we find a *variety* of practice; differing from the established customs of other butter-dairy districts; as Yorkshire, Suffolk, &c.; where *skim-milk cheeses* are invariably made; the *whey*, there, being the beverage of swine:—whereas, in Buckinghamshire, the *skimmed milk*, itself, goes immediately to the hog tub.—This may serve to account for the extraordinary care bestowed on separating the cream from it:—in order, it is more than probable, to obtain a supply of secondary butter, —*for home consumption:*—under the same intention as the good houswives of the prime-cheese districts extract butter, of a secondary quality, from whey.

Thus, we have three *differential* practices.—In Glocestershire, Cheshire, &c. the milk from the cow is separated into prime cheese, whey butter, and skimmed whey for hogs.—In Yorkshire, Suffolk, &c. it is divided, by a varying process, into butter, secondary cheese, and skimmed milk whey, for the hogs.—In Buckinghamshire, by another analysis, into prime butter, skimmed milk butter, and doubly skimmed milk for the hogs.

Calves of butter-dairy Cows.—P. 296. "The calves are generally sold to sucklers at an age from four to twelve days old, except a few which are fattened or kept to supply the dairy. Those intended for the dairy, either at home or elsewhere, are chosen by their white faces, white eyelids, and white noses;" (!)* "calves with such points will generally sell for 5*s.* each more than others."

SUCKLING CALVES, for Veal.—P. 303. "The practice of suckling calves in Bucks, is declining. Those who suckle keep the calves in pens, boarded and kept as clean as possible

* This, in Yorkshire, is a hateful point (see my YORKSHIRE). How vague, and frequently ridiculous, are popular "signs."

sible. A small crib is placed at one end for chalk, of which they have a handful each every day.

"—— Ward, Esq. of Newport Pagnel, pays great attention to cleanliness in suckling of calves, insomuch, that he ties them up whilst they are with the cows to prevent them from licking any dirt or filth upon the cows. By this care, and by giving chalk, the calves are not bled before they are slaughtered, and no veal is whiter.

"At Lord Carrington's, the calves are tied to a crib by the neck, in the same manner as fatting stock."

P. 304. "Mr. Foster, of Wendover, used to suckle; but he found the sale of calves so precarious, having often received from his salesman not half what he expected, that he has given up the practice.

"Mr. Davis, of Cheynies, suckles a few. Calves thus suckled are sent to Smithfield, to be sold by salesmen"

P. 305. "The scouring of calves is cured by Mr. Dodd, of Cheynies, by sprinkling their loins with cold water." (?)

SWINE.—320. "Hogs form an important article in the account of the profits of a farmer in Bucks. Upon the arable farms where the growth of corn arrests the whole attention of the farmers, the management of pigs makes but a small part of their system. They breed some, and keep stores in the yards, but the dairy farmers regularly buy stores, fat them upon the skimmed milk of the dairy, of which they give them the whole, and then sell them as bacon, between Michaelmas and Christmas, and send porkers to London market from that time till the spring."

P. 321. "The breed, in general, is the Berkshire, on account of its being kindly disposed to fatten, and attaining a large size. The Chinese is a favourite breed with some, as is also the Suffolk. There is also a cross between the Berkshire and the Chinese, which is said to give a stronger inclination to fatten."

P. 324. "From the time that the bacon hogs go to market to May, porkers are fattened for London. They are killed at home, and sent to salesmen in London to sell at market; the price of which, with carriage, is about 6½*d*." (6*s*) "per stone. The following is a copy of a salesman's bill for selling two porkers at Newgate-market:

Mr. B. 4th May, 1808.

Pigs, 8st. 4lb. at 6*s*.	£.2	11	0
Two heads,	0	2	6
	£.2	13	6
Selling,	0	1	7
	£.2	11	11
Paid carriage,	0	3	4
Paid to R. D.	£.2	8	7

Note.

"*Note.*—Mr. B. is the salesman, and R. D. is the carrier. The carrier received the above on Thursday; they were sold on Friday, and within a day or two the money was paid by the carrier to the person who sent the pigs."

P. 325. "The pigs are kept upon grass, and brought home into the yard at night, until they are put to milk."

P. 326. "Porkers are put up to fatten at about a quarter of a year old, from four to six weeks, and weigh from 5 to 10 stone."

P. 329. "Pigs are very subject to a huskiness with a bound hide, called the *garget;* in which case Mr. Dodd, of Cheynies, uses with success a mixture of madder and the flour of brimstone, one pound of each, and puts half a pint into a pail of their food."

It would be wrong not to record, here, the subjoined notice: to show the inattention with which REPORTERS from ENQUIRY are liable to make their memoranda.

P. 328. "Mr. Heart, of Wing, says, some persons there keep breeding sows, which are suffered to have one or two litters, and then they are fattened: but in general pigs are bought at one year old at Aylesbury or Leighton, kept a year, and then sent *as porkers* to London, or fattened as bacon:"—*Two years old porkers!*

SHEEP.—*Object.*—P. 307. "The principal object to be attained by sheep in this county, is to produce fat lambs for London market as early as possible. Hence those sheep which will produce the earliest and the greatest number of lambs, are most valuable; for whilst, after having kept lambs from the time of yeaning to Midsummer, the Norfolk breeder gets from 20*s*. to 25*s*. a-piece for his lambs, the Buckinghamshire farmer gets in the spring from 35*s*. to 40*s*. each: for which purpose, the Dorsetshire breed seems to be most esteemed, but not the most prevalent; next to these the Gloucester, and then the Berkshire. South Downs are gaining ground in Bucks, amongst such farmers as pay attention to wool and grazing."

House Lamb.—"Mr. Langton, of Chippenham Court, keeps the Dorsetshire and Somersetshire ewes for early lambs: they take the ram in May, and yean in October. The method of making ewes *blossom* (*i. e.* willing or desirous to receive the ram), is to increase the richness of their food, by first putting them to inferior food, and then giving them vetches, or other food equally rich, having previously kept the rams and ewes apart from each other."

Breeding Sheep.—The following passage is truly interesting.—P. 309. "Mr. Langton, of Chippenham Court, who puts rams to ewes very early, as has been stated before.

fore, never trusts to one ram only, and in this respect breeders would do well to imitate him: for there is now no doubt made of the doctrine of superfœtation; and from a remarkable circumstance which occurred lately in the flock of a breeder of sheep in Norfolk, there is strong reason for supposing, that two rams amongst a given number of ewes, will get more lambs than one ram alone. Mr. Seppings, of Creak in Norfolk, had a flock of Norfolk ewes, to which he put Norfolk and Leicester rams. Several of the ewes which had twin lambs, had one lamb a true Norfolk, and the other a half-bred between the Leicester and the Norfolk. I do not recollect the exact number, but it was between 50 and 100 ewes which were so circumstanced."

If the ewes, in that case, were thoroughly bred, without any admixture, by former crossings, of Leicestershire blood in them, the above incident, alone, (admitting it of course to be accurately recorded) may be considered as a proof of the position advanced.—In cases, that are common, in which lambs are intended, as such, for the butcher,—experiments of that sort may be made, on a small scale, without any material injury or loss.

Management of Sheep.—P. 310. "In the *dairy-farms* there appeared but one method of managing sheep, which was, to buy ewes with lamb in the autumn, to keep them in winter upon hay, to fatten their lambs and send them to London market in the spring, and the ewes afterwards in the summer. This is the universal practice of those who have no folding, and the number of sheep kept is, upon an average, nearly two to five acres.

"Upon the *Chiltern Hills*, the general practice is to buy ewes and wethers, the former to produce fat lambs and then to be fattened, and the latter to be fattened. For instance, a farm of 400 acres has 300 sheep—200 wethers to be fattened upon turnips, and 100 ewes to produce lambs to be sent fat to market, and then to be themselves fattened. This, Mr. Jagger, of Beacons-field, informed me, was the common practice of that neighbourhood, and this, with very little deviation, seemed to be the method of managing sheep with most of the best farmers."

P. 312. "At Wing, and on all farms of a mixed nature, besides the ewes and lambs which are fattened for market, a flock is kept for folding, and after *working* one year is fattened."

P. 313. "*Recapitulation.*—From this statement, and the account given in Chap. IV. Sect. 2, it will be seen, that the number of sheep kept upon the dairy farms are nearly two to five acres, upon the arable farms five to six acres, and

and upon those of a mixed nature five to seven acres: that upon the dairy farms, where there is no folding, ewes with lamb are bought in the autumn, and the lambs and ewes fattened in the spring and summer following; and that excepting a very few instances upon the arable farms, and those of a mixed nature, as many lambs are fattened as possible, with their ewes, and that stores are kept as *working* sheep for folding, and then after a certain time fattened. Such as are not wanted for folding or stores are sold."

Many thanks are due to Mr. P. for this agreeable repast;—this well given information.

RABBITS.—P. 330. "Although rabbits are not very numerous, nor any where kept upon warrens, yet not a small number are sent yearly and weekly to London markets from hence. They are kept by poor men in houses."

POULTRY.—*Ducks.*—The following information is curious; and is a proper companion to the account given of geese, in Lincolnshire. See EASTERN DEPARTMENT.

P. 331. "Ducks form a material article at market from Aylesbury and places adjacent: they are white, and as it seems of an early breed: they are bred and brought up by poor people, and sent to London by the weekly carriers. One poor man whom I visited, had before his door a small pit of water, about three yards long and one yard broad: at two corners of this pit are places of shelter for the ducks, thatched with straw: at night the ducks are taken into a house. In one room belonging to this man (the only room he had to live in), were ducks of three growths, on the 14th of January, 1808, fattening for London market: at one corner about seventeen or eighteen four weeks old; at another corner a brood a fortnight old; and at a third corner a brood a week old. In the bed-room were hens brooding ducks' eggs in boxes, to be bought off at different periods: ducks six weeks old at that time for 12*s.* a couple. Besides the above, there are other persons who breed many more ducks than the person now mentioned, and as far as it was possible to discover, I understood this person sends 400 ducks in a year to London. Allowing then forty persons to send only as many, at an average of 5*s.* per duck, the return of ducks from Aylesbury alone will amount to 4000*l.* per annum. This return has been magnified into 20,000*l.* per annum: but upon such conjecture the whole neighbourhood must be taken into consideration, and I have not sufficient *data* to ascertain the truth of it."

PIGEONS.—The Reporter describes a pigeon house. A minutia belonging to it is entitled to mention, here.—P. 39.

"Very

"Very properly the lockers are white-washed: this serves in a great measure to keep them free from bugs."

BEES.—The following suggestion may, in suitable situations, be entitled to attention.—P. 332. "Bees are every where too much neglected. They are very profitable, and might serve the poor well towards paying their rent. Many a poor man would keep bees had he the means of raising a stock. Surely it would answer the purpose of a parish well, to enable poor men to effect this."

PROFIT.—P. 97. "There is no county in this island, where the variation of expenses and of profit is greater than in Bucks: from excessive expenditures upon the Chiltern Hills, arising from poorness of soil, high chalky hills, difficult to cultivate and difficult to manure, to the bare ploughing of rich and fertile spots of ground upon the farms of a mixed nature, which produce, without manure, a succession of abundant crops of barley, oats, and wheat, after one another from seven quarters to ten quarters of the first and second, and then from 30 to 35 bushels of the third. Such land must make rich farmers; and accordingly I was informed of one farmer, under a very kind and good landlord, who, in the course of a few years (less than 20), accumulated a sum of money between 18,000*l.* and 20,000*l.*, upon a farm less than 300 acres. This farmer upon entering the farm upon which he realized the sum now mentioned, had not enough capital to stock his farm, but was obliged to borrow of his landlord! he had, however, permission to break up old rich pastures in the dearest of years, and thus acquired the profits now stated."

This corroborates what I have long been led to believe; namely, that few men have made much money by farming; excepting those who have fortunately had FRESH LAND to work upon.—See remarks on this subject, page 57, aforegoing: which were written before I opened the book that is now before me.

P. 99. "It would not only be highly gratifying to my own personal feelings, but extremely interesting to the cause in which I am engaged, if I had met with such accounts so fairly kept, of the different methods of farming pursued in Bucks, that a communication of the precise expenses and profits upon different farms in the several methods, could have been made to the Board and the public. Such accounts were not given, and conjecture must not be indulged."—These sentiments, I have pleasure in saying, appear to me highly creditable to Mr. PRIEST.

BEDFORDSHIRE,

BEDFORDSHIRE.

THE COUNTY of BEDFORD (as those of Oxford and Buckingham) enters within the *Southern* Department;—has a portion of Chalk Hill within its boundary. The extent of *this*, however is not great. The principal part of the County is situated in the MIDLAND DEPARTMENT; forming a considerable part of its southern margin.

Bedfordshire aptly breaks into DISTRICTS, or PASSAGES, according to its soils; as will be seen in the extracts, from *Mr. Batchelor's Report*, ensuing.

"GENERAL VIEW

OF THE

AGRICULTURE

OF THE

COUNTY OF BEDFORD;

WITH

OBSERVATIONS ON THE MEANS OF IMPROVEMENT.

BY THOMAS STONE,

LAND-SURVEYOR, GRAY'S-INN.

1794."

THIS is an "original Report;" being the third which was delivered in, to the Board of Agriculture, by the same writer; namely, one from *Huntingdonshire*, in the wane of 1793,—one from *Lincolnshire*, in February 1794,—and the one which is now under review, in July 1794. None of them has been reprinted.

In bringing the second of these sketches forward (see the EASTERN DEPARTMENT) I endeavoured to make a due estimate

estimate of the QUALIFICATIONS of this Reporter; and, in noticing his Huntingdonshire, page 399, aforegoing, I have briefly spoken my sentiments, on that performance. What is there said, might, with little alteration, be repeated, here. The sketch of Bedfordshire, however, is fuller, and more interesting than that of Huntingdonshire. For altho we find but little which resembles a *Report* of *established practices*, we discover some good *general remarks*, on rural subjects.

Number of pages, seventy.

No Map.

NATURAL ECONOMY.

EXTENT.—P. 10. "The extent of this county is computed at 35 miles from North to South, and 20 miles from East to West, and 145 miles in circuit, containing an area of 480 square miles or 307,200 acres."

WATERS.—P. 10. "The principal river is the Ouse which runs across the county from the Buckinghamshire side, through the town of Bedford to St. Neots in Huntingdonshire. The Ivel empties itself into the Ouse at Tempsford; besides which rivers are the Lea and other smaller streams of no considerable importance."

SOILS.—P. 13. "Every soil and every mixture of soil, commonly seen upon high land in the united kingdoms, may be found in this county, from the strongest clay to the lightest sand."

N. P. 13. "When I began to inspect the land it was my intention to represent by a map, the mixtures and connexions of different soils, but having upon experiment frequently found that one and the same parish produced four or five different soils, nothing but a particular survey could have answered the purposes of delineation, which would have been foreign from the present design."

POLITICAL ECONOMY.

STATE of APPROPRIATION.—P. 11 "Of the 307,200 acres contained in this county, from the best information I have been able to obtain upon the subject, it may be computed that 68,100 acres are inclosed meadow, pasture and

and arable land; 21,900 acres of woodland, and 217,200 acres of open or common fields, common meadows, commons and waste lands."

P. 25. "From the statement I have already made, of the large quantity of land, yet remaining in a state of common and arable fields, common meadows, and waste lands, it must appear, that very little land has been inclosed of late years; every parish which is commonly understood to be open, consists of a certain portion of antient inclosed land near the respective villages, but that proportion, compared with the open common fields in each respective parish, does not on an average exceed one-tenth of the whole."

Common Pastures.—P. 25. "There are not any extensive commons of this description in the county, and those which remain, are mixed with, or appendant on the common fields, and are held according to the antient system of farming, as necessary for the depasture of sheep, in order to fold upon the arable common fields."

Common Fields.—There is good sense, and practical knowledge, in the following remarks; which may serve as a valuable hint to proprietors, to lose no time,—when an act of appropriation is likely to take place,—in putting their lands into good condition.

P. 61. "It has frequently occurred to me in practice, that some of the occupiers of a common field, are pursuing the best possible mode of management the situations are capable of, whilst others are reducing land, intermixed therewith, to the lowest state of poverty, beggary, and rubbish, making the respective value of the inheritance to vary three, four, or more years purchase; and upon the inclosure of common fields it frequently occurs, that commissioners are obliged to consider such worn-out land of considerably less value than such parts as have been well farmed; of course, the proprietors, whose misfortune it has been to have their land badly occupied, have had a smaller share, upon the general division of the property, than they otherwise would have had, in case their land had been better farmed."

MANUFACTURES —P 10. "The making of thread lace forms the principal part of the manufactures."

INLAND TRAFFIC.—P. 10. "The chief importation is coals for fuel, and blacksmith's work, deals, fir, timber and salt; its exports are *fuller's earth*, oak-timber, and corn."

TITHE —In speaking of the advantages to arise, from dividing and inclosing common fields, Mr. Stone says, page 59,—"It may be here observed, that the Bishop of LIN-

COLN

COLN has, with very great prudence and judgement, suggested a regulation for a commutation of tithes in his diocese (of which this county is a part) when common fields are inclosed, which is found to answer so well, that it is to be hoped it will be every where adopted. By this plan, the money payments for tithes, vary according to the price of corn from time to time, a procedure equitable towards the land-owners and occupiers, and highly secure for the clergy, because it prevents the abuses which too frequently have befallen the interest of the clergy, in consequence of the mismanagement of the allotments which have been made to them of land, given in lieu of tithes: for it cannot be supposed, that gentlemen, bred up merely in scholastic pursuits, are always competent to let the land they receive, so as to preserve the permanency of its yearly value. It is with pleasure I add, wherever this plan has been carried into effect, it has been attended with the desired success. Those who may be desirous of obtaining further information upon this subject, may consult the regulations in the Act of Parliament lately passed, respecting the inclosing of Milton Bryant, in Bedfordshire, and Tealby, in Lincolnshire."

Thanks are due to Mr. Stone for these explicit remarks, on the Bishop of Lincoln's plan of a SUBSTITUTION for TITHES.—See EASTERN DEPARTMENT, p. 91.

EMBANKMENT.—For an instance of its being required, in Bedfordshire,—see *Grass Land*, ensuing.

Markets.—P. 10 "Corn is chiefly vended by the growers on the North part of the county at St. Neotes in Huntingdonshire, and on the South and East at Hertfordshire, so that except in the town of Bedford, very little business is done in the corn trade, and with regard to several of the other towns very little more than the name of market remains. Before a dreadful fire which happened a few years ago at Potton, that town possessed a very flourishing market for corn, &c. but since that time, it has not been much resorted to."

RURAL ECONOMY.

TENANTED ESTATES.

TENANCY.—Mr. Stone is a staunch *lessean*. But it is high time that the subject of *long leases* (leases for twenty-one years) should go to sleep:—at least, for a while*.

The

* This was written in May 1813.

The subjoined COVENANT BY CUSTOM is entitled to a place, here. It is not however peculiar to Bedforshire.

N. P. 15. "It may not be here improper to remark, that the occupiers of common field farms, as tenants at will, are entitled to hold possession for a round of cropping, according to the number of seasons, upon this sort of land (where it is farmed in three years) and an ejectment will not lie upon the common notice to quit at the end of a year."

RENT and CHOICE of TENANTS.—P. 23. "I am as great an enemy as any man to the racking up the rentals of farms beyond a fair yearly value, and wherever the best mode of agriculture is adopted, and the best and most suitable stock of cattle and sheep are produced, or in other words wherever any given spot is made as productive as it can possibly be, the land-owner ought to be careful that he does not require a greater rent than the occupier can live well under and pay with cheerfulness, reserving the interest of his money employed in business at least, and a fair gain for his skill and personal exertion. It is the groveling, prejudiced, unskilful, obstinate farmer, that I point at, who rents his land at half the real value, and therefore exerts but half his industry, great part of which is employed in endeavouring to conceal from the land-owner or his agents the real state of his property, and who carefully turns his face aside from any improvements least his landlord should reap a part of the successful advantages to be derived from them."—These are well grounded, valuable remarks.

WOODLANDS.

THE subjoined censorial strictures; tho they elicit nothing new; may serve as useful hints, in different parts of the kingdom, to the owners of woods.—P. 33. "The woods or woodlands, consist chiefly of oak timber and any kinds of rude underwood, that, by chance, may spring up under it, so that it is not unusual, to see throns produced, where a more valuable crop might be cultivated; it not being an object of general attention at every fall of underwood, which is cut at about twelve or fourteen years growth, either to root out such productions as are the least profitable, and to fill up the vacant places with a better stock. It is not unusual, to observe in the woods, considerable quantities of land, either quite vacant, or producing a small crop of any thing; indeed so inconsiderable is the crop of underwood, in the estimation of some persons who

who have had the management of woods, that instead of felling the necessary timber at the time the underwood is cut, they have returned years afterwards to cut more timber, throwing it down upon such of the young shoots of the underwood as were produced, which, if a tolerable crop, would be greatly injured by such means, and also by the conveying it away."

AGRICULTURE.

THE STATE of HUSBANDRY, in Bedfordshire, in 1794.—On this topic, the Reporter is somewhat severe.—P. 10. "The County of Bedford, though so near the metropolis, is not remarkable for the excellence of its agriculture or attention to its breeds of cattle or sheep."

P. 11. "Upon a view of the neglected state of the agriculture of this district, by a person acquainted with the improved agriculture of many other parts of England on similar soils, and who should be unacquainted with its geographical situation, he would naturally conclude, that instead of its centre being not more than 50 miles from the metropolis, that it was 500. Instead of its being desirably circumstanced in having a navigable river running from its centre to the ocean, possessing almost every other advantage which nature or art could give it for exporting or converting its produce to the greatest advantage, he would rather conclude, that it was inaccessible by means of bogs and barriers, and that its produce had no other market than that which arose from the mere consumption of its inhabitants."

He endeavors to account for it.—P. 12. "One principle cause of this delay in the improvement of the agriculture of this county, has been the inattention, which, till of late, gentlemen of landed property, have shewn towards advancement in rural œconomy, and to improvement in a science in which they are so materially interested.

"The frequently committing the management of their country concerns into the hands of persons, who are totally unacquainted with agriculture, or, in other words, considering that one and the same person, who receives and pays with great integrity, is equally competent to suggest or enforce improvements in the uses or prevent abuses in the management of land, whilst, in fact, with the same propriety might a mere husbandman be called from the plough, to amputate a limb, in the expectation of his having the skill of an experienced surgeon, or a seaman be directed to draw a marriage settlement, with the technical accuracy, and legal knowledge, of an experienced conveyancer."

And,

And, in a subsequent page, he thus softens off the preceding severities.—P. 21. "In a district so large as the county of Bedford there is certainly a diversity of management both with regard to the interests of landlord and tenant, and instances may be adverted to where the landowners are noblemen and gentlemen of the first fortunes and highest respectability, pursue a line of conduct extremely steady and liberal towards their tenantry, and on the other hand instances occur where the occupiers approach nearer towards perfection than in others, nevertheless but a small part of the land in this county is managed in conformity to the most approved modes of agriculture which have long been practiced in the best cultivated counties upon similar soils."—But closes, with re-assumed censure.—P. 26. "In but few instances, have we seen improved systems of farming, adopted upon the new inclosures which have taken place, and except Lidlington, the property of the Earl of UPPER OSSORY; Sundon, the property of Sir JOHN BUCHANAN RIDDELL, Bart. and Potton; it does not appear, that any regular systems of farming, were laid down upon the inclosing of land, or have been since pursued upon it, but it has been a practice for the persons who were the tenants in the open field state, to take the new inclosed land at a considerable advance of rent, without any knowledge of or view towards improved agriculture, and generally without any salutary restrictions as to management, or any example or encouragement towards good husbandry. No wonder that such tenants pursued prospects of immediate gain, without any view to future advantage; the land was cropped successively with the most exhausting crops, it became poor and foul, and such proceedings have brought the measure of inclosing very undeservedly into disrepute in this county."

PLAN of MANAGEMENT.—*Common Fields.*—Strong Lands.—P. 14. "The common fields of those descriptions of soils, are generally divided into three parts, seasons, or fields, one of which is annually fallowed, a moiety of which fallow field (according to the best mode of management) is annually folded with sheep and sowed with wheat, the other moiety of such fallowed land is dunged and sown with barley in the succeeding spring, and that part which produces wheat is in succession sown with oats, that which is next after fallow sown with barley, is in the succeeding year sowed with beans, peas, or other pulse, and then such land being again to be fallowed, that part which in the previous course of husbandry was sown with wheat, comes in rotation to be sowed with barley, by which procedures the same kind or sort of grain is only produced every sixth year."

P. 15.

P. 15. "There are but few instances in this county where the arable land is divided into four fields or seasons, and where it is so circumstanced, nothing like system prevails, and the occupiers are generally at liberty to exhaust the soil at pleasure."

Common Fields.—Light Lands.—P. 18. "The common fields of these descriptions of soil are generally understood to be divided into three, and in a few instances four, parts or seasons, and here turnips are sown upon considerable parts of the fallow land, which are succeeded by barley sown with clover, which clover remains one year for a crop, and is sometimes saved for seed, and the fourth crop is generally wheat; but where there are but three fields, the crop of clover is considered as a breach crop instead of beans, peas, or oats, and the land which produces clover, is in succession fallowed, and that apportionment intended for barley is first sowed with turnips; but these practises are not pursued systematically; the occupiers not being generally confined to any particular modes of farming, follow such as seem to promise them the most immediate gain, without any direct view to the future."

Inclosures.—Light Land.—P. 21. "The inclosed estates of the last mentioned descriptions of soil are generally managed in a manner proportionably unproductive of advantage with the common fields."

WORKPEOPLE.—P. 56. "There not being any manufactures in this district deserving notice, agriculture is the only means of occupation; but from the uninclosed and uncultivated state of the country, and the little employment and encouragement given to the husbandmen, in respect to constant work throughout the year, the labourers continue with the farmers during the winter season, to thrash out their grain, and on the approach of summer, many of them set off for more cultivated counties, where labour is more required."

WORKING ANIMALS.—P. 44. "The farmers teams are chiefly kept up, by yearling and two-years old colts, brought by dealers from the Fens of Huntingdonshire and Lincolnshire. Some farmers practice the selling off their cart horses for more valuable purposes to profit at 6 or 7 years old, but the practice is not general. In the southern part of the county, where the farmers keep a road team to carry the produce of the land towards London, and to bring back London manure, such as sheeps trotters, horn shavings, rabbits and fowls dung, &c. &c. such teams are kept very high, and of course at a very great expence."

ARABLE CROPS.—The established practice of Bedfordshire, regarding this main branch of husbandry, does not appear

appear to have been thought an object of attention, by this Reporter. I find no information, that is here noticeable, relating to it; excepting that which is above extracted, concerning the general *state* of *husbandry* and *plan* of *Farm Management*.

GRASS LANDS.—Nor, on this sister branch, do we meet with any thing concerning the established practice of Bedfordshire;—other than as a ground of censure, on which to build the Reporter's own *plans* of *improvement*. And even in *these*, I perceive nothing sufficiently new or excellent to require insertion, here.

Meadow Land.—P. 67. "It has been already remarked, that the Ouze is the principal river which runs though this county; along its banks is a considerable quantity of rich meadow land, which is subject to be overflowed at all seasons of the year. When the water comes down from Buckinghamshire with any considerable rapidity, it frequently happens, that the crops of hay are either considerably damaged, or totally carried away."

Pasture Land.—P. 17. "The pasture land not being manured is here devoted to every possible reduction of condition, the drainage is mostly neglected, poached up in winter, and suffered to be over-run with ant-hills, bushes, rushes and sedge, and in many instances repeatedly mown."

LIVESTOCK.—On this, the other principal division of the practice of husbandry, we find a somewhat more satisfactory account.

HORSES.—P. 44. "The breeding of horses is not a practice in this county worthy of particular observation, but few are bred except those designed for pleasurable uses:"—that is to say, horses of draft are seldom bred in the County; but are bought in:—as appears in the foregoing page.

CATTLE.—*Breed.*—P. 28. "The cattle bred in this county, are for the most part of a mixed kind, differing, according to various mixtures, from the Holderness, Lancashire and Leicestershire to the Alderney sorts, and as it has not been a general practice, to attend nicely to the breeding from the best or any particular sorts, we find them of a very inferior nature, but most particular with regard to their intrinsic value of feeding for beef, *after the first intention for the dairy is over;* a circumstance, which it is presumed ought to be weighed by those breeders, who are desirous of making the greatest profit from their occupations. We generally find them large in their heads, bones and bellies, and coarse in their horns, throats and necks; narrow in their hips, plates, chines, shoulders and bosoms, and high in their rumps."

Rearing Cattle.—P. 29. "But few calves are reared."

Suckling

Suckling Calves.—P. 29. " Those made fat for veal, are generally of a very nice quality, and sent up from Bedford and many other towns in the county, killed and dressed in provision waggons, for the supply of the London market; a reformation in this article I consider to be very practicable. It but too often occurs in the course of a summer, that in very wet or tempestuous weather, the Thames becomes the receptacle of large quantities of meat thus conveyed to London, by which circumstance, not only the interests of the parties immediately concerned, but that of the community are deeply injured I should recommend an experiment, of making the bodies of provision waggons, to convey in the the summer season the calves alive to London, whilst a frame might be constructed over them, upon which to place hampers and baskets of less perishable provision."

DAIRY.—*District.*—P. 28. " A considerable quantity of land, in the southern part of the county, is used for dairies, and butter is from thence consigned for the London market. In the middle and northern part, there is not so large a portion of land applied to the maintenance of cows as in the southern part, and that which is so applied, is divided between the dairy, and suckling calves for the London market, as well as for home consumption. The butter made in the south part of the county, is generally much superior in quality to that made in the central and northern parts, which I attribute to the degree of attention necessary to be paid to the manufacturing it for the London market, for unless it was sent thither in a good state it would not be sold."

Soil of Dairy Farms.—P. 39. " Dairy Farming.—This mode of employing land, is of all others the most im poverishing, and more especially upon cold or wet land, with a clayey bottom, or where the superstratum is in any degree retentive of water, because the poaching of the cattle, when the land is in a wet state, is extremely injurious to it:"—Unfortunately, however, for the lovers of good butter and cheese, the lands, above proscribed, are the only kind on which, the latter at least, can be produced of a superior quality.

SHEEP.—*Breed.*—Common Field.—P. 31. " They are generally of a very unprofitable quality, but more especially those bred in the common fields, where the provision intended for their maintenance, is generally unwholesome and scanty; it is impossible to give a description of any particular sort as the general breed of the county, because jobbers are constantly driving various sorts from fair to fair, and selling them in the different counties, and from the

undrained

undrained state of the commons and common fields, the stock of sheep depastured upon them, is but too frequently swept away by the rot; and it being absolutely necessary, according to the present system of farming, that their places should be constantly supplied with others for the folding of the land, under such circumstances of casualty and necessity, the healthiness of the animal when purchased, is the first and almost the only object of consideration with the farmers, with that view, sheep are purchased by them of any country and of any description, the horned and polled are mixed together, and as a pretty general description of them I may venture to observe, that they are coarse in their heads and necks, proportionably large in their bones, high on the leg, narrow in their bosoms, shoulders, chines and quarters, and light in their thighs, and their wool is generally of a very indifferent quality, weighing from three to four pounds per fleece. A few exceptions may be made to this description, in the sheep at Goldington, St. Leonard's, Ickwell, and a few other places, but generally speaking, upwards of nine tenths of the sheep of the common fields of the county, are of this description."

Inclosures.—P. 32. "*The sheep bred upon the inclosures*, are generally of a much superior quality, being for the most part a mixture between the Lincolnshire and Leicestershire sorts, but they are not equal to the most perfect of either kinds, though very useful and profitable."

Fatting Sheep.—P. 32. "The weathers are generally sent to market from the inclosures when shorn twice, called *two shear*, and are sold when very fat at from 35*s.* to 40*s.* per head. Their fleeces generally weigh from seven to nine pounds each."

RABBITS—P. 41. "Rabbit Warrens.—This mode of occupying land, is very little practised in this county, and is chiefly confined to two or three parishes."

BEES — I cannot refrain from giving a place to the following *calculation!*—as it incalculably out does all the other calculations, which I have yet found, in the Board's Reports.

P. 54. "The means of producing the greatest possible profit that can be derived from soil, cannot be completely pursued, until the production of honey and wax is fully attended to. Upon a moderate calculation, in which I have been assisted by Mr. WILDMAN, of Holborn, a person, who has made this species of profit his particular study for many years—every square mile in Great Britain, would produce in those articles, on an average 100*l.* sterling in value, admitting that an increase of product would reduce the price

of

of those articles. But such an increase in the quantity of bees-wax, would consequently tend to render the importation, not only of those articles, but of tallow, unnecessary to the present extent. The value of these articles, on this statement, far exceeds the idea of the most sanguine friend to the prosperity of the country. There are in England alone, 49,450 square miles, and in Scotland 27,794—total 77,244; which at 100*l.* per square mile, would produce 7,724,400*l.* per annum. At only 20*l.* per square mile, the produce would be 1,544,880*l.* This is an object well worth attending to, being in addition to every other profit derived from the soil."

"GENERAL VIEW

OF THE

AGRICULTURE

OF THE

COUNTY OF BEDFORD.

DRAWN UP BY ORDER OF

THE BOARD OF AGRICULTURE

AND INTERNAL IMPROVEMENT.

BY THOMAS BATCHELOR,

FARMER.

1808."

THIS is a second Report of Bedfordshire. See the preceding article.

QUALIFICATIONS of the REPORTER.—Still we are left in the dark, regarding the required biographical sketches of the Board's Reporters.—The designation, affixed to the present author's name, does not well agree with the internal evidence of his book.—Mr. Batchelor, it is obvious, naturally possesses a considerable compass of mind. But his

his attainments would seem to be those of a man of general reading; and an amateur of science; rather than those of a practical husbandman:—an acquirement which is doubtlessly intended to be conveyed, by the addition, "Farmer."

Chemistry, the vegetable economy, and *experiments* in husbandry, are his favorite themes.—The established provincial practice of Bedfordshire frequently appears in the back-ground; and occupies, even there, a minor portion, only, of the bulky volume under view.

The method of collecting that portion of information,—the MODE of SURVEY,—does not evidently appear. The subjoined passage is all I find respecting it.—Preface, p v. "To obtain as much information as possible, *inquiries* have been made in nearly every Parish in the County; but there are so few variations of practice, arising either from caprice or ingenuity, that the result of many inquiries has only tended to explain and confirm a variety of popular opinions on the minor subjects of Husbandry, in which nearly all Farmers are unanimous." Ha! ha! What a morsel! Can it be Mr. Batchelor's own?

"The minor objects of Husbandry, in which nearly all farmers are *unanimous*." Rather let it be put—the minutiæ of practice, in which nearly all farmers *differ*; and on which the EXCELLENCIES and DEFECTS of the RURAL ART principally depend.

See, in any township of the kingdom, in which the *outline* of management is the same, among its professional occupiers,—its *farmers*,—the striking effects produced by minute variations in practice;—by which, alone, one man's crops are seen of twice the value of those of his neighbour; and the states of the lands, after the crops have been reaped, bearing the like superiority or debasement; and this merely through a rightly directed attention to "the minor subjects of husbandry." No *plan* can succeed, unless it be duly *executed*; whether in agricultural, or in any other art or profession.

Beside the MATERIALS COLLECTED, and the *Reporter's* own *remarks*, and *theoretic observations*,— a considerable portion of *adscititious matter* is found. Much of it is drawn from the "ANNALS of AGRICULTURE;" the rest being chiefly communicated by J. FOSTER, Esq. of Bedford; the Rev. H. Y. SMITHIES; and a few other contributors.

Only one copy of the ORIGINAL REPORT from BEDFORDSHIRE appears to have been returned to the Board, with marginal notes thereon.—The Report, itself, however, has not been altogether overlooked.

In the MATERIALS AT LARGE of the volume under review, we

we certainly find many interesting passages, and some useful information; as will be seen in the following abstract of them. But there can be no injustice in saying, that by far the greater part of them is irrelevant to a Report of the practice of a County. And if it were proper that those should have met the public eye, they ought, I conceive, to have appeared in the form of a treatise; or as a "communication" to the Board.

Mr. BATCHELOR is a great friend to *experiments* (as every *farmer* ought;) but we find no rules, nor even an intimation, how to prosecute experiments, with advantage; nor any evidence of his having, himself, had much *experience* in that very difficult art. Indeed, he appears to be, even of this his favorite object, an ill informed admirer, only *.— His end and aim would seem to be to set up *experiments*, in opposition to *experience!*—Mr. B. being the first public writer, I have met with, who has ventured to decry, in effect, PRACTICE and EXPERIENCE!! †.

Regarding

* Preface, p. vi.—"It has been my endeavour, in various parts of this Survey, to impress on the mind of the reader the utility and necessity of minute experimental investigations: though I have been so circumstanced, as to be able to make very few experiments myself."

† P. vii.—"I conceive the discussions which are inserted in various parts of this Survey, may tend to prove, that theory is not so fallible, nor practice so infallible a guide, as many have asserted."

And, having spoken of "Experiments on Manures, by Dr. CARTWRIGHT of Woburn,"—the Reporter has the temerity to assert,—page 522,—"A few experiments of this kind, would promote scientific agriculture, more in five years, than plodding dullness, miscalled experience, will ever achieve to the end of time."

EXPERIENCE.

The writer of those sentiments was either playing off a *hoax*; or was, at the time he wrote, unacquainted with the import of the word *experience*.

EXPERIENCE and SCIENCE are nearly synonimous; and it were equally rash to decry the one as the other. Experience is an accumulation of facts; whether they may have arisen through the mean of human intention, by the process of experiment; or have entered the human mind, thro the instructive tuition of accidents. *Experiments* in agriculture, and *incidents* in its practice, are, with regard to their effects in SCIENCE, precisely the same.—It is well known that most of the great discoveries, in science, have been made, *incidentally*; and have not been brought to light by the "plodding dulness" of *theoretical experimenters!*

If, in practice, a doubt arise, concerning an important point, let experiment be called in, to endeavour to remove it. If a valuable fact present itself, *incidentally*, under complex and dubious circumstances, set experiment to work, to prove whether it can be profitably introduced, into

Regarding Mr. Batchelor's MANNER, as a Reporter, I have chiefly to say, that it is above the par of that which I have hitherto found among the publications of the Board. It may, however, be remarked, that there is sometimes, a sort of modesty, bordering on shyness, observable in his work. He rarely brings himself, or his own practice, forward;—in this particular, forming a striking contrast with some of his coadjutors;—and, when he does, it is in so indirect and inexplicit a way, as to render it sometimes doubtful, whether it is himself, or another, of whom he is speaking.——His theories, however, tho frequently drawn out, at length, and sometimes loosely written, may generally be *read*, without disgust, or much fatigue; being in this unlike the generality of those which are found in the Reports to the Board.—The *Editorship*, too, is reputable. The matter is mostly commendably digested; tho, here and there, we find a loose, miscellaneous section; and, not unfrequently, different notices and remarks, on one and the same subject, straying, as will be observable, in distant parts of the work. An intelligent index is added.

The number of pages—six hundred and thirtysix.

A map of soils; and a few engravings of buildings and implements.

SUBJECT

into *general* practice. But what can experiments avail, without experience to plan, superintend, and introduce their useful results into practice? *Experiment* cannot otherwise act, with propriety, than as an *agent* of EXPERIENCE; and certainly ought to be constantly employed, by MEN of SCIENCE, as a *valuable assistant*, in the FIELD of AGRICULTURE.

Before Mr. Batchelor shall venture, again, to *profane* the name of EXPERIENCE, I advise him (tho I may be thought presumptuous in doing it) to read, with due attention, what I wrote on this important subject, toward half a century ago (in the MINUTES and EXPERIMENTS of AGRICULTURE); but which I had not reconsidered, for several years, until I was induced, by the above-quoted remarks, and others of a like mischievous tendency, which are dispersed, in the volume under review; and I am gratified in being able to say, that, after a length of extensive and attentive experience, I find, in what I have there written, nothing to retract; and but little, if any thing, to add.

I have been urged to those general remarks, the rather, as it is not in agriculture, only, but in a sister art and science, that the dangerous doctrine, here combated, is now under propagation;—dangerous, not merely to the comforts of life, but to health, and life itself. It is no longer a mystery how scientific nations have reverted to a state of savage ignorance. In this, the sun of science appears to be setting.

SUBJECT THE FIRST.

NATURAL ECONOMY.

EXTENT.—P. 1. "Authors have not been very unanimous with respect to the area of this county. Mr. Stone, in the original Report, states it at 307,200 acres; Dr. Halley estimates it at no more than 260,000 acres: in the observations in the *Poor's-rate Abstract*, it is said to contain (according to the latest authorities) 275,200 acres; Mr. Beake, in his pamphlet on the income-tax, supposes it to contain 293,059 acres; and by an admeasurement taken of a map, reduced from the large one of Jefferys to a scale of three-fourths of an inch to a miles, it appears to contain 297,600 acres, or 465 square miles."

CLIMATURE.—P. 4. "The most prevalent winds, as far as observations has been made, are those from the south-west; these are very general in summer, and not unfrequent in winter; while those from the north-easterly points are usually regarded as both a sign and cause of a cold ungenial season in summer, and of frost and snow in winter."

SOILS &c.—P. 4. "The various kinds of soil are frequently found in such small portions, and so much surrounded and intermixed with each other, that no very accurate delineation of them can be made; but as much accuracy as the subject admits of, will probably be found in the Map which accompanies this Survey."

Sandy Soils.—P. 5. "The sandy district, which extends, with a small interval, from Leighton to Potton, is in length about 25 miles; the general width is about three miles, but it varies from five miles to one, as between Woburn and Leighton, where it extends several miles into the county of Buckingham. Very little sand is to be met with in any part of the county beyond the boundaries marked in the Map, which appears to occupy about 42,000 acres. This sandy belt, as it has been termed, mostly presents a hilly surface, with clay and various loams in the intervening vales, and sometimes clay on the tops of the hills. If to these be added the ferruginous peats of Tingrith, Fletwick, Westoning, Flitton, Maulden, &c. it is probable that the real quantity of sand may be found not to exceed 30,000 acres."

P. 6. "The parish of Sandy, is generally supposed to contain the best garden ground in the county. The prevailing soil of the parish has been described as 'a rich sand

sand two or three feet deep.' But this description, if true, must only be understood of some of the low, flat vales, which, like all others in the same circumstances, have received all that the rains, &c. could dissolve and carry away from the hills for many centuries."

Chalky Soils.—P. 6. "The district consisting principally of chalk, which is bounded toward the north by the Chiltern hills, contains about 36,000 acres."

P. 7. "Some of the hills at Luton, are clay toward their summits, with chalk and gravel descending to the vales; and at Sundon, and Streatley, we find the chalky basis covered to various depths by a stratum of clay, gravel, or gravelly loams."

"The chiltern hills are the outcrop of the chalky stratum, which passes under the whole" (?) "county of Hertford, &c."

P. 467. "The chalky downs that meet the eye of every traveller who enters the county at Luton, or Dunstable, have been estimated at 4000 acres."

Gravelly Soils.—P. 7. "The principal part of the gravelly loams found in this county, follow the course of the rivers Ivell and Ouse, and comprise a space of about 34,000 acres.

"A considerable quantity of clay is however included within the boundaries marked in the Map, but it is probable that the insulated spots of gravel which are met with in other parts of the county, may make the total quantity of soil which is more or less gravelly, nearly equal to the above statement. The meadows of the Ouse and Ivell, consist of gravels of various degrees of fineness, mixed with clay and sand, composing loams of several descriptions. Gravels are also found beyond the district marked in the Map, and frequently appear in the slopes of the hills which attend the meandering course of the Ouse from Turvey to Bletsoe."

Clayey Soils.—P. 10. "Clays of every description, comprise about two-thirds of the whole, or 197,600 acres. The clays of the southern part of the county, extend without interruption from Billington to Cockayne Hatley.

"They are mostly stiff and tenacious, interspersed with small portions of gravels, and loams on a wet basis. The clays near the Chiltern hills, contain in general a mixture of chalk, and are therefore called white land, though it appears the term *maumy* or *marme*, is used in some parts, to disignate soils of this description.

"The clays of the central district occupy the southern part of the Vale of Bedford, in which but little gravel appears on the surface, though it is found at various depths in in some parts of Marston, Houghton Regis, &c. The general flat surface of the Vale, is in this and most other instances, an indication that the soil is not unfertile," (?) "and perhaps no other part of the county contains an equal extent of clays, which is not of inferior fertility. The Vale of Bedford is bounded by a range of hills, which toward the east and south divide it from the sandy belt which crosses the county. The soil of much of this tract is denominated *woodland*, and woods occupy much of its surface."

P. 11. "There are several varieties of this soil, but as it generally occurs on the summits and declivities of the hills, the staple is mostly shallow, and the subsoil is either a blue or yellow *golt* clay, or a marl abounding with chalkstones of various degrees of friability. The surface soil is generally a light spongy clay, which does not derive its friability from a mixture of sand, nor perhaps often from chalk or the remains of putrefied vegetables.

"As this kind of soil is commonly in the vicinity of woods, it is probable, and indeed certain, that in the early stages of cultivation, such hilly clays were neglected, as proper for little else than the growth of wood, and some of them which have been long reclaimed from a state of nature, produce little, if any, profit to the occupier.

"The north western part of the county possesses many points of similarity to the district last described; in both of these hilly divisions, we frequently meet with cold, thin stapled clays, which are sometimes so tenacious as to 'hold water like a dish.'

"In other instances they are light and marly, permitting the feet to sink deep into them in winter. At Harrold, Mr. Pickering describes some of the soil as consisting of clay, which, when slightly wetted, is as sticky as glue, intermixed with many white stones which are a kind of limestone gravel. The woodlands, though often of a blackish colour, are sometimes, as in a part of Old Warden, described as of a pale red, or a kind of orange colour. On the declivities of the hills, as near Marston Thrift, the furrows are sometimes 'washed away, and the light stones driven in heaps by heavy rains;' and in many instances, the winter frosts are described as rendering this kind of soil 'as porous as a honeycomb.'"

It is not necessary to say that Mr. Batchelor's account of the soils of Bedfordshire is very satisfactory. I cannot, however, forego the pleasure of saying it. In my present undertaking, I meet with so few instances which will admit of praise, that I am ever happy to notice them.

For further particulars, relating to this subject, see the head *Appropriation*, ensuing.

FOSSILS.

FOSSILS.—*Limestones.*—P. 8. "The last-mentioned district" ("the slopes of the hills which attend the meandering course of the Ouze, from Turvey to Bletsoe") "is also distinguished by a stratum of flat, hard limestone, which is thus described by the late Mr. Cooper. 'The usual strata on opening a pit are these: good earth two feet more or less: a light-coloured marl, which soon incorporates itself with the mortar, under which is a small stone, short, thick, and hard, called the pendle rock; under this sometimes a thin washy mortar, then again pendle rock, under which lies the solid rock: this is sometimes twelve feet below the surface. There are frequently in the rock, veins of bluish stone. Under the rock is penny-earth, used for malting floors, barn floors, &c.'"

P. 14. "Some of the limestone of Pavenham has been used formerly for grave-stones, and some churches have been floored with it; but a better or cheaper kind of stone, found at Halston and Dusson, in Northamptonshire, has superceded the use of it.

"Many church porches were built with the *freestone* of Tottenhoe, and it is said, a block of 40 tons weight has been raised in those quarries.

Clunch is one of the names of *this kind of limestone*; but the hard chalk which lies near the surface of the hills, and is used at Ampthill, Husborn Crawley, for lime, is usually known by the name of *hurlock*."

Is it, by this inexplicit notice, to be understood that a calcareous freestone is quarried out of the face of the hill;—being the substructure of the chalk which rises above it, to near the surface?

Coals.—P. 14. "Small quantities of imperfect coal have been found in the parish of Goldington, and it is said some signs of this substance have been discovered in other places; but it is said" (?) "that the usual disposition of the strata o the earth, gives no reason to expect coal of any value to be found in this county."

SUBJECT THE SECOND.

POLITICAL ECONOMY.

APPROPRIATION.—*Common Pastures.*—P. 467. "In the sandy district, the parishes of Clophill, Flitton, Steppinly, and Heath and Reach, with Leighton, contain a quantity

quantity of hilly common ground, the principal product of which is heath or ling.

"Leighton-heath, which is probably the largest, is said to contain 400 acres."

P. 468. "Few of the unenclosed towns in the rest of the county contain any considerable extent of commons, except the roads, and the Lammas or half-year ground. At Yielding there is, however, a common of 80 acres; at Sharnbrook, 50 acres; and at Cranfield, 40. In addition to these, may be mentioned the low wet common at Billington, and a considerable one at Biggleswade, which would appear to be of some value, as the right of keeping sheep on it is made a subject of legal decision."

Common Fields.—P. 217. "In the original Report it was supposed that three-fourths of the county, or 217,200 acres, were at that time in the state 'of open or common fields, common meadows, commons and waste lands.' Into the accuracy of this estimate it is not necessary at present to inquire: it will be seen, however, that the business of enclosing has made much progress since the period referred to, as about fifty enclosures have taken place within the last thirteen years."

Mr. B. has inserted a table of the parishes, which he found (or understood to be) in a state of inclosure, in 1807 (I suppose); but does not mention those which remained in the openfield state, at that time.—However, in a section entitled "Divisions," the total number of parishes appear to be 124; and in his table of those inclosed, there are only 81:—so that, on these data, there then remained 43, in the commonfield state; being rather more than one third of the County.

The Reporter's chapter, "Enclosing," fills three or four sheets of paper; some considerable part of which is taken up with extracts from, "ANNALS of AGRICULTURE."—

P. 220. "In the 42d. vol. of the *Annals*, Mr. Young has given so ample a collection of minutes, concerning parliamentary enclosures in this county, that it was deemed proper to add them to this Work."

Memoranda, respecting other parishes, are furnished by "B." (?) Others are without signature.—The matter of those several minutes and memoranda is miscellaneous. Nothing of digestion appears; nor any results, or practical inferences, drawn from them.

The latter part of the section (nearly half of it) is filled up with "extracts from parochial registers,"—"made with a view to discover the effects of inclosing, on the increase of population."—The following are Mr. Batchelor's observations concerning them.

P. 270.

P. 270. "By the preceding tables it appears, that the population had not increased very remarkably till about the year 1770; and it is observable, that the increased price of provisions, and the rapid growth of the taxes and the national debt, took place at nearly the same time.

"The tables seem to indicate nearly an equal increase of population in the unenclosed parishes, as in those which have been enclosed many years; yet it is evident, a greater number of instances must be collated before any satisfactory evidence is procured."

MANUFACTURES.—P. 594. "The manufactures of this county are almost entirely confined to the plaiting of straw, and the making of thread lace; the latter probably employs three-fourths of the female population, with the exception of servants, &c.

"Straw-plaiting was formerly confined to the chalky part of the county; but has been so much encouraged within the last few years, that it has spread rapidly over the whole southern district, as far as Woburn, Ampthill, and Shefford."

P. 596. "The prevalence of lace making causes a scarcity of maid-servants, but the same tends to keep down the poor's-rates. The families of those women who do not understand this useful art, are often extremely troublesome to the parishes.

"Spinning of hemp and cotton is almost entirely laid aside, and very few women attend to any of the business of agriculture.

"A considerable quantity of mats are made near the Ouse, to the north-west of Bedford."

For further remarks, on the effects of the *lace* manufacture, see *Workpeople*, ensuing.

POOR RATES.—P. 40. "The general average of the county is not supposed to exceed 3 *s.* 6 *d.* in the pound on the true rent."

P. 612. "Many clubs are under regulations of questionable propriety, and the members are sometimes expelled for trivial deviations from the rules; but their utility, in preventing many applications for parochial relief, is well established. They consist, however, in general, of such as would not, under common circumstances, be chargeable to a parish, such as the lower order of tradesmen, &c. The injurious effects of box clubs (real or imaginary) are, I believe, entirely unknown in the county of Bedford."

This is the first *mention*, I have met with, of the "injurious effects of box clubs."

TITHES.—P. 35. "About half the parishes in the county are vicarages, and the great tithes of these are mostly in

lay

lay hands. There are but few of the enclosed parishes which remain subject to tithes. The tithe is taken in kind in the parishes of Stagsden, Sharnbrook, Harlington, Stotfold, Eggington, Billington, Tingrith, and a few others."

P. 36. "The tithes of several parishes lately enclosed, are paid by a corn rent, which is regulated by the average price of corn for the 20 years preceding the enclosure, and after a certain number of years is subject to future regulations. The land is generally given to the lord of the manor, and provision is made in the Act for the Clergyman, to take and enter upon the land so allotted for tithe, in case of non-payment of the corn-rent.

"The following extracts from the tithe accounts of the parish of Milton Bryan, in the year 1649, many serve to furnish some idea of the expenses and profits of taking tithes in kind."

P. 38. "From the above it appears, that the expense which attends the taking of tithes in kind, amounts to considerably more than one-third of their value, and as the expense would be considerably less to the farmer, from whose fields they are carried to a great distance, there seems to be mutual reasons why they should never be taken in kind."

P. 39. "An equitable commutation of the tithes is extremely desirable, and would conduce to the benefit of all the parties concerned, and perhaps the allotment of land is a preferable mode, as the revenues of the clergy would then be increased or diminished by the same means and in the same proportions as that of the landed interest in general."

EMBANKMENTS.—The following observations show, pretty plainly, a *want* of this valuable improvement, in Bedfordshire.—P. 492. (sect. Irrigation) "Connected with this subject is that of embankments, of which there are none in this county, except those which confine the mill-streams on the rivers, &c. The river-meadows on the Ouse are perhaps 40 poles wide on the average, which, as the circuitous course of the river extends through the space of about 50 miles, amount to perhaps 4000 acres. These meadows are lett in many places at about 40 *s.* per acre; and perhaps about half the quantity receive the benefit of winter irrigation, and perhaps equal injury at other seasons, by the sudden swells of the river after heavy rains.

"The farmers who occupy these meadows, seems to have more dread of the inundations of the river, than hope of the benefit resulting from watering."

CANALS.—P. 588. "The Grand Junction Canal passes through a very small part of the county, and is productive of of all the advantages in its vicinity, which result from a cheap intercourse with the metropolis, and the north-western counties, in the articles of corn, coal, salt, iron, &c. Various projects have been mentioned for extending the internal navigation of Bedfordshire. By one of these it is proposed to carry a navigable canal from Biggleswade to Shefford, the expense of which was estimated at about 1000 *l.* per mile."

ROADS.—P. 588. "The form of the roads is generally convex, and the few concave or wash-ways that may be observed, seem rather the effect of accident than design, and are not likely to be extensively adopted. They are sometimes observed to form a kind of ditch, the sides of which are kept perpendicular by the friction of the wheels of carts, &c. Where a foot-path crosses such roads, it is composed of four posts, between which the wheels and horses pass, and whatever conveniencies many belong to wash-ways in general, they seem little prized in this county."

For the history of concave roads, see my MIDLAND COUNTIES.

MARKETS.—P. 591. "Though it is customary to bring much of the corn to some of the markets toward the southern part of the county, selling by sample is often practised in all of them; neither does there appear any weighty objection to the practice.

"Selling corn at *pitched markets*, as they are termed, is always attended with an extra expense and trouble, while the selling by sample is performed with great facility. The farmers meet together in some customary place, which is sometimes in the street, but often over a pot of the best home-brewed ale the town affords, where new bargins are made; and the corn which was sold the preceding week is usually paid for, with the customary deduction of 1 *s.* or 1 *s.* 6 *d.* on every ten sacks."

"Biggleswade had formerly a very considerable barley market, but in consequence of the plan adopted by several maltsters and brewers, of fixing the highest price which they choose to give for barley each market-day, many quarters are sent by the farmers without any previous bargain; and the apparent quantity of corn sold in the market is much reduced."

Corn Measure.—P. 592. "Corn is sold by the Winchester bushel, five of which are commonly put into each sack.

"Wheat, rye, beans, pease, and tares, are sold by the load of five bushels; but oats and barley are invariably sold by the quarter. The customary bushel of Bedfordshire, is said to have exceeded the statute measure about two pints, till

till the general regulation which took place a few years since."

Cattle Weights.—P. 594. "The stone of 8 lbs. is in use among the butchers of the south of this county; but north of the Ouse, that of 14 lbs. is more prevalent."*

The VALUE OF MONEY, at MARKET.

In a section headed "Comparison of Times" (a quaint, but convenient, mode of expression, invented,—not by Mr. Batchelor,—to avoid the use of the odious phrase—"depreciation of money")—a series of lists, tables, and remarks, to the extent of twenty or thirty pages, are inserted.—They are thus premised.

P. 44. "As the very considerable, and, in some degree, gradual advance in the price of every article of agricultural labour and produce, must have been owing to some cause or causes, the greater part of which are not of an accidental or temporary nature, it is important to preserve every record that may tend, in any degree, to elucidate a comparison of the ancient and modern situation of the agriculturist."

The situation of the agriculturist has been much the same, in regard to this matter, in all ages.—The amount of his expenditure, and the value of his products, have ever kept company,—jogged pretty cordially on, together; and, in their nature, must, while a state of agriculture shall continue, be inseparable companions.—The prices of rent, labor, and corn, must necessarily correspond. Like liquids they naturally tend to preserve a degree of level.—Though storms and tempests, winds and weather, or other temporary circumstances, may occasionally disturb them,—and, for a while, destroy their equiponderance,—they cannot fail, in time, to regain their level.

Whether the rent of wheat land be one shilling or thirty-six shillings, an acre,—the rate of day labor be one penny or three shillings,—and the price of a bushel of wheat, at market, be four pence, or twelve shillings,—the situation of the farmer, the laborer and the community,—so far as it is effected by the price of bread,—must, necessarily, be pretty much the same; and, with the price of bread, that of the other

* WEIGHT of CATTLE and BUTCHER'S MEAT.—The *nominal stone* of eight pounds, whatever may have been its origin, is now very improper; as interfering, and of course creating a degree of confusion, with the *legitimate English Stone.* It is, I believe, peculiar to the southern districts of England, including the metropolis. Its extent to the northward appears, by the above notice, to reach no farther than the middle of Bedfordshire.

other indispensible articles of human food, are principally regulated. Personal taxes,—such as come home to the farmer's pocket, doubtlessly effect his condition, during a a length of time proportioned to the term of his holding.—But these, tho in reality taken out of the pocket of the tenant, devolve, at the end of his term, on the proprietor of the lands he rents. For if he had not such taxes to pay, he could *afford* to give, and, through the influence of competition, he *would* give, proportionally more for the use of them*.

The subjoined is the first, and most interesting item, in Mr. B's collection.—P. 44. "The most early mention which I have met with of the prices of corn in Bedfordshire, I have extracted from the Annales of Dunstable, by Hearne.

"1253. Before autumn, wheat sold for 5*s.* a quarter; but so great was the scarcity, that it afterwards rose to 8*s.* per quarter.

"1254. Each acre of wheat or oats for 2*s.*

"1255. A scarcity of corn, that, except for last year's, many must have starved.

"1258. Such a scarcity of corn this summer, that wheat at Northampton was 20*s.* per quarter; at Bedford 17*s.*; here, one marc. A quarter of common malt 6*s.* 8*d.* Oxen used for ploughing at Dunstable.

"1277. Wool, 6*d.* a fleece.

"1283. Sheep had the itch, for which was used successfully, stale hog's-lard, quicksilver, and verdigrease.

"1287. Such a plenty, that a quarter of wheat was sold generally for 20*d.* and a quarter of beans and oats 12*d.*

"1294. A quarter of wheat, at the Peak, 21*s.*; here, 16*s.* 8*d.*; 1 quarter of salt 16*s.*"

The rest are of more modern date.—Their value, however, may not be the less, on that account. They may have their use, *as far as they go.*—But a few scraps, incidentally picked up, can be of little avail; and ought not, I conceive, to have encumbered a provincial report.

An AMPLE and WELL AUTHENTICATED DETAIL, chronologically digested, of the relative value or POWER of MONEY, with regard to the market prices of bread corn, and other necessaries

* MAY, 1814.—This, it may be well to say, was verbally written in June, 1813. The subject is, now, under public discussion; but is not, yet, it would seem, sufficiently well understood; for the purpose of legislation.

necessaries of life, from the earliest account, to the present time, is much to be desired.

The SOCIETY of ANTIQUARIES are, probably, in possession of materials sufficient to form such an authentic statement.—If, in reality, they are, they would be doing political economy a valuable service, in giving to the public so essential a document.

The *remarks* which Mr. Batchelor has interspersed, among the different articles of his collection, on this subject, are many of them *ingenious;* but they are not always well grounded. The concluding paragraphs of his section, "Comparison of Times" are, however, sensible, and, I believe, just.

P. 69. "The average price of wheat from 1595 to 1685, was 1*l.* 18*s.*; but from the average of 20 years, from 1730 to 1749, it appears a depreciation of price had taken place to the amount of nearly 10*s.* per quarter. Money obtained from any permanent source, had consequently become more valuable in an inverse ratio.

"The depreciation of money, which was the consequence of the importation of the precious metals, had therefore ceased, and the depreciation of the present times must be deduced from a source entirely distinct, which, it is thought, will be readily found in the modern system of commercial credit, paper money, and national mortgage."

SOCIETIES of AGRICULTURE, &c.—P. 618. "The establishment of an Agricultural Society in Bedfordshire, took place in the year 1801, and, in the words of J. Foster, Esq. 'was founded by him, to whom we justly look up as the author and patron of all our rural improvements, the late Duke of Bedford.'"

P. 622. "The formation of provincial agricultural societies, is undoubtedly very conducive to local improvement: but this depends greatly on the number and amount of the subscriptions which are applied to its support, and the subjects for which the premiums are offered.

"Common farmers cannot be expected to subscribe very liberally in any case, but especially if their own interest in the business is not very obvious."

"Common Farmers," I am clearly of opinion, ought to be FREE MEMBERS; not "Subscribers."—Let men of property provide assets, and discharge the expenditure of the society; and invite, to their meetings, such of their tenants, or other well informed practical men, as are most capable of assisting them, in the designs of their institution.

SUBJECT THE THIRD.

RURAL ECONOMY.

TENANTED ESTATES.

ESTATES.—Mr. Batchelor gives a list of the principal *proprietors*, with the parishes in which their largest estates are situated (p. 16);—but does not convey an idea of the prevailing *sizes* of estates (excepting an inadequate one of those of the Duke of Bedford, Lord St. John, and Mr Whitbread,) nor say, under the legitimate head, whether that valuable class of society, yeomanry, or small proprietors, are numerous, or otherwise. But see *Occupiers*, ensuing.

TENURES.—P. 18. "Copyhold estates are numerous in some parishes, but nothing occurs respecting them that is worthy of particular detail."

IRRIGATION.—P. 484. "This mode of improvement was introduced into the county by the late Duke of Bedford, and various instances may be seen in the parishes of Woburn, Crawley, Ridgmount, Flitwick, and Maulden."

P. 488. "The late Duke of Bedford procured the insertion of a clause in the Acts of Enclosure for Maulden, Ridgmount, and Crawley, by which a liberty was given to make use of the various brooks for the purposes of irrigation, by turning their course through old enclosures, &c. as might appear most convenient, making due satisfaction to the parties injured."

This, in many situations, as in calcareous districts, and districts through which calcareous waters pass, is a sensible, and can scarcely fail of being a highly beneficial, regulation, in a bill of inclosure.

SODBURNING.—P. 477. "The practice of paring and burning is not at present pursued to any great extent. On the first breaking up of peaty soils, it is in common use, and no doubts have arisen of its present and ultimate utility. Neither the farmers nor proprietors are under any apprehension of destroying a soil of six feet deep."

Much more is said, on this subject.—A lengthened string of hearsay information, with *remarks* thereon, follow. But *these* are little more than theoretic wanderings;—the DAY DREAMS of INEXPERIENCE.

MANAGEMENT of ESTATES.—*Managers.*—P. 18. "The management of estates affords little ground for observation they are sometimes committed to the care of attorneys, o

land

land-agents; but the estates of some of the principal proprietors are superintended by such as are themselves considerable farmers."

LETTING FARMS.—*Choice* of *Tenants.*—P. 35. "The mode of letting of land by secret auction, has been lately introduced in one part of the county, and is esteemed to be as illiberal a mode as can be easily invented. A price is not set upon the land, as in all other cases of the exchange of property, but the farmers are required to make what offers they choose, upon which they are generally informed that a greater price has been already offered, but without producing any proof that such is a true statement of the case. It is easy to conceive, that agriculture will not be promoted by secret and mysterious proceedings, which are calculated to destroy the mutual respect and confidence which ought to subsist between a landlord and tenant."

TENANCY.—P. 40. "The farms in this county are in general held only from year to year, or for the usual three years course of cropping in the unenclosed parishes.

"There are, however, a few farms held on lease in every part of the county; but such leases as have been executed within the last ten or twelve years, are mostly for a short term, as eight, or at most, fourteen years, and some of them are voidable upon half a year's warning from either landlord or tenant.

"It does not appear that leases have at any former period been very prevalent in this county, and the great depreciation of the value of money, which was effected by the circumstances that distinguished the termination of the last century, has apparently contributed to prevent their introduction to general use, and by that means sensibly retarded the improvement of the various parts of agriculture."

P. 41. "Some of the leases or agreements, contain a desire, that white corn may not be sown successively on the same land, and in other cases it is prohibited under a penalty of 20*l.* per acre. But this rule, which is deemed to be founded on just argument in this county, as well as in most other parts of England, is frequently violated by farmers of great property and intelligence, in various parts of the sandy and gravelly districts, and there are few who would deem it prudent to enforce this rule with severity."

P. 43. "The custom of holding farms from year to year, though in some respects unfavourable to great exertions in improvement, is known to promote a friendly intercourse between landlord and tenant, and is in reality more conducive to permanency of occupation than long leases.

"The farms of Bedfordshire generally descend from father to

to son through a long series of years, and perhaps as frequently change their owners as their occupiers. The large farmers, therefore, are secure in their possessions, and the benefit of their improvements, if not overburdened with increased rents, descends to their children."

Nevertheless, Mr. B as appears in different parts of his book, is a *lessean;*—a decided advocate for twentyone years leases.

Toward the close of his volume, however, perceiving, perhaps, on more mature reflection, their impropriety, under existing circumstances, he proposes a more rational and eligible plan;—safer, while these circumstances continue, both for the proprietor and the holder; namely, a LAW OF REMUNERATION.—In this proposal, with a single, but very material, alteration, I readily and cordially agree with Mr. Batchelor.

P. 620 "The measures which are calculated to improve this county, are equally applicable to the whole kingdom; and in this intention the removal of obstacles is necessarily the first step. Tenants sometimes injure the land previous to leaving it, and commit dilapidations which the landlord cannot always prevent or punish; but on the other hand, the tenantry who make extensive improvements, and invest a great portion of their capital in the bowels of the earth, are not considered, *in the eye of the law*, to have any claim on the landlord for remuneration.

"It is easy to conceive, that the legislature of ancient times could not foresee, without a spirit of prophesy, the expensive improvements which would be undertaken by the cultivators of the present age. It is therefore the interest, as well as the duty, of those distinguished characters who devote their influence to the advancement of agriculture, to give the improvers of the soil *a legal right* to remuneration of the capital employed in any improvement of a farm, which they may be induced or compelled to leave."

The required alteration is obvious. It is not "the capital employed, in any improvement" for which the tenant ought to have a legal right of remuneration; but the *remainder* of that capital.—The tenant, himself, may have received the principal part of the benefit to arise from an improvement; and, in all cases, unless he quit presently after the improvement has been made, he has received of course some share of the benefit.—It is only that share of it which he *leaves behind him*, when he quits,—that which the proprietor of the soil, or his next incoming tenant, will reap, for which he is entitled to remuneration.

It is not the money expended, perhaps improperly, or foolishly,

foolishly, by an outgoing tenant; but the advantage which his successor will receive, for which he is to be remunerated. If he has laid out money, imprudently, he ought to bear the loss.

It is on this principle my TRIENNEAL LEASE may be said to be founded; and on which, I am, by long experience, fully convinced, ought to be extended to all leases and agreements, entered into between landlords and tenants, in husbandry.

There are men,—weak, or wicked, or both,—who set their faces against all plain, simplex, obvious improvements; and who, I understand, cavil at the right of remuneration, in the case which is now under view,—on account of the difficulty with which the quantity of right can be settled. But is there no other difficulty, than this, in settling, in an equitable manner, the various matters which necessarily arise, in arbitrating between outgoing and incoming tenants? —how much easier it is to estimate the value of the remainder of an improvement, with the data—the facts belonging to it,—before the eye, than to say, at ladyday, what a crop of wheat will be worth at harvest?—an estimate which is not unfrequently made. The remuneration for the value of the improvement, which the outgoing tenant is about to leave behind him, forms only one item, among many others, that are usually submitted to the judgment of two men of experience and character;—such as are to be found in every district.

I have only to add, that, in nearly twenty years experience, I have not found any difficulty or dispute arise between a proprietor and a tenant, relative to remuneration for improvements. A man of large property has little to fear. He has, or ought to have, upon his own estate, men who are quite equal to the business of estimation, and who can of course sufficiently guard him against imposition *.

RENT.—P. 33. "Of the modern rise of rent in this county, no accurate account can be obtained. In many of the new enclosures the nominal rent has been doubled; in other cases it has been raised 40 or 50 per cent. and sometimes not more than 20 or 30 per cent. There are even a considerable number of cases, under a few indulgent landlords, where the rent has experienced no alteration in 40 or 50 years; and instances are not wanting, of rents which were raised at the end of the last century, that are again increased at the present time.

"The

* See my TREATISE on LANDED PROPERTY. Also my WEST of ENGLAND, &c. &c.

"The circumstances before stated, are sufficient to prove that the rent is not an invariable criterion of the value of the land. The average rent of any particular parish, is frequently as little known to many of the farmers who occupy it as to a person at a distance, as it is a question which would scarcely be asked among neighbours, in a direct way, without giving offence."

P. 34. "The open fields dispersed over the county are in many places about 10*s*. per acre."

Several instances of the rents of enclosed lands are enumerated; but no average, or general rate, is attempted.

Receiving Rents.—P. 32. "At the middle of the last century, it was common about Lidlington, and probably in other places, to pay half a year's rent at the time when a year and a half's rent was become due; but at present, it is customary with some of the principal proprietors, to receive half a year's rent, when it has been due only three months, by which means, it will be perceived, that an additional capital, equal to three-fourths of a year's rent, is necessary to stock a farm, and that the rent is raised 3*l*. 15*s*. per cent. without any alteration in the nominal sum."

WOODLANDS.

At the close of an extract from Mr. Stone's Report, Mr. Batchelor says, page 461, "Thus far I have extracted from the original Report. But I consider the quantity of Woodland mentioned in page 10 of that Report, as a very erroneous statement. From an enumeration of the acres in each of the principal woods, with which I was favoured by the Rev. Mr. Marsh, with due allowances for deficient accounts, it appears that the true quantity is about 7000 acres, or less than one-third of the original statement.

"The woods are found almost invariably on the slopes of the hills, which consist of cold, marly, woodland clays.

"A considerable portion of them occupy the hills which extend from Ampthill towards Blunham, between the sandy district and the vale of Bedford. After an interval of some miles they again make their appearance on the western side of the vale, at Holcut and Marston, and from thence are dispersed over the whole north west of the county.

"Wood is very scarce in several places in the south and east of the county.

"The *management* of this necessary article presents nothing very peculiar; the underwood of a few small copses is is sometimes lett with the farms, but nearly all those of any considerable extent, are under the care of agents appointed by the respective landlords. The underwood and timber are felled late in the autumn, and a day of sale is appointed in the course of the winter for the disposal of the former, which consists principally of hazel, and a few ash-poles, which are used, according to circumstances, for hurdles, hedging, and fire-wood. The underwood is commonly sold in divisions of ten poles each, the felling of which by the woodmen costs, in some places, 7*d.* with a good ash or hazel pole, which is termed a *crutch*, which the workmen claim for each day's work.

"The value of wood varies not a little from its situation. If the subsoil is either a limestone, or ferruginous sandy rock, into which the tap-roots of the timber and other wood find no access, the vegetation is necessarily checked, and there are instances of both in the county.

"Woods are sometimes cut at twelve years' growth, but fourteen years is the usual period, and is, on every account, the most proper for obtaining a due size in the poles, and lessening the general expenses."

AGRICULTURE.

FARMS.—*Sizes.*—P. 25. "It does not appear that a consolidation of farms has taken place in this county, to the extent in which it is said to have been practised in several districts of Great Britain; but it is evident that the prevalence of the enclosing system, and other causes, have diminished the number of farms within the last fifty years to a considerable amount."

P. 27. "The greatest number of large farms are in the southern and central part of the county. Much of the district north of the Ouse, is a poor clay soil, which affords no great temptation to opulent farmers; small occupations are therefore more numerous in that part of the county; and according to the representation of a gentleman in that neighbourhood, several of the farmers have been formerly menial servants, and have obtained their situations by persevering industry and economy. There are, however, many large farms in almost every part of the county, some of which are as high as 700*l.* or 800*l.* per annum, and there are not any considerable number of parishes that do not contain one or more farms from 200 to 500 acres. It has been said, that the farms of His Grace the Duke of Bedford

ford are not larger on the average than 80 acres, but if this assertion be correct, it must include, in all probability, such small occupations as five or ten acres; several of which may be rented by farmers whose principal farm belongs to some other proprietor. The farms of Lidlington have been stated at 100 acres each, exclusive only of the cottages, but there are probably more small farmers in this parish than in many others, notwithstanding a decrease of more than one-third in half a century.

"If the cottage allotments, which seldom exceed two acres, be excluded, it seems probable that all the other farms in the county may amount on the average to 150 acres each, a size which forms what is properly deemed a moderate farm among the great body of farmers in Bedfordshire."—This may well be deemed considerate Report.

Plans of Farms.—P. 19. "The farm-houses are generally situated on low ground, by the sides of public and other roads; in consequence of which, the drainings of the dung-yard are washed away by the rains, without any possibility, in most cases, of applying it to the use of irrigating the pasture land. The buildings, which have been erected at various times, and enlarged or diminished as occasions offered, are often inconveniently situated, and are seldom found at the centre of the farm to which they belong. It appears, however, that the practical inconvenience of removing the house and buildings belonging to a large farm, is generally deemed of more consequence than the extra trouble and expense of occupying lands at a great distance, as the farm-houses which have been rebuilt commonly occupy their former positions."

Draining Farm Lands.—Mole Plow.—P. 476. "In the draining of pasture, I find it recommended by several, and practised by Mr. Foster, to open a furrow with a common plough previous to the use of the mole-plough. The furrow is afterwards returned to its place, to prevent the sun from cracking the ground."

This, by dividing the labor, must greatly facilitate it; and tend to do away the main objection to the mole plow; namely that of requiring extraordinary strength, and of course *weight*, of animals to work it.

OCCUPIERS.—What I am able to pick out of the present Report, relative to this material head of enquiry, lies scattered under different divisions of the volume; and is so entangled with other matters of Report, as not to be easy of digestion. I therefore place the few articles, which I have considered to be of sufficient value for extraction, in the order in which they stand in the book.

Yeomanry.—P. 19. (sect. "Farm Houses.")—"There are

are several farm-houses in the county, that were formerly the seats of gentlemen who appear to have farmed their own estates; and there seems much reason to believe, that this class of proprietors is considerably diminished since the commencement of the last century."

Working Farmers.—For a notice, respecting this class of occupiers, see *Farms*, aforegoing.

Common Farmers.—After having allowed Mr. Foster to indulge himself, in terms adulatory, to mention the *late* Duke of Bedford, Mr. Whitbread, and Mr. Lee Antonie, as promoters of the rural profession,—Mr. Batchelor thus proceeds.

P. 31. (sect. "Farmers") "The unwillingness with which the common farmers adopt any new improvement, has been often remarked; yet it cannot be denied, that this reluctance is frequently well founded, as the recommendation of new improvements often comes in a questionable shape. They are told, that two horses a-breast will draw as much as three at length; but who has applied the spring steel-yard, or the dynamometer, to prove the assertion? It is said, that oxen are more profitable as beasts of draught than horses; but whence are they to draw the information of the comparative expense of either? If a small farmer be advised to drill or dibble his beans, he will perhaps inquire what is the most proper distance of the rows, and quantity of seed; or, if dibbled, whether one, two, three, four, or five beans ought to be put into each hole: but these are inquiries that perhaps no agriculturist in Great Britain will venture to answer. In the article of dibbling beans, however, the large farmers of this county will not accuse the small ones of obstinate incredulity, as in several towns in the centre of the county, such as have possessed from one to twenty acres of arable, seem to have been the first who introduced the practice, and several of them have persevered in it for many years. The north of the county, though it contains several large and good farmers, is, on the testimony of the resident gentlemen, less distinguished for enterprise and experiment than any other part of the county. Such as have conducted experiments with a degree of attention which is necessary to render them of any public utility, are aware, that much trouble and some expense attends them; hence it will be readily believed, that the occupiers of small and moderate farms deposit in their memory all that they wish to preserve of the past, and trust to that too often treacherous guide, the eye, in the valuation of all things present."

Great Farmers.—P. 32. "The large farmers, though" (?) "men of liberal minds and considerable experience, freely

freely confess, that the chemical nature of soils, and the first principles of vegetation and animalization, are *desiderata* in agriculture, in the investigation of which, the occupier of 50 or of 1000 acres is almost equally at a loss."

P. 613 (sect. "Obstacles to Improvement.") "Those who occupy considerable tracts of land, are seldom known to acquire any great accession of wealth, without the aid of other profitable occupations; but the occupiers of poor soils, such as abound in some of the towns north of the Ouse, are said to be as poor as the soil. A considerable farmer in that district observed, that most of the neighbouring farmers were far from affluence, and rather struggled for existence than flourished in their occupations."

PLAN of MANAGEMENT.—In the volume under review, the prolific subject, "Course of Crops," occupies more than twenty pages. The three short passages which follow, comprise all the information which I conceive to be of sufficient use to practical agriculture to claim the right of insertion in this register.

P. 337. "Perhaps no district in the kingdom affords a greater number of varieties in the succession of crops, than are to be met with in this county."

Management of *Strong Soils*.—The following is substantial evidence in favor of (occasionally at least) SUMMERFALLOWING lands of this description.

P. 348. "A great number of farmers remain in various parts of the county, who under no restrictions but what originate in their own sentiments, and having every means of information within their reach, still pursue the old open-field rotation of two crops and a fallow, with no other variations than tares on a part of the fallow, and clover perhaps once in nine years, on a part of the bean or oat-stubble, or more commonly instead of those second crops. Some of them stoutly maintain that clay soils cannot be kept clean by any other means. And that it may not be deemed, as it probably would, that such opinions prevail only among small occupiers, it may be proper to say, that such is the practice of a considerable farmer who occupies his own estate, and of another who keeps, I believe, twelve or thirteen horses, and has been a farmer considerably more than half a century."

Management of *lighter Lands*.—P. 349. "The rotations of crops on the gravels, sands, and loams on a chalky basis, consist in general of a turnip fallow, succeeded by barley, and the various kinds of clover, &c."

WORKPEOPLE.—P. 580. "The greatest part of the business of husbandry is performed by day-labourers in every part of the county. It is common, however, on most farms of of considerable size, to retain annual servants in the capacity of horse-keeper, cow-man, shepherd, and kitchen-maid, though the great advance in the price of provisions has apparently contributed to diminish the number of domestic servants of every description.

"It seems generally agreed, that the horse-keeper ought to attend his horse at four o'clock in the morning, to allow them a sufficient time to feed, and get them properly geared for their work before he takes his breakfast. The team is taken to work as soon as it is light in the winter; at six o'clock, or the time when the day-labourers come, in the spring; and about five, or as soon as convenient, in harvest. About ten o'clock, an interval of a quarter of an hour, or more, is allowed for the servants to feed. This is called *beaver time;* but when the business of ploughing is performed by day-labourers, who have no *mess* in the house with the servants, they sometimes delay their breakfast till nine, which generally occupies half an hour.

"It is common to finish ploughing from one to two o'clock. The horse-keeper attends his horse in the afternoons, and frequently does not entirely leave them for the night till eight o'clock."

Food of Farm Servants, in 1807.—P. 582. "It is common for the servants to dine at the same table as their master, wherever the farms are not very large: some little distinction is made occasionally; but the servants seldom look forward with eager expectation to the pleasures of a separate table." Very well!

"The breakfast and supper of men-servants consists in general of a *mess* of milk. In addition to this, bread and cheese, and sometimes meat is allowed.

"In respect to female servants, tea in the morning and afternoon, is of late years, become nearly a general practice; and the custom of employing them in milking the cows, is fallen into general disuse."—Their *wages* are not satisfactorily set forth.

Employments of Farm Laborers.—P. 598. "In this district many of the boys, and some of the men, make lace, in the winter at least, for want of other employment.

"In the western district, or the hundred of Redbournstoke, lace-making is little practised by the males, and much less than was formerly the case.

"From this part of the county occasional, but not numerous, emigrations take place, to assist in hay-making in the neighbourbood of London; a circumstance evidently owing to the small quantity of sward in several parishes. In the east of the county, the population seems comparatively

tively deficient, and they have been commonly supplied with many harvest-men from other parts of this county, as also from the counties of Northampton and Buckingham.

"There is no deficiency of employment in the southern district, where the straw manufacture furnishes employment for many males, as well as nearly the whole female population."

An extraordinary *Custom* concerning them.—P. 608. "The increase of population has caused a deficiency of employment, which is so remarkable in some seasons, that a great proportion of the labourers "*go the rounds.*" This practice is not modern; but as it is not supposed to be sanctioned by law, it may be proper to describe the nature of it, and its general consequences. When a labourer can obtain no employment he applies to the acting overseer, from whom he passes on to the different farmers all *round* the parish, being employed by each of them after the rate of one day for every 20*l.* rent. The allowance to a labourer *on the rounds*, is commonly 2*d.* per day below the pay of other labourers, which is found to be a necessary check upon those who love liberty better than labour. Boys receive from 4*d.* to 6*d.* per day *on the rounds*, the whole of which is often repaid to the farmers by the overseer. About half the pay of the men is returned in the same manner, and the farmers often receive in this way the amount of from 2*d.* to 4*d.* in the pound rent, which consequently causes the apparent expense of the poor to exceed the truth. The practice in question has a very bad effect on the industry of the poor: they are often employed in trivial business, the boys in particular, are of little use in the winter season."

In the district of Yorkshire in which I am writing, old men who are no longer able to do a full day's work, and younger men who are infirm, and sometimes fatherless boys, "go by house row." This custom, when confined to persons of the above description, is far from having any other bad effect, than that of incurring a degree of unpleasantness on those who have to receive them into their families. The men must feel themselves inexpressibly more comfortable in a farmer's kitchen (to which in their youth they had been habituated) than in a workhouse; or languishing in a hut, on a pauper's pittance, barely sufficient, perhaps, to satisfy the cravings of nature. And it is surely much better for the boys to be in that manner initiated, in the various works of which they may be capable, and to have opportunities of seeing, at an age when ideas make deep impressions, different methods of performing the same operation,—than to receive parish pay, and acquire,

acquire, under maternal indulgencies, habits of idleness and other vices.—It is in agricultural villages, however, in which regulations of this kind can be most eligibly established.

IMPLEMENTS.—The chapter, bearing this title, comprises fiftysix pages of letterpress, and a few engravings;—in itself a well sized pamphlet. Yet I have not been able to select a passage of it, which would materially add to the value of this register; and this, notwithstanding the writer of it is, himself, pretty evidently, an active implementarian;—dealing much in the didactic, and evincing a greater share of *experience*, in this, than in any other chapter of his book.

Nothing, however, I think it may be fairly said, either new or excellent, appears in his composition, on this head. Even as a "communication" to the Board, it could have claimed little merit. As a *Report* to it, concerning the implements in use, in a *particular province*, it requires to be censured.—Excepting an ingenious invention or two of Mr. SALMON (formerly clerk of the works carried on at Woburn)—particularly his *chaf-cutting machine*,—which I remember to have much admired at the time of its construction,—we find scarcely any one implement brought forward, that Bedfordshire can call its own; and the drawing and verbal description of the straw-cutter are copied from "Annals of Agriculture."

The following circumstance, in the history of "modern agriculture," is entitled to a place, here.—Having copied, from Annals of Agriculture, the account of trials of the merits of plows, which were made at the Woburn sheep-shearing, in 1803, and having mentioned one which was invented by Mr. Salmon, Mr. Batchelor has deemed it right to inform the Board of Agriculture (page 173) that "the draught of this plough, compared with that of the Northumberland, according to the statement of Mr. Young, * is as two to three, which is considerable, and render it a subject of regret, that the only instance of an attempt to improve a single plough, which was probably called into existence by the stimulus of His Grace the Duke of Bedford's premium, has been suffered to be forgotten."

MANURES.—On this subject, too, we have a section of some length; together with part of another.—That section, however, is not altogether barren of information, concerning "the agriculture of the County of Bedford."

Marl.—P. 494. "Marl, *or* clay, is in common use on the

* Secretary to the Board of Agriculture?

the light sandy soils; but very little, if at all, on the gravels. The quantity which is usually laid on an acre, is 60 cart loads of a cubic yard each; but it varies from 40 to 80."

Of the specific quality of this marl we are not informed,—by this friend to agricultural chemistry *.

Chalk.—P. 495. "Chalk is used by several farmers at Studham, Whipsnade, &c. Pits are sunk of various depths, in the middle of a piece of six or seven acres; and the chalk is drawn from them in buckets, in the same manner as in Hertfordshire."

Lime.—P. 496. "The use of lime, or burned chalk, is very little known in Bedforshire"

Yard Dung.—P. 504. "This is the principal, and indeed the only manure, used by most of the farmers to the north of the Chiltern-hills. A great diversity prevails in the management of this important article, and while the opinions of more scientific men than the Bedfordshire farmers pretend to be, remain unsettled and discordant, it is presumed they are not imprudent in taking that side of the question which is the least expensive."

After some miscellaneous observations, concerning the modern controversy, between the advocates for "long dung" and "short dung," Mr. Batchelor closes them with the following remarks.

P. 507. "The process of fermentation disengages a great quantity of carbonic acid, and amonia, or volatile alkali, by which the weight of the manure is much lessened, but its value increased. After about six weeks fermentation, it assumes a soponaceous greasy appearance, and in this state it is applied to the land by the best farmers in this county. Those who choose to give it repeated turnings, and keep what has been termed *over-year muck*, must probably submit to lay ten loads per acre instead of twenty or thirty. There is even reason to believe that dung laid in heaps for only six months, loses half its weight and much of its value; but such as has been heaped from one to two years, *I have been informed*, has sometimes *appeared* to produce no effect whatever on the land where it was applied. If this county produces a few who may be said to

* "Preface," p. vi. "The various theoretical observations that may be met with, must of course be considered as the author's own opinion, which, being founded on modern chemistry, could not be laid before the public in any other shape, or in a smaller compass."—Other intimations serve to convey the Reporter's pretentions to chemical science.

to lessen the quantity of manure as much as possible, it is probable the public inns will furnish some advocates for straw scarcely discoloured by the horses. I observed some manure of this kind spread on the lands near Dunstable, and was told it was a matter of course, and done to save trouble.* On the whole, there is a reason to believe that dung, like every thing else, will pay for some attention and management; but there is in all things a certain point, where resides the maximum of profit, beyond which is nothing but loss."

Peat.—P. 510. "*Peat-Ashes and Peat-Dust.*—The use of these substances as manures has prevailed for some years, and seems to be on the increase, particularly in the chalky district of this county. The bog from which the principal part of this manure is derived, is in the parish of Tingrith; but much peat of a similar nature is found near almost every stream of water in the sandy district."

Peat *Dust.*—P. 512. "At the request of Mr. Willaume, of Tingrith, Dr. Pearson analyzed the peat-dust, &c. and communicated a full and correct account of the circumstances attending its use as a manure, to the Board of Agriculture."

The Reporter gives what he terms the "substance" of that account. But it is not *done* in away that entitles it to a place, here.

Peat *Ashes.*—P. 513. "The turf or surface, and such parts as do not appear to be of the best quality for domestic fuel, are laid up in considerable heaps, and reduced to ashes, which are of a red colour."

"These ashes are carried by higglers on asses in sacks, to such distances, that they must come very dear to the consumer."

P. 514. "The dust is sold at the moor at 1½*d.* per bushel, and the ashes at 2*d.*"

P. 515. "They are commonly laid on clover or grass; and their effect, where they are said to be useful, is, to increase the growth of white clover, and to produce it where none grew before."

Town Manures.—P. 518. "In addition to the common farmyard manures, the chalky district is supplied with various light dressings from London, and there are some instances of gentlemen farmers at greater distances, as, Sir Hugh Inglis, of Milton Bryan, G. Edwards, Esq. of Henlow, &c. who have made use of London manure; but the expense in such cases must leave little hopes of ultimate profit,

* This I had not read when I wrote the remarks, p. 483, aforegoing.

profit. Mr. Thompson, of Sundon, expends nearly a pound per acre, or 300*l.* per annum, in purchasing manures, and adds, that they are forced to purchase a crop of wheat ere they have it."

Sheepfold.—P. 560. "The farmers of Bedfordshire are almost invariably advocates for this practice, under all soils and circumstances. The fold is esteemed peculiarly advantageous to the wheat crop. Nothing perhaps except a wet spewy soil, will prevent the folded crops of wheat from being distinguished at a considerable distance, by its deep olive green colour in the spring, when such as has been manured with common yard-dung often looks pale and sickly, and the straw and ears are small at harvest, and the corn not well filled. Its superiority to other manure is often equally perceptible in the crop of barley.

"The necessity of folding in the common fields is sufficiently obvious; the manure is useful, and there is no other mode of obtaining it; at the same time, it is apparent, that the sheep of the fallow fields never obtain a sufficiency of food to improve their condition in any considerable degree, and are employed, as it were, for no other purpose than to carry the produce of the commons, &c. upon the arable land in the shape of manure.

"The folding system in the enclosures bears somewhat of a different complexion, as tares may be grown on the fallows for the support of the sheep; yet there are many occupiers of clay land farms, particularly in the north of the county, who appropriate a part of the pasture to the use of the folding flock. These are termed *sheep-walks*, and are treated in every respect like the ancient commons.

"The value of the sheep-fold bears an high estimate in Bedfordshire.

"I am informed that a farmer, who lived many years on the farm where these pages are written, used to say, that 300 sheep folded for one week on an acre of land, would increase the produce five bushels per acre.

"According to the average price of a load of wheat for the last five years, the value of a sheep's manure (as above) is precisely one farthing per night, which forms a remarkable coincidence with the same opinion derived from other sources."

P. 561. "Mr. Wilson, of Ravensden, observes, that the fallow-field folding of that district, consisting of poor starveling sheep, is valued at about 30*s.* per acre; but when the sheep are well fed it is worth 40*s.* or more. Ten sheep are supposed to fold an acre in half a year; but if the sheep are small, ill fed, or mixed with many lambs, twelve, fourteen, or fifteen, are allowed.

"Mr.

"Mr. Brown, of Dunton, observes, that moderate folding is worth 40*s.* per acre, and is cheaper at that price than any other manure. Mr. Platt estimates the folding at 40*s.* per acre, which is performed after the rate of twelve sheep to a square pole.

"Mr. Atterbury, of Hockliffe, supposes that if the sheep are well fed, such a fold as above described would be worth 50*s.* per acre, which amounts to one-third of a penny each night, or 3*d.* in nine days. On the whole, there is reason to suppose the value of a sheep's manure is worth one farthing per night, or about one-third of the value of their summer food, under every mode of feeding. Each sheep is supposed to manure a space of $2\frac{2}{7}$ square yards per night; and the value of 180 days folding is 3*s.* 9*d.* per head."

TILLAGE.—*Depth of Plowing.*—P. 276. "The usual depth of this operation varies from four to five inches, and many people entertain the opinion, that if land be ploughed six inches deep, it *requires* more manure than usual. It will be readily acknowledged, that if this opinion be well-founded, the question is decided in favour of moderate depths; but it has always appeared to me in the light of a theory, which was contrived for the defence of ancient customs. In the parish of Ridgmount, a road was made across the ends of some ridged lands, and in this operation, the cultivated soil of the ridges was cast into the hollows. The field was afterwards sown with barley, and the scattered corns which grew where the soil was accumulated in the ancient furrows, formed a remarkable contrast with the rest of the field. The produce of the barley crop was little more than three quarters per acre, while that which grew on the same poor soil, accumulated perhaps a foot deep, was remarkably luxuriant; many of the corns producing from ten to twenty stalks, and the ears large in proportion. This effect can be ascribed to no other cause than the *depth* of the soil."

I register this incident in practice; tho it is not directly in point. The stratum, which caused the luxuriance of growth, was *made earth*,—an accumulation of cultured surface soil,—and contained, of course, a more than ordinary portion of prepared vegetable food.

Plow Team.—P. 277. "Till of late, upon all our clays, ploughing was performed by three, four, five, and even six horses, lengthways, and a driver. Those who have tried two a-breast, find that, independent of the vast saving, the work is performed easier and better. The ploughman, however averse at first to this mode, will, when once accustomed to it, think it a hardship to go in the old way, which

which sometimes, however, may be requisite in January or February, when the tread of the horses a-breast would injure the rich earth. Yet even in the most workable soils, such is the effect of prejudice and a determination not to be instructed, that by far the most farmers persevere in using three or more horses, and a driver.—*J. Foster, Esq.*"

For the *Hours of Work*, see *Workpeople*, aforegoing.

Dayswork of *Plowing*.—P. 278. "An acre is called a day's work for a plough; but on the general average, including bad weather, accidents, &c. it is probable that three roods are nearer the truth.'

Harrowing.—P. 278. "His Grace the Duke of Bedford has a machine, which was invented by Mr. Wildes, of Nottinghamshire, for the purpose of enabling the farmer to harrow the land, while the horses walk only in the furrows. The machine consists of a long axle-tree with a small wheel at each end, and a pair of shafts for the thill-horse to draw with; and the harrows are attached to the machinery at any distance from the furrow which may be required."

A contrivance of that sort (which is not singular) is convenient, where a retentive soil is laid in wide flat beds; but is far less eligible than concave harrows, working on gently convex narrower lands. See MINUTES of AGRICULTURE.

Width of Ridges.—P. 280. "Stitches of a yard wide, or two-bout lands, are common in the chalky district, and are thought useful; but it seems difficult to define the nature of their utility on dry soils, unless it be supposed to consist in the depth of the tilth, which is by that means increased."

For strictures on *Fallowing*, see Plan of Management, aforegoing.

Quantity of Tillage.—P. 391. (Section "Barley") "The occupier of a part of the light sands on Millbrook-warren, 30 or 40 years ago, is said to have been remarkable for giving his barley-land a great number of repeated ploughings, harrowings, and rollings, for the purpose of obtaining the most complete pulverization; in consequence of which, he found two bushels and a half of barley amply sufficient for the purpose of seed.

"This observation is derived from very respectable authority, and is here inserted to prove, that the effects of frequent stirring, and of fallowing in general, deserve an experimental investigation previous to the general adoption of those theoretical opinions, according to which it would appear, that *air*, *heat*, and *light* destroy, instead of increasing, the fertility of soils exposed to their action."—Very well!—If *such* be "modern husbandry," away with it!

SEMINATION.

SEMINATION.—P. 282. (The head "Row Culture.")—"This term comprehends the various operations of drilling, dibbling, horse-hoeing, and hand-weeding, which in the opinion of the most intelligent writers on the subject, ought to be considered as essentially connected with each other. There are a considerable number of farmers who have made partial attempts at drilling, in different parts of the county; but the number of those who have practised the *row culture*, as above defined, is very small."

Mr. Batchelor is, or was at the time he wrote his book, a keen drillist; and had carried off a premium; tho he writes like a Tyro in his favorite art. It is, therefore, no wonder that he has filled thirty or forty pages, with words, about the "rowculture" (a good term);—a subject which has long been exhausted.

The following result of *experience*, by a *practical* man of some consideration, is worthy of a place, here.—P. 301. "Mr. RUNCIMAN, of Woburn, who is the most considerable driller in this neighbourhood, has had little success in drilling wheat, and approves of the drill almost entirely on account of the facility which it affords of destroying the innumerable weeds that infest his sandy soil. When this business is effected, Mr. R. hopes to gain a good crop of broad-cast wheat, from an opinion that drilled corn has farther to search for its food, and that it would grow better if set singly at equal distances."

Mr. B. however, sticks to the row culture, to the end of the chapter.—P. 319. "In so intricate and complicated a subject as the row culture, it appears to me improper to regard the number of those who have have practised the drill husbandry and have returned to the broad-cast, unless every step of the process be mentioned, in which I conceive it will commonly be found, that the management has been deficient in some essential point."

WEEDS of Arable Lands.—P. 320. "On this subject I can say but little, from a want of botanical knowledge, which is common among the cultivators of the soil; and I think it a subject of no less regret, that botanists are frequently led into mistakes of much consequence, from a deficient acquaintance with agriculture."

Nevertheless the Reporter "stains" half a sheet of paper with uninteresting observations on the subject.

VERMIN of Arable Lands.—P. 616. "When wheat is sown late on sandy soils, perhaps the lark destroys more of it, when first appearing above the ground, than any other bird, nor is it possible to drive them away by any ordinary means."

This is the first charge of misdemeanor, which I have found

found to be brought against this cheering little songster.

ARABLE CROPS.

WHEAT.—*Tillage.*—P. 330. "Many farmers concur in opinion, that all the tillage of fallows intended for wheat, should be performed, if possible, as soon as the beginning of August, as the wheat is best put in upon an old tilth."—This information was probably gathered on the chalk hills.

Manure for Wheat.—P. 358. "It is the common practice in every part of the county, to fold as much as possible of the land which is intended for wheat, and its success is an unquestionable proof of the propriety of the practice, in all cases where it is deemed proper to sow wheat after a summer-fallow. The dark green colour of the wheat in spring, marks with much accuracy, the extent over which the fold has passed; while the parts which have been manured with yard-dung, present in general, a pale and sickly appearance."

Produce of Wheat.—P. 386. "The average produce of wheat on the gravels and sands, is probably below 20 bushels. On good clay loams, 25 bushels may be expected after clover, but on clays in general, probably not more than 22 bushels, varying however, according to the skill and good fortune of the farmer, from 17 to 27 bushels, and in extreme cases, including mildew, &c. from 6 bushels to 40 per acre."—This is praiseworthy Report.

RYE.—P. 386. "The quantity of this corn which is grown in Bedfordshire, is much decreased of late years. It is little in demand for making of bread, and the price is consequently too low to render it an object of profit to the occupier of any soil of moderate fertility."

BARLEY.—*Tillage.*—P. 388. "The usual tillage for barley consists of one ploughing on every kind of soil, with scarcely a solitary deviation, unless on account of the foulness of the land after turnips."—See the general head, *Tillage*, aforegoing.

Manure for Barley.—P. 389. "In the unenclosed fields, the yard-dung is generally laid on the barley fallows, the sheep-fold being preferred for the wheat crop."

Quantity of *Seed.*—P. 390. "The quantity of seed is generally four bushels per acre, in most kinds of soil."—But see as above.

Harvesting Barley.—I insert the subjoined passage, without meaning, thereby, to vouch for the truth of it. It has probability, I think, in its favor.—P. 392. "It is generally believed, that barley is benefited by a shower of rain while lying in the field; and that a slight sweat in the mow

mow takes away its *steeliness*, and causes it to make better malt."

Produce of Barley.—P. 391. "The general reply to queries of this kind is, about four quarters per acre."

OATS.—P. 394. "The culture of oats is very little attended to in any part of this county, as beans are supposed more profitable, and less exhausting on clay soils."

BEANS.—P. 400. "This kind of pulse is cultivated on all the clays and strong loams, but generally in the broadcast manner."

Produce of Beans.—P. 403. "The opinions which have been obtained on this subject, vary from three to five loads per acre; but very little grain can be expected from twenty bushels per acre, and fifteen will not pay the expenses on the poorest soils. The average is probably about twenty-three bushels."

PEASE.—P. 398. "Pease are considered as a hazardous crop in all cases, and the hazard is increased, but not caused, by their frequent repetition. Sandy soils of moderate fertility will often produce tolerable crops at intervals of six years."

Produce of Pease.—P. 400. "The produce is stated by several farmers to be about twenty bushels per acre, on the average of soils and seasons.

"The produce of drilled pease, on soils of moderate fertility, varies from twenty to fifty bushels per acre."?

TARES.—P. 404. "Winter and summer tares are grown in every part of the county, and their importance is generally known and acknowledged."

RAPE SEED.—P. 418. "Mr. Maxey, of Knotting, sows coleseed for sheep, and sometimes permits it to stand for seed, which is thrashed in the field. Various other instances occur, of the use of this vegetable in the north and east of the county, where it is generally the first crop after paring and burning old sour pastures."

POTATOES.—P. 421. "The culture of potatoes, which is common in gardens, is a fallow crop, almost unknown."

Nevertheless, and notwithstanding that fact, the Reporter has extended his section, on the subject, to the length of several pages; in which he classes the potatoe among "the ameliorating or improving crops"!

TURNEPS.—P. 411. "Turnips are commonly sown on the sands and gravels of this county; they are also common on the chalky soils, and are sometimes grown on the light hen-mould clays or woodlands."

"In the only original Report which was returned to the Board of Agriculture from Bedfordshire," (!) "I find the following

lowing observation by Edward Rudd, Esq. of Biggleswade: 'At Biggleswade, and six miles distant either way, the cultivation of land in general is as well managed, and the crops as productive, as any lands in the counties of Norfolk or Suffolk, containing such a quantity of acres, and the turnips in general have made from two to three pounds per acre more for the last two years, than those in the county of Hertford.'"

This superiority of practice, it is to be feared, is confined to the district of Biggleswade; as I find nothing of excellence reported, concerning this practice, in the County at large.

CULTIVATED HERBAGE.—*Red Clover.*—P. 428. "On light blowing sands (according to the experience of Mr. Gresham, of Chicksands, and others), it is useless to sow broad clover, as it will not grow, though never sown in the same place before."?

For *Tare Herbage*, see *Tares*, and for *Rape Herbage*, see *Rape*, aforegoing.

GRASS LANDS.

QUANTITY and QUALITY.—P. 440. "The quantity of land in a state of pasture is not very considerable. In the north, and some other parts of the county, there are several parishes that are almost entirely under tillage, and others contain a quantity of worthless sward, covered with sedge, ant-hills, &c. and producing little advantage either to the occupier or the public."

P. 445. "A farmer in the north of the county, remarked that it had been said (I believe in print), that Bedfordshire contained no land sufficiently rich to fatten an ox; but though this assertion is to be considered as very erroneous, the county is certainly not remarkable for rich feeding land.

"Some of the pastures in the south west of the county, have been let from 50*s.* to 60*s.* per acre, though much of the grass land is worth only from 20*s.* to 30*s.* per acre; and Mr. Wilson, of Ravensden, observes that a milch cow will scarcely maintain herself in tolerable condition in that and several other parishes in that part of the county."

P. 447. "The breaking up of grass land has been practised of late years to some extent, particularly in the north and east of the county, and paring and burning is commonly the first step in the business; but there are still remaining considerable portions of coarse sward, producing scarcely any thing but sedge, and other rubbish, which no animal will eat, and which the tenants are restricted from ploughing

ploughing, though many an open field common is far superior in public utility to such enclosures."

Breaking up old Grass Land.—P. 449. (Mr. Foster)—"It is to be observed, that burnt land will not soon again turn to good grass; if, therefore, in breaking up old grass land, it is intended soon to lay it down again, it is better to plough it up without burning."—There is much good sense, in this remark.

MEADOWS.—See the head *Embankment*, aforegoing.

ORCHARDS and GARDENS.

P. 458. "*Orchards* are in general very small in this county. There are a few that may contain 100 fruit trees of various kinds, and new ones of an acre or two may be occasionally met with, planted sometimes in squares of about seven yards between each tree, but there are frequently no other orchards than what are included in gardens, consisting of four or five trees."

P. 456. "The *gardens* of Sandy and Girtford have been long celebrated in Bedfordshire, and the adjacent counties, for the excellence and abundance of their culinary vegetables. It does not appear, however, that any particular process is employed, which is not known to all professional gardeners."

LIVESTOCK.

THEIR IMPROVEMENT.—P. 571. "The improvement of the breed of animals has almost monopolized the attention of modern agriculturists; yet as they have not been unanimous in opinion, it may be proper to make a few remarks on what are deemed the fundamental principles of the art."—This the Reporter attempts; but I find nothing new in his strictures. They are, however, *readable*.

HORSES.—See Mr. STONE's Report, aforegoing.

CATTLE.—*Breed.*—After inserting an extract from Mr. Stone's Report, Mr. Batchelor says, p. 525. "At the present time, Bedfordshire, though occupied by many good farmers, makes no pretensions to any peculiar or excellent breed of cattle."

DAIRY.—*District.*—P. 525. "The chief dairy district is in the west of the county, consisting in many of the towns which surround Ampthill and Woburn."

"Very little butter is made in the north of the county, except what is required for family use. Much of the grass land is very poor. Mr. Wilson, of Ravensden, observes, that a milch-cow will scarcely maintain her condition in that neighbourhood."

Cows.

Cows.—P. 525. "Broad-horned cows are kept in many parts of the county; but a rather general opinion seems to prevail among many of the principal dairy farmers, in favour of the large Holderness short-horned breed.

"They are generally called Yorkshires, in this neighbourhood, and are purchased in that county by professed dealers. Many others are obtained from the Fens, &c. being purchased at St. Ives' market, in Huntingdonshire."

Food of Cows.—P. 525. "Artificial food, such as chaff, turnips, &c. is seldom used. The summer food is principally natural pasture. Red clover is found to be a very improper food for milking cows, as, though it does not diminish the quantity of the milk, it makes it poor in quality, as has been sufficiently experienced at Lidlington. It is supposed that more than one half of the pasture grounds which are appropriated to the dairy, must be annually mown, to support the cows in winter; but they are often supplied with clover-hay, and the clover, in its dry state, is not supposed to injure the quantity or quality of the butter."

Milking.—P. 526. "Where the quantity of cows is not very considerable, they are commonly milked between the hours of five and six, both in the morning and evening."

"The milk is kept in *leads*, or sometimes in wooden *kivers*, of a shallow construction."

Butter.—P. 526. "The butter is generally churned twice a week, and sent to London the succeeding day, by the common carriers, or provision waggons. The carriage is paid by the London dealers, who purchase the butter for half a year, or sometimes a year, at two different prices, which have varied within the last few years between 12*d.* and 15*d.* per pound. The money is commonly returned once a month.

"The inferior kind, which is called *under-butter*, or *after-butter*, is taken at the regular price, as this is the only mode to improve the quality of the prime sort."

Are we, from this not very intelligent account, to conclude that milk, in Bedfordshire, as in Buckinghamshire, is skimmed more than once?—See p. 546, aforegoing.

Calves.—P. 525. "Are generally sent to Leighton-market, and sold for the purpose of suckling."

SWINE.—*Breed.*—P. 570. "The swine of Bedfordshire are mostly mixed breeds, many of which partake more or less of the Berkshire kind."

Foods of Swine.—P. 570. "Mr. Pickford, of Market-street, keeps 4 or 500 of these animals. He gives them green tares, and frequently clover, in summer, and Swedish turnips in winter, which are capable of keeping them in good store condition."

P. 571. "I have been told, that some person of Hockliffe formerly kept hogs without either wash or water, by filling one trough with beans, and another with raw potatoes."

SHEEP.—*Breed.*—P. 537. "In the only copy of Mr. Stone's original Report which was returned from Bedfordshire, are the following observations by Edward Rudd, Esq. of Biggleswade.

"'Upon wet, cold clay lands, where sheep are driven a great way to fold, in common fields, the horned sheep, that are short' (?) 'legged, and well made, are the most beneficial to be kept; but on dry land, or pasture ground, the better sort of polled sheep, where they are not driven far to fold, are the most profitable. Good *sheep* of the above description, of either sort, if kept sound, are the most advantageous of any *cattle*' (!) 'to the farmer.'

"Since the above was written (1794), the prevalence of the enclosing system, and the influence and example of the late Duke of Bedford, have contributed materially to improve the sheep stock of the county. The New Leicester breed has been introduced into many parishes, and various crosses of this breed with the Wiltshires, and other kinds, have found their way even into the open fields.

"There are, however, a great many farmers, who granting the superior merit of the Dishley sheep, are yet found to maintain that this, like many other improvements, costs as much, and sometimes more than it is worth; and that some years must elapse ere the profit overbalances the previous expenses of tups, &c. Hence it may be observed, that there are other reasons, in addition to prejudice of education, &c. that prevent a hasty adoption of new practices.

"The horned sheep which remain in the county, occupy many of the towns which are yet unenclosed; as in the angle of the county from Leighton to Whipsnade, and many other places."

Food of Sheep.—P. 559. "The flocks of the common fields are kept on the commons, and *balks* between the lands, and among the crops of beans in the spring.

"In the winter they are kept on the grass land, or sent to turnips, where they can be procured.

"Sometimes they are fed with bean-straw, hay, &c. in littered yards, and in the south-east part of the county, where neither turnips nor grass can be procured, the sheep are frequently wintered on the grass land about Barnet, &c.

"In the enclosures, tares, clover, &c. are grown for their support in summer, and turnips in winter.

"The ewes are seldom put to turnips in winter, as the succulent nature of the turnip is supposed by some to make the

the lambs too large previous to their birth. And it seems advisable to give hay along with turnips in all cases, as their cold nature seems to increase in sheep a disposition to the *red-water*, and other diseases. (?)

"The Swedish turnip, though much esteemed for fattening, is generally thought to produce an insufficient supply of milk for lambs in the spring." (?)

For the *Folding* of Sheep, see the article *Manure*, page 594, aforegoing.

Shearing Sheep.—P. 565. "Farmers are not anxious to shear the sheep in that extremely neat and close manner which has been recommended, as they suppose that the expense would be increased by this means as much perhaps as the wool; and when the skin is thus suddenly exposed to the burning rays of the sun, the sheep are liable to sustain much injury."

RABBITS.—P. 574. "This kind of live stock, which formerly made a conspicuous figure on the warrens of Sandy, Ampthill, Millbrook, Steppingly, &c. appears at this time to be little attended to with a view to profit, except on a small warren in the latter parish."

BEES.—P. 579. "Mr. Maxey, of Knotting, had a crop of rape, which was seeded last year (1806), and produced such abundant employ for the bees, that Mr. Maxey supposed one man, who kept a considerable number of hives, would gain 5*l*. by the seeding of the rape."

EXPENCE and PROFIT.—In endeavoring to comply with the standing order of the Board, Mr. Batchelor has evinced extraordinary exertions of ingenuity and labor:—not in collecting data among the occupiers of Bedfordshire; but in suppositious calculations; and has struck out a NEW METHOD of estimating the EXPENCES of HUSBANDRY;—by entering into, and putting down separately, the various minutiæ belonging to them:—a work which gives pain in the contemplation. It fills nearly one hundred pages:—not merely with pound-shilling-and-pence estimates; but with numerous tablets, and more complex tables; which have necessarily cost much time, and some thought, to form.

It were needless to say that a work of this sort is a heavy encumbrance on a provincial Report. But having found it in one, I have thought it right, briefly to notice it. The subjoined extract is the opening of the section.

P. 70. "To ascertain the expenses and profits of agriculture, in all its various shapes and circumstances, is a subject of more than ordinary difficulty, and though it does not appear that it has been, in any case, minutely investigated, so many erroneous or partial estimates have been laid before the public, as to induce some to believe, that no tolerable

tolerable approximation to the truth can ever be obtained. The fundamental error of many calculations, appears to consist in the rejection of averages, and making use of local and temporary prices to serve as the basis of general deductions, in consequence of which, several of the cattle crops, the intrinsic merit of which is still considered by some as not well established, have been represented as capable of affording more profit in the fallow season, than is commonly obtained by the whole subsequent course of cropping under the management of a good farmer.

"That there is some latent source of delusion in such calculations is not to be doubted, and nothing short of a very minute inquiry into every step of the business, is likely to furnish a proper basis of calculations applicable to all times and circumstances. It is impossible to ascertain the average size and shape of the farms; but thus far is well known, that the dwelling house and offices are seldom found in the centre of a farm, whether it be large or small, and that there are great irregularities in the size of the fields, and the number of acres allotted to each season, as it is here termed, or to each kind of crop in the regular course of husbandry. The average size of arable farms in this county, has been estimated at 150 acres, and with the exception of gentlemen's parks, open fields, and cottage allotments, it is probable that the average size of enclosed pastures is ten acres, and of enclosed arable fields is 15 acres each.

"The subsequent calculations are intended to apply more particularly to a farm of the above description, which may be considered as possessing at least an average share of the conveniences of occupation which are commonly met with in this county."

A sketch of the supposed farm having been previously drawn, the calculations commence with the subject of

DOMESTIC EXPENCES.—This subject is subdivided, as follows:—

Farmer's Bread.	Firing.
Homebrewed Ale.	Food for Servants.
Meat and Vegetables.	Washing and Mending.

After discussing, separately, these several items, with a minuteness that is creditable to the perseverance of a mind which is capable of investigating more enlarged subjects,—the author presents us with the following tablet. P. 78.

"General

" General Expenses of Servants, &c.	House-keeper (or Mistress.)			Kitchen or Dairy-maid			Horse-keeper, or Man-servant.			Boy, 12 Years old.		
	£.	s.	d.	£.	s.	d.	£.	s.	d.	£.	s.	d.
Diet, 4*s.* 4*s.* 5*s.* 2*s.* 6*d.* per week,	10	8	0	10	8	0	13	0	0	6	10	0
Wages,..................	10	10	0	5	5	0	10	10	0	2	12	0
Lodging, and wear and tear of furniture, ...	1	6	0	1	6	0	1	6	0	1	6	0
Firing, ...	0	18	$2\frac{1}{2}$	0	18	$2\frac{1}{2}$	0	18	$2\frac{1}{2}$	0	18	$2\frac{1}{2}$
Cooking, ...	2	3	4	2	3	4	2	3	4	1	1	8
Washing, mending, &c.	1	10	5	1	10	5	...			...		
Total per annum,......	26	16	0	21	11	0	27	17	6	12	7	10
Average per week, ...	0	10	$3\frac{1}{2}$	0	8	$3\frac{1}{4}$	0	10	$8\frac{1}{2}$	0	4	9"

I had conceived the idea of making out a list of the almost innumerable heads and subheads of this elaborate section. But they are too loosely thrown together, to serve as a model for other writers to work by.

It is possible, however, that Mr. B. may be induced to revise, reconsider, abridge, and digest more sedulously, the matters of this and the other sections of his book, which do not belong, especially, to the *practice* of *Bedfordshire;* and either to publish the selection, separately, or send it in, as a *communication* to the Board of Agriculture.

Should Mr. Batchelor adopt a plan of that sort, I hope he will not overlook the following suggestion, relative to the subject, which is now more immediately under consideration.—It is this: instead of calculating on the " average value," *at the time* of *writing*, let more *integral* prices be employed.—Thus, in estimating the cost of " farmer's bread," calculate on ten shillings a bushel, instead of 8*s.* 9*d.*; and in reckoning that of " home-brewed ale," put the price of barley at five shillings, instead of 4*s.* $3\frac{3}{8}$ *d.* For, seeing the fluctuation of the prices of corns, at all times, and that of money at present, the cost of bread and ale will be incessantly varying. But, by founding the calculations on *whole numbers*, instead of *fractional parts*, the cost, at any time, might be the more readily found, by the rule of proportion.

Having proceeded thus far, in the thankless office of advice, I will risk another, suggestion;—namely that of using, freely, but cautiously, the valuable art of *compression*, throughout the work above suggested.—Half a century ago, when WRITTEN AGRICULTURE was in its nonage, any thing that was published on the subject was read with avidity;

avidity;—no matter how frivolous, or ridiculously void of useful information, it might be. But, now, when the several subjects belonging to it have been discussed, by various writers, and have received a degree of scientific existence,—a less diffuse, a closer, and more considerate, style of writing is required. It is become requisite before a man sit down to write, on PRACTICAL AGRICULTURE, as on any other art or science, that he should well study his subject; digest his ideas, with due consideration; and compose with clearness, yet with conciseness.—Unwinnowed corn is no longer marketable. It is, now, required that the chaff and weeds should be separated from it, before it be offered for sale.

I hope Mr. Batchelor will pardon me for placing these observations, here. They certainly are not particularly aimed at the author of the Bedfordshire Report; but are intended as a general intimation to writers on rural subjects.

CAMBRIDGESHIRE.

CAMBRIDGESHIRE.

THIS is a most untoward subject of departmental division. Like Oxfordshire, it extends into three departments.

Its fens and other *water-formed lands*, as well as the *upper grounds*, that are situated to the *eastward* of them,—together forming about three fourths of the County,—are natural parcels of the *Eastern* Department; and have, *there*, passed in review.

The *chalky lands* of Cambridgeshire, which border on Hertfordshire, form the eastern termination of the line of chalk hills that are the northern limits of the *Southern* Department. While that part of the County,—the *strong lands*,—which naturally, and agriculturally, unite with Huntingdonshire and Bedfordshire, inseparably belong to the *Midland* Department.

The difficulty arises in drawing a line of separation, between the *Midland* and the *Southern* Departments. The *clayey* and the *chalky* lands are so much intermixed, in a considerable breadth of country which lies between them, as to admit of no strongly marked *agricultural* line of demarcation. The most *natural* line is that branch of the river Cam, which enters the County at the point of contact of Bedfordshire and Hertfordshire, and descends in in a northeasterly direction toward Cambridge; and that line giving the largest share, of those intermixed lands, to the MIDLAND DEPARTMENT, I will insert the *whole* of the useful matter which I may find relative to the UPPER GROUNDS of CAMBRIDGESHIRE, *westward of its fens*, in *this* place; and refer to it (should reference be required) for what may particularly regard the southern department. I am weary of dissecting *County* Reports.

" GENERAL

"GENERAL VIEW OF THE AGRICULTURE IN THE COUNTY OF CAMBRIDGE, WITH OBSERVATIONS ON THE MEANS OF ITS IMPROVEMENT

By CHARLES VANCOUVER,

1794."

CONSIDERABLE attention has been already paid to this Report; and much useful matter extracted from it, in going over the *Eastern Department*; it being to the *marsh-lands* and *fens* of CAMBRIDGESHIRE, that Mr. VANCOUVER has been more particularly attentive, in surveying and reporting it.

To its UPPER GROUNDS, and HIGHER LANDS, however, he has not been inattentive:—And whatever may be deemed suitable for abstraction, concerning these, will be incorporated here, with the other useful materials that have been sent in to the Board, from the MIDLAND DEPARTMENT.

Mr. Vancouver's QUALIFICATIONS have been noticed in the EASTERN DEPARTMENT.

His MODE of SURVEY is there given, at length, in his own words. It is briefly this.—Each parish of the County was visited, and most of them "surveyed," or rather examined, and separately reported,—as to the subjoined particulars. In a comparatively few, no information was procured.

The primary object attended to, in these parochial Surveys, was the STATE of APPROPRIATION.

In many of the *commonfield parishes*, each "field" is mentioned, as to its *size*, its *soils*, and the *rents* paid for them.—The *state* of *drainage*.—The *general state* of *husbandry*,

bandry, and the *average produce* of each crop; with the breeds and number of *sheep*; and sometimes the *cattle* of a parish are noticed; and mostly the *size* of the *largest farm* in each; but without mentioning the more common and prevailing sizes The ordinary *tenancy* of farms, is also not unfrequently put down; together with *incidental remarks* and observations, which arose in the survey. But of these, not many *.

In the *inclosed parishes*, similar notices were taken; tho, in general, with less regard, than in the open ones. But the number of parishes that were wholely appropriated and inclosed, at the time of Mr. V's survey, in 1793-4, are few, in comparison with those which still remained subject to feudal restraints and inconveniencies. The proportion being in 1794, nearly as one to ten.

In

* Mr. Vancouver's Parochial Journal. The subjoined is a specimen of it. Page 114.

"GAMLINGAY." (*A commonfield parish.*)

"The soil of this parish, on the east of the village, and adjoining the meadows, is a loamy sand, proper for the culture of barley, turnips, rye, and clover; of this there are about sixty acres, which are rented at eight shillings per acre. The remainder of this field, amounting to about three hundred and forty acres, extending to, and binding upon Mr. Quintin's wood, is a thin, cold, hungry clay, lying upon a gault, proper for the culture of wheat, beans, peas, clover, and black oats. South of the village, and also adjoining the meadows, there are about eighty acres of a deep, loamy, sandy nature; thence towards Potton wood, are about four hundred and seventy acres, of a similar cold, and clayey nature, with that before described. North of the village, and immediately adjoining thereto, the sandy land prevails, to the extent of about sixty acres; thence towards Warsley, are about four hundred and ninety acres, of a cold, clayey soil. The meadow, or half-yearly land, is of a moory nature, contains about eighty acres, and is on an average, rented with the open field arable, at eight shillings the acre.

"The largest farm is held at will, at the annual rent of one hundred and fifty pounds. The common husbandry, with turnips, or rye, on the sandy lands, in the place of a thorough summer fallow, assisted occasionally with hand-dressings, to the amount of forty shillings per acre, produces

16	bushels of	Wheat
24	ditto	Barley
22	ditto	Oats
12	ditto	Peas and Beans per acre.

"There are about twelve hundred of the common Cambridgeshire sheep kept in this parish, three hundred and forty of which, perished in the course of last last year, by the rot, and the mortality at this time still continues This dreadful disease is here imputed to the bad state

of

In the arrangement of the materials, collected by the Reporter, he has set the "plan of the Board" at naught. He has divided his work into TWO PARTS.

The FIRST PART contains his *parochial journal*,—formed on the plan above described,—and including a valuable *communication* of Mr. STONE of Leverington (not the Reporter of Bedfordshire) concerning three of the principal fen parishes, in the nothern extreme of the County. This mass of local information fills nine tenths of the volume.

The SECOND PART consists of *general information*,—arranged under the following miscellaneous heads;—namely,

Arable.	Half Year Meadows.	Provisions.
Inclosure.	Highland Common.	Labor.
Tenures.	Heath Sheep Walk.	Horses.
Grass.	Sheep.	Implements.
Paring &c.	Cows.	Hemp
Fens.	Woodland.	Roads.
Moor Commons.	Population.	Recapitulation.

In reviewing the Volume before me, with the attention bent toward the Eastern Department, I extracted several articles of the parochial journal; being anxious to collect every thing I could, of any value, concerning the FENS of ENGLAND; and within the limits of Cambridgeshire, as much or more than in any other County, information concerning them is to be obtained.

But, among the UPLAND PARISHES of CAMBRIDGESHIRE, which were chiefly, at the time of Mr. V's survey, in a state of common field, a less considerable portion of useful or interesting information was to be expected I will, however examine the unexplored part of the Volume; and register, here, what I may find,—whether in the *parochial journal*, *Mr. Stone's communication*, or Mr. Vancouver's *second part*,—as I may think will throw additional light on the rural affairs of the department which is now under consideration.

The

of the drainage, in the open fields, which in the event of their being enclosed, as is much desired, would be hollow drained, and improved to very great advantage; and until the herbage is made better by inclosure, no improvement can possibly be made in the stock and husbandry of this parish; which contains four hundred and five cottagers, in the whole, seven hundred souls. The poor's rates are three shillings, with an annual donation for the support of ten widows, out of the estate of the Earl of Macclesfield.

"N. B. Chiefly college lands."

The number of pages—two hundred and nineteen:—octavo-sized pages, on quarto paper; this being an "original report;" and of course remains *unpublished.*

An intelligent map of the County, and the adjacent Fens, is prefixed to the *volume,*—or rather *pamphlet*; it being—bulky as it is—stitched in the pamphlet manner.

SUBJECT THE FIRST.

NATURAL ECONOMY.

EXTENT.—A general view, not only of the County at large, but of the agricultural state, and rental value, of its several descriptions of lands, is seen in the subjoined statement; which I insert, here, as a proper place of reference. —P. 193.

" Description of Land.	Number of Acres.	Present Rental, or Value, per Acre.		
		£.	s.	d.
Enclosed Arable	15000	0	18	0
Open Field Arable	132000	0	10	0
Improved Pasture	52000	1	0	4
Inferior Pasture	19800	0	10	9
Wood Land	1000	0	15	0
Improved Fen	50000	0	15	0
Waste and Unimproved Fen ...	150000	0	4	0
Half Yearly Meadow Land	2000	0	12	6
Highland Common	7500	0	10	0
Fen or Moor Common	8000	0	3	0
Heath Sheep Walk	6000	0	2	6"
	443300			

SOILS.—In the parochial journal, as has been said, the soils of each parish are particularized; tho sometimes in terms not sufficiently defined; and we meet with no general statement of the soils of the County at large;—nor with any classification of them, into DISTRICTS or passages; any other than the ordinary distinctions of "Highlands," and "Fens."

In the next article—*Appropriation*—under the subhead "Heathsheep Walk"—will be found an uncommon, but not singular, kind of land, satisfactorily described.

SUBJECT

SUBJECT THE SECOND.

POLITICAL ECONOMY.

APPROPRIATION.—A general view of the state of appropriation may be seen under the head, *Extent*, aforegoing.

P. 203. " *Fen or Moor Common.* In the highland part of the county, there are about eight thousand five hundred acres of this description, which at present, contribute little to the support of the stocks, though greatly to the disease of the rot in sheep and cows: These commons generally lie well for draining, and are otherwise capable of very great improvement; but until a Court of Sewers shall be established, with powers to oblige the mills upon the several streams which pass through these moors, to be pitched lower; so that the mill-dams shall not hold the water up to its present height, and over-ride the surface of the commons as they now do; no remedy can be applied to this very serious evil, which must necessarily be removed, before any improvement can be undertaken.

" *Half Yearly Meadow Land.* These lands lying dispersed through the hollows of the open fields, and receiving the richest juices of the surrounding lands, even in their present neglected state, are rented on an average, at twelve shillings and six-pence per acre only; but would by proper draining, and being put into severalty, readily be improved to thirty shillings per acre, as the crop which is now only mown twice in three years, would then be annually secured.

" *Highland Common.* There are about seven thousand five hundred acres of this land in the county, which in severalty, would be readily improved, to the annual rent of a guinea per acre. In its present state, it cannot possibly be valued at more than half that price; though no alteration in the present mode of depasturing, can apparently be made, to encrease the present estimated value.

" *Heath Sheep Walk.* This land appears to be chiefly appropriated to the original design of nature; the surface or skin, forming a tender and wholesome food for the sheep, which are generally depastured thereon. The staple of the land is in general so very dry, and thin, that once broken, it will be ages before it can acquire an equally valuable turf or covering with that it now produces. The substratum is generally

generally a chalk, though in some places, there is found a deep, rank sand, abounding with flints, and where the surface is broken, the sand in the dry season of summer, is very liable to be driven by the wind, to the inconvenience not only of the adjoining lands, but of those at some distance. Where these plains in severalty, and were it practicable to raise live fences upon them, trefoil, cinquefoil, and rye grass, would be found the most profitable grasses to cultivate: The less however that this kind of land is disturbed, the better."

The following general remarks of this Reporter will serve to corroborate many other of a similar tendency, which I have thought right to place before the public, concerning the ENTIRE APPROPRIATION of the TERRITORY of ENGLAND *

P 195. "The laying of the intermixed property together, and in severalty, which is now dispersed in the common open fields; and enclosing, where such a measure shall be found advisable, appear to be indispensibly necessary, as previous steps, to the general improvement of the highland part of the county; but as these objects involve a great diversity of interests, and as it is material that the Board should understand the general disposition as fully as possible, I have made it my particular care, to mix, and converse with the yeomanry of the county, and in their sedate, and sober moments, to possess myself fully of their experience, and local knowledge; and finally, to ascertain the general sentiment, as to this important innovation upon the establishment of ages. A few have given an unqualified dissent, but they were flock-masters; others have concurred under certain limitations, but the mass of the farmers are decidedly for the measure in question. The general average of the rent of the enclosed arable, compared with that of the open common field arable, in the whole county, exceeds the latter in the proportion of eight shillings per acre, and the average produce of the former, exceeds that of the latter, as under

	Bushels.	Pecks.
Wheat	3	1
Rye	0	3
Barley	15	1
Oats	1	1
Peas	2	1

But if a single instance be adverted to, and a comparison made between the parishes of Childersley, which is enclosed, and

* That of SCOTLAND, I believe, has long been in the required state.

and Hardwicke, which remains in open common field, and which parishes, appear by the journal, to consist of a perfectly similar soil, and are divided only by a hedge row; the excess of the produce in favour of the enclosed, will appear infinitely more abundant, viz.

Childersley enclosed		Hardwicke open	Excess of produce
24 bushels of	Wheat	16 bushels	8 bushels
36 ditto	Barley	18 ditto	18 ditto
36 ditto	Oats	18 ditto	18 ditto
20 ditto	Peas and Beans	8 ditto	12 ditto

"Now if the good effects of enclosing were even to stop here, surely sufficient benefit is apparent to justify the general principle; but when to that is added the exemption from a disease, the dreadful consequences of which, have desolated the sheep walks in most of the neighbouring parishes, whilst in Childersley and Knapwell (both of which are enclosed) not the least shadow of the disease, has made its appearance; it is surely reasonable to conclude that it is highly expedient; relying fully on the wisdom of parliament, for all the arrangements which necessarily apply to the complete adjustment of so complicated a business."

The severe losses, occasioned by the rot in sheep, in the commonfield parishes, will be seen under the head, *Sheep;* and for other cogent reasons, for that salutary measure, see the head *Rent*, ensuing.

PROVISIONS.—P. 212. "The general average price from repeated statements in different parts of the county, appears on the several articles to be as under, viz.

Beef 4½d. per lb.	Mutton 4¾d. per lb.	Pork 5½d. per lb.
Veal 5¼d. per lb.	Cheese 6d. per lb.	Flour 1s. 11½d. per stone,
Butter 10d. per lb.	Potatoes 1s. 4d¾ per bush.	or 2s. 3d. the peck loaf."

MANUFACTURES.—P. 71. "The spinning woollen, or worsted yarn, for the Norwich and north country markets, has a good effect, in giving employment to the women and children in this neighbourhood."

What an admirable and most eligible connexion is this, between AGRICULTURE and MANUFACTURES! How easily, and profitably might a plan of that sort be adopted, and executed, in any non-manufacturing district.—A man, with a moderate capital, and some knowledge of wools, and their manufacture, placing himself in such a district, might benefit himself and thousands of industrious wives and daughters of farm laborers, that are now existing in a state of idleness and poverty, through a total want of employment, in the winter season.—He would purchase the wools

wools of the district, *from the growers*, and sell the yarn to the manufacturers to whose particular lines of business they might be best adapted.

It will readily be perceived, however, that before a permanent blessing to the Country, so great as that plan would not fail to be, could be enjoyed, *to its full extent*, a law would previously be required to prohibit the use of spinning mills; which the next generation, if not the present, will consider as one of the most ruinous inventions that ever was unfortunately adopted, by a FLORISHING NATION:—A nation which required not "tricks of trade" to secure its LASTING PROSPERITY.

POOR RATE.—From a general table of the rate of each parish, the average comes out 2*s.* 6½*d*, in the pound; (table opposite p. 121.)—But on what principle of valuation is not expressed.

TITHE.—P. 71. "The tithes of this, and the neighbouring parish of Triplow, are taken in kind, by a gentleman, who, much to his honor, allows the farmers one tenth part of the first cost, of all the artificial manure, or foreign composts, which they purchase."

This is a well judged policy; which any man, who *takes tithe* in *kind*, or by the *valuation* of *crops*, might adopt.

PUBLIC DRAINAGE.—See the head, *Appropriation*, p. 613, aforegoing.

ROADS.—P. 218. "The public roads in general through the county, are tolerably good; the private roads are very indifferent; and it is not very probable that they will be much improved under the present regulation of the surveyors of the highways. The materials for mending them in many places are extremely scarce, and lying at a considerable distance, are not to be obtained, without more particular attention is paid to the statute duty of each parish, and the present laws for keeping them in repair."

SUBJECT THE THIRD.

RURAL ECONOMY.

TENANTED ESTATES.

TENANCY.—P. 193 "There is no greater error in the whole economy of country business, than that which the gentlemen of Cambridgeshire, are too apt to fall into, respecting the tenures" (tenancy) "they grant of their estates.

Few

Few are inclined to give their tenants such assurances of the certain and quiet enjoyment of their improvements, as reason dictates and justice demands. Had the same jealously prevailed in Norfolk, on the early improvement of that county, in vain would the landlords, in conjunction with their tenants, have expended such large sums in claying, *marling*, and otherwise improving their estates; if the tenant had not been assured of an eventual benefit, and reward for his expence and labour, under the protection and encouragement of a lease for twenty-one years."

It should have been previously made appear that *Cambridgeshire* and *Norfolk* are alike circumstanced; and that a *commonfield County*, *without marl* (for any thing to the contrary that appears in this report), and an inclosed County which abounds in it, require the same sort of tenancy.

RENT.—For the average rents of the several descriptions of lands, in Cambridgeshire, see the statement, under the head, *Extent*, p. 612, aforegoing.—It there appears that the rent of inclosed arable lands is *eighteen shillings*, that of commonfield lands *ten* shillings; which is not much more than the half of what their value would be, in a state of COMPLETE APPROPRIATION*.

The following extraordinary circumstance places, in a still stronger point of view, the absurdity of keeping valuable lands in that unproductive, and, to all classes in society, unprofitable state. It is, however, so contrary to ordinary circumstances as to render its authenticity doubtful. The truth may have been strictly told; but, it is probable, not all the truth.

P. 97. "It may not be amiss to observe, that Mr. BENDITCHE has documents by him, which shew that a considerable part of his estates in this parish," (Barrington, a commonfield parish) "and at Foxton, were let a century ago, at an actually higher rent than is given at this time. This cannot be ascribed to old grants, and tenures, because the estates were held chiefly by tenants at will; but it strongly proves, that so far from the agriculture in this neighbourhood having been progressively improving, for the last hundred years, it has been greatly on the decline, and the country of course, taking the value of money, &c. &c. into the account, must at present be far less productive, than at that period."

WOODLANDS.

* RENT and PRODUCE.—And it may be fairly reckoned that the value of their products, at market, would, on a par of years, be nearly proportionate to their rental values; which are of course grounded on the market values of their produce:—From which, however, in the case under notice, something is to be deducted for the conveniency of cultivation, which belongs to lands that are wholely appropriated.

WOODLANDS.

P. 210. "Few woods, it may be presumed, afford less matter for observation in the kingdom, than the woodlands of Cambridgeshire, which are thinly dispersed; and this nakedness must remain, so long as the county continues in an uninclosed state."

AGRICULTURE.

STATE of the LANDS.—A general view of the agricultural state of the lands, in Cambridgeshire may be seen, p. 612, aforegoing. It there appears that nine tenthss of the arable lands of the County were, at the time that statement was made, 1794, in the state of common field; only one tenth part (or a few acres more) being then wholely appropriated, and in the state of inclosure; and this, mostly, of modern date.

PLAN of MANAGEMENT.—I find nothing entitled to extraction, on this subject in the *commonfield* husbandry. Some deviations from the general plan of the kingdom are observable. But none of them, I think, are of superior excellence. And the few parishes, that are in a state of *inclosure*, appear to have continued the openfield course of husbandry; some very few excepted.

WORKPEOPLE.—P. 212. "The general average of men-servants wages through the county, is ten pounds per ann. maid-servants four pounds ten shillings; that of boys forty-five shillings, and girls, washing included, thirty-eight shillings a year. During eight months of the year, the wages to the day labourer is seven shillings per week, after which, for the next two months, it is increased to nine shillings; and the remaining two months, during the time of hay and corn harvest, he receives two shillings and six-pence per day, or fifteen shillings per week; amounting in the whole to twenty-two pounds four shillings, if the labourer is blessed with constant health and employment during the whole year. To this may be added the casual earnings of his wife and children, which if estimated at three pounds sixteen shillings, will make the total amount of the earnings of a poor family, twenty-six pounds per ann."

WORKING ANIMALS.—P. 214. "Nothing in the husbandry of Cambridgeshire is more replete with error, and abuse, or more capable of reform, under the present circumstances

cumstances of the county, than the feeding, and working management of farm horses."

P. 216. "The scarcity of pasture ground, the want of proper attention in the farmers to the raising of green food for soiling their horses in summer, and the great neglect in the culture of artificial grasses, all conduce to an expence in supporting the farm horses *in the upper parts of the country*, that is absolutely enormous. They are kept in the stable throughout the year, each horse is fed with a peck of corn per day, with as much chaff, chopped straw, and hay, as they can eat, and work but one journey in the day; which seldom exceeds seven hours, but never eight."

ARABLE CROPS.—In a table of "highland produce, in bushels per acre," in the several parishes of the County, the "averages" stand, thus; (facing p. 121.)

	B.	P.		B.	P.
Wheat, *Inclosures*,	23	3	—*Open Field*	20	2
Rye, ...	20	2	....	19	3
Barley	36	1	....	21	0
Oats	26	2 (!)	....	25	1
Pease	18	3	....	16	2
Beans	17	0 (!)	....	20	0 (!)
Peabeans	16	1	....	17	0

For remarks on these products, see *Appropriation*, p. 613, aforegoing.

GRASS LANDS.—P. 199. "The principal divisions of the pasture grounds which are noticed, are first, those which produce a rich tender grass and herbage, from a loose black soil, proper for feeding or grazing cattle, and worth from twenty-five to thirty shillings per acre. The second, a more coarse, but luxuriant grass and herbage, produced upon a close, moist soil, proper for the depasturage of milch cows, and store cattle, worth from fifteen to twenty shillings per acre. The third class produces very coarse, sharp, sour grass and herbage, vegetating very late in the spring from wet, cold, and compact clays, worth from five to ten shillings per acre: this last division owes its inferiority, to the wet, cold, and compressed state, in which it has lain for ages."

In the subjoined extract, we see *another* instance of the wanton waste committed, by our infatuate and overbearing ancestors, during "the dark ages;" and which, it would seem, by this not very satisfactory account, is suffered to impart some share of its baleful influence, in "these enlightened times."—See my GLOCESTERSHIRE, &c. &c. &c.

P. 67. "The meadow land contains about twenty acres, enter-common with Whittlesford, from the end of hay harvest

harvest until Lady Day, *with a bite on Easter Sunday;* this bite formerly destroyed the whole crop of hay: for although the Whittlesford cattle were only allowed from six o'clock in the morning of Easter Sunday, till the end of the morning church service, still the multitudes that were driven on to this common, during that time, either eat up, or destroyed every prospect of a crop of hay: at present, as Easter falls so much earlier, this custom is not so injurious."

CATTLE.—*Breed.*—P. 207. "The various mixtures of *this cattle* that are found in this county, are not easily enumerated: the Suffolk polled, the Craven, the short-horned Yorkshire, the Derby, the Welch, the Leicester, the Fifeshire, Gloucester-brown, and the common Cambridgeshire, are the breeds of cow cattle most generally preferred; nor is it conceived possible to mould this variety into any one uniform sort, until the open field lands, are laid in severalty, and the coarse and low lands, drained and improved, so, that by subsequent cultivation, it shall be ascertained, what are the species of cattle most proper for the then improved grasses and herbage, in the several districts of the county."

Diseases of Cattle.—P. 208. "To the considerations of the general inferiority of the cows in the *upper part of the county*, are to be added some important evils, which are perhaps, scarcely to be paralleled in any other county in the kingdom; (viz.) the frequency of slipping calf, and the perishing by the rot; a few conjectures may be hazarded upon the cause of the former, whilst the cause of the latter, evidently speaks for itself; arising from the foulness of the herbage in the low grounds, on which the cows depasture."

The author's conjectures on abortion appear, to me, to be far from well founded. That carrion and blood (the latter more particularly) are capable of causing it, in cows at least, is a pretty general opinion. But, as is by this writer justly observed (p. 209)—"in the instances before us, taken from the journal, it does not appear possible to ascribe so general a calamity, to such partial and accidental causes."

Mr. V. blames the exhaustion caused by the unnatural practice of milking the cows "beyond a certain point;" yet recommends "repeated bleedings."—There may be propriety in those ideas; but I do not perceive it.

The ABORTION of DOMESTIC ANIMALS is a subject of serious consideration to the livestock farmer; and is not unworthy of scientific research.

P. 87. (Parish of Shingay) "A very serious calamity prevails amongst the cows, that are here depastured, that of slipping their calves; this accident generally happens when the cow has gone twenty-one weeks, or rather better than

than half her time, with her *second calf;* which at the time of exclusion is found to be much smaller than might reasonably be expected, and in general appears to have been dead for some length of time. In this parish, within these five years in a dairy of twenty-three cows, a loss of ninety calves has been sustained."

P. 56. (Babraham) "The Gloucester brown, and the Suffolk poll'd cows answer; but, they are however subject to a disease called the joint garget, the first symptom of which is a partial relaxation of the nerves and tendons; this soon becomes general, and the whole frame of the animal is so far deranged, as to render it, as incapable, as it seems indifferent, about seeking its food; when in motion the bones are heard to rattle; a fever and great costiveness prevail the whole time the animal lingers, which generally does not exceed two months, and then dies. This disease appears to be but little understood by the cow doctors."

DAIRY.—*Cottingham Cheese.*—P. 127. (Cottingham) "The cheese so famous through England, by the name of this parish, is made here, and the neighbouring villages; the superiority of which, is not to be ascribed to any particular mode in the management of the dairies, but solely to the nature of the herbage on the commons." ?

Suckling Calves.—P. 127. (same parish) "The suckling of calves for the London market, is carried on here to great advantage; it commences at Michaelmas, and is continued to Lady Day. The common allowance is the milk of two cows to a calf, which is considered as the winter profit, and answers very well."

SHEEP.—*Number* and *Breeds.*—P. 205. "It appears from the general average, that one thousand and sixty-two sheep is the proportion per parish in the sixty-two parishes, in which the number kept was ascertained. This ratio multiplied by one hundred and forty-four, the number of parishes in which sheep are kept in this county, is equal to one hundred and fifty-two thousand nine hundred and twenty-eight sheep, for an extent of *highland* country of about two hundred and forty-three thousand and three hundred acres, which is not quite one and a half acres per sheep. This general stock may be divided into three distinct breeds, though there are many intermediate shades amongst them. The Norfolk, the West Country, and the Cambridgeshire, are the principal ones. The three years old wethers of the former when fattened will average about sixteen pounds per quarter, and about two and three quarter pounds per fleece; and the West Country breed will average about eighteen pounds per quarter, and four pounds per

per fleece. These two sorts are generally found between the Cam and Mildenhall rivers, extending along the plains of Newmarket Heath, towards Linton, Foulmire, and Roysston, binding upon the counties of Suffolk, Essex, and part of Hertfordshire, and to the head of the valley distinguished by the name of the Dairies—Crossing this Valley, and extending thence westwardly towards Caxton, and northwardly towards the fens, binding east on the river Cam, and south and westwardly upon Bedford and Huntingdonshires, the common Cambridgeshire breed prevails; the three years old wethers, of which sort when fattened to the bone, will average about fourteen pounds per quarter, and two and a quarter pounds to the fleece."

Diseases of Sheep.—Rot.—P. 107. (Dry Drayton) "About one thousand sheep, of the common breed, are kept in this parish, one half of which fell a sacrifice to the rot in the course of last year, imputed to the bad state of drainage in the open fields."

P. 112. (Croxton) "About fourteen hundred sheep of the common breed are here kept, one thousand of which, were carried off by the rot in the course of the last year. To prevent so dreadful a calamity, and to improve the stock in general, and the husbandry of the parish, an inclosure is desired."

Similar accounts were registered, in other parishes.

The following is Mr. Vancouver's theory of the *ordinary rot* in Sheep.—P. 206. "This part of the country, north of Wisbech, is very happily exempt from the ravages of the *rot;* the cause of which, so far as the enquiries and observations made in the course of the survey will lead to a conjecture, seems to arise from an extremely wet season in summer. Extremely wet winters do not produce this disease. The moors, low grounds, and wastes, in the common open fields, upon which the sheep are by necessity obliged to feed, as well in wet, as in dry summers, frequently in wet seasons, become overflowed with the highland waters, which leave prodigious quantities of filth and sullage upon the grass and herbage, in which is most probably involved the germin, or egg of those snails or insects, which being conveyed with the food into the stomach of the sheep, and there meeting with a proper nidus become vivified, and invited by the gall, their proper aliment, pass the bileducts into the liver, where, in a certain stage of the disease, they encrease to the frightful size and number which destroy the animal."

P. 111. (Eltsley) "There are about twelve hundred sheep, of the common Cambridgeshire breed kept here, seven

seven hundred of which, perished by the rot, in the course of last year; the present prospect is something mended, though as the sheep still continue to die, it is greatly apprehended, that most of the diseased sheep, will be carried off in the course of the spring. It has been observed, that in the first stage of this disease, the liver has not been infected with the snails, or plaice; it has preserved a vivid sound appearance, but when touched, was found tender, and rotten, and in every respect like cold, and coagulated blood. This stage of the disease, or rather the disease itself, is called the blood rot."

From this notice, it would seem as if there were another species of rot, prevalent in Cambridgeshire; and, toward the close of his work, Mr. V. gives a more intelligible account of it.

P. 207. "Another species of rot, was noticed on the survey, which does not appear to be ascribeable to the like cause. This is called by the farmers, the *blood rot*. The liver appears to the eye in these cases to be perfectly sound, and as free from disease, as in the most healthy animal; it is however covered with an extremely thin transparent membrane, as tender as a spider's web, but which the smallest pressure imaginable, immediately ruptures; when the whole liver resembles a mass of coagulated blood, without any cohesion whatsoever; the liver and intestines, at this time, are free from any appearance of insects, alive or dead; nor was it understood from the farmers, that the liver in the state before mentioned, was offensive to the smell; though certain it is, that in its progress to that condition, it must have been rendered gradually inert, and corrupt, as it became disorganized."

And I have still to register another, and yet more alarming, disorder of this useful species of animal.—P. 12. (Ashley) "One thousand, three hundred sheep, of the Norfolk breed, amongst which, a growing disease prevails, equally alarming with the rot, though these sheep walks, are happily free from that calamity; the first appearance of which, is indicated by the wool changing to a brown colour; and as the disease advances, drops off at the roots, and leaves the skin quite clean and naked. At this time, the animal appears extremely uneasy, constantly rubbing its head against the hurdles and fences, and scratching its back and sides, with its horns, starting suddenly, running a few steps, then falling down, where it will remain a short time, and then rise, and begin feeding, as if in perfect health. The skin is perfectly free from eruption, or other appearance of disease; nor are there any traces of the disorder discoverable

able, by examination of the entrails, the body, or head of the animal; and as no instance of a cure has occured, in any of the surrounding parishes; and moreover as this disorder is considered to be infectious, the sheep are usually killed on the appearance of the first symptoms; though some have been known, to have languished under its fatal influence, for ten or twelve weeks together. In the parish of Dallham in *Suffolk*, which is distant only a few miles from hence, out of a flock of five hundred sheep, the owner sold last year, as many skins at ten-pence each, as amounted to ten pounds; every sheep of which, was either killed in consequence of, or perished by this disease."

Has this destroying malady ceased? No mention is made of it in the *Suffolk* Report; nor in any of the Reports of *Essex*.

DEER.—What is remarkable, and entitled to notice, here, —a similar disorder, to that last mentioned, made ravages among the deer of Wimpole Park (Lord Hardwick's). The subjoined is Mr. V's notice of it.

P. 94. " It is necessary to state the following curious fact. Wimple park, contains about four hundred acres, and is at present, depastured by deer, sheep, and cow cattle; amongst the former, a disease does, and has prevailed for some years past, which in some degree, may be compared, from its resemblance with the very extraordinary one, observed amongst the sheep, in the neighbourhood of Ashley. The first symptom of the disorder, observable in the deer, is similar to that amongst the sheep; which is an apparent uneasiness in the head, and the rubbing of its horns against the trees, (this action however is common to deer, at particular seasons, in all countries, whether in a perfectly wild, or more domesticated state) but the most extraordinary effect of this disease is, that the animal appears to labour under a sort of madness, in pursuing the herd, which now flee before him, and endeavour to forsake him; trying to bite or otherwise annoy them, with all his strength and power, which soon being exhausted, he becomes sequestered from the rest of the herd, and in that deplorable state of the disease, breaks his antlers against the trees, gnaws large collops of flesh, from off his sides, and hind quarters, appears convulsed for a short time, and soon expires."

IMPROVEMENTS.—At the close of Mr. Vancouver's work that has now passed under review, is placed the following statement of the various species of improvement which, he conceives, the County of Cambridge is capable of receiving.

P. 219.

	£	s.	d.
P. 219. "From the preceding statements, and from a due consideration of the information acquired on the survey and contained in the journal, it appears clearly evident that the complete and effectual *drainage* of one hundred and fifty thousand acres of *fen land* in this county, would produce an additional revenue to the proprietors only, an augmented rent of..	£75,000	0	0
That the laying into severalty, or generally *enclosing* one hundred and thity-two thousand acres, of open *common field* arable, land would yield an additional rent of	58,600	0	0
That a general *improvement* of the coarse and *rough pastures*, amounting to about nineteen thousand eight hundred acres, would produce an increased rent of..	9,487	10	0
That the *enclosing* in severalty seven thousand five hundred acres of *highland common*, would produce in addition to its present estimated value, an increased income of	4,125	0	0
That the *draining*, properly improving, *and enclosing* eight thousand acres of fen or *moor common*, would necessarily produce an increased rent upon its present value of	4,000	0	0
That laying into severalty, draining, and improving two thousand acres of *half yearly meadow land*, would produce an encreased rent of	850	0	0
Total improvement of which the county is capable, according to the foregoing statements, is	146,262	10	0
Stating the increased produce, at thrice the increased rent, hence per annum to the public	438,787	10	0
Which at thirty years purchase, would increase the value of the national capital to the amount of............................	13,163,625	0	0"

If the several sums, here set down, have but a near resemblance of accuracy, they reflect, on the natural turn of mind, exertion, and perseverance of Mr. Vancouver, very great credit.

CALCULATIONS

CALCULATIONS of *this sort* have GOOD SENSE and MEANING in them; and are capable of promoting the permanent welfare of a Country;—if not in themselves, immediately;—as a groundwork on which to raise more correct statements.

"GENERAL VIEW

OF THE

AGRICULTURE

OF THE

COUNTY OF CAMBRIDGE

DRAWN UP FOR THE

CONSIDERATION OF THE BOARD OF AGRICULTURE

AND INTERNAL IMPROVEMENT.

BY THE REV. W. GOOCH, A. B.

1811." *

THIS performance was examined, and some extracts taken from it, relating to the fens of Cambridgeshire, in reviewing the Reports from the EASTERN DEPARTMENT.

The UPLANDS, or NATURAL GROUNDS of the County situated *westward* of the fens, form a portion of the MIDLAND DEPARTMENT.

Regarding Mr. GOOCH'S QUALIFICATIONS, as a Rural Reporter, they appear in his book (which is the only criterion I have to judge by) to be such as a gentleman of his profession may be conceived to possess. It were a crime, we are told, to assert, that the clergy "are not unmindful of temporal concerns." † Nevertheless, this reverend Reporter would seem to have borne that moral and

* The preface is dated, "Whatfield Parsonage, Suffolk, 1807"; which is four years prior to the publication of the volume!

† See "the parson's review."

and "praiseworthy" principle in mind, while he was composing his work. He was, of course, careful of *his own good things*;—keeping himself in the back ground (on one occasion only excepted, on which he appears in a clerical group) and placing, in the forward ranks, the sentiments and sayings of other men.

Of his MODE of SURVEY (as it is called) the time spent in it, or the route he took, not a footstep or any trace appears.—His mean of information was evidently that of *enquiry*; without, may we be allowed to say, sufficient experience, to appreciate the value of the answers given.

The ORIGINAL MATTER collected is not considerable. The *extracts* from Mr. VANCOUVER'S Report,—from "Annals of Agriculture,"—the "Beauties of England and Wales,"—and other erudite works,—form the principal part of the volume;—which is not large *.

The Reporter's *own* chiefly consists, let it be put, of assertions and opinions of *others*;—strung together, much in the *Secretarian* manner; and interspersed with remarks, and perchance calculations, which rarely convey any practical information.—This, however, is not uniformly the case.

The number of pages three hundred and three.

An engraved sketch of the River Ouse, near Lynn.—No map.

SUBJECT THE FIRST.

NATURAL ECONOMY.

EXTENT.—Mr. Gooch copies Mr. VANCOUVER'S table;—see page 612, aforegoing.

WATERS.—P. 28. "The Cam enters the county to the west of Guilden-Morden, thence flowing to the north-east, it receives several rivulets, and near Grantchester has its current enlarged by united waters which flow into this county from Essex; hence, taking a northerly direction, the Cam *glides through the walk* of the principal colleges at Cambridge, and having passed several villages, falls into the Ouse, at Harrimere in the parish of Stretham. The Nene is likewise a considerable river, it runs by Wisbech to

* A somewhat novel method, this, of making up a Report, by a *Surveyor*, employed by a public Board.

to the sea. The old and new Bedford rivers *run upwards* of twenty miles from Erith to Denver. These rivers are all navigable, and merchandize is conveyed on them by gangs of barges, from 4 to 7 and 8 each gang."

SOILS.—The Reporter likewise copies Mr. V's account of soils;—and extracts the passages relating to them, from his PAROCHIAL JOURNAL:—thus bringing the whole together.—This may be deemed the most laudable part of Mr. Gooch's performance;—as it places, in a comprehensive light the most minute and interesting account of the soils of a County which, perhaps, has been exhibited:—Yet which, had it not been for Mr. Gooch's labors, would never, it is more than probable, have been *published!*—It is too bulky (filling twenty pages), and not of sufficient *public* importance, to be inserted, here.

The subjoined is *this* Reporter's unsatisfactory account of the soils of Cambridgeshire.—P. 26. "To these accounts it may perhaps be superfluous to add a word, the observations however of individuals are entitled to notice; I therefore, will add those made to me on this subject. The arable soil which is most esteemed in the county, is called 'white-land,' which is particularly adapted to the growth of wheat; the celebrated seed-wheat called Burwell-wheat, is grown on this soil, which is not only found in the fields of that parish, but in those of many of the adjoining ones, and in others in various distant districts, and is that described by Mr. Vancouver as 'a deep, rich, white loam, lying upon a chalk or gault;' it is however in general, not of a *deep* staple but *fleet*, (not more than three or four inches), and it has been found that ploughing into the substratum *(chalk or gault)*, * and bringing it up, has rendered the land nearly barren for many years; this soil has been found unfavourable to turnips; they die when their root comes to the clunch; this soil, on the least rain, becomes soapy, and poaches so as considerably to injure stock (particularly sheep) feeding on it. As the Cambridgeshire farmers call this, their favourite soil, 'white land,' so they have a soil they call 'red land,' which name indeed is too frequently applied by them to all light lands, but properly only to the soil composed of a reddish sand, with a mixture of chalk and gravel which is suitable to turnips. That the substratum of the white lands has not been found *in all cases* to produce the effect generally imputed to it, when brought upon the surface, appears from the following communication from Wimpole."

SUBSTRUCTURE.

* See the next article!

SUBSTRUCTURE.—P. 26. "In digging wells at Wimpole, Lord Hardwicke penetrates one hundred and forty feet of what in Cambridgeshire is called *gault*, that is *a pale, blue clay*, seemingly free from sand, and consisting of impalpable particles." *

MINERALS.—P. 27. "There are no mines in the County."

SUBJECT THE SECOND.

POLITICAL ECONOMY.

APPROPRIATION.—For the *species* and *extents* of the unappropriated, and partially appropriated, lands of Cambridgeshire, in 1793-4, see Mr. Vancouver's statement, p. 612, aforegoing; which Mr. G. has copied.—The subjoined is Mr. Gooch's account of them, in 1806.

P. 2. "The open-field arable, waste and unimproved fen, half-yearly-meadow, highland-common, fen or moor-common, and sheep-walk heath, are much lessened now (1806), full 43,000 acres of the open-field arable, being now enclosed arable and pasture; and great part (supposed about 20,000 acres) of the waste and unimproved fen, half-yearly meadow, highland-common, fen or moor-common, sheep-walk heath, being now become also enclosed arable and pasture, and the total rental increased, in open field more than double, and on the other lands three times at least" (?) "(in the opinion of most persons) that of the former rents and value."

The Reporter's chapter, "Enclosing," ocupies nearly forty pages. Its prefatory remarks are these.

P. 56. "Cambridgeshire has gone far into this measure since 1770, and in consequence its farmers have an opportunity of redeeming the county from the imputation it has so long lain under, of being the worst cultivated in England, and of proving (the fact) that the same industry, spirit and skill which have been manifested in other parts of the kingdom, exist also in this, the open-field state and system

* What incoherent writing. Are we to understand by it, that *gault*, otherwise *chalk*, otherwise *blue clay*, may be "brought upon the surface," from the depth of one hundred and forty feet, by "ploughing"?

system precluding the possibility of exercising them. It is somewhat singular, and is a striking proof of the snail-like progress of improvements in agriculture, that the very same ideas which are now entertained by the advocates for enclosures, existed and were published in 1650 by Walter Blyth, who has pointed out the evils of a 'Champion country,' and the benefits to be expected from its enclosure, with as much zeal and ability as any writer of the present day. In 1783 queries were sent to the parishes in this county, which had been enclosed in his present Majesty's reign, up to that time, with a view of ascertaining the effects of enclosures. It is necessary to state these queries and the answers to them, and to make some observations on them.

"*Queries.*

"1st, What number of acres in your parish were enclosed under the act passed?

"2nd, Was the land then enclosed, heath, down, fen, waste land, common, or common-field?

"3dly, What number of acres then enclosed were annually sown with wheat before such enclosure, according to the best information you can obtain?

"4thly, What number of acres then enclosed have been annually sown with wheat, since such enclosure?

"5thly, Is the annual quantity of wheat grown in your parish, increased or diminished since the enclosure, and in what proportion?

"6thly, Is the produce in other articles in your parish, increased or diminished since the enclosure? State which are increased, and what diminished, and in what proportion."

By whom, or to what end, those queries were sent into Cambridgeshire, is not explained. But, as the whole of the answers, that have names affixed to them, except one, are by clergymen,—we may conjecture that the plan was of clerical origin. And this idea is strengthened by the ample remarks of the Reporter;—the main object and drift of which appear, pretty evidently, to have been that of ascertaining the effect of enclosing, on the incomes of tithe owners.

After five or six pages, filled with "answers,"—we find the subjoined observation.—P. 63. "It will be observed that the answers vary in a great degree, and it may perhaps be safely asserted, they are as much for as against enclosures, indeed nothing can be determined from them on either side of the question, unaccompanied by explanation, and further information."

Nevertheless, the Reporter has expended on the subject, two sheets of letterpress, *more;* and, after all, his readers still find themselves inveloped in a darksome atmosphere;—and still treading uncertain ground.

FUEL.—P. 290. "Coals, 40*s*. per chaldron; turf, 7*s*. per thousand; sedge, 9*s*. to 12*s*. per hundred; at Cambridge all fuel except coals rapidly advancing; cow-dung dried is used as firing for dairy purposes and by the poor; it is spread on grass, (common or waste-land) about one inch and a half thick, and cut into pieces about eight to twelve inches square, and lies till dry."

POOR RATES.—P. 36. "These were stated by six returns made to the Board of Agriculture in 1804 to have risen, from 1790 to 1803, from 2*s*. 11*d*. to 4*s*. 8¾*d*. in the pound. The information I received on this subject in 1805 and 1806, warrants my stating them at much more than even the latter sum, at 6*s*. to 7*s*. and in many parishes at 10*s*. to 12*s*. and even higher."

P. 293. "Nothing singular in the management of the poor, their dwellings in general bad. No hundred-houses as in Norfolk and Suffolk."

TITHES.—P. 35. "These are taken in kind in many parishes, particularly in those consisting of open field, the hirer giving from 3*s*. 4*d*. to 5*s*. 4*d*. statute acre for the *great thithes*. Where tithes are compounded for, an equal composition is paid on the average of the county, in many instances a much higher. Under the late acts of enclosure, tithes have been abolished for one-fifth of arable, one-eighth of pasture, one-ninth of fen, allotted and fenced in at expence of proprietors at large."

P. 264.—"One-tenth of the cost of purchased manures is allowed the farmer by many tithe-gatherers."

RIVER NAVIGATION.—See *Waters*, p. 627, aforegoing.

CANALS.—P. 291. "The fens in this county are intersected in all directions, by cuts for the conveniency of districts and individuals; the last made was from Wisbech to the river Nene at Outwell, and thence to the river Ouse at Salter's Lode sluice, opening a communication with Norfolk, Suffolk, &c. &c. It was opened in 1797, and has been of great service in draining its neighbourhood, as well as having benefited the town of Wisbech, and the adjacent country, considerably, by the increase of trade."

ROADS.—P. 291. "Excepting the turnpikes, the roads in this county are miserably bad, owing to the scarcity and dearness of materials. Most roads running through the fens, are frequently almost impassable, even the turnpike one from Downham to Wisbech, not excepted; the 'mending,' being only the silt, viz. a sand formerly left by the sea,

sea, and not a stone amongst it. The turnpike in the high-land parts of the county are excellent, as is that from Cambridge through Chatteris, March, &c."

MARKETS.—*Weight* of *Corn*, &c.—P. 298. "The stone is 14 lbs. Wool is sold by tod, of 28 lbs. Cheese, by cwt. of 120 lbs. Corn, by coomb," (4 bushels) "or by load of five bushels. Oats of fen, by last of 21 coomb."

P. 300. "Field corn is heavier than fen-corn one stone and a half to two stone (of 14 lbs.) Weight of fen-corn at Thorney, oats, nine stone; barley, fourteen stone: wheat, sixteen stone, per Co. Hence the weight of field corn is (taking the difference at two stone per Co.) oats, eleven stone; barley, sixteen stone; wheat, eighteen stone; from which it may be suspected that the fen-corn is over-rated in weight."

SUBJECT THE THIRD.

RURAL ECONOMY.

TENANTED ESTATES.

ESTATES.—*Sizes*.—P. 29. "The estates vary very much in size; there are many large ones, viz. those of Lord Hardwicke, Duke of Bedford, Duke of Rutland, Sir Henry Peyton, Mr. Thorpe, &c. &c. The greatest part of the county is perhaps in estates from 200*l*. to 500*l*. and 1000*l*. per annum; there are however many from 20*l*. to 50*l*. and 400*l*. per year, many occupied by the owners. Great part of the county (I had no means of ascertaining what proportion) belongs to colleges and other public bodies."

TENURES.—P. 29. "Every kind of tenure is in this county; there are vast numbers of leaseholds, under the college and other public bodies; chiefly for 21 years, renewable every 7 years, paying also an annual rent, called a reserved rent; the usual fee for renewal, is from $1\frac{1}{4}$ to $1\frac{1}{2}$ years rent; some are grants for a number of years, and some for life or lives."

RECLAIMING WILD LANDS.—*Sodburning*.—After filling a series of pages with proandcon opinions, the Reporter favors us, somewhat indirectly, with his own ideas, on the subject.

P. 257.

P. 257. " Such are the opinions of individuals in Cambridgeshire on this subject, and the arguments here advanced against the measure in question have been answered again and again, proving that the evils stated have not arisen from the burning when properly done, but from the succeeding treatment of the land, and particularly from an unmerciful and injudicious cropping."

IRRIGATION.—It is no longer a matter of surprize that calcareous waters are suffered to run waste, in nine places of ten, or ninetynine of one hundred, in which they might be profitably employed,—when we hear of a work which was formerly executed,—and it would seem, from the account here given of it, with judgement,—now lying in a state of neglect!—Without appearing to have excited, at any time, a spirit of imitation in its neighbourhood.

P. 258. " Colonel Adeane, of Babraham, has a large tract of meadows, which have been irrigated from the time of Queen Elizabeth. Of these Mr. A. Young thus writes: ' the only watered meadows of any consequence on this side of the kingdom, are those I believe at Babraham, in Cambridgeshire, belonging to Thomas Adeane, Esq.; their history is remarkable. Pallavicino, who was collector of Peter's pence in England, at the death of Queen Mary, having 30,000*l.* or 40,000*l.* in his hands, had the art to turn protestant on the accession of Queen Elizabeth, and appropriated the money to his own use; he bought with it the estate at Babraham, and other lands near Bournbridge; and procuring a grant from the crown, of the river which passes through them, was enabled legally to build a sluice across it, and throw as much of the water as was necessary into a new canal of irrigation, which he dug to receive it in the method so well known, and commonly practised in Italy long before that period. In the first week of April I examined the works.' "

P. 259. " The canals and the sluices are all well designed, and are the work of a man evidently well acquainted with the practice; but in taking the water from them for spreading it by small channels over the meadows, there does not seem to be the least intelligence or knowledge of the husbandry of watering. No other art is exerted, but that merely of opening in the bank of the river small cuts for letting the water flow on to the meadows always latterally, and never longitudinally, so necessary in works of this kind. The water then finds its own distribution, and so irregularly, that many parts receive too much, and others none at all. From the traces left of small channels in different parts of the meadows, I suspect that the ancient distribution formed under Pallavicino is lost, and that we see nothing at present

sent but the miserable patch-work of workmen ignorant of the business."

This is one of those striking facts that *instinctively* rouse the attention. But, in the case under notice, we have no information, as to the specific quality of the *water* (no intimation as to the strata out of which it issues), nor any description of the *soil*, over which it is spread, nor of the *substratum* on which the soil rests. It would therefore be rashness to condemn, altogether, the conduct of the present proprietors and occupiers.—*It is possible*, an error was committed, in the first instance, by the projector—a *foreigner*—who might mistake the nature of the water, the soil, or the subsoil.—This being as it may, the lands under notice must lie a disgrace to the district in which they are situated, until the truth be ascertained.

CHOICE of TENANTS.—For *Capital*, see the head *Profit*, ensuing.

TENANCY.—P. 38. "In great part of the county none are granted, this system (if it may be so called) cannot however continue, if the benefits looked for from enclosures are to be realized. Where enclosures have taken place, leases have in general been granted, and the usual covenant respecting cropping has been two crops and a fallow, viz. the course allowed before enclosing, and the course observed by many since."

RENT.—P. 32. "Correct information on this subject however desirable, is not attainable by an indifferent person, nor indeed can it be reasonably expected from those whose interests may be, and there is reason to believe has been, affected by such communication."—Mr. G. however, has ventured to put down several items, which we are told he had "from a respectable quarter":—a sort of *authenticity*, this, which does not entitle them to a place, here.

AGRICULTURE.

FARMS.—*Sizes*.—P. 32. "From 20 to 100" (1000) "acres; a few only exceeding 1000 acres: many from 100 acres to 1000."

DRAINING Farms.—*Mole Plow*.—P. 244. "At Madinglay. Sir Charles Cotton has used the mole-plough with success on pasture: draws the drains at about a rod distance; each drain goes into an open ditch; depth of drain about a foot only; they have been done seven or eight

eight years, and are now perfect, and work well; have made the pasture perfectly dry; twelve and fourteen horses did fifteen acres a day; attendance one man to hold the plough, five men to attend horses, &c. the expense therefore in *labour*, may be estimated at 3*s*. 1*d*. per acre."

HOMESTEADS.—P. 30. "The farm-houses and premises are in general bad, inconvenient, and of such materials as must subject the owners to heavy expence in repairs. Lath and plaster, or clay and wattle, are the most common materials; in many places, clunch-walls, which are found very warm, dry, and durable, if attended to. There are many newly erected premises on the late enclosures, most of them defective in arrangement and conveniences, and almost all over-barned."

Building Materials.—P. 292. "Excellent white bricks are also made there" (Ely) "and at Chatteris, and Cambridge."

COTTAGES.—P. 31. "These are wretchedly bad, speaking generally. Lord Hardwicke has set an example worthy of imitation, in having built several comfortable cottages, and having attached gardens to them; some few other gentlemen have done the like; but, it is to be lamented, it is only a few."

PLAN of MANAGEMENT.—P. 98. "The common open-field course is fallow, wheat, barley."

In this short extract, we see all that is worthy of preservation (excepting one on the *fens*, heretofore extracted) out of more than twenty pages, which are found within the Reporter's section, "Course of Crops";—an exhaustless subject, as I have repeatedly said, that gives unbounded scope to the expatiatory writings of listening amateurs.

WORKPEOPLE.—The Reporter inserts a table of communications, which "were made to the Board of Agriculture, from this county, in 1804," (p. 285);—by *whom* does not appear; and no average is drawn from them. At the foot of the table, the Reporter adds a few items;—the fruits of his own enquiries.—But still, we have no average rates of labor.

P. 289. "The farmers not only complain of the rapid advance of wages, but of the difficulty of procuring steady and deserving labourers; they are much less industrious and respectable than in many counties."

WORKING ANIMALS.—P. 279. "Farm horses are kept at great expense in the upland part of the county, being in the stable all the year at hay, corn, and chaff; very few farmers, comparatively speaking, giving them grass, tares, clover, or any green food. The expense per year, per horse 20*l*. to 30*l*. thus estimated,

"Oats

	£.	s.	d.
"Oats 1½ bushels per week the year round, viz. 19½ Co. at 12*s*.	11	14	0
Hay one cwt. per week, that is 52 cwt. at 3*s*.	7	16	0
Shoeing	1	1	0
Farrier	0	10	0
Interest on capital, say on 30*l*.	1	10	0
Decrease in value in seven years, supposing the first cost 30*l*. say 15*l*. which is per year say	2	2	0
	24	13	0

"There is also a further expense for chaff, which in general consists of cavings of corn, trodden down hard, kept in a heat by watering it; the farmers begin to get a stock at Michaelmas, but don't wish to use it till after barley-sowing; till which time, from Michaelmas use chaff or cut-straw untrodden."

IMPLEMENTS.—*Oil-cake Drill*.—P. 47. "Mr. Shepherd" (of Chippenham) "claims the invention of the drill for drilling oil-dust and turnip-seed together, and for which Mr. Burwell of Thetford in Norfolk, undeservedly as Mr. Shepherd terms it, obtained a silver cup of Mr. Coke, in 1803. Mr. Burwell as confidently asserts he was the inventor."—How extraordinary, that a *useful* invention has seldome been brought to light, without two individuals claiming the credit of it.

MANURES.—*Dung*.—P. 264. "At Chatteris, and indeed in many parishes bordering on the fens, there is such abundance of muck that the farmers know not what to do with it."

Sheepfold.—P. 274. "Folding, is universally practised, its value variously estimated.

At Horse-Heath, Mr. Sanxter ....at...... 40*s*. per acre.
At Islesham .... 18*s*.
At Barnwell, Mr. Burleigh .... 26*s*.
At Burwell, Mr. Dunn .... 25*s*.

"At Westley Bottom, Mr. Wedge. 'Take away my fold, take away my flock.' At Trumpington, Mr. Wedd at 30*s*. per acre, if done well between August and Michaelmas, when he considers it of the most value. At Abington, Mr. Mortlock's bailiff, at 40*s*. per acre."

Lime.—P. 292. "Lime is burnt at Wisbech, Mepal, Cherryhinton, &c. &c. but that in greatest estimation is burnt at Reach (a hamlet of Burwell), and is fetched many miles."

TILLAGE.—P. 95. "Ploughing is done on light soils and in the fens by two, and in some instances in the latter, by by three horses abreast; on heavy soils (up-lands) by three and sometimes by four horses at length. When more than two horses at length are used, a boy is also employed to drive them. From three-fourths of an acre to an acre is a day's work in the uplands; and one and an half acre in the fens."

P. 96. "Mr. Wedge, of Wesley-Bottom, (on a very light soil), has his stetches contain an acre, for the more easily seeing if his men have done a day's work."

"Fallowing is practised through the county with very few exceptions, which are on what is called (in consequence of such exemptions perhaps) 'every year land.'"

BARN MANAGEMENT.—*Thrashing Mills.*—These we are told,—p. 50,—are "becoming general."

After having entered, with a degree of minuteness, into the different articles of expence and profit of a thrashing mill, the Reporter makes the following statement.

P. 54. "It appears then that the expense per day of a threshing machine, on a farm of 150 acres arable, is as follows:

	£.	s.	d.
Four horses	0	8	0
Four men	0	8	0
Four boys or women	0	4	0
Interest on first cost of machine 4 *l.* per year equal on 23 days, to per day	0	3	5½
Repairs of machine 4 *l.* per year, equal on 23 days, to per day	0	3	5½
Decrease of value of machine in 14 years, is per year, 4 *l.* 5 *s.* 9 *d.* equal on 23 days, to per day	0	3	8¼
	£.1	10	7¼

"Total expense, therefore, of threshing 20 Co. of corn by the machine, and on the farm assumed, is 1 *l.* 10 *s.* 7¼ *d.* viz. 1 *s.* 6 *d.* per Co. round, much above the price by hand."*

THRASHING MILLS, like many other things, are good or bad, right or wrong, eligible, or ineligible,—according to given circumstances.—On farms of size, in a district where flail men are few, they become a positive and great good. On the contrary, in a country which is fully supplied with farm workmen, they are *parochial* evils; tho they

* See MURRAY'S WARWICKSHIRE! (p. 322, aforegoing.)—So much for *arbitrary arrangements of figures!*

they may be convenient and profitable to *large occupiers*. In every situation, there is one benefit to arise from them. They are calculated to preserve the *health* of laborers; hand thrashing being one of the most unwholesome of rural imployments. Against this, however, the *accidents* which attend mill thrashing, require to be placed.

In districts where laborers are in sufficient number, and wages moderate, there are two valuable advantages, which attach to thrashing mills, and which must be obvious to all practical men; tho seldome, if ever, noticed by writers on the subject*;—namely that of employing *yearly servants* (plowmen and carters) as well as *full-fed horses*, in *rainy* and *frosty weather*; when, without such mean of employment, they might remain, in a degree, idle.

The other advantage is that of being able to catch a *profitable market*; especially at the close of harvest, in years when corn is at high prices;—as was, last year, 1812, the case in *this* neighbourhood;—when wary thrashing-mill farmers got their wheats to market, at an advance of four or five shillings, a bushel, above what mere flail thrashers could obtain, in any considerable quantity.

In the latter point of view, *water*, *wind*, and *steam mills*, gain an additional superiority, to those that are worked by *animals*; which, at that time of the year, have generally full employment.—The advantage, above noticed, however, was gained by *horse mills*.

Arable Crops.—More than sixty pages are filled with words and figures, on this subject. I find very few of them, however, that are so applied, as to render them entitled to transcription, into this register of useful information. They are chiefly, it would seem, the conversational saysos of interrogatees; who, being asked questions, thought it right, in these talking times, to say something.

Wheat.—*Gleaning*.—P. 132. "Gleaning is a general evil in this county, and is unlimited, extending to every grain and without any regulations, the gleaners going amongst the shocks of wheat, and following the rakers of soft corn so closely, and in so disorderly a manner, as to cause perpetual dispute and complaint."

Turnips.—P. 145. "The cultivation of this plant has hitherto been very confined in this county, owing to so great a part of it having been in open field, the system of cropping which, and the flock masters' right of going over the whole fallow-field, precluding it; the Cambridgeshire farmers, however, appear as sensible of the value of this root

* The above was written, before Mr. Murray's Warwickshire was published.

root as the Norfolk ones, having introduced it into the rotation of cropping adopted on new enclosures, on suitable soils, where it is likely to prove, as might be expected, a great acquisition; one circumstance is indeed to be lamented, namely, that this plant does not succeed on the best" (?) "lands of the county; namely 'the white lands,' the soil of which is *very fleet*, and the substratum a *clunch*." (?)

On thin calcareous lands, whether on chalk or limestone, turnips require to be cultivated on ridgets, in the Tweedside manner; and ought, perhaps even under that culture, to be allowed an extra quantity of seed.

RAPE HERBAGE.—P. 144. "Begin *feeding it*" (!) "about Michaelmas. Is given to ewes after they have lambed, (will injure them before lambing), and to fattening sheep. Mr. Wedd, of Trumpington, thinks cole should be *fed* by hurdling it off, a piece at a time, and that it should be given to old sheep. Mr. Scott, of Chatteris, thinks the sheep should be turned into the whole field of cole at once. Mr. Boyce, of Whittlesea, hurdles it off if he gives it to store-sheep, but turns into the whole at once, when he gives it to fattening ones; for when hurdled off and fed bare, the sheep bite so close as to eat the crown of the plant; which they prefer to the leaf, and will not eat the latter afterwards, but 'pine for the former, and will not in consequence get on well.'"

This is readily to be conceived; as the common rape is, doubtlessly I believe, the parent of the BULBOUS RAPE, or RAPE TURNEP; namely of what is incongruously called, the "Swedish Turnip," or, more sillily, "Swedes"!

SAINFOIN.—P. 152. "The after grass is fed by sheep, but many think it should not be very closely fed. When it stands for seed, produce three to six Co. per acre. When for hay, from one to two tons per acre. It is a remark of a gentleman of Landwade, that, 'sheep ruin it. I make it into hay, and get a ton an acre.' Mr. Wedge, of Westley Bottom, sheep destroy it.' Professor Harwood, makes it into hay. Feeds the rowen till Michaelmas. Mr. Sanxter mows it and does not feed the rowen. Mr. Hammon, of Ashley, mows about two tons per acre, and feeds after-grass with sheep; he has grown eight Co. per acre *seed*.

"Mr. Eaton, of Stetchworth, says, sheep injure it if fed near winter.

"About Babraham neighbourhood it is made into hay, and never fed close. The Rev. Mr. Lane, of Carlton, gives it made into hay, and cut, to horses: grows great crops of it.

"Duration. At Landwade, remains about nine years.

"At Ashley. About seven or eight years. (Mr. Hammond.)

"At

" At Stetchworth. If it remains more than four years, the crop which succeeds it, (oats) is likely to fail."

Under such treatment, the surprize excited is, that the sainfoin crop should last, even four years. The *first* shoots of sainfoin ought to be mown, every year; and the *second* growth to be left untouched, until autumn.—GLOCESTERSHIRE and KENT are the proper schools, in which to study the culture of sainfoin; not CAMBRIDGESHIRE;—if the above bear any resemblance of its best practice.

GRASS LANDS.—P. 184. " This county contains a great quantity of grass lands. Some under no management, and of so little value in their present state that the town charges of many parishes in which they are, would be a high rent for them; indeed from their appearance one would conclude they are not deemed by the farmer worthy his attention; there are, however, many thousand acres of pasture of the first quality, and under the best management."

Inferior Pastures. " These are dispersed chiefly over the upland part of the county, on heavy, wet soils; they are miserably poor, and abounding with every thing but what they ought, yet capable of *vast improvement*, with the prospect of paying amply."

This assertion would seem to be too broad; seeing that " opinions vary on the mode of improving them."

Superior Pastures.—P. 186. " The greater part of these is situated in the parishes of Soham, Ely, Chatteris, March, Wisbech, Outwell, Upwell, Thorney, Whittlesea, and other parishes in and bordering upon the fens. The district called the ' Wash,' is also most valuable pasture; it is the receptacle of the upland waters, it is called in the map the ' 100 foot Wash,' running by the side of the old Bedford river, being nearly twenty miles long, and from one-fourth of a mile to three miles wide. This land has been *sold* at 10*l.* per acre," (?) " for growing oziers, but it is chiefly applied to feeding; some mow it, running the hazards of floods. Its quality is such that in six weeks it will fatten a bullock or horse, though put unto it bone lean; it rots sheep. Its fertility is attributed to the earth of the upland arable lands, brought and deposited at every flood:"—rather, shall we say, to the warp, or sea mud, deposited, heretofore, by the tide?

Management of Grass Lands.—P. 187. " The sheep pastures are fed all the year, reducing the number in March, for a week or two, to about half the summer-stock. Bullock-pastures are spared about a month or five weeks in the spring. Mr. Jennyns, of Bottisham, sows on his pastures, where they fail of plants, ray-grass in autumn; and folds after

after it directly."—This is an accuracy of management which does Mr. Jennyns credit.

LIVESTOCK.—*Grazing*.—P. 189. "The perfection of grazing is reckoned to consist not only in the choice of stock, but in nicely proportioning it to the breadth of land; being under-stocked is considered a great evil, as long grass is found prejudicial to any cattle. On grazing, the farmers of this county with reason pride themselves."—Yet this may be said to be all the explicit information we are favored with, in this Report, of their practice; saving the few words that are contained in the preceding extract.

HORSES.—P. 279. "The farmers in this county think themselves unrivalled in cart horses; in the fens they are a source of great profit, they are very large and bony, and the greatest number black; long hair, from the knee to the fetlock and trailing on the ground, is reckoned an excellency. Mr. Johnson, of Whittlesea, shines as a breeder of these horses, perhaps as much as any gentleman in the county; he has a cart stallion for which he gave by auction 255 guineas; the colts of this horse have sold off the mare, at 60*l.* and year olds at 100 guineas. Mr. Johnson one year sold twenty-two year old cart colts (not the breed of this horse) at 40*l.* each. Mr. Edes, of Wisbech, is also a great breeder of this stock, he sells at two and three years old; average price of late years, two year old, 20*l.* three year old 25*l.*: the present prices of cart-horses and brood-mares, are high beyond belief; 40*l.* to 50*l.* is thought a low price, for a good, strong, common, three or four year old. They are generally sold at two years old: while these prices remain, stock will pay equal to them."

CATTLE.—The Reporter, in treating of this species of livestock, separates it into "cows" and "bullocks";—appropriating a distinct section to each;—under the latter head, he speaks of "rearing cattle." But no matter. I shall digest the few articles of useful information, which the chapter contains, under their natural heads.

Breed of Cattle.—P. 266. "Cows.—These are mostly the horned breed of the county, and are called by its name; there are, however, cows of various kinds in every parish."

Rearing Cattle.—P. 269. "1st, Wean at a few days old, keep in house four to nine months on milk, turnips, potatoes, &c. &c. put them to grazing, at three, four, or five years old, generally at three years.

"2d, Wean and sell to graziers at age for fattening.

"3d, Buy in year olds, and keep them till of age to graze.

"4th, Buy at an age for grazing."

Grazing Cattle.—P. 268. "These are of various sorts; the stock of the county, and from Norfolk to Suffolk are the

the kinds generally reared. Those bought at an age for grazing,are Galloway, Scots, and other north country breeds, and for the best part of the fens and superior pastures, large beasts: chiefly the short-horned, the Lincolnshire, Yorkshire, Fifeshire, and Irish."

Purchasing Cattle.—P. 269. "This is generally done at autumn, and return succeeding autumn, keeping on hay and grass, in winter, and finishing them from grass.

"Buy at the spring, and if not forward enough to sell fat in the autumn, finish on corn, or oil cake."

DAIRY.—P. 267. "Mr. Darnton, of Babraham, keeps the South Wales cow, and thinks they produce less milk than the Suffolk, but of so superior a quality that it yields more cream; this was acknowledged by his dairy-woman, a Suffolk one. He thinks cows have paid him better than grazing."

"At Cottenham (where the famous cheese called by its name are made), I inquired whether the excellency of their cheese was to be ascribed to any particular process in making them, or to what other cause; and the general opinion seemed to be that it was owing to the nature of their grass."

P. 268. "The farmers whose wives attend the dairy, say nothing pays better than cows; but all agree they are unprofitable unless that is the case. The butter is sold rolled up in pieces of a yard long, and about two inches in circumference, this is done for the conveniency of colleges, where it is cut into pieces called 'parts,' and so sent to table; its quality is no where excelled."

SUCKLING.—P. 268. "Suckling of calves, and making of butter is the chief cow system; there is not much cheese made, except the noted ones of Soham and Cottenham. The suckling season is from Michaelmas to Lady-day. It requires on an average two cows to fatten a calf."

Diseases of Cattle.—P. 266. "I did not find the rot in cows, and their frequency of slipping calf existing to the degree mentioned by Mr. Vancouver."

SHEEP.—*Breed.*—P. 272. "The most prevalent sort in the fens (where the greatest number in the county is kept) is a cross between the Leicester and Lincoln; there are, however, many other breeds, viz. Norfolks, West-country, Cambridgeshire, Berkshire, Hertfordshire, South Down, Lincoln, and Leicester."—The Southdown breed appear to have been, at the time Mr. Gooch wrote, the favorite of fashion.

General Management of Sheep.—"System."—P. 274. "1st, Breed and sell lamb, fat from ewe; then fat ewe and sell her, buying in every autumn fresh ewes.

"2d

"2d, Breed and rear produce, and return it fat at three years old, keeping ewes as long as they are 'whole mouthed;' set ewes from own stock.

"3d, Buy at one or two years old, and return fat, within the year.

"4th, Keep regular folding flock."

Summer Management.—P. 275. "In feeding upland layers with ewes and lambs, the almost general practice is, to let the lambs go before the ewes into fresh feed, through 'nooses in the hurdles, going to and from the ewes at pleasure. The lambs are found not to be so liable to be hoven by clover as sheep are.'"

Winter Management.—Same page. "Rev. G. Jennyns, and Mr. Tharpe, have excellent fold-yards fenced in by *open* pales; in these yards well littered, they lodge their sheep in bad weather; they conceive a *close fence* would be injurious to the sheep." There may be truth in that conception.

Folding Sheep.—See *Manure*, p. 636, aforegoing.

Diseases of Sheep—P. 276. "Mr. Vancouver has ably and fully described the disorders prevalent amongst the sheep in the county. I did not, however, find them existing to the degree, (or any thing like it) which he states."

What Mr. Vancouver says of the rot, is chiefly confined to that of 1793-4. Mr. Gooch *mentions*, after Mr. V., the alarming disorder which took place in the neighbourhood of Ashley, about that time.—See p. 623, aforegoing. But tho (professionally) a *Suffolk man*, he says nothing of its alarming extention into that County. So that we are still in the dark, as to its duration.—Either Mr. V. has been a credulous, or Mr. G. an inattentive, Surveyor.

SWINE.—P. 283. "These are as various as the county itself, and the adjacent ones produce; there are many of the Suffolk breed, viz. short, white, and short eared, which are gaining ground. Some of the Cambridgeshire are so large as to fatten to forty stone, fourteen lbs. to the stone, at two years old; twenty to thirty such stones, a common size."

PROFITS of FARMING.—I am glad to find Mr. Gooch aiding in the exposure of a false principle of calculation, which has been adopted by agricultural writers, regarding the PERCENTAGE which an occupier is entitled to, on the CAPITAL he employs.—See the NORTHERN DEPARTMENT, p. 106; and EASTERN DEPARTMENT, p. 420.

P. 40. "I did not meet with farmers enough in the county, keeping sufficiently accurate accounts from which any valuable information on this subject could be extracted. To the question, 'what per cent. per annum on the capital employed

employed, is cleared *in addition to common interest* by the generality of farmers in the county?' Answer, from 5 to 10 per cent; now nothing less than the latter appears adequate to the maintenance of a family, much less to the getting a fortune, except on very large occupations; for supposing the opinion prevalent in the county, to be well founded, viz. that not more than 7 *l.* per acre is employed on the average of arable occupations (though much more, is employed in many instances), the following will be the profit, taking it at 10 per cent., on farms of the sizes specified.

Number of acres.		Capital 7 *l.* per acre £.		Profit being 10 per cent. £.
50	-	350	-	35
100	-	700	-	70
150	-	1050	-	105
200	-	1400	-	140
250	-	1750	-	175
300	-	2100	-	210
350	-	2450	-	245
400	-	2800	-	280
450	-	3150	-	315
500	-	3500	-	350

"Shewing that farming on a small scale deserves not the attention of men of skill and ability. The farmer, however, whose capital is his own, would have to *spend* one-third more than the above sums, viz. the 5 per cent. on his capital, made in addition to these profits, viz. the farmer having 50 acres, would have an *income* of 52 *l.* 10 *s.* he with 300" (500) " acres, 525 *l.* per annum. By having these sums to *spend,* is to be understood he would have them for the purpose of paying such of his domestic and other expenses, as are not absolutely chargeable to his farm; for when it is said that a profit of 10 per cent is made, no other part of the farmer's house expenses, &c. are supposed to be charged to the farm, than the board of servants, &c. kept for the express purpose of carrying on the farm, and who are solely employed thereon."

Mr. G. pursues the subject, with general remarks; and enters upon calculations of some length, concerning it. But what he, afterward, says, toward the close of the volume, under the head "Statistical Division of the Produce of Land," will serve as a sufficient reason for not inserting them, here.

P. 295. "Mr. A. Young, in his Chapter on this subject in his 'Suffolk Report,' observes that he inserted it as an attempt which may in time be ameliorated in more able hands; as *mine* are not those hands, I must decline a similar attempt; indeed the accuracy of Mr. Young's calculations

tions under this head may be suspected, (he himself observes they are very far from perfection), as the result of them is such as proves farming so beggarly an employ (except on a *very large scale)* that no man with two ideas in his head and a hundred pounds in his pocket would engage in it; and that these estimates are very far from the truth, may be taken for granted from the apparent, and, it is to be hoped, real, situation of the farmers in the kingdom, and above all from the impossibility of their living, reaping such profits only *. Till accounts absolutely accurate, be produced, and those from various respectable quarters, every communication of this nature must be defective in so great a degree, as to be of little individual or national utility."

* "Viz. 5 per cent. profit, on £5 capital per acre."

THE END.

Mr. Marshall's other Works on Rural Subjects.

1.

In two Volumes, Octavo, price 15s. in Boards,

Minutes and Experiments on Agriculture; containing his own Practice in the Southern Counties; and moreover conveying to practical Men in general, an accurate Method of acquiring Agricultural Knowledge, scientifically, from the Results of their Experience.

2.

In twelve Volumes, Octavo, price 4l. in Boards,

The established Practices of the higher Orders of Professional Men, in the six Agricultural Departments of England:

The Practice of the Northern Department being shown, in the Rural Economy of Yorkshire; price 12s.

That of the Western Department, in the Rural Economy of Glocestershire; price 12s.

That of the Midland Department, in the Rural Economy of the Midland Counties; price 14s.

That of the Eastern Department, in the Rural Economy of Norfolk; price 12s.

That of the Southern Department, in the Rural Economy of the Southern Counties; price 15s.

That of the South-western Department, in the Rural Economy of the West of England; price 15s.

3.

In two Volumes, Octavo, price 16s. in Boards,

A general Work on Planting and Rural Ornament; with the Management of Woodlands and Hedgerow Timber.

4.

In one Volume, Quarto, price 2l. 2s. in Boards,

An elementary and practical Treatise on the Landed Property of England: comprising the Purchase, the Improvement, and the executive Management of Landed Estates; and moreover containing what relates to the general Concerns of Proprietors, and to such Subjects of Political Economy, as are intimately connected with the Landed Interest.

5.

In one Volume, Octavo, price 10s. 6d. in Boards,

A general Work on the Management of Landed Estates; being an Abstract of the above Treatise; for the Use of professional Men: including whatever relates to the Business of Estate Agency; whether it be employed in the Purchase, the Improvement, or the executive Management of Estates.

Also,

INDEX.

INDEX.

Inland

From the Office of
THOMAS WILSON and SONS,
High-Ousegate, York.